**Mean square within**

$$MSW = \frac{SSW}{dfw}$$

**Mean square between**

$$MSB = \frac{SSB}{dfb}$$

**F ratio**

$$F = \frac{MSB}{MSW}$$

# CHAPTER 13

### Least-squares regression line

$$Y = a + bX$$

**Slope**

$$b = \frac{n\Sigma XY - (\Sigma X)(\Sigma Y)}{n\Sigma X^2 - (\Sigma X)^2}$$

**Y intercept**

$$a = \overline{Y} - b\overline{X}$$

**Pearson's r**

$$r = \frac{n\Sigma XY - (\Sigma X)(\Sigma Y)}{\sqrt{[n\Sigma X^2 - (\Sigma X)^2][n\Sigma Y^2 - (\Sigma Y)^2]}}$$

# CHAPTER 14

### Partial correlation coefficient

$$r_{yx.z} = \frac{r_{yx} - (r_{yz})(r_{xz})}{\sqrt{1 - r_{yz}^2}\sqrt{1 - r_{xz}^2}}$$

### Least-squares multiple regression line

$$Y = a + b_1X_1 + b_2X_2$$

### Partial slope for $X_1$

$$b_1 = \left(\frac{s_y}{s_1}\right)\left(\frac{r_{y1} - r_{y2}r_{12}}{1 - r_{12}^2}\right)$$

### Partial slope for $X_2$

$$b_2 = \left(\frac{s_y}{s_2}\right)\left(\frac{r_{y2} - r_{y1}r_{12}}{1 - r_{12}^2}\right)$$

### Y intercept

$$a = \overline{Y} - b_1\overline{X}_1 - b_2\overline{X}_2$$

### Beta-weight for $X_1$

$$b_1^* = b_1\left(\frac{s_1}{s_y}\right)$$

### Beta-weight for $X_2$

$$b_2^* = b_2\left(\frac{s_2}{s_y}\right)$$

### Standardized least-squares regression line

$$Z_y = b_1^*Z_1 + b_2^*Z_2$$

### Coefficient of multiple determination

$$R^2 = r_{y1}^2 + r_{y2.1}^2(1 - r_{y1}^2)$$

# *Statistics*
## A TOOL FOR
## SOCIAL RESEARCH

Fourth Canadian Edition

Joseph F. Healey

*Christopher Newport University*

Steven G. Prus

*Carleton University*

Riva Lieflander

*University of Ottawa*

**NELSON**

# NELSON

**Statistics: A Tool for Social Research, Fourth Canadian Edition**

by Joseph F. Healey, Steven G. Prus, and Riva Lieflander

**Vice President, Product Solutions:**
Claudine O'Donnell

**Publisher, Digital and Print Content:**
Leanna MacLean

**Marketing Manager:**
Claire Varley

**Technical Reviewer:**
Catherine Gelinas

**Content Manager:**
Maria Chu

**Photo and Permissions Researcher:**
Natalie Barrington

**Production Project Manager:**
Fiona Drego

**Production Service:**
MPS Ltd.

**Copy Editor:**
Wendy Yano

**Proofreader:**
Shilbhadra Maity

**Indexer:**
May Hasso

**Design Director:**
Ken Phipps

**Higher Education Design PM:**
Pamela Johnston

**Interior Design:**
Colleen Nicholson

**Cover Design:**
Colleen Nicholson

**Cover Image:**
tai11/Shutterstock

**Compositor:**
MPS Ltd.

**Library and Archives Canada Cataloguing in Publication Data**

Healey, Joseph F., 1945-, author
   Statistics: a tool for social research / Joseph F. Healey, Christopher Newport University, Steven G. Prus, Carleton University, Riva Lieflander, Carleton University. — Fourth Canadian edition.

Includes index.
Issued in print and electronic formats.
ISBN 978-0-17-672508-2 (softcover). —ISBN 978-0-17-685378-5 (PDF)

   1. Social sciences—Statistical methods—Textbooks.
2. Statistics—Textbooks.
3. Textbooks. I. Prus, Steven G. (Steven Gerald), 1967-, author
II. Lieflander, Riva, 1966-, author
III. Title.

HA29.H42 2018    519.5
C2018-901700-7
C2018-901701-5

ISBN-13: 978-0-17-672508-2
ISBN-10: 0-17-672508-3

# Brief Contents

# Detailed Contents

**Online Chapters (available at *nelson.com/student*)**

Introduction to Probability

Other EPSEM Sampling Techniques, Systematic, Stratified, and Cluster Samples

Nonparametric Hypothesis Testing for Variables Measured at the Ordinal Level

Linear Regression with Dummy Variables

Regression with a Dichotomous Dependent Variable: an Introduction to Logistic Regression

Elaborating Bivariate Tables

# Preface to the Fourth Canadian Edition

Sociology and the other social sciences, including political science, social work, public administration, criminology, and gerontology, are research-based disciplines, and statistics are part of their everyday language. To join the conversation, you must learn the vocabulary of research, data analysis, and scientific thinking. Knowledge of statistics will enable you to understand the professional research literature of your discipline as well as the research reports you encounter in everyday life. Knowledge of statistics will enable you to conduct quantitative research and to contribute to the growing body of social science knowledge.

Although essential, learning statistics can be a challenge. Students in statistics courses typically have a wide range of mathematical backgrounds and an equally diverse set of career goals. They are often puzzled about the relevance of statistics for them, and, not infrequently, there is some math anxiety to deal with.

This textbook introduces statistical analysis for the social sciences while addressing these challenges. The textbook makes minimal assumptions about mathematical background (the ability to read a simple formula is sufficient preparation for virtually all of the material in the textbook), and a variety of special features help students analyze data successfully. The textbook is sufficiently flexible to be used in any program with a social science base.

The textbook is written at a level intermediate between a strictly mathematical approach and a mere "cookbook." We have not sacrificed comprehensive coverage or statistical correctness, but theoretical and mathematical explanations are kept at an elementary level, as is appropriate in a first exposure to social statistics. For example, we do not treat formal probability theory per se. Rather, the background necessary for an understanding of inferential statistics is introduced, informally and intuitively, in Chapters 4 and 5 while considering the concepts of the normal curve and the sampling distribution. The textbook makes no claim that statistics are "fun" or that the material can be mastered without considerable effort. At the same time, students are not overwhelmed with abstract proofs, formula derivations, and mathematical theory, which can needlessly frustrate the learning experience at this level.

## GOALS AND FEATURES OF THE TEXTBOOK

The textbook has three primary goals, which are collectively designed to help students to develop the skills necessary to become statistically literate. The first goal is to develop an appreciation for the role of statistics in the research process. The second is to cultivate a competence to perform basic statistical calculations. The third is to develop a capability to critically read statistical information, especially as reported in the professional research literature. The following discussion considers each goal in more detail and how it is achieved through the many special features of the textbook.

**1. An Appreciation of Statistics.** To appreciate statistics is to understand the relevance of statistics for research, to analyze and interpret the meaning of a statistical test, and to select and use an appropriate statistic for a given purpose and a given set of variables. This textbook develops these qualities, within the framework of an introductory course, in the following ways:

- *The relevance of statistics.* The textbook stresses the importance of statistics as a means of analyzing and manipulating data to answer research questions. This central theme of relevance is reinforced by a series of boxes labelled "Applying Statistics," each of which illustrates some specific way in which statistics can be used to answer questions.

  Furthermore, the end-of-chapter problems are labelled by the social science discipline or subdiscipline from which they are drawn: SOC for sociology, SW for social work, PS for political science, CJ for criminology and criminal justice, PA for public administration, and GER for gerontology. By identifying problems with specific disciplines, students can more easily see the relevance of statistics to their own academic interests. (Not incidentally, they will also see that the disciplines have a large subject matter in common.)
- *Interpreting statistics.* For most students, interpretation—saying what statistics mean—is a big challenge. The ability to interpret statistics can be developed only by exposure and experience. To provide exposure, we have been careful, in the example problems, to express the meaning of the statistic in terms of the original research question. To provide experience, the end-of-chapter problems almost always call for an interpretation of the statistic calculated. To provide examples, many of the answers to odd-numbered computational problems in the back of the textbook are expressed in words as well as numbers. The "Interpreting Statistics" sections provide additional, detailed examples of how to express the meaning of statistics.
- *Using statistics: Ideas for research projects.* Appendix E offers ideas for independent data-analysis projects for students. The projects require students to use a computerized statistical package to analyze a data set. They can be assigned at intervals throughout the semester or at the end of the course. Each project provides an opportunity for students to practise and apply their statistical skills and, above all, to exercise their ability to understand and interpret the meaning of the statistics they produce.

**2. Computational Competence.** Students should emerge from their first course in statistics with the ability to perform elementary forms of data analysis—to execute a series of calculations and arrive at the correct answer. To be sure, computers and calculators have made computation less of an issue today. Yet computation and statistics are inseparable, and since social science majors frequently do not have strong quantitative backgrounds, we have included a number of features to help students cope with these challenges:

- *Step-by-step computational algorithms* are provided for each statistic.
- *Extensive problem sets* are provided at the end of each chapter. Most of these problems use fictitious data and are designed for ease of computation.
- *Cumulative exercises* are included at the end of each part to provide practice in choosing, computing, and analyzing statistics. These exercises present only data sets and research questions. Students must choose appropriate statistics as part of the exercise. The Cumulative exercises can be found at nelson.com/students.
- *Solutions* to odd-numbered computational problems are provided so that students may check their answers.

**3. Critically Read Statistical Information.** A statistically literate person can comprehend and critically evaluate statistical information reported in research written by others. The development of this quality is a particular problem at the introductory level since (1) the vocabulary of professional researchers is so much more concise than the language of the textbook, and (2) the statistics featured in the literature are generally more advanced than those covered at the introductory level. To help bridge this gap, we have included a series of boxes labelled "Reading Statistics," beginning in Chapter 1. In each box, we briefly describe the reporting style typically used for the statistic in question and try to alert students about what to expect when they approach the professional literature. These inserts include excerpts from the Canadian research literature and illustrate how statistics are actually applied and interpreted by social scientists.

**Additional Features.** A number of other features make the textbook more meaningful for students and more useful for instructors as they help develop students' statistical literacy:

- *Readability and clarity.* The writing style is informal and accessible to students without ignoring the traditional vocabulary of statistics. Problems and examples have been written to maximize student interest and to focus on issues of concern and significance. For the more difficult material (such as hypothesis testing), students are first walked through an example problem before being confronted by formal terminology and concepts. Each chapter ends with a summary of major points and formulas and a glossary of important concepts. A list of frequently used formulas inside the front cover and a glossary of symbols inside the back cover can be used for quick reference.

- *Organization and coverage.* The textbook is divided into four parts. Overview sections have been included with each of the four parts of the textbook. These provide a "road map" of the material that follows and help students see why the chapters are organized as they are. Most of the coverage is devoted to the first three parts of the textbook: descriptive statistics, estimation, and hypothesis testing. Estimation and hypothesis testing are the two main applications of inferential statistics. The distinction between description and inference is introduced in Chapter 1 and maintained throughout the textbook. In selecting statistics for inclusion, we have tried to strike a balance between the essential concepts with which students must be familiar and the amount of material students can reasonably be expected to learn in their first (and perhaps only) statistics course, while bearing in mind that different instructors will naturally wish to stress different aspects of the subject. Thus, the textbook covers the full gamut of the usual statistics, with each chapter broken into subsections so that instructors may choose the particular statistics they wish to include.
- *Flow charts.* Flow charts that help students select appropriate statistics are provided in the textbook. The flow charts depict the selection process in detailed form at the beginning of each chapter.
- *Learning objectives.* Learning objectives are stated at the beginning of each chapter. These are intended to serve as "study guides" and to help students identify and focus on the most important material.
- *Review of mathematical skills.* A comprehensive review of all of the mathematical skills that will be used in this textbook (Prologue) is included. Students who are inexperienced or out of practice with mathematics may want to study this review early in the course and/or refer to it as needed. A self-test is included so that students may check their level of preparation for the course.
- *Statistical techniques and end-of-chapter problems are explicitly linked.* After a technique is introduced, students are directed to specific problems for practice and review. The "how-to-do-it" aspects of calculation are reinforced immediately and clearly.
- *End-of-chapter problems are organized progressively.* Simpler problems with small data sets are presented first. Often, explicit instructions or hints accompany the first several problems in a set. The problems gradually become more challenging and require more decision making by the student (e.g., choosing the most appropriate statistic for a certain situation). Thus, each problem set develops problem-solving abilities gradually and progressively.

- *Computer applications.* To help students take advantage of the power of the computer, this textbook integrates Version 24 of IBM SPSS Statistics for Windows, though Versions 10 through 23 are completely compatible with the textbook. IBM SPSS Statistics, colloquially referred to here as "SPSS," is a leading, state-of-the-art computerized statistical package. Alternatively, students can download a full working evaluation copy of SPSS. This free 14-day trialware can be downloaded after registering at the IBM SPSS website.

  The last part of each chapter, labelled "You Are the Researcher," offers demonstrations and exercises in using SPSS to produce the statistics presented in the chapter. All SPSS outputs from the demonstrations are shown in the textbook and are unedited. Students choosing to replicate the demonstration will see the same output on their computer screen. SPSS exercises are provided below the demonstrations and give students the opportunity to actually use SPSS to compute statistics. Appendix E provides additional SPSS exercises, and Appendix F gives a general introduction to SPSS.

  Overall, detailed instructions and demonstrations on how to use SPSS for each exercise are provided in this textbook. SPSS can be taught at a basic level from this textbook without the aid of an SPSS supplementary text.

  A manual for Stata (Version 15 for Windows), another commonly used statistical software package, is also available for the textbook. Like SPSS, Stata provides a variety of tools for statistical analyses that are easy to learn and use. The manual can be downloaded for free from the textbook's website. The manual is accompanied by two databases, allowing students to practise their statistical skills in a Stata computing environment.

- *Real data.* Four databases for SPSS application give students a wide range of opportunities to practise their statistical skills on "real-life" data: (1) a shortened version of the 2013 Canadian General Social Survey (labelled *2013_GSS_Shortened.sav*); (2) a shortened version of the 2012 Canadian Community Health Survey (*2012_CCHS_Shortened.sav*); (3) the full version of the 2013 Canadian General Social Survey (*2013_GSS_Full.sav*); and (4) the full version of the 2012 Canadian Community Health Survey (*2012_CCHS_Full.sav*). The databases are described in Appendix G and are available in SPSS format (i.e., the ".sav" file format) on the website for the textbook.

## KEY CHANGES IN THE FOURTH CANADIAN EDITION

This edition of the textbook remains focused on developing the skills necessary for students to become statistically literate. It is written for students with varying levels of mathematical proficiency, providing an accessible yet comprehensive examination of statistics, and continues to expose students to statistics from a uniquely Canadian perspective. With this in mind, various changes were made in the fourth edition. The following are the most important changes:

- The textbook has been reorganized to better integrate the discussion of hypothesis tests and measures of association.
- New statistics and methods—index of qualitative variation, five-number summary, measures of central tendency/dispersion for grouped data, and eta-squared—have been added.
- The "Reading Statistics" inserts have been updated. Likewise, data cited in the text have been updated.
- The textbook, at the time of printing, uses the latest version of IBM SPSS Statistics for Windows (Version 24), along with the new 2013 Canadian General Social Survey data set.

## ANCILLARIES INSTRUCTOR RESOURCES

The **Nelson Education Teaching Advantage (NETA)** program delivers research-based instructor resources that promote student engagement and higher-order thinking to enable the success of Canadian students and educators. Visit Nelson Education's **Inspired Instruction** website at nelson.com /inspired/ to find out more about NETA.

The following instructor resources have been created for *Statistics: A Tool for Social Research*, Fourth Canadian Edition. Access these ultimate tools for customizing lectures and presentations at nelson.com/instructor.

## NETA TEST BANK

Full-Circle Assessment®

This resource was written by Markus Schafer of the University of Toronto. It includes over 500 multiple-choice questions written according to NETA guidelines for effective construction and development of higher-order questions. Also included are more than 40 problems.

The NETA test bank is available in a new, cloud-based platform. **Nelson Testing Powered by Cognero®** is a secure online testing system that allows instructors to author, edit, and manage test bank content from anywhere Internet access is available. No special installations or downloads are needed, and the desktop-inspired interface, with its drop-down menus and familiar, intuitive tools, allows instructors to create and manage tests with ease. Multiple test versions can be created in an instant, and content can be imported or exported into other systems. Tests can be delivered from a learning management system, the classroom, or wherever an instructor chooses. Nelson Testing Powered by Cognero for *Statistics: A Tool for Social Research*, Fourth Canadian Edition, can be accessed through nelson.com/instructor.

**NETA POWERPOINT**

Microsoft® PowerPoint® lecture slides for every chapter have been created by Irene Boeckmann University of Toronto. There is an average of 25 slides per chapter, many featuring key figures, and tables, from *Statistics: A Tool for Social Research*, Fourth Canadian Edition. NETA principles of clear design and engaging content have been incorporated throughout, making it simple for instructors to customize the deck of their courses.

**IMAGE LIBRARY**

This resource consists of digital copies of figures and short tables, used in the book. Instructors may use these jpegs to customize the NETA PowerPoint or create their own PowerPoint presentations. An Image Library Key describes the images and lists the codes under which the jpegs are saved.

**INSTRUCTOR'S MANUAL**

The Instructor's Manual to accompany *Statistics: A Tool for Social Research*, Fourth Canadian Edition, contains answers to even-numbered end-of-chapter problems and detailed answers to selected textbook problems. It also provides a "What can I do in class?" feature that includes 2–3 lesson ideas per chapter, and a "What can I do online?" feature, which includes 2–3 suggestions per chapter for engaging and instructing students using Web resources.

**APLIA**

**Aplia™** is a Cengage Learning online homework system dedicated to improving learning by increasing student effort and engagement. **Aplia** makes it easy for instructors to assign frequent online homework assignments. **Aplia** provides students with prompt and detailed feedback to help them learn as they work through the questions, and features interactive tutorials to fully engage them in learning course concepts. Automatic grading and powerful assessment tools give instructors real-time reports of student progress, participation, and performance, and while **Aplia's** easy-to-use course to management features let instructors flexibly administer course announcements and materials online. With **Aplia**, students will show up to class fully engaged and prepared, and instructors will have more time to do what they do best . . . teach.

**STUDENT ANCILLARIES**

Founded in 2000 by economist and Stanford professor Paul Romer, **Aplia™** is an educational technology company dedicated to improving learning by increasing student effort and engagement. Currently, **Aplia** products have been used by more than a million students at over 1,300 institutions. **Aplia** offers a way for you to stay on top of your coursework with regularly scheduled homework assignments that increase your time on task and give you prompt feedback. Interactive tools and additional content are provided to further increase your engagement and understanding. See Aplia.com for more information. If **Aplia** isn't bundled with your copy of *Statistics:*

*A Tool for Social Research*, Fourth Canadian Edition, you can purchase access separately at NELSONbrain.com. Be better prepared for class with **Aplia!** The **Aplia** course for *Statistic: A Tool for Social Research,* Fourth Canadian Edition, was prepared by text author Steven Prus.

 The **Student Companion Site** for *Statistics* at nelson.com/student is a comprehensive, resource-rich location for students to find pertinent information. As well as SPSS data sets used for the end-of-chapter SPSS demonstrations and exercises in the textbook, they'll find additional review and study materials, including online chapters, tables of frequently used formulas and random numbers, and more! It contains:

- **Data Sets and Code Books:** These data sets were written for use with Version 24 of IBM SPSS Statistics for Windows, but Versions 10 through 23 are completely compatible.
- **Cumulative exercises** at the end of each part provides practice in choosing, computing, and analyzing statistics. These exercises present only data sets and research questions. Students must choose appropriate statistics as part of the exercise.
- **Online Chapters:** Several online chapters to accompany the text.

## ACKNOWLEDGMENTS FOR THE FOURTH CANADIAN EDITION

I would like to first and foremost acknowledge and thank Dr. Teresa Abada, Western University; Dr. Alex Bierman, University of Calgary; Dr. Stephen Gyimah, Queen's University; Dr. Michelle Maroto, University of Alberta; Dr. Owen Temby, McGill University; and Dr. Michael Weinrath, University of Winnipeg, for their very helpful comments and advice in writing this textbook. The textbook and its various supplements and ancillaries have also greatly benefited from the reviews, suggestions, and guidance provided by many others. I am grateful to Catherine Gelinas, who worked diligently as technical reviewer on the textbook and solutions.

Along with others who prefer to remain anonymous, they include:

Edward Akmetshin, *University of British Columbia*
Liqun Cao, *University of Ontario Institute of Technology*
Daniel Cohn, *York University*
Lesley Frank, *Acadia University*
John Jayachandran, *Concordia University*
Zhiqiu Lin, *Carleton University*
Amir Mostaghim, *University of Ontario Institute of Technology*
Patricia Pakvis, *King's University College*
Jason Roy, *Wilfrid Laurier University*
Markus Schafer, *University of Toronto*
Gerry Veenstra, *University of British Columbia*

I wish to express a special thank you of gratitude to Riva Lieflander. This edition received extraordinary authorship from Riva. She worked on many of the key changes and additions in the fourth edition. Riva's dedication and insight have enriched and led to the successful completion of this textbook.

Maria Chu at Nelson Education provided the utmost effort and dedication to this project, and I am very thankful for her support. Finally, I would like to thank my wonderful children, Laura, Mandy, and Michael, and wife Kristen Presta. I dedicate this textbook to them.

We lastly acknowledge and are grateful to the Literary Executor of the late Sir Ronald A. Fisher, F.R.S., to Dr. Frank Yates, F.R.S., and to Longman Group Ltd., London, for permission to reprint Appendixes B, C, and D from their book *Statistical Tables for Biological, Agricultural and Medical Research* (6th ed., 1974). We are also grateful to Statistics Canada, for providing the General Social Survey and Canadian Community Health Survey data sets used in this textbook.

Steven G. Prus

# Prologue: Basic Mathematics Review

You will probably be relieved to hear that first courses in statistics are not particularly mathematical and do not stress computation per se. While you will encounter many numbers to work with and numerous formulas to use, the major emphasis will be on understanding the role of statistics in research and the logic by which we attempt to answer research questions empirically. You will also find that, at least in this textbook, the example problems and many of the homework problems have been intentionally simplified so that the computations will not unduly distract you from the task of understanding the statistics themselves.

On the other hand, you may regret to learn that there is, inevitably, some arithmetic that you simply cannot avoid if you want to master this material. It is likely that some of you haven't had any math in a long time, others have convinced themselves that they just cannot do math under any circumstances, and still others are just rusty and out of practice. However, you will find that even the most complex and intimidating operations and formulas can be broken down into simple steps. For those of you who have forgotten how to cope with some of these steps or are unfamiliar with these operations, this section is designed to ease you into the skills you will need to do all of the computation in this textbook.

**CALCULATORS AND COMPUTERS**

A calculator is a virtual necessity for this textbook. While you could do all the arithmetic by hand, a calculator will save you time and effort. Furthermore, calculator applications are conveniently available on most smartphones. While standard functions of addition, subtraction, multiplication, division, and square root are all you really need, you may want the learn additional features on your calculator including the memory and some pre-programmed functions.

Along the same lines, many of you probably have access to computers and statistical packages. If so, take the time now to learn how to use them, because they will eventually save you time and effort. This textbook includes a guide to a statistical package called IBM SPSS Statistics, but many other programs are available that will help you accomplish the goals of saving time and avoiding drudgery while generating precise and accurate results.

In summary, you should find a way at the beginning of this course—with a calculator, a statistical package, or both—to minimize the tedium and hassle of mere computing. This will permit you to devote maximum effort to the truly important goal of increasing your understanding of the meaning of statistics in particular and social research in general.

**VARIABLES AND SYMBOLS**

Statistics are a set of techniques by which we can describe, analyze, and manipulate variables. A variable is a trait that can change values from case to case or from time to time. Examples of variables include height, weight, level of education, and political party preference. The possible values associated with a given variable might be numerous (e.g., income) or relatively few (e.g., gender). We will often use symbols, usually the letter $X$, to refer to variables in general or to a specific variable.

Sometimes we will need to refer to a specific value or set of values of a variable. This is usually done with the aid of subscripts. So, the symbol $X_1$ (read "$X$-sub-one") would refer to the first score in a set of scores, $X_2$ ("$X$-sub-two") to the second score, and so forth. Also, we will use the subscript $i$ to refer to all the scores in a set. Thus, the symbol $X_i$ (read "$X$-sub-eye") refers to all of the scores associated with a given variable (e.g., the test grades of a particular class).

**OPERATIONS**

You are all familiar with the four basic mathematical operations of addition, subtraction, multiplication, and division and the standard symbols ($+$, $-$, $\times$, $\div$) used to denote them. Some of you may not be aware, however, that the latter two operations can be symbolized in a variety of ways. For example, the operation of multiplying some number $a$ by some number $b$ may be symbolized in (at least) six different ways:

$$a \times b$$
$$a \cdot b$$
$$a * b$$
$$ab$$
$$a(b)$$
$$(a)(b)$$

In this textbook, we will commonly use the "adjacent symbols" format (i.e., $ab$), the conventional times sign ($\times$), or adjacent parentheses to indicate multiplication. On most calculators and computers, the asterisk (*) is the symbol for multiplication.

The operation of division can also be expressed in several different ways. In this textbook, we will use either of these two methods:

$$a/b \quad \text{or} \quad \frac{a}{b}$$

Several of the formulas with which we will be working require us to find the square of a number. To do this, simply multiply the number by itself. This operation is symbolized as $X^2$ (read "$X$ squared"), which is the same thing as $(X)(X)$. If $X$ has a value of 4, then

$$X^2 = (X)(X) = (4)(4) = 16$$

or we could say that "4 squared is 16."

The square root of a number is the value that, when multiplied by itself, results in the original number. So the square root of 16 is 4 because (4)(4) is 16. The operation of finding the square root of a number is symbolized as

$$\sqrt{X}$$

Be sure you have access to a calculator with a built-in square root function.

A final operation with which you should be familiar is summation, or the addition of the scores associated with a particular variable. When a formula requires the addition of a series of scores, this operation is usually symbolized as $\Sigma X_i$. The symbol $\Sigma$ is the uppercase Greek letter sigma and stands for "the summation of." So the combination of symbols $\Sigma X_i$ means "the summation of all the scores" and directs us to add the value of all the scores for that variable. If four people had family sizes of 2, 4, 5, and 7, then the summation of these four scores for this variable could be symbolized as

$$\Sigma X_i = 2 + 4 + 5 + 7 = 18$$

The symbol $\Sigma$ is an operator, just like the + or × signs. It directs us to add all of the scores on the variable indicated by the $X$ symbol.

There are two other common uses of the summation sign, and unfortunately, the symbols denoting these uses are not, at first glance, sharply different from each other or from the symbol used above. A little practice and some careful attention to these various meanings should minimize the confusion. The first set of symbols is $\Sigma X_i^2$, which means "the sum of the squared scores." This quantity is found by *first* squaring each of the scores and *then* adding the squared scores together. A second common set of symbols will be $(\Sigma X_i)^2$, which means "the sum of the scores, squared." This quantity is found by *first* summing the scores and *then* squaring the total.

These distinctions might be confusing at first, so let's see if an example helps clarify the situation. Suppose we had a set of three scores: 10, 12, and 13. So,

$$X_i = 10, 12, 13$$

The sum of these scores would be indicated as

$$\Sigma X_i = 10 + 12 + 13 = 35$$

The sum of the squared scores would be

$$\Sigma X_i^2 = (10)^2 + (12)^2 + (13)^2 = 100 + 144 + 169 = 413$$

Take careful note of the order of operations here. First, the scores are squared one at a time and then the squared scores are added. This is a completely different operation from squaring the sum of the scores:

$$(\Sigma X_i)^2 = (10 + 12 + 13)^2 = (35)^2 = 1{,}225$$

To find this quantity, first the scores are summed and then the total of all the scores is squared. The value of the sum of the scores squared (1,225) is not the same as the value of the sum of the squared scores (413). In summary, the operations associated with each set of symbols are as follows:

| Symbols | Operations |
|---|---|
| $\Sigma X_i$ | Add the scores |
| $\Sigma X_i^2$ | First square the scores and then add the squared scores |
| $(\Sigma X_i)^2$ | First add the scores and then square the total |

## OPERATIONS WITH NEGATIVE NUMBERS

A number can be either positive (if it is preceded by a + sign or by no sign at all) or negative (if it is preceded by a − sign). Positive numbers are greater than zero, and negative numbers are less than zero. It is very important to keep track of signs because they will affect the outcome of virtually every mathematical operation. This section will briefly summarize the relevant rules for dealing with negative numbers. First, adding a negative number is the same as subtraction. For example,

$$3 + (-1) = 3 - 1 = 2$$

Second, subtraction changes the sign of a negative number:

$$3 - (-1) = 3 + 1 = 4$$

Note the importance of keeping track of signs here. If you neglected to change the sign of the negative number in the second expression, you would arrive at the wrong answer.

For multiplication and division, there are various combinations of negative and positive numbers you should be aware of. For purposes of this textbook, you will rarely have to multiply or divide more than two numbers at a time, and we will confine our attention to this situation. Ignoring the case of all positive numbers, this leaves several possible combinations. A negative number multiplied by a positive number results in a negative value:

$$(-3)(4) = -12$$

or

$$(3)(-4) = -12$$

A negative number multiplied by a negative number is always positive:

$$(-3)(-4) = 12$$

Division follows the same patterns. If there is a single negative number in the calculations, the answer will be negative. If both numbers are negative, the answer will be positive. So,

$$\frac{-4}{2} = -2$$

and

$$\frac{4}{-2} = -2$$

but

$$\frac{-4}{-2} = 2$$

Note that negative numbers do not have square roots, because multiplying a number by itself cannot result in a negative value. Squaring a negative number always results in a positive value (see the multiplication rules above).

**ACCURACY AND ROUNDING OFF**

A possible source of confusion in computation involves the issues of accuracy and rounding off. People work at different levels of accuracy and precision and, for this reason alone, may arrive at different answers to problems. This is important, because if you work at one level of precision and the textbook (or your instructor or your study partner) works at another, the resulting solutions will be at least slightly different. You may sometimes think you've gotten the wrong answer when all you've really done is round off at a different place in the calculations or in a different way.

There are two issues here: *when* to round off and *how* to round off. In this textbook, we have followed the convention of working with as much accuracy as our calculator or statistics package will allow and then rounding off to two places of accuracy (two places beyond the decimal point) at the very end. If a set of calculations is lengthy and requires the reporting of intermediate sums or subtotals, we will round the subtotals off to two places also.

In terms of how to round off, begin by looking at the digit immediately to the right of the last digit you want to retain. If you want to round off to 100ths (two places beyond the decimal point), look at the digit in the 1000ths place (three places beyond the decimal point). If that digit is greater than 5, round up. For example, 23.346 would round off to 23.35. If the digit to the right is less than 5, round down. So, 23.343 would become 23.34. If the digit to the right is 5, round up if the digit immediately to the left is even and round down if the digit is odd. So, 23.345 would become 23.35 and 23.355 would round to 23.35.

Let's look at some more examples of how to follow the rounding rules stated above. If you are calculating the mean value of a set of test scores and your calculator shows a final value of 83.459067, and you want to round off to two places beyond the decimal point, look at the digit three places beyond the decimal point. In this case the value is 9 (greater than 5), so we would round the second digit beyond the decimal point up and report the mean as 83.46. If the value had been 83.453067, we would have reported our final answer as 83.45. A value of 83.455067 would round to 83.45, and a value of 83.445067 would be 83.45.

**FORMULAS, COMPLEX OPERATIONS, AND THE ORDER OF OPERATIONS**

A mathematical formula is a set of directions, stated in general symbols, for calculating a particular statistic. To "solve a formula" means that you must replace the symbols with the proper values and then manipulate the values through a series of calculations. Even the most complex formula can be rendered manageable if it is broken down into smaller steps. Working through these steps requires some knowledge of general procedure and the rules of precedence of mathematical operations. This is because the order in which you perform calculations may affect your final answer. Consider the following expression:

$$2 + 3(4)$$

Note that if you do the addition first, you will evaluate the expression as

$$5(4) = 20$$

but if you do the multiplication first, the expression becomes

$$2 + 12 = 14$$

Obviously, it is crucial to complete the steps of a calculation in the correct order.

The basic rules of precedence are to find all squares and square roots first, then do all multiplication and division, and finally complete all addition and subtraction. So the following expression:

$$8 + 2 \times 2^2/2$$

would be evaluated as

$$8 + 2 \times \frac{4}{2} = 8 + \frac{8}{2} = 8 + 4 = 12$$

The rules of precedence may be overridden when an expression contains parentheses. Solve all expressions within parentheses before applying the rules stated above. For most of the complex formulas in this textbook, the order of calculations will be controlled by the parentheses. Consider the following expression:

$$(8 + 2) - 4(3)^2/(8 - 6)$$

Resolving the parenthetical expressions first, we would have

$$(10) - 4 \times 9/(2) = 10 - 36/2 = 10 - 18 = -8$$

Without the parentheses, the same expression would be evaluated as

$$8 + 2 - 4 \times 3^2/8 - 6$$
$$= 8 + 2 - 4 \times 9/8 - 6$$
$$= 8 + 2 - 36/8 - 6$$
$$= 8 + 2 - 4.5 - 6$$
$$= 10 - 10.5$$
$$= -0.5$$

A final operation you will encounter in some formulas in this textbook involves denominators of fractions that themselves contain fractions. In this situation, solve the fraction in the denominator first and then complete the division. For example,

$$\frac{15 - 9}{6/2}$$

would become

$$\frac{15 - 9}{6/2} = \frac{6}{3} = 2$$

When you are confronted with complex expressions such as these, don't be intimidated. If you're patient with yourself and work through them step by step, beginning with the parenthetical expression, even the most imposing formulas can be managed.

**EXERCISES**

You can use the problems below as a "self-test" on the material presented in this review. If you can handle these problems, you're ready to do all of the arithmetic in this textbook. If you have difficulty with any of these problems, please review the appropriate section of this prologue. You might also want to use this section as an opportunity to become more familiar with your calculator. Answers are given on the next page, along with some commentary and some reminders.

**1.** Complete each of the following:
    **a.** $17 \times 3 =$
    **b.** $17(3) =$
    **c.** $(17)(3) =$
    **d.** $17/3 =$
    **e.** $(42)^2 =$
    **f.** $\sqrt{113} =$

**2.** For the set of scores ($X_i$) of 50, 55, 60, 65, and 70, evaluate each of the expressions below:

$\Sigma X_i =$

$\Sigma X_i^2 =$

$(\Sigma X_i)^2 =$

**3.** Complete each of the following:

**a.** $17 + (-3) + (4) + (-2) =$

**b.** $15 - 3 - (-5) + 2 =$

**c.** $(-27)(54) =$

**d.** $(113)(-2) =$

**e.** $(-14)(-100) =$

**f.** $-34/-2 =$

**g.** $322/-11 =$

**4.** Round off each of the following to two places beyond the decimal point:

**a.** 17.17532

**b.** 43.119

**c.** 1,076.77337

**d.** 32.4651152301

**e.** 32.4751152301

**5.** Evaluate each of the following:

**a.** $(3 + 7)/10 =$

**b.** $3 + 7/10 =$

**c.** $\dfrac{(4 - 3) + (7 + 2)(3)}{(4 + 5)(10)} =$

**ANSWERS TO EXERCISES**

**1. a.** 51    **b.** 51    **c.** 51 (The obvious purpose of these first three problems is to remind you that there are several different ways of expressing multiplication.)

**d.** 5.67 (Note the rounding off.)    **e.** 1,764    **f.** 10.63

**2.** The first expression translates to "the sum of the scores," so this operation would be

$$\Sigma X_i = 50 + 55 + 60 + 65 + 70 = 300$$

The second expression is the "sum of the squared scores." So

$$\Sigma X_i^2 = (50)^2 + (55)^2 + (60)^2 + (65)^2 + (70)^2$$

$$\Sigma X_i^2 = 2{,}500 + 3{,}025 + 3{,}600 + 4{,}225 + 4{,}900$$

$$\Sigma X_i^2 = 18{,}250$$

The third expression is "the sum of the scores, squared":

$$(\Sigma X_i)^2 = (50 + 55 + 60 + 65 + 70)^2$$

$$(\Sigma X_i)^2 = (300)^2$$

$$(\Sigma X_i)^2 = 90{,}000$$

Remember that $\Sigma X_i^2$ and $(\Sigma X_i)^2$ are two completely different expressions with very different values.

**3. a.** 16    **b.** 19 (Remember to change the sign of $-5$.)    **c.** $-1{,}458$
   **d.** $-226$    **e.** 1,400    **f.** 17    **g.** $-29.27$

**4. a.** 17.17    **b.** 43.12    **c.** 1,076.77
   **d.** 32.47    **e.** 32.47

**5. a.** 1    **b.** 3.7 (Note again the importance of parentheses.)    **c.** 0.31

# 1

# Introduction

**LEARNING OBJECTIVES**

By the end of this chapter, you will be able to

1. Describe the limited but crucial role of statistics in social research.
2. Distinguish between the two general classes of statistical techniques (descriptive and inferential) and identify situations in which each is appropriate.
3. Distinguish between discrete and continuous variables and cite examples of each.
4. Identify and describe three levels of measurement and cite examples of variables from each.

## 1.1 WHY STUDY STATISTICS?

Students sometimes approach their first course in statistics with questions about the value of the subject matter. What, after all, do numbers and statistics have to do with understanding people and society? In a sense, this entire textbook will attempt to answer this question, and the value of statistics will become clear as we move from chapter to chapter. For now, the importance of statistics can be demonstrated, in a preliminary way, by briefly reviewing the research process as it operates in the social sciences. These disciplines are scientific in the sense that social scientists attempt to verify their ideas and theories through research. Broadly conceived, **research** is any process by which information is systematically and carefully gathered for the purpose of answering questions, examining ideas, or testing theories. Research is a disciplined inquiry that can take numerous forms. Statistical analysis is relevant only for those research projects where the information collected is represented by numbers. Numerical information is called **data**, and the sole purpose of statistics is to manipulate and analyze data. **Statistics**, then, are a set of mathematical techniques used by social scientists to organize and manipulate data for the purpose of answering questions and testing theories. Sometimes, the numbers obtained after applying these techniques are also called statistics.

What is so important about learning how to manipulate data? On the one hand, some of the most important and enlightening works in the social sciences do not utilize any statistical techniques. There is nothing magical about data and statistics. The mere presence of numbers guarantees nothing about the quality of a scientific inquiry. On the other hand, data can be the most trustworthy information available to the researcher and, consequently, deserve special attention. Data that have been carefully collected and thoughtfully analyzed are the strongest, most objective foundations for building theory and enhancing understanding. Without a firm base in data, the social sciences would lose the right to the name *science* and would be of far less value.

Thus, the social sciences rely heavily on data analysis for the advancement of knowledge. Let us be very clear about one point: it is never enough merely to gather data (or, for that matter, any kind of information). Even the most objective and carefully collected numerical information does not and cannot speak for itself. The researcher must be able to use statistics effectively to organize, evaluate, analyze, and interpret the data. Without a good understanding of the principles of statistical analysis, the researcher will be unable to make sense of the data. Without the appropriate application of statistical techniques, the data will remain mute and useless.

Statistics are an indispensable tool for the social sciences. They provide the scientist with some of the most useful techniques for evaluating ideas, testing theory, and discovering the truth. The next section describes the relationships among theory, research, and statistics in more detail.

## 1.2 THE ROLE OF STATISTICS IN SCIENTIFIC INQUIRY

Figure 1.1 graphically represents the role of statistics in the research process. The diagram is based on the thinking of Walter Wallace and illustrates how the knowledge base of any scientific enterprise grows and develops. One point the diagram makes is that scientific theory and research continually shape each other. Statistics are one of the most important means by which research and theory interact. Let's take a closer look at the wheel.

Because the figure is circular, it has no beginning or end, and we could begin our discussion at any point. For the sake of convenience, let's begin at the top and follow the arrows around the circle. A **theory** is an explanation of the relationships among phenomena. People naturally (and endlessly) wonder about problems in society (such as prejudice, poverty, child abuse,

**FIGURE 1.1    The Wheel of Science**

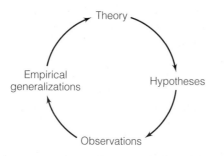

Source: Adapted from W. Wallace, *The Logic of Science in Sociology*. Copyright © 1971 by Transaction Publishers. Reprinted by permission of the publisher.

or serial murders), and in their attempts to understand these phenomena, they develop explanations ("lack of education causes prejudice"). This kind of informal "theorizing" about society is no doubt very familiar to you. One major difference between our informal, everyday explanations of social phenomena and scientific theory is that the latter is subject to a rigorous testing process. Let's take the problem of health inequality as an example to illustrate how the research process works.

Why do people differ in their health? One possible answer to this question is provided by the *materialistic theory*. This theory was stated over 30 years ago in the groundbreaking *Black Report*, named after the physician Sir Douglas Black, on health inequalities in the United Kingdom.* It has been tested on a number of occasions since that time.

According to the materialistic theory, health is affected by social class. We often think it is the individual who chooses whether to have a healthy diet, participate in leisure exercise, protect his or her own health and prevent illness (e.g., annual physical, flu shot), and so on. The materialist theory asserts that such "individual choices" are constrained by one's social class. Social class is linked to health by one's access to resources such as health care; preventative health care services; adequate diet; and safe housing, living, and working conditions that are necessary to maintain and improve health.

The materialistic theory is not a complete explanation of health inequality, but it can serve to illustrate a sociological theory. This theory offers an explanation for the relationship between two social phenomena: (1) health inequality and (2) social class. People of a lower social class will have poorer health, and those of a higher social class will have better health.

Before moving on, let us examine theory in a little more detail. The materialistic theory, like most theories, is stated in terms of causal relationships between variables. A **variable** is any trait that can change values from case to case. Examples of variables would be gender, age, ethnicity, or political party affiliation. (Remember that a variable must be able to vary—so if your study includes only women, then gender would not be a variable.) In any specific theory, some variables will be identified as causes and others will be identified as effects or results. In the language of science, the causes are called **independent variables** and the effects or result variables are called **dependent variables**. In our theory, social class is the independent variable (or the cause) and health is the dependent variable (the result or effect). In other words, we are arguing that social class is a cause of health condition or that an individual's level of health depends on his or her social class.

---

*Source: P. Townsend and N. Davidson (eds). 1982. *Inequalities in Health: The Black Report*. Harmondsworth, UK: Penguin Books.

Diagrams can be a useful way of representing the relationships between variables:

$$\text{Social Class} \rightarrow \text{Health}$$

$$\text{Independent Variable} \rightarrow \text{Dependent Variable}$$

$$X \rightarrow Y$$

The arrow represents the direction of the causal relationship, and "$X$" and "$Y$" are general symbols for the independent and dependent variables, respectively.

So far, we have a theory of health and an independent and a dependent variable. What we do not know yet is whether the theory is true or false. To find out, we need to compare our theory with the facts—we need to do some research. The next step in the process would be to define our terms and ideas more specifically and exactly. One problem we often face in conducting research is that scientific theories are too complex and abstract to be fully tested in a single research project. To conduct research, one or more hypotheses must be derived from the theory. A **hypothesis** is a statement about the relationship between variables that, while logically derived from the theory, is much more specific and exact.

For example, if we wish to test the materialistic theory, we have to say exactly what we mean by social class and health. There has been a great deal of research on the effects of social class on health, and we would consult the research literature to develop and clarify our definitions of these concepts. As our definitions develop and the hypothesis takes shape, we begin the next step of the research process, during which we decide exactly how we will gather our data. We must decide how cases will be selected and tested and how the variables will be measured. Ultimately, these plans will lead to the observation phase (the bottom of the wheel of science), where we actually measure social reality. Before we can do this, however, we must have a very clear idea of what we are looking for and a well-defined strategy for conducting the search.

To test the materialistic theory, we would begin by considering people from all sections of society (rich, poor, healthy, unhealthy, and so on). Then, we need to decide what our measures of social class and health status are. In other words, we need to operationalize the concepts of social class and health status. For example, we may decide to use those measures used in the *Black Report*: occupation and chronic illness as measures of social class and health, respectively. We would then administer a survey that asked each person, "What is your current main occupation?" and "How many long-term or chronic medical conditions diagnosed by a health professional do you have?" Our goal would be to see whether people with higher occupational status have fewer chronic illnesses.

Now, finally, we come to statistics. As the observation phase of our research project comes to an end, we will be confronted with a large collection of numerical information or data. If our sample consisted of 2,000 people, we would have 2,000 completed surveys measuring social class and health. Try to imagine dealing with 2,000 completed surveys. If we had asked each respondent five questions about their health, instead of just one question, we would have a total of 10,000 separate pieces of information to deal with. What do we do? We need to have some systematic way to organize and analyze this information; at this point, statistics will be very valuable. Statistics will provide us with many ideas about "what to do" with the data (we will begin to look at some of the options in Chapter 2). For now, let us stress two points about statistics.

First, statistics are crucial. Simply put, without statistics, quantitative research is impossible. Without quantitative research, the development of the social sciences would be severely impaired. Only through the application of statistical techniques can mere data help us shape and refine our theories and understand the social world better. Second, and somewhat paradoxically, the role of statistics is rather limited. As Figure 1.1 makes clear, scientific research proceeds through several mutually interdependent stages, and statistics become directly relevant only at the end of the observation stage. Before any statistical analysis can be legitimately applied, the preceding phases of the process must have been successfully completed. If the researcher has asked poorly conceived questions or has made serious errors of design or method, then even the most sophisticated statistical analysis is valueless. As useful as they can be, statistics cannot substitute for rigorous conceptualization, detailed and careful planning, or creative use of theory. Statistics cannot salvage a poorly conceived or designed research project. They cannot make sense out of garbage.

Conversely, inappropriate statistical applications can limit the usefulness of an otherwise carefully done project. Only by successfully completing *all* phases of the process can a quantitative research project hope to contribute to understanding. A reasonable knowledge of the uses and limitations of statistics is as essential to the education of the social scientist as is training in theory and methodology.

As the statistical analysis comes to an end, we would begin to develop empirical generalizations. While we would be primarily focused on assessing our theory, we would also look for other trends in the data. Assuming that we found that social class was linked to health in general, we might go on to ask if the pattern applies to males as well as females or to older respondents as well as younger ones. As we probed the data, we might begin to develop some generalizations based on the empirical patterns we observe. For example, what if we found that social class was linked to health for older respondents but not for younger respondents? Could it be that material advantages and disadvantages have a cumulative effect on health, so that the social class–health link does not emerge until old age? As we developed tentative explanations, we would begin to revise or elaborate our theory.

If we change the theory to take account of these findings, however, a new research project designed to test the revised theory will be called for and the wheel of science will begin to turn again. We (or perhaps some other researchers) will go through the entire process once again with this new—and, hopefully, improved—theory. This second project might result in further revisions and elaborations that would (you guessed it) require still more research projects, and the wheel of science would continue turning as long as scientists were able to suggest additional revisions or develop new insights. Every time the wheel turned, our understandings of the phenomena under consideration would (hopefully) improve.

This description of the research process does not include white-coated, clipboard-carrying scientists who, in a blinding flash of inspiration, discover some fundamental truth about reality and shout, "Eureka!". The truth is that, in the normal course of science, it is a rare occasion when we can say with absolute certainty that a given theory or idea is definitely true or false. Rather, evidence for (or against) a theory gradually accumulates over time, and ultimate judgments of truth are likely the result of many years of hard work, research, and debate.

Let's briefly review our imaginary research project. We began with an idea or theory about social class and health. We imagined some of the steps we would have to take to test the theory and took a quick look at the various stages of the research project. We wound up back at the level of theory, ready to begin a new project guided by a revised theory. We saw how theory can motivate a research project and how our observations can cause us to revise the theory and, thus, motivate a new research project. Wallace's wheel of science illustrates how theory stimulates research and how research shapes theory. This constant interaction between theory and research is the lifeblood of science and the key to enhancing our understandings of the social world.

The dialogue between theory and research occurs at many levels and in multiple forms. Statistics are one of the most important links between these two realms. Statistics permit us to analyze data, to identify and probe trends and relationships, to develop generalizations, and to revise and improve our theories. As you will see throughout this textbook, statistics are limited in many ways. They are also an indispensable part of the research enterprise. Without statistics, the interaction between theory and research would become extremely difficult, and the progress of our disciplines would be severely retarded. *(For practice in describing the relationship between theory and research and the role of statistics in research, see Problems 1.1 and 1.2.)*

## 1.3 THE GOALS OF THIS TEXTBOOK

In the preceding section, we argued that statistics are a crucial part of the process by which scientific investigations are carried out and that, therefore, some training in statistical analysis is a crucial component in the education of every social scientist. In this section, we address the questions of how much training is necessary and what the purposes of that training are. First, this textbook takes the point of view that statistics are tools. They can be a very useful means of increasing our knowledge of the social world, but they are not ends in themselves. Thus, we will not take a "mathematical" approach to the subject. The techniques will be presented as a set of tools that can be used to answer important questions. This emphasis does not mean we will dispense with arithmetic entirely, of course. This textbook includes enough mathematical material to help you develop a basic understanding of why statistics "do what they do." Our focus, however, will be on how these techniques are applied in the social sciences.

Second, all of you will soon become involved in advanced coursework in your major fields of study, and you will find that much of the literature used in these courses assumes at least basic statistical literacy. Furthermore, many of you, after graduation, will find yourselves in positions—either in a career or in graduate school—where some understanding of statistics will be very helpful or perhaps even required. Very few of you will become statisticians per se (and this textbook is not intended for the pre-professional statistician), but you must have a grasp of statistics in order to read and critically appreciate your own professional literature. As a student in the social sciences and in many careers related to the social sciences, you simply cannot realize your full potential without a background in statistics.

Within these constraints, this textbook is an introduction to statistics as they are utilized in the social sciences. Its general goal is to develop an appreciation—a "healthy respect"—for statistics and their place in research. You should emerge from this experience with the ability to use statistics intelligently and to know when other people have done so. You should be familiar with the advantages and limitations of the more commonly used statistical techniques, and you should know which techniques are appropriate for a given set of data and a given purpose. Lastly, you should develop sufficient statistical and computational skills and enough experience in the interpretation of statistics to be able to carry out some elementary forms of data analysis by yourself.

## 1.4 DESCRIPTIVE AND INFERENTIAL STATISTICS

As noted earlier, the general function of statistics is to manipulate data so that research questions can be answered. There are two general classes of statistical techniques that, depending on the research situation, are available to accomplish this task. Each is introduced in this section.

**Descriptive Statistics.**   The first class of techniques is called **descriptive statistics** and is relevant in several different situations:

1. When the researcher needs to summarize or describe the distribution of a single variable. These statistics are called *univariate* (one variable) descriptive statistics.

**2.** When the researcher wishes to describe the relationship between two or more variables. These statistics are called *bivariate* (two variables) or *multivariate* (more than two variables) descriptive statistics.

To describe a single variable, we would arrange the values or scores of that variable so that the relevant information can be quickly understood and appreciated. Many of the statistics that might be appropriate for this summarizing task are probably familiar to you. For example, percentages, graphs, and charts can all be used to describe single variables.

To illustrate the usefulness of univariate descriptive statistics, consider the following problem: Suppose you wanted to summarize the distribution of the variable "family income" for a community of 10,000 families. How would you do it? Obviously, you couldn't simply list all incomes in the community and let it go at that. Imagine trying to make sense of a list of 10,000 different incomes! Presumably, you would want to develop some summary measures of the overall income distributions—perhaps an arithmetic average or the proportions of incomes that fall in various ranges (such as low, middle, and high). Or perhaps a graph or a chart would be more useful. Whatever specific method you choose, its function is the same: to reduce these thousands of individual items of information into a few easily understood numbers. The process of allowing a few numbers to summarize many numbers is called **data reduction** and is the basic goal of univariate descriptive statistical procedures.

By contrast, bivariate and multivariate descriptive statistics are designed to help the investigator understand the relationship between two or more variables. These statistics, also called **measures of association**, allow the researcher to quantify the strength and direction of a relationship. These statistics are very useful because they enable us to investigate two matters of central theoretical and practical importance to any science: causation and prediction. These techniques help us disentangle and uncover the connections between variables. They help us trace the ways in which some variables might have causal influences on others; and, depending on the strength of the relationship, they enable us to predict scores on one variable from the scores on another. Note that measures of association cannot, by themselves, prove that two variables are causally related. However, these techniques can provide valuable clues about causation and are therefore extremely important for theory testing and theory construction.

For example, suppose you were interested in the relationship between "time spent studying statistics" and "final grade in statistics" and had gathered data on these two variables from a group of university students. By calculating the appropriate measure of association, you could determine the strength of the bivariate relationship and its direction. Suppose you found a strong, positive relationship. This would indicate that "study time" and "grade" were closely related (strength of the relationship) and that as one increased in value, the other also increased (direction of the relationship).

You could make predictions from one variable to the other ("the longer the study time, the higher the grade").

As a result of finding this strong, positive relationship, you might be tempted to make causal inferences. That is, you might jump to such conclusions as "longer study time leads to (causes) higher grades." Such a conclusion might make a good deal of common sense and would certainly be supported by your statistical analysis. However, the causal nature of the relationship cannot be proven by the statistical analysis. Measures of association can be taken as important clues about causation, but the mere existence of a relationship can never be taken as conclusive proof of causation.

In fact, other variables might have an effect on the relationship. In the example above, we probably would not find a perfect relationship between "study time" and "final grade." That is, we will probably find some individuals who spend a great deal of time studying but receive low grades, and some individuals who fit the opposite pattern. We know intuitively that other variables besides study time affect grades (such as efficiency of study techniques, amount of background in mathematics, and even random chance). Fortunately, researchers can also incorporate these other variables into the analysis and measure their effects.

**Inferential Statistics.** This second class of statistical techniques becomes relevant when we wish to generalize our findings from a **sample** to a **population**. A population is the total collection of all cases that the researcher is interested in and wishes to understand better. Examples of possible populations would be all eligible voters in Canada, unemployed youth in the Greater Toronto Area, or students enrolled at the University of British Columbia.

Populations can theoretically range from inconceivable in size (all humanity) to quite small (all professional hockey players residing in the City of Ottawa) but are usually fairly large. In fact, they are almost always too large to be measured. To put the problem another way, social scientists almost never have the resources or time to test every case in a population. Hence the need for **inferential statistics**, which involve using information from a sample (a carefully chosen subset of the population) to make inferences about a population. Because they have fewer cases, samples are much cheaper to assemble, and—if the proper techniques are followed—generalizations based on these samples can be very accurate representations of the population.

There are two general uses of inferential statistics: estimation and hypothesis testing. While many of the concepts and procedures involved in inferential statistics may be unfamiliar, most of us are experienced consumers of them—most familiarly, perhaps, in the form of public opinion polls and election projections. When a public opinion poll reports that 36 percent of the Canadian electorate plans to vote for a certain political party, it is essentially reporting a generalization to a population (the "Canadian electorate," which numbers about 24 million people) from a carefully drawn sample (usually about 1,500 respondents).

**The Descriptive-Inferential Statistics Divide.**   The textbook is divided into four parts, with each part focusing on one or both of the two fundamental (descriptive and inferential) classes of statistics. Part 1 reviews statistical procedures that describe the distribution of a single variable (i.e., univariate descriptive statistics). These procedures include frequency distributions and graphs (Chapter 2), measures of central tendency and dispersion (Chapter 3), and $Z$ scores and the normal curve (Chapter 4).

Part 2 of the textbook provides a transition from description to inference. Chapter 5 looks at the logic behind inferential statistics and Chapter 6 looks at one of the two main applications of inferential statistics: estimation.

In Part 3 we turn our attention to bivariate relationships, where both measures of association (descriptive statistics) and hypothesis testing (the other main application of inferential statistics) are discussed. This part of the textbook is organized according to the *level of measurement* of the variables (to be discussed in Section 1.6) whose relationship we are going to examine. We begin with a discussion of hypothesis testing for "nominal" or "ordinal" variables in Chapter 7. Next, we look at measures of association designed for situations where both variables are measured at the nominal level in Chapter 8 and ordinal level in Chapter 9. Before we move on to situations where both variables are measured at the "interval-ratio" level (Chapter 13), we first consider measures of association and hypothesis testing for situations where we have a combination of nominal, ordinal, and interval-ratio variables, in Chapters 10 through 12. Part 4 introduces multivariate descriptive statistics used to describe the relationship between three or more interval-ratio variables. Multiple regression and partial correlation (Chapter 14) are multivariate extensions of the techniques introduced in Chapter 13.

In summary, Figure 1.2 provides a diagram outlining the structure of this textbook, in which descriptive and inferential statistical procedures are divided by type of analysis (univariate, bivariate, multivariate) and uses of inferential statistics (estimation, hypothesis testing). As we will see in the next two sections of this chapter, the nature of the variable(s) under consideration largely determines what statistical procedure to use in our research. *(For practice in describing different statistical applications, see Problems 1.3 and 1.7.)*

## 1.5 DISCRETE AND CONTINUOUS VARIABLES

In Chapter 2, you will begin to encounter some of the broad array of statistics available to social scientists. One aspect of using statistics that can be puzzling is deciding when to use which statistic. You will learn specific guidelines as you go along, but we will introduce some basic and general guidelines at this point. The first of these concerns discrete and continuous variables; the second, covered in the next section, concerns level of measurement.

A variable is said to be **discrete** if it has a basic unit of measurement that cannot be subdivided. For example, number of people per household

**FIGURE 1.2  An Overview of Statistical Procedures, by Type of Analysis and Inferential Statistic**

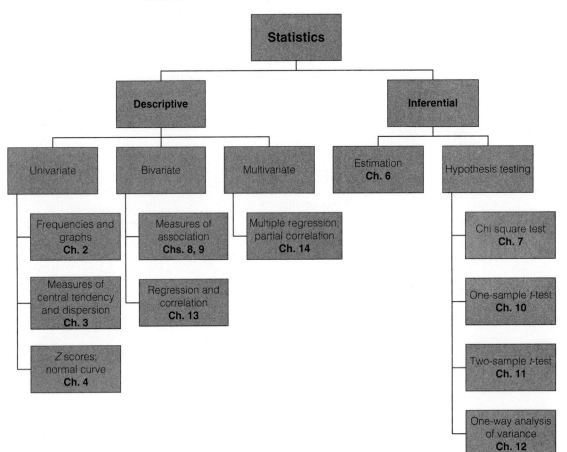

is a discrete variable. The basic unit is people, a variable that will always be measured in whole numbers: you'll never find 2.7 people living in a specific household. The scores for a discrete variable will be zero, one, two, three, or some other whole integer. Other discrete variables include number of siblings, children, or cars. To measure these variables, we count the number of units for each case and record results in whole numbers.

A variable is **continuous** if the measurement of it can be subdivided infinitely—at least in a theoretical sense. One example of a continuous variable would be time, which can be measured in minutes, seconds, milliseconds (thousandths of a second), nanoseconds (billionths of a second), or even smaller units. In a sense, when we measure a continuous variable, we are always approximating and rounding off the scores. We could report somebody's time in the 100-metre dash as 10.7 seconds or 10.732451 seconds, but, because time can be infinitely subdivided (if we have the technology to make the precise measurements), we will never be able to report the exact time elapsed. Since we cannot work with infinitely long numbers, we must report the scores on continuous variables as if they were discrete.

The distinction between these two types of variables relates more to measuring and processing the information than to the appearance of the data. This distinction between discrete and continuous variables is one of the most basic in statistics and will constitute one of the criteria by which we will choose among various statistics and graphic devices. *(For practice in distinguishing between discrete and continuous variables, see Problems 1.4–1.8.)*

## 1.6 LEVEL OF MEASUREMENT

A second basic and very important guideline for the selection of statistics is the **level of measurement** or the mathematical nature of the variables under consideration. The best way to identify a variable's mathematical nature is to look at its **response categories**. Response categories are a variable's possible attributes, qualities, or characteristics. For example, the response categories of a variable measuring a person's first-learned language might be "English," "French," "English and French," and "Neither English nor French." In other words, where the discrete-continuous distinction looks at a variable's *unit of measurement*, the level of measurement distinction looks at a variable's *response categories*.

Variables at the highest level of measurement have numerical scores and can be analyzed with a broad range of statistics. Variables at lower levels of measurement have "scores" that are really just labels, not numbers at all. Statistics that require numerical variables are inappropriate, and often completely meaningless, when used with non-numerical variables. When selecting statistics, you must be sure that the level of measurement of the variable justifies the mathematical operations required to compute the statistic.

For example, consider the variables age (when measured in years, rather than in year ranges) and income (when measured in dollars, rather than in dollar ranges). Both of these variables have numerical scores and could be summarized with a statistic such as the mean or average (e.g., "The average income of this city is $43,000." "The average age of students on this campus is 19.7 years.").

However, the mean or average would be meaningless as a way of describing gender or area codes, which are variables with non-numerical scores. Your personal area code might *look* like a number but it is merely an arbitrary label that happens to be expressed in digits. These "numbers" cannot be added or divided, and statistics like the average cannot be applied to this variable: the average area code of a group of people is a meaningless statistic.

Determining the level at which a variable has been measured is one of the first and most foundationally important steps in any statistical analysis, and we will consider this matter at some length. We will make it a practice throughout this textbook to introduce level-of-measurement considerations for each statistical technique.

The three levels of measurement, in order of increasing sophistication, are nominal, ordinal, and interval-ratio. Each is discussed separately. To reiterate an important point: We need to examine a variable's response categories—rather than the variable's definition—in order to identify the variable's level of measurement.

**Nominal Level of Measurement.** Variables measured at the **nominal** level simply classify observations into "scores" or categories. Examples of variables at this level include gender, area code, province of residence, religious affiliation, and place of birth. At this lowest level of measurement, the only mathematical operation permitted is comparing the relative sizes of the categories (e.g., "there are more females than males in this residence"). The categories or scores of nominal-level variables cannot be ranked with respect to one another and cannot be added, divided, or otherwise manipulated mathematically. Even when the scores or categories are expressed in digits (such as area codes or street addresses), all we can do is compare relative sizes of categories (e.g., "the most common area code on this campus is 221"). The categories themselves are not a mathematical scale: they are different from one another but not more or less, or higher or lower than one another. Males and females differ in terms of gender, but neither category has more or less gender than the other. In the same way, an area code of 621 is different from but not "more than" an area code of 221.

Although nominal variables are rudimentary, we need to observe certain criteria and procedures in order to ensure adequate measurement. In fact, these criteria apply to variables measured at *all* levels, not just nominal variables. First, the categories of nominal-level variables must be "mutually exclusive" so that no ambiguity exists concerning classification of any given case. There must be one and only one category for each case. Second, the categories must be "exhaustive," that is, a category must exist for every possible score that might be found, even if it is only an "other" or miscellaneous category.

Third, the categories of nominal variables should be relatively "homogeneous," that is, our categories should include cases that are comparable. To put it another way, we need to avoid categories that lump apples with oranges. There are no hard and fast guidelines for judging whether a set of categories is appropriately homogeneous. The researcher must make that decision in terms of the specific purpose of the research. Categories that are too broad for some purposes may be perfectly adequate for others.

Table 1.1 demonstrates some errors of measurement in four different schemes for measuring the variable "religious affiliation." Scale A in the table violates the criterion of mutual exclusivity because of the overlap between the categories Catholic and Christian and Protestant and Christian. Scale B is not exhaustive because it does not provide a category for people who belong to religions other than the eight listed or for people with no religious affiliation (None). Scale C uses a category (Non-Catholic) that would be too broad for many research purposes. Scale D represents the way religious affiliation is often

**TABLE 1.1  Four Scales for Measuring Religious Affiliation**

| Scale A (not mutually exclusive) | Scale B (not exhaustive) | Scale C (not homogeneous) | Scale D (an adequate scale) |
|---|---|---|---|
| Catholic | Catholic | Catholic | Catholic |
| Protestant | Protestant | Non-Catholic | Protestant |
| Christian | Other Christian | | Other Christian |
| Jewish | Jewish | | Jewish |
| Muslim | Muslim | | Muslim |
| Buddhist | Buddhist | | Buddhist |
| Hindu | Hindu | | Hindu |
| Sikh | Sikh | | Sikh |
| Other religions | | | Other religions |
| None | | | None |

measured in Canada, but note that these categories may be too general for some research projects and not comprehensive enough for others. For example, an investigation of issues that have strong moral and religious content (assisted suicide, abortion, or capital punishment) might need to distinguish between the various Protestant denominations (e.g., United Church, Presbyterian, Lutheran, Anglican, Baptist, Jehovah's Witness, Pentecostal, Mormon), and an effort to document religious diversity would need to add categories for other Eastern or Christian religions (e.g., Bahai, Greek Orthodox). Likewise, Scale D does not capture the variety within Islam, Judaism, and other non-Christian religions.

Numerical labels are often used to identify the categories of variables measured at the nominal level. This practice is especially common when the data are being prepared for computer analysis. For example, the various religions might be labelled with a 1 indicating Catholic, a 2 signifying Protestant. Remember that these numbers are merely labels or names and have no numerical quality to them. They cannot be added, subtracted, multiplied, or divided. The only mathematical operation permissible with nominal variables is counting and comparing the number of cases in each category of the variable.

**Ordinal Level of Measurement.**   Variables measured at the **ordinal** level are more sophisticated than nominal-level variables. They have scores or categories that can be ranked from high to low so that, in addition to classifying cases into categories, we can describe the categories in terms of "more or less" with respect to one another. Thus, with variables measured at this level, not only can we say that one case is different from another; we can also say that one case is higher or lower, more or less, than another.

For example, the variable socioeconomic status (SES) is usually measured at the ordinal level. The categories of the variable are often ordered according to the following scheme:

4. Upper class
3. Middle class
2. Working class
1. Lower class

Individual cases can be compared in terms of the categories into which they are classified. Thus, an individual classified as a 4 (upper class) would be ranked higher than an individual classified as a 2 (working class), and a lower-class person (1) would rank lower than a middle-class person (3). Other variables that are usually measured at the ordinal level include attitudes and opinions—for example, prejudice, alienation, or political conservatism.

The major limitation of the ordinal level of measurement is that a particular score represents only position with respect to some other score. We can distinguish between high and low scores, but the distance between the scores cannot be described in precise terms. Although we know that a score of 4 is more than a score of 2, we do not know if it is twice as much as 2.

Because we don't know the exact distances from score to score on an ordinal scale, our options for statistical analysis are limited. For example, addition (and most other mathematical operations) assumes that the intervals between scores are exactly equal. If the distances from score to score are not equal, 2 + 2 might equal 3 or 5 or even 15. Thus, strictly speaking, statistics such as the average or mean (which requires that the scores be added together and then divided by the number of scores) are not permitted with ordinal-level variables. The most sophisticated mathematical operation fully justified with an ordinal variable is the ranking of categories and cases (although, as we will see, it is not unusual for social scientists to take some liberties with this strict criterion).

## READING STATISTICS 1: Introduction

By this point in your education you have developed an impressive array of skills for reading words. Although you may sometimes struggle with a difficult idea or stumble over an obscure meaning, you can comprehend virtually any written work that you are likely to encounter.

As you continue your education in the social sciences, you must develop an analogous set of skills for reading numbers and statistics. To help you reach a reasonable level of literacy in statistics, we have included a series of boxed inserts in this textbook labelled "Reading Statistics." These will appear in most chapters and will discuss how statistical results are typically presented in the professional literature. Each instalment will include an extract or quotation from the professional literature so that we can analyze a realistic example.

As you will see, professional researchers use a reporting style that is quite different from the statistical language you will find in this textbook. Space in research journals and other media is expensive, and the typical research project requires the analysis of many variables. Thus, a large volume of information must be summarized in very few words. Researchers may express in a word or two a result or an interpretation that will take us a paragraph or more to state.

Because this is an introductory textbook, we have been careful to break down the computation and logic of each statistic and to identify, even to the point of redundancy, what we are doing when we use statistics. In this textbook we will never be concerned with more than a few variables at a time. We will have the luxury of analysis in detail and of being able to take pages or even entire chapters to develop a statistical idea or analyze a variable. Thus, a major theme of these boxed inserts will be to summarize how our comparatively long-winded (but more careful) vocabulary is

*(continued)*

translated into the concise language of the professional researcher.

When you have difficulty reading words, your tendency is (or at least, should be) to consult reference books (especially dictionaries) to help you identify and analyze the elements (words) of the passage. When you have difficulty reading statistics, you should do exactly the same thing. One tip that might be helpful is to write out a list of your questions

as you read and attend classes. Then make sure that you obtain answers to your satisfaction. Another helpful tip is to ask questions as they arise, so that your questions do not build up as you go along. We hope you will find this textbook a valuable reference book, but if you learn enough from this textbook to be able to use any source to help you read statistics, this textbook will have fulfilled one of its major goals.

**Interval-Ratio Level of Measurement.**\*   The categories of nominal-level variables have no numerical quality to them. Ordinal-level variables have categories that can be arrayed along a scale from high to low, but the exact distances between categories or scores are undefined. Variables measured at the **interval-ratio** level not only permit classification and ranking but also allow the distance from category to category (or score to score) to be exactly defined.

That is to say, interval-ratio variables are measured in units that have equal intervals. For example, asking people how old they are will produce an interval-ratio level variable (age) because the unit of measurement (years) has equal intervals (the distance from year to year is 365 days). Similarly, if we asked people how many siblings they had, we would produce a variable with equal intervals: two siblings are one more than one and thirteen is one more than twelve. Other examples of interval-ratio variables are income in dollars, number of children, and years married. All mathematical operations are permitted for data measured at the interval-ratio level.

Table 1.2 summarizes this discussion by presenting the basic characteristics of the three levels of measurement. Note that the number of permitted mathematical operations increases as we move from nominal to ordinal to interval-ratio levels of measurement. Ordinal-level variables are more sophisticated and flexible than nominal-level variables and interval-ratio-level variables permit the broadest range of mathematical operations.

**Level of Measurement and Discrete Versus Continuous Variables.**   The distinction made earlier between discrete and continuous variables is a concern only for interval-ratio-level variables. Nominal- and ordinal-level variables are discrete, at least in the way they are usually measured. For example, to measure marital status, researchers usually ask people to choose one category

---

\*Many statisticians distinguish between the interval level (equal intervals) and the ratio level (equal intervals and a true zero point, indicating the absence or complete lack of whatever is being measured). We find the distinction unnecessarily cumbersome in an introductory textbook, and since most statistical analysis that is appropriate for interval variables is also appropriate for ratio variables, we will treat these two levels as one.

**TABLE 1.2** **Basic Characteristics of the Three Levels of Measurement**

| Levels | Examples | Measurement Procedures | Mathematical Operations Permitted |
|---|---|---|---|
| Nominal | Sex, race, religion, marital status | Classification into categories | Counting number of cases in each category of the variable; comparing sizes of categories |
| Ordinal | Socioeconomic status (SES), attitude and opinion scales | Classification into categories plus ranking of categories with respect to one another | All operations above plus judgments of "greater than" and "less than" |
| Interval-Ratio | Age, number of children, income | All of above plus description of distances between scores in terms of equal units | All of above plus all other mathematical operations (addition, subtraction, multiplication, division, square roots, etc.) |

from a list: married, living common-law, widowed, and so on. What makes this variable discrete is that respondents can place themselves into a single category only; no subcategories or more refined classifications are permitted.

The distinction is usually a concern only for interval-ratio-level variables, of which some are discrete (number of times you've been divorced) and others are continuous (income or age). Remember that because we cannot work with infinitely long numbers, continuous variables have to be rounded off at some level and reported as if they were discrete. The distinction relates more to our options for appropriate statistics or graphs, not to the appearance of the variables.

**Level of Measurement: A Summary.** Levels of measurement can be depicted as steps on a ladder, as illustrated in Figure 1.3. As we climb up the ladder, each step possesses the characteristics of the preceding step, plus adds a new characteristic. The bottom or first step of the ladder is the nominal level. Nominal-level variables simply classify observations into categories. The second or middle step of the ladder is the ordinal level. Ordinal-level variables classify observations into categories, but the categories also have an intrinsic ordering—they can be naturally ranked from low to high. The top or third step of the ladder is the interval-ratio level. Interval-ratio variables classify observations into ordered categories or scores, but there is also an equal distance between any two adjacent categories or scores.

Thus, to ascertain the level of measurement of a variable you need to ask two successive questions about a variable's categories (or scores). The first is: "Do the categories of the variable have an intrinsic order?" If the answer is no, it is a nominal-level variable and no further question is asked. For example, gender is a nominal variable because its scores do not have an intrinsic order—they can be stated in *any* order: (1) male, (2) female or (1) female, (2) male.

If the answer to the first question is yes, then the variable is *at least* ordinal, so a second, follow-up question is asked: "Is there an equal distance between

**FIGURE 1.3  Characteristics for Levels of Measurement**

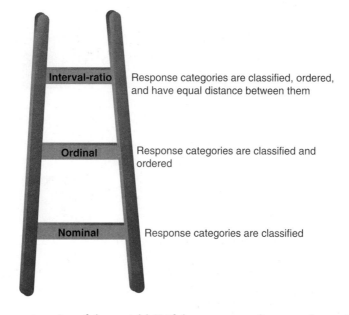

Interval-ratio — Response categories are classified, ordered, and have equal distance between them

Ordinal — Response categories are classified and ordered

Nominal — Response categories are classified

categories of the variable?" If the answer to the second question is no, it is an ordinal-level variable; if the answer is yes, it is an interval-ratio variable.

Consider a scale measuring self-rated health with the following categories: (1) poor, (2) fair, (3) good, (4), very good, and (5) excellent. Individuals in excellent health are healthier than those in very good health, individuals in very good health are healthier than those in good health, and so on. Scores on self-rated health have an intrinsic order; however, the distance between adjacent scores is different and unequal. For instance, the distance between a score of 4 (very good) and a score of 5 (excellent) is not the same as the distance between a score of 1 (poor) and a score of 2 (fair). That is, people with scores of 4 and 5 are likely to be in a very similar state of health, while people with scores of 1 and 2 are likely to be in quite different states of health—the distance in health status between a score of 4 and a score of 5 is narrower than the distance between a score of 1 and a score of 2. Thus, self-rated health is only an ordinal-level variable.

To help find the level of measurement of a variable, Figure 1.4 provides a flow chart of the two questions and how to proceed when answered. The One Step at a Time box further demonstrates how the two questions can be used to determine the level of measurement of three different variables that measure health. As you can see in this demonstration, the level of measurement is not an inherent feature of what a variable measures, but is instead a characteristic of the variable's response categories.

Remember that the level of measurement of a variable is important because different statistics require different mathematical operations. The level

**FIGURE 1.4   Finding the Level of Measurement of a Variable**

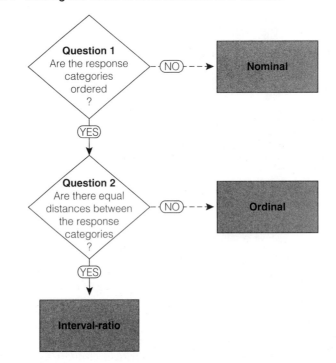

of measurement of a variable is the key characteristic that tells us which statistics are permissible and appropriate. Ideally, researchers utilize only those statistics that are fully justified by the level-of-measurement criteria. In this imperfect world, however, the most powerful and useful statistics (such as the mean) require interval-ratio variables, while most of the variables of interest to the social sciences are only nominal (sex, marital status) or ordinal (attitude scales). Relatively few concepts of interest to the social sciences are so precisely defined that they can be measured at the interval-ratio level. This disparity creates some very real difficulties for social science research. On the one hand, researchers should use the most sophisticated statistical procedures fully justified for a particular variable. Treating interval-ratio data as if they were only ordinal, for example, results in a significant loss of information and precision. Treated as an interval-ratio variable, the variable "age" can supply us with exact information regarding the differences between the cases (e.g., "Individual A is three years and two months older than Individual B"). Treated only as an ordinal variable, however, the precision of our comparisons would suffer and we could say only that "Individual A is older (or greater than) Individual B."

On the other hand, given the nature of the disparity, researchers are more likely to treat variables as if they were higher in level of measurement than they actually are. In particular, variables measured at the ordinal level, especially when they have many possible categories or scores, are often treated

## ONE STEP AT A TIME   Finding the Level of Measurement of a Variable

**Health1**, **Health2**, and **Health3** are three variables that measure health, but each of these variables measures health in a different way.

### Health1

Health1 is based on the question, "In the past 12 months, did you contact a medical practitioner to discuss your health?" The response categories of Health1 are

    1 = No
    2 = Yes

*Question 1:* Are the response categories ordered? No. Health1 is therefore a *nominal* variable. (There is no need to proceed to Question 2.)

### Health2

Health2 is based on the question, "In the past 12 months, how many times did you contact a medical practitioner to discuss your health?" The response categories of Health2 are

    1 = 0–1
    2 = 2–3
    3 = 4–5
    4 = 6 or more

*Question 1:* Are the response categories ordered? Yes.
*Question 2:* Are there equal distances between the response categories?
No. Even though each of the first three response categories has the same size, the exact distance cannot be calculated. For example, if one person chooses the first response category, and a second person chooses the fourth response category, it is impossible to calculate the exact difference in the number of medical visits between these two people. This is because we do not know if the first person contacted a medical practitioner 0 times or 1 time, and we do not know how many times the second person contacted a medical practitioner (we only know that it was 6 or more times). Without knowing the exact number of times each person contacted the medical

practitioner, all we can say is that the second person contacted the medical practitioner more often than the first person. Health2 is therefore an *ordinal* variable.

### Health3

Health3 is based on the question, "In the past 12 months, how many times did you contact a medical practitioner to discuss your health?" The response categories of Health3 are

    1 = 0
    2 = 1
    3 = 2
    4 = 3
    5 = 4
    6 = 5
    7 = 6
    8 = 7

and so on, with each code value representing the specific number of times the respondent contacted a medical practitioner.
*Question 1:* Are the response categories ordered? Yes.
*Question 2:* Are there equal distances between the response categories?
Yes. For example, if one person chooses the first response category, and a second person chooses the third response category, we can calculate the exact difference in the number of medical visits between these two people. This is because we know that the first person contacted a medical practitioner exactly 0 times, and the second person contacted a medical practitioner exactly 2 times. The exact difference in the number of medical visits between these two respondents is therefore 2 − 0 = 2. Health3 is therefore an *interval-ratio* variable.

### Transformation of Variable Level of Measurement

What the above examples also illustrate is that it is often possible to "transform" a variable's level of measurement from a higher level to a lower level. This procedure can be done simply by collapsing

*(continued)*

or grouping the response categories of the higher-level variable. For example, Health3 (interval-ratio) could be transformed into an ordinal variable by collapsing/grouping its values to correspond to the values of Health2, or it could even be transformed into a nominal variable by collapsing/grouping its categories to correspond to the values of Health1, as follows:

| Health3 | | Health2 | | Health1 | |
|---|---|---|---|---|---|
| Code | Variable Value | Code | Variable Value | Code | Variable Value |
| 1 | 0 | 1 | 0–1 | 1 | No |
| 2 | 1 | | | 2 | Yes |
| 3 | 2 | 2 | 2–3 | | |
| 4 | 3 | | | | |
| 5 | 4 | 3 | 4–5 | | |
| 6 | 5 | | | | |
| 7 | 6 | 4 | 6 or more | | |
| 8 | 7 | | | | |

Note, however, that transformation is a downward-sloping, one-way street based on the simplification of variable response categories. So an interval-ratio variable can be transformed into an ordinal or a nominal variable, and an ordinal variable can be transformed into another ordinal or a nominal variable. However, an interval-ratio variable can never be transformed into another interval-ratio variable, an ordinal variable can never be transformed into an interval-ratio variable, and a nominal variable can never be transformed into an ordinal or an interval-ratio variable.

as if they were interval-ratio because the statistical procedures available at the higher level are more powerful, flexible, and interesting. This practice is common, but researchers should be cautious in assessing statistical results and developing interpretations when the level-of-measurement criterion has been violated. Level of measurement is a very basic characteristic of a variable, and we will always consider it when presenting statistical procedures. Level of measurement is also a major organizing principle for the material that follows, and you should make sure you are familiar with these guidelines. *(For practice in determining the level of measurement of a variable, see Problems 1.4 – 1.8.)*

## SUMMARY

1. In the context of social research, the purpose of statistics is to organize, manipulate, and analyze data so that researchers can test their theories and answer their questions. Along with theory and methodology, statistics are a basic tool by which social scientists attempt to enhance their understanding of the social world.

2. There are two general classes of statistics. Descriptive statistics are used to summarize the distribution of a single variable and the relationships between two or more variables. Inferential statistics provide us with techniques by which we can generalize to populations from random samples.

3. Two basic guidelines for selecting statistical techniques were presented. Variables may be either discrete or continuous and may be measured at any of three different levels. At the

nominal level, we can compare category sizes. At the ordinal level, categories and cases can be ranked with respect to one another. At the interval-ratio level, all mathematical operations are permitted. Interval-ratio-level variables can be either discrete or continuous. Variables at the nominal or ordinal level are almost always discrete.

## GLOSSARY

**Continuous variable.** A variable with a unit of measurement that can be subdivided infinitely.

**Data.** Any information collected as part of a research project and expressed as numbers.

**Data reduction.** Summarizing many scores with a few statistics. A major goal of descriptive statistics.

**Dependent variable.** A variable that is identified as an effect, result, or outcome variable. The dependent variable is thought to be caused by the independent variable.

**Descriptive statistics.** The branch of statistics concerned with (1) summarizing the distribution of a single variable or (2) measuring the relationship between two or more variables.

**Discrete variable.** A variable with a basic unit of measurement that cannot be subdivided.

**Hypothesis.** A statement about the relationship between variables that is derived from a theory. Hypotheses are more specific than theories, and all terms and concepts are fully defined.

**Independent variable.** A variable that is identified as a causal variable. The independent variable is thought to cause the dependent variable.

**Inferential statistics.** The branch of statistics concerned with making generalizations from samples to populations.

**Interval-ratio variable.** A variable whose response categories can be classified, ordered, and have equal distance between them.

**Level of measurement.** The mathematical characteristic of a variable and the major criterion for selecting statistical techniques. It is determined from an examination of the variable's response categories. Variables can be measured at any of three levels, each permitting certain mathematical operations and statistical techniques. The characteristics of the three levels are summarized in Table 1.2.

**Measures of association.** Statistics that summarize the strength and direction of the relationship between variables.

**Nominal variable.** A variable whose response categories can be classified but not ordered.

**Ordinal variable.** A variable whose response categories can be classified and ordered.

**Population.** The total collection of all cases in which the researcher is interested.

**Research.** Any process of gathering information systematically and carefully to answer questions or test theories. Statistics are useful for research projects in which the information is represented in numerical form or as data.

**Response category.** A variable's possible attributes, qualities, or characteristics.

**Sample.** A carefully chosen subset of a population. In inferential statistics, information is gathered from a sample and then generalized to a population.

**Statistics.** A set of mathematical techniques for organizing and analyzing data. Sometimes the term refers to the numbers obtained with statistical techniques.

**Theory.** A generalized explanation of the relationship between two or more variables.

**Variable.** Any trait that can change values from case to case.

## PROBLEMS

**1.1** In your own words, describe the role of statistics in the research process. Using the "wheel of science" as a framework, explain how statistics link theory with research.

**1.2** Find a research article in any social science journal. Choose an article on a subject of interest to you and don't worry about being able to understand all of the statistics that are reported.

a. How much of the article is devoted to statistics per se (as distinct from theory, ideas, discussion, and so on)?

b. Is the research based on a sample from some population? How large is the sample? How were subjects or cases selected? Can the findings be generalized to some population?

c. What variables are used? Which are independent and which are dependent? For each variable, determine the level of measurement and whether the variable is discrete or continuous.

d. What statistical techniques are used? Try to follow the statistical analysis and see how much you can understand. Save the article and read it again after you finish this course to see if you understand more.

1.3 Distinguish between descriptive and inferential statistics. Describe a research situation that would use both types.

1.4 Below are some items from a public opinion survey. For each item, indicate the level of measurement and whether the variable will be discrete or continuous. *(HINT: Remember that only interval-ratio-level variables can be continuous.)*

a. What is your occupation? _____

b. Exactly how many years of school have you completed? _____

c. If you were asked to use one of these four names for your social class, which would you say you belonged in?
_____ Upper _____ Middle
_____ Working _____ Lower

d. What is your exact age? _____

e. In what country were you born? _____

f. What is your grade point average? _____

g. What is your major? _____

h. The only way to deal with the drug problem is to legalize all drugs.
_____ Strongly agree
_____ Agree
_____ Undecided
_____ Disagree
_____ Strongly disagree

i. What is your astrological sign? _____

j. Exactly how many brothers and sisters do you have? _____

1.5 Below are brief descriptions of how researchers measured a variable. For each situation, determine the level of measurement of the variable and whether it is continuous or discrete.

a. **Sex.** Respondents were asked to select a category from the following list:
_____ Male _____ Female

b. **Honesty.** Subjects were observed as they passed by a spot on campus where an apparently lost wallet was lying. The wallet contained money and complete identification. Subjects were classified into one of the following categories:
_____ Returned the wallet with the money.
_____ Returned the wallet but kept the money.
_____ Did not return the wallet.

c. **Social class.** Subjects were asked about their family situation when they were 16 years old. Was their family
_____ very well off compared to other families?
_____ about average?
_____ not so well off?

d. **Education.** Subjects were asked exactly how many years of schooling they and each parent had completed.

e. **Sex integration on campus.** Students were observed during lunchtime at the cafeteria for a month. The exact number of students sitting with students of the opposite sex was counted for each meal period.

f. **Number of children.** Subjects were asked: "How many children have you ever had? Please include any that may have passed away. Did you have:
_____ 0 children
_____ 1–2 children
_____ 3–4 children
_____ 5 or more children"

g. **Student seating patterns in classrooms.** On the first day of class, instructors noted where each student sat. Seating patterns were remeasured every two weeks until the end of the semester. Each student was classified as
_____ same seat as last measurement;
_____ adjacent seat;
_____ different seat, not adjacent;
_____ absent.

h. **Physicians per capita.** The number of practising physicians was counted in each of 50 cities, and the researchers used population data to compute the number of physicians per capita.

i. **Physical attractiveness.** A panel of 10 judges rated each of 50 photos of a sample of males and females for physical attractiveness on a scale from 0 to 20 with 20 being the highest score.

j. **Number of accidents.** The number of traffic accidents for each of 20 busy intersections in a city was recorded. Also, each accident was rated as

_____ minor damage, no injuries;

_____ moderate damage, personal injury requiring hospitalization;

_____ severe damage and injury.

**1.6** For each of the first 20 items in the General Social Survey (see Appendix G), indicate the level of measurement and whether the variable is continuous or discrete.

**1.7** For each research situation summarized below, identify the level of measurement of all variables and indicate whether they are discrete or continuous. Also, decide which statistical applications are being used: descriptive statistics (single variable), descriptive statistics (two or more variables), or inferential statistics. Remember that it is quite common for a given situation to require more than one type of application.

a. The administration of your university is proposing a change in parking policy. You select a random sample of students and ask each one whether he or she favours or opposes the change.

b. You ask everyone in your social research class to tell you (1) the highest grade he or she ever received in a math course and (2) the grade on a recent statistics test. You then compare the two sets of scores to find out whether there is any relationship.

c. Your aunt is running for mayor and hires you (for a huge fee, incidentally) to question a sample of voters about their concerns in local politics. Specifically, she wants a profile of the voters that will tell her exactly what percent belong to each political party, what percent are male or female, and what percent favour or oppose the widening of the main street in town.

d. Several years ago, a country reinstituted the death penalty for first-degree homicide. Supporters of capital punishment argued that this change would reduce the homicide rate. To investigate this claim, a researcher has gathered information on the number of homicides in the country for the two-year periods before and after the change.

e. A local automobile dealer is concerned about customer satisfaction. He wants to mail a survey form to all customers for the past year and ask them if they are satisfied, very satisfied, or not satisfied with their purchases.

**1.8** For each research situation below, identify the independent and dependent variables. Classify each in terms of level of measurement and whether or not the variable is discrete or continuous.

a. A graduate student is studying sexual harassment on university campuses and asks 500 female students if they personally have experienced any such incidents. Each student is asked to estimate the frequency of these incidents as either "often, sometimes, rarely, or never." The researcher also gathers data on age and major to find out whether there is any connection between these variables and frequency of sexual harassment.

b. A supervisor in the Solid Waste Management Division of a municipal government is attempting to assess two different methods of trash collection. One area of the city is served by trucks with two-person crews who do "backyard" pickups, and the rest of the city is served by "high-tech" single-person trucks with curbside pickup. The assessment measures include the exact number of complaints received from the two different areas over a six-month period, the amount of time per day required to service each area, and the cost per tonne of trash collected.

c. The adult bookstore near campus has been raided and closed by the police. Your social research class has decided to poll the student body and get their reactions and opinions. The class decides to ask each student if he or she supports or opposes the closing of the store, how many times each one has visited the store, and if he or she agrees or disagrees that "pornography is a direct cause of sexual assaults on women." The class also collects information on the sex, exact age, religious and political philosophy, and major of each student to see if opinions are related to these characteristics.

**d.** For a research project in a political science course, a student has collected information about the quality of life and the degree of political democracy in 50 nations. Specifically, she used infant mortality rates to measure quality of life and the percentage of all adults who are permitted to vote in national elections as the measure of democratization. Her hypothesis is that quality of life is higher in more democratic nations.

**e.** A highway engineer wonders if a planned increase in speed limit on a heavily travelled local avenue will result in any change in number of accidents. He plans to collect information on traffic volume, exact number of accidents, and number of fatalities for the six-month periods before and after the change.

**f.** Students are planning a program to promote "safe sex" and awareness of a variety of other health concerns for university students. To measure the effectiveness of the program, they plan to give a survey measuring knowledge about these matters to a random sample of the student body before and after the program.

**g.** Several provinces have drastically cut their budgets for mental health care. Will this increase the number of homeless people in these provinces? A researcher contacts a number of agencies serving the homeless in each province and develops an estimate of the size of the population before and after the cuts.

**h.** Does tolerance for diversity vary by race, ethnicity, or gender? Samples of males and females from various racial and ethnic groups have been given a survey that measures their interest in and appreciation of cultures and groups other than their own.

## You Are the Researcher

### Introduction to the Canadian General Social Survey, Canadian Community Health Survey, and SPSS

Two types of exercises are located at the end of each chapter of this textbook. While the "Problems" exercises are based on fictitious data for the most part and are designed to be solved with a simple hand calculator, the "You Are the Researcher" computer-based exercises provide a more realistic experience and use actual social science data from two Canadian social surveys, the Canadian Community Health Survey (CCHS) and the Canadian General Social Survey (GSS).

The GSS is an annual public opinion poll, administered by Statistics Canada, of a representative sample of Canadians. It has been conducted since 1985 and explores a broad range of social issues. Each year the survey collects information on specific aspects of society relevant to social policy. Since survey topics are often repeated every few years, GSS data can also be used to track trends and changes in these characteristics over time. The GSS has proven to be a very valuable resource for testing theory, for learning more about Canadian society, and for informing public debates.

The 2013 GSS is supplied and used in this textbook. It collected information on social identity in Canada. Using the 2013 GSS data, students can describe

Canadians' contacts with their friends and family, civic participation in groups and organizations, knowledge of Canadian history and national symbols, work–life balance, and sense of belonging and trust. Students can further examine whether variables such as gender, age, and province of residence are associated with social networks and patterns of civic participation in Canada.

Two versions of the 2013 GSS are supplied with this textbook. The first version, named *2013_GSS_Full.sav*, contains the original random sample. The second (*2013_GSS_Shortened.sav*) is a shortened version with 1,500 cases randomly selected from the original random sample.

The CCHS provides information on the determinants of health, health status, and use of health care services for a random sample of Canadians. The CCHS is conducted annually by Statistics Canada. The 2012 CCHS is provided here. Using CCHS data, students can describe many aspects of the health of Canadians and the factors that determine it, such as health care access, alcohol and tobacco use, stress, and socioeconomic status.

The 2012 CCHS contains dozens of variables for a sample of thousands of Canadians. As with the GSS, we provide both the complete version of the CCHS (*2012_CCHS_Full.sav*) containing the original random sample and a shortened version (*2012_CCHS_Shortened.sav*) with 1,500 randomly selected cases.

The four databases (*2013_GSS_Shortened.sav*, *2012_CCHS_Shortened.sav*, *2013_GSS_Full.sav*, and *2012_CCHS_Full.sav*) and the user's guide for the 2013 GSS (*2013_GSS_Guide.pdf*) and 2012 CCHS (*2012_CCHS_Guide.pdf*) can be downloaded from our website at nelson.com/student. The user's guides provide a detailed description of each survey; however, for quick reference, a list of the variables in each database is shown in Appendix G.

One of the problems with using "real-life" data such as the GSS and CCHS is that they very often contain too many cases to be analyzed with just a simple hand calculator. Computers and statistical packages are almost always needed to analyze the data. A statistical package is a set of computer programs for data analysis. The advantage of these packages is that, since the programs are already written, you can capitalize on the power of the computer with minimal computer literacy and virtually no programming experience.

This textbook utilizes IBM SPSS Statistics for Windows, referred to in this book simply as "SPSS." Version 24 of SPSS is used, though all recent versions of SPSS are compatible with the textbook. In the "You Are the Researcher" exercise sections at the end of each chapter, we will explain how to use this package in various ways to manipulate and analyze the GSS or CCHS data, and we will illustrate and interpret the results. Be sure to read Appendix F, which gives a general introduction to SPSS, before attempting any data analysis.

As a final note, there are two versions of SPSS: a full version and a student version. The student version, created for classroom instruction, is, in essence, the full version of the SPSS base software package but is limited to a maximum of 50 variables and 1,500 cases. The student version is compatible with the *2013_GSS_Shortened.sav* and *2012_CCHS_Shortened.sav* data files.

# Part 1 Descriptive Statistics

Part 1 has three chapters, each devoted to a different application of univariate descriptive statistics. Chapter 2 covers "basic" descriptive statistics, including percentages, ratios, rates, frequency distributions, and graphs. It is a lengthy chapter, but the material is relatively elementary and at least vaguely familiar to most people. Although the statistics covered in this chapter are "basic," they are not necessarily simple or obvious, and you should consider the explanations and examples carefully before attempting the end-of-chapter problems or using them in actual research.

Chapter 3 covers measures of central tendency, dispersion, and distribution shapes. Measures of central tendency describe the typical case or average score (e.g., the mean), while measures of dispersion describe the amount of variety or diversity among the scores (e.g., the range or the distance from the high score to the low score). Distribution shape, meanwhile, takes both central tendency and dispersion into account, in order to describe the pattern or form of the distribution of variable values. Central tendency and dispersion are presented in a single chapter to stress the point that they depend on each other to describe the characteristics of a variable, and are both important for distribution shape. You will come to realize that both measures are necessary and commonly reported together. You will also see the usefulness of graphs and charts to provide a visual sense of the relationship between central tendency, dispersion, and distribution shape. To reinforce the idea that measures of centrality and dispersion are complementary descriptive statistics, many of the problems at the end of Chapter 3 require the simultaneous computation of a measure of central tendency and dispersion.

Chapter 4 is a pivotal chapter in the flow of the textbook. It takes some of the statistics from Chapters 2 and 3 and applies them to the normal curve, a concept of great importance in statistics. The normal curve is a type of frequency polygon (Chapter 2) that can be used to describe the position of scores using means and standard deviations (Chapter 3). Chapter 4 also uses proportions and percentages (Chapter 2).

Besides playing a role in descriptive statistics, the normal curve is a central concept in inferential statistics, a core topic in Parts 2 and 3 of the textbook. Thus, Chapter 4 serves a dual purpose: It ends the presentation of univariate descriptive statistics and lays essential groundwork for the material to come.

# 2

# Basic Descriptive Statistics
## Percentages, Ratios and Rates, Tables, Charts, and Graphs

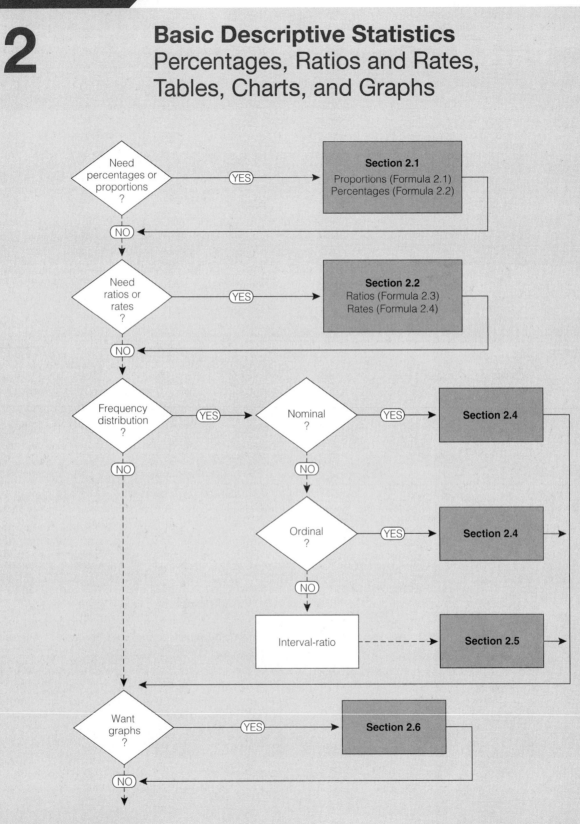

**LEARNING OBJECTIVES** ██████████████████████████████

By the end of this chapter, you will be able to

**1.** Explain the purpose of descriptive statistics in making data comprehensible.

**2.** Compute and interpret percentages, proportions, ratios, and rates.

**3.** Construct and analyze frequency distributions for variables at each of the three levels of measurement.

**4.** Construct and analyze bar and pie charts, histograms, and frequency polygons.

Research results do not speak for themselves. They must be organized and manipulated so that whatever meaning they have can be quickly and easily understood by the researcher and by his or her readers. Researchers use statistics to clarify their results and communicate effectively. In this chapter, we will consider some commonly used techniques for presenting research results: percentages and proportions, ratios and rates, tables, charts, and graphs. Mathematically speaking, these univariate descriptive statistics are not very complex (although they may not be as simple as they appear at first glance), but as you will see, they are extremely useful for presenting research results clearly and concisely.

## 2.1 PERCENTAGES AND PROPORTIONS

Consider the following statement: "Of the 113 survey respondents, 60 are female." While there is nothing wrong with this statement, the same fact could have been more clearly conveyed if it had been reported as a percentage: "About 53% of survey respondents are female."

Percentages and proportions supply a frame of reference for reporting research results in the sense that they standardize the raw data: percentages to the base 100 and proportions to the base 1.00. The mathematical definitions of **proportions** and **percentages** are

**FORMULA 2.1**
$$\text{Proportion}(p) = \frac{f}{n}$$

**FORMULA 2.2**
$$\text{Percentage}(\%) = \left(\frac{f}{n}\right) \times 100$$

where $f$ = frequency, or the number of cases in any category
$n$ = the number of cases in all categories

To illustrate the computation of percentages, consider the data presented in Table 2.1. How can we find the percentage of males in the

**TABLE 2.1  Sex of Respondents**

| Sex | Frequency (f) | Proportion (p) | Percentage (%) |
|---|---|---|---|
| Male | 53 | 0.4690 | 46.90 |
| Female | 60 | 0.5310 | 53.10 |
| | $n = 113$ | 1.0000 | 100.00 |

© Cengage Learning

sample? Note that there are 53 males ($f = 53$) and a total of 113 cases in all ($n = 113$). So,

$$\text{Percentage}(\%) = \left(\frac{f}{n}\right) \times 100 = \left(\frac{53}{113}\right) \times 100 = (0.4690) \times 100 = 46.90\%$$

Using the same procedures, we can find the percentage of females:

$$\text{Percentage}(\%) = \left(\frac{f}{n}\right) \times 100 = \left(\frac{60}{113}\right) \times 100 = (0.5310) \times 100 = 53.10\%^*$$

Both results could have been expressed as proportions. For example, the proportion of females in Table 2.1 is 0.5310:

$$\text{Proportion}(p) = \frac{f}{n} = \frac{60}{113} = 0.5310$$

Percentages and proportions are easier to read and comprehend than frequencies. This advantage is particularly obvious when attempting to compare groups of different sizes. For example, Table 2.2 provides actual data collected by Statistics Canada in the 2011 National Household Survey on major field of study of undergraduate university graduates from across Canada. Based on the field-of-study information presented in the table, which sex has the higher relative number of majors in business, management, and public administration? Because the total numbers of graduates are much different, comparisons are difficult to make from the raw frequencies. Computing percentages eliminates the difference in size of the two groups by standardizing both distributions to the base of 100. The same data are presented in percentages in Table 2.3.

The percentages in Table 2.3 make it easier to identify both differences and similarities between the sexes. We now see that a greater percentage of males than females graduated with a business, management, and public administration degree from Canadian universities, even though the absolute number of female business, management, and public administration

---

*If you are wondering why 0.530973451 . . . has been rounded up to 0.5310 rather than down to 0.5309, check the subsection called "Accuracy and Rounding Off," in the textbook's prologue.

**TABLE 2.2** **Major Field of Study\* for Female and Male Undergraduate University Graduates**

| Major | Female | Male |
|---|---|---|
| Education | 359,411 | 120,377 |
| Visual and performing arts | 77,772 | 47,751 |
| Humanities | 251,081 | 146,188 |
| Social and behavioural sciences, and law | 385,089 | 266,716 |
| Business, management, and public administration | 346,857 | 340,552 |
| Physical and life sciences and technologies | 128,862 | 126,720 |
| Mathematics, computer and information sciences | 50,155 | 107,910 |
| Architecture, engineering, and related technologies | 72,783 | 342,139 |
| Agriculture, natural resources, and conservation | 24,071 | 36,595 |
| Health and related fields | 280,487 | 76,251 |
| Personal, protective, and transportation services | 2,484 | 7,092 |
| Other | 654 | 97 |
| | $n = 1,979,706$ | $n = 1,618,388$ |

\*Major field of study, primary groupings (based on CIP Canada 2011).

Source: Data from Statistics Canada 2011 National Household Survey.

---

## Applying Statistics 2.1: Communicating with Statistics

Not long ago, in a large social service agency, the following conversation took place between the executive director of the agency and a supervisor of one of the divisions:

> *Executive director:* Well, I don't want to seem abrupt, but I've only got a few minutes. Tell me, as briefly as you can, about this staffing problem you claim to be having.
>
> *Supervisor:* Ma'am, we just don't have enough people to handle our workload. Of the 177 full-time employees of the agency, only 50 are in my division. Yet 6,231 of the 16,722 cases handled by the agency last year were handled by my division.
>
> *Executive director (smothering a yawn):* Very interesting. I'll certainly get back to you on this matter.

How could the supervisor have presented his case more effectively? Because he wants to compare two sets of numbers (his staff versus the total staff and the workload of his division versus the total workload of the agency), proportions or percentages would be a more forceful way of presenting results. What if the supervisor had said, "Only 28.25% of the staff is assigned to my division, but we handle 37.26% of the total workload of the agency"? Is this a clearer message?

The first percentage is found by

$$\% = \left(\frac{f}{n}\right) \times 100 = \frac{50}{177} \times 100$$

$$= (0.2825) \times 100 = 28.25\%$$

and the second percentage is found by

$$\% = \left(\frac{f}{n}\right) \times 100 = \left(\frac{6231}{16,722}\right) \times 100$$

$$= (0.3726) \times 100 = 37.26\%$$

**TABLE 2.3 Major Field of Study* for Female and Male Undergraduate University Graduates (Based on Table 2.2)**

| Major | Female (%) | Male (%) |
|---|---|---|
| Education | 18.15 | 7.44 |
| Visual and performing arts | 3.93 | 2.95 |
| Humanities | 12.68 | 9.03 |
| Social and behavioural sciences, and law | 19.45 | 16.48 |
| Business, management, and public administration | 17.52 | 21.04 |
| Physical and life sciences and technologies | 6.51 | 7.83 |
| Mathematics, computer and information sciences | 2.53 | 6.67 |
| Architecture, engineering, and related technologies | 3.68 | 21.14 |
| Agriculture, natural resources, and conservation | 1.22 | 2.26 |
| Health and related fields | 14.17 | 4.71 |
| Personal, protective, and transportation services | 0.13 | 0.44 |
| Other | 0.03 | 0.01 |
| | 100.00 | 100.00 |
| | (1,979,706) | (1,618,388) |

*Major field of study, primary groupings (based on CIP Canada 2011).

Source: Data from Statistics Canada 2011 National Household Survey.

graduates is more than that of male business, management, and public administration graduates. How would you describe the differences in the other major fields? *(For practice in computing and interpreting percentages and proportions, see Problems 2.1 and 2.2.)*

Some further guidelines on the use of percentages and proportions:

1. When working with a small number of cases (say, fewer than 20), it is usually preferable to report the actual frequencies rather than percentages or proportions. With a small number of cases, the percentages can change drastically with relatively minor changes in the data. For example, if you begin with a data set that includes 10 males and 10 females (i.e., 50% of each gender) and then add another female, the percentage distributions will change noticeably to 52.38% female and 47.62% male. Of course, as the number of observations increases, each additional case will have a smaller impact. If we started with 500 males and females and then added one more female, the percentage of females would change by only a tenth of a percent (from 50% to 50.10%).

2. The first guideline leads to a follow-up, general best practice guideline about reporting results. Always report the number of observations along with proportions and percentages. This permits the reader to judge the adequacy of the sample size and, conversely, helps prevent the researcher from lying with statistics. Statements like "two out of three people questioned prefer courses in statistics to any other course" might impress you, but the claim would lose its gloss if you learned that only three people were tested. *You should be extremely suspicious of reports that fail to state the number of cases that were tested.*

> **ONE STEP AT A TIME**   **Finding Percentages and Proportions**
>
> **1:** Determine the values for *f* (number of cases in a category) and *n* (number of cases in all categories). Remember that *f* will be the number of cases in a *specific category* and *n* will be the number of cases in *all* categories and that *f* will be smaller than *n*, except when the category
>
> and the entire group are the same. Therefore, proportions cannot exceed 1.00, and percentages cannot exceed 100.00%.
> **2:** For a proportion, divide *f* by *n*.
> **3:** For a percentage, multiply the value you calculated in step 2 by 100.

**3.** Percentages and proportions can be calculated for variables at the ordinal and nominal levels of measurement, even though they require division. This is not a violation of the level-of-measurement guideline (see Table 1.2). Percentages and proportions do not require the division of the *scores* of the variable (as would be the case in computing the average score on a test, for example) but rather the *number of cases* in a particular category (*f*) of the variable by the total number of cases in the sample (*n*). When we make a statement like "43% of the sample is female," we are merely expressing the relative size of a category (female) of the variable (gender) in a convenient way.

## 2.2 RATIOS AND RATES

Ratios and rates provide some additional ways of summarizing results simply and clearly. Although they are similar to each other, each statistic has a specific application and purpose.

**Ratios.**   **Ratios** are especially useful for comparing categories of a variable in terms of relative frequency. Instead of standardizing the distribution of the variable to the base 100 or 1.00, as we did in computing percentages and proportions, we determine ratios by dividing the frequency of one category by the frequency of another. Mathematically, a ratio can be defined as

**FORMULA 2.3**
$$\text{Ratio} = \frac{f_1}{f_2}$$

where $f_1$ = the number of cases in the first category

$f_2$ = the number of cases in the second category

To illustrate the use of ratios, we will use actual information from the 2015 Canadian Election Study, which is an inter-university project that regularly conducts a survey of Canadian voters on a variety of political issues. One of the survey questions asked whether respondents strongly agreed, somewhat agreed, somewhat disagreed, or strongly disagreed with the following statement: "It should be mandatory to vote in Canadian federal elections. Electors who do not vote should receive a fine." Of those polled, 2,774 people said that they agreed somewhat or strongly with the statement, while 3,302 said that they disagreed somewhat or strongly.* What is the relative size of these two groups? To find the ratio of those who think non-voters should be fined ($f_1$) to those who think non-voters should not be fined ($f_2$), divide 2,774 by 3,302:

$$\text{Ratio} = \frac{f_1}{f_2} = \frac{2,774}{3,302} = 0.84$$

The resultant ratio is 0.84, which means that for every Canadian who think non-voters should not be fined, there are 0.84 Canadians who think non-voters should be fined.

Ratios can be very economical ways of expressing the relative predominance of two categories. In our example, it is obvious from the raw data that Canadians who think non-voters should be fined are outnumbered by Canadians who do not think non-voters should be fined. Percentages or proportions could have been used to summarize the overall distribution (e.g., "45.65% Canadians think non-voters should be fined, and 54.34% think non-voters should not be fined"). In contrast to these other methods, ratios express the relative size of the categories: They tell us exactly how much one category outnumbers (or is outnumbered by) the other.

Ratios are often multiplied by some power of 10 to eliminate decimal points. For example, the ratio computed above might be multiplied by 100 and reported as 84 instead of 0.84. This would mean that, for every 100 Canadians who think non-voters should not be fined, there are 84 Canadians who think non-voters should be fined. To ensure clarity, the comparison units for the ratio are often expressed as well. Based on a unit of ones, the

---

### Applying Statistics 2.2: Ratios

In Table 2.2, how many male social and behavioural sciences, and law undergraduate university graduates are there compared to male business, management, and policy administration graduates? This question could be answered with frequencies, but a more easily understood way of expressing the answer would be with a ratio. The ratio of male social and behavioural

sciences, and law to business, management, and policy administration graduates would be

$$\text{Ratio} = \frac{f_1}{f_2} = \frac{266,716}{340,552} = 0.78$$

For every male business, management, and policy administration graduate, there are 0.78 male social and behavioural sciences, and law graduates.

---

*Source: Canadian Election Study, *2015 Canadian Election Study.*

ratio of Canadians who think non-voters should be fined to Canadians who think non-voters should not be fined would be expressed as 0.84:1. Based on hundreds, the same statistic might be expressed as 84:100. *(For practice in computing and interpreting ratios, see Problems 2.1 and 2.2.)*

**Rates.** **Rates** provide still another way of summarizing the distribution of a single variable. Rates are defined as the number of actual occurrences of some phenomenon divided by the number of possible occurrences per some unit of time.

**FORMULA 2.4**
$$\text{Rate} = \frac{f_{\text{actual}}}{f_{\text{possible}}}$$

where    $f_{\text{actual}}$ = the number of actual occurrences of a phenomenon

$f_{\text{possible}}$ = the number of possible occurrences of the phenomenon

Rates are usually multiplied by some power of 10 to eliminate decimal points. For example, the crude death rate for a population is defined as the number of deaths in that population (actual occurrences) divided by the number of people in the population (possible occurrences) per year. This quantity is then multiplied by 1,000. The formula for the crude death rate can be expressed as

$$\text{Crude death rate} = \frac{\text{Number of deaths}}{\text{Total population}} \times 1,000$$

---

### Applying Statistics 2.3: Rates

In 2015, there were 388,729 births in Canada, within a population of 35,851,774 persons. In 1972, when the population of Canada was only 22,218,463, there were 351,256 births. Is the birth rate rising or falling? Although this question can be answered from the preceding information, the trend in birth rates will be much more obvious if we compute birth rates for both years. Like crude death rates, crude birth rates are usually multiplied by 1,000 to eliminate decimal points. For 1972:

$$\text{Crude birth rate} = \frac{351,256}{22,218,463} \times 1,000 = 15.81$$

In 1972, there were 15.81 births for every 1,000 people in Canada. For 2015:

$$\text{Crude birth rate} = \frac{388,729}{35,851,774} \times 1,000 = 10.84$$

In 2015, there were 10.84 births for every 1,000 people in Canada. With the help of these statistics, the decline in the birth rate is clearly expressed.

Source: Statistics Canada, CANSIM, Tables 051-0001 and 051-0004.

---

**ONE STEP AT A TIME** **Finding Ratios and Rates**

**To Find Ratios**

**1:** Determine the values for $f_1$ and $f_2$. The value for $f_1$ will be the number of cases in the first category, and the value for $f_2$ will be the number of cases in the second category.
**2:** Divide the value of $f_1$ by the value of $f_2$.
**3:** You may multiply the value you calculated in step 2 by some power of 10 when reporting results.

**To Find Rates**

**1:** Determine the number of actual occurrences. This value will be the numerator of the formula.

**2:** Determine the number of possible occurrences. This value will usually be the total population for the area in question and will be the denominator of the formula.
**3:** Divide the number of actual occurrences (step 1) by the number of possible occurrences (step 2).
**4:** Multiply the value you calculated in step 3 by some power of 10. Conventionally, birth rates and death rates are multiplied by 1000 and crime rates are multiplied by 100,000.
**5:** Remember to state the period of time (e.g., per year) on which the rate is based.

---

In 2012, a total of 246,596 deaths were registered in Canada. With a population of 34,751,476,* Canada's crude death rate for that year was

$$\text{Crude death rate} = \frac{246{,}596}{34{,}751{,}476} \times 1{,}000 = (0.00710) \times 1{,}000 = 7.10$$

Or, for every 1,000 Canadians, there were 7.10 deaths in 2012.

Rates are often multiplied by 100,000 when the number of actual occurrences of some phenomenon is extremely small relative to the size of the population, such as homicides in Canada. Canadian police reported 516 homicides** in 2014, hence the homicide rate was

$$\text{Homicide rate} = \frac{516}{35{,}543{,}658} \times 100{,}000 = (0.0000145) \times 100{,}000 = 1.45$$

Or, for every 100,000 Canadians, there were 1.45 homicides in 2014. *(For practice in computing and interpreting rates, see Problems 2.3 and 2.4.)*

**2.3 FREQUENCY DISTRIBUTIONS INTRODUCTION**

Table 2.1 above is an example of what is formally called a **frequency distribution**. A frequency distribution is a table that summarizes the distribution of a variable's values by reporting the number of cases contained in each category of the variable. It is a very helpful and commonly used way of organizing and working with data. In fact, the construction of a frequency distribution is almost always the first step in any statistical analysis.

---

*Source: Statistics Canada, CANSIM, Tables 051-0001 (population) and 102-0503 (deaths).
**Source: Statistics Canada, CANSIM, Tables 051-0001 (population) and 253-0001 (homicides).

**TABLE 2.4   Data from Health and Counselling Services Survey**

| Student | Sex | Type of Health Professional Seen[1] | Satisfaction with Services[2] | Age |
|---|---|---|---|---|
| A | Male | Medical doctor | 1 | 18 |
| B | Male | Counsellor | 2 | 19 |
| C | Female | Medical doctor | 4 | 18 |
| D | Female | Medical doctor | 2 | 19 |
| E | Male | Counsellor | 1 | 20 |
| F | Male | Medical doctor | 1 | 20 |
| G | Female | Counsellor | 4 | 18 |
| H | Female | Medical doctor | 3 | 21 |
| I | Male | Medical doctor | 2 | 19 |
| J | Female | Other | 3 | 23 |
| K | Female | Medical doctor | 3 | 24 |
| L | Male | Counsellor | 3 | 18 |
| M | Female | Medical doctor | 1 | 22 |
| N | Female | Counsellor | 4 | 26 |
| O | Male | Medical doctor | 3 | 18 |
| P | Male | Counsellor | 4 | 19 |
| Q | Female | Counsellor | 2 | 19 |
| R | Male | Other | 1 | 19 |
| S | Female | Other | 4 | 21 |
| T | Male | Medical doctor | 2 | 20 |

US Census Bureau and Statistics Canada

[1]Based on the question, "What type of health professional did you see or talk to during your visit?"
[2]Measured on a scale from 1 (very dissatisfied) to 4 (very satisfied).

To illustrate the construction of frequency distributions and to provide some data for examples, let's assume a hypothetical situation in which students who recently visited the health and counselling services centre at a university were sent an e-mail asking them to complete a brief patient-satisfaction survey. Any realistic evaluation research would collect a variety of information from a large group of students, but for the sake of this example, we will confine our attention to just four variables and 20 students. The data are reported in Table 2.4.

Note that even though the data in Table 2.4 represent an unrealistically low number of cases, it is difficult to discern any patterns or trends. For example, try to ascertain the general level of satisfaction of the students from Table 2.4. You may be able to do so with just 20 cases, but it will take some time and effort. Imagine the difficulty with 50 cases or 100 cases presented in this fashion. Clearly the data need to be organized in a format that allows the researcher (and his or her audience) to understand easily the distribution of the variables's values.

One general rule that applies to all frequency distributions is that the categories of the frequency distribution must be exhaustive and mutually exclusive. In other words, the categories must be stated in a way that permits each case to be counted in one and only one category. This basic principle applies to the construction of frequency distributions for variables measured at all three levels of measurement.

**TABLE 2.5** **Sex of Respondents, Health and Counselling Services Survey**

| Sex | Tallies | Frequency (f) |
|---|---|---|
| Male | ⫽⫽⫽  ⫽⫽⫽ | 10 |
| Female | ⫽⫽⫽  ⫽⫽⫽ | 10 |
| | | $n = 20$ |

## 2.4 FREQUENCY DISTRIBUTIONS FOR VARIABLES MEASURED AT THE NOMINAL AND ORDINAL LEVELS

Beyond this rule, there are only guidelines to help you construct useful frequency distributions. As you will see, the researcher has a fair amount of discretion in stating the categories of the frequency distribution (especially with variables measured at the interval-ratio level). We will identify the issues to consider as you make decisions about the nature of any particular frequency distribution. Ultimately, however, the guidelines we state are aids for decision making, nothing more than helpful suggestions. As always, the researcher has the final responsibility for making sensible decisions and presenting his or her data in a meaningful way.

**Nominal-Level Variables.** For nominal-level variables, construction of the frequency distribution is typically very straightforward. For each category of the variable being displayed, the occurrences are counted and the subtotals, along with the total number of cases ($n$), are reported. Table 2.5 displays a frequency distribution for the variable "sex" from the health and counselling services survey. For purposes of illustration, a column for tallies has been included in this table to illustrate how the cases would be sorted into categories. (This column would not be included in the final form of the frequency distribution.) Take a moment to notice several other features of the table. Specifically, it has a descriptive title, clearly labelled categories (male and female), and a report of the total number of cases at the bottom of the frequency column. These items must be included in all tables regardless of the variable or level of measurement.

The meaning of the table is quite clear. There are 10 males and 10 females in the sample, a fact that is much easier to comprehend from the frequency distribution than from the unorganized data presented in Table 2.4.

For some nominal variables, the researcher might have to make some choices about the number of categories he or she wishes to report. For

**TABLE 2.6** **Type of Health Professional Seen by Respondents, Health and Counselling Services Survey**

| Health Professional | Frequency (f) |
|---|---|
| Medical doctor | 10 |
| Counsellor | 7 |
| Other | 3 |
| | $n = 20$ |

**TABLE 2.7  Type of Health Professional Seen by Respondents, Health and Counselling Services Survey**

| Health Professional | Frequency (f) |
|---|---|
| Medical doctor | 10 |
| Non-medical doctor | 10 |
|  | n = 20 |

example, the distribution of the variable "type of health professional seen" could be reported using the categories listed in Table 2.4. The resultant frequency distribution is presented in Table 2.6. Although this is a perfectly fine frequency distribution, it may be too detailed for some purposes. For example, the researcher might want to focus solely on "non-medical doctor" as distinct from "medical doctor" as the type of health professional seen by respondents during their visit to the health and counselling services centre. That is, the researcher might not be concerned with the difference between respondents who saw a "counsellor" and respondents who saw any "other" type of health professional but may want to treat both as simply "non-medical doctor." In that case, these categories could be grouped together and treated as a single entity, as in Table 2.7. Notice that, when categories are collapsed like this, information and detail will be lost. This latter version of the table would not allow the researcher to discriminate between the two types of non-medical doctor health professionals.

**Ordinal-Level Variables.**  Frequency distributions for ordinal-level variables are constructed following the same routines used for nominal-level variables. Table 2.8 reports the frequency distribution of the "satisfaction" variable from the health and counselling services survey. Note that a column of percentages by category has been added to this table. Such columns heighten the clarity of the table (especially with larger samples) and are common adjuncts to the basic frequency distribution for variables measured at all levels.

This table reports that students were neither satisfied nor dissatisfied with health and counselling services. Students were just as likely to be "satisfied" as "dissatisfied." *(For practice in constructing and interpreting frequency distributions for nominal- and ordinal-level variables, see Problem 2.5.)*

**TABLE 2.8  Satisfaction with Services, Health and Counselling Services Survey**

| Satisfaction | Frequency (f) | Percentage (%) |
|---|---|---|
| (4) Very satisfied | 5 | 25 |
| (3) Satisfied | 5 | 25 |
| (2) Dissatisfied | 5 | 25 |
| (1) Very dissatisfied | 5 | 25 |
|  | n = 20 | 100 |

## 2.5 FREQUENCY DISTRIBUTIONS FOR VARIABLES MEASURED AT THE INTERVAL-RATIO LEVEL

**Basic Considerations.** In general, the construction of frequency distributions for variables measured at the interval-ratio level is more complex than for nominal and ordinal variables. Interval-ratio variables usually have a large number of possible scores (i.e., a wide range from the lowest to the highest score). The large number of scores requires some collapsing or grouping of categories to produce reasonably compact frequency distributions.

Note that a frequency distribution, constructed from collapsed or grouped categories of interval-ratio variable values, will closely resemble the frequency distribution of an ordinal variable. When we talk of collapsing or grouping interval-ratio variable values, in order to create a frequency distribution, we are therefore only looking for a way to summarize the interval-ratio variable values in a table form. In other words, we are not replacing the actual variable values with the grouped values, as would be the case with a level of measurement transformation. To construct frequency distributions for interval-ratio-level variables, you must decide how many categories to use and how wide these categories should be. For example, suppose you wished to report the distribution of the variable "age" for a sample drawn from a community. Unlike the university data reported in Table 2.4, a community sample would have a very broad range of ages. If you simply reported the number of times that each year of age (or score) occurred, you could easily wind up with a frequency distribution that contained 70, 80, or even more categories. Such a large frequency distribution would not present a concise picture. The scores (years) must be grouped into larger categories to heighten clarity and ease of comprehension. How large should these categories be? How many categories should be included in the table? Although there are no hard and fast rules for making these decisions, they always involve a tradeoff between more detail (a greater number of narrow categories) and more compactness (a smaller number of wide categories).

**Constructing the Frequency Distribution.** To introduce the mechanics and decision-making processes involved, we will construct a frequency distribution to display the ages of the students in the health and counselling services centre survey. Because of the narrow age range of a group of university students, we can use categories of only one year (these categories are often called **intervals** when working with interval-ratio data). The frequency distribution is constructed by listing the ages from youngest to oldest, counting the number of times each score (year of age) occurs, and then totalling the number of scores for each category. Table 2.9 presents the information and reveals a concentration or clustering of scores in the 18 and 19 intervals.

Even though the picture presented in this table is fairly clear, assume for the sake of illustration that you desire a more compact (less detailed) summary. To do this, you will have to group scores into wider intervals.

**TABLE 2.9**   **Age of Respondents, Health and Counselling Services Survey (interval width = one year of age)**

| Interval | Frequency (f) |
|---|---|
| 18 | 5 |
| 19 | 6 |
| 20 | 3 |
| 21 | 2 |
| 22 | 1 |
| 23 | 1 |
| 24 | 1 |
| 25 | 0 |
| 26 | 1 |
| | $n = 20$ |

By increasing the interval width (say to two years), you can reduce the number of intervals and achieve a more compact expression. The grouping of scores in Table 2.10 clearly emphasizes the relative predominance of younger respondents. This trend in the data can be stressed even more by the addition of a column displaying the percentage of cases in each category.

Note that the intervals in Table 2.10 have been stated with an apparent gap between them (i.e., the intervals are separated by a distance of one unit). At first glance, these gaps may appear to violate the principle of exhaustiveness; but because age has been measured in whole numbers, the gaps actually pose no problem. Given the level of precision of the measurement (in years, as opposed to 10ths or 100ths of a year), no case could have a score falling between these intervals. In fact, for these data, the set of intervals contained in Table 2.10 constitutes a scale that is exhaustive and mutually exclusive. Each of the 20 respondents in the sample can be sorted into one and only one age category.

However, consider the difficulties that might have been encountered if age had been measured with greater precision. If age had been measured in 10ths of a year, into which interval in Table 2.10 would a 19.4-year-old

**TABLE 2.10**   **Age of Respondents, Health and Counselling Services Survey (interval width = two years of age)**

| Interval | Frequency (f) | Percentage (%) |
|---|---|---|
| 18–19 | 11 | 55 |
| 20–21 | 5 | 25 |
| 22–23 | 2 | 10 |
| 24–25 | 1 | 5 |
| 26–27 | 1 | 5 |
| | $n = 20$ | 100 |

subject be placed? You can avoid this ambiguity by always stating the limits of the intervals at the same level of precision as the data. Thus, if age were being measured in 10ths of a year, the limits of the intervals in Table 2.10 would be stated in 10ths of a year. For example:

$$17.0–18.9$$
$$19.0–20.9$$
$$21.0–22.9$$
$$23.0–24.9$$
$$25.0–26.9$$

To maintain mutual exclusivity between categories, do not overlap the intervals. If you state the limits of the intervals at the same level of precision as the data (which might be in whole numbers, tenths, hundredths, etc.) and maintain a "gap" between intervals, you will always produce a frequency distribution with which each case can be assigned to one and only one category.

**Midpoints.** On occasion, you will need to work with the **midpoints** of the intervals, for example, when constructing or interpreting certain graphs such as the frequency polygon (see Section 2.6). Midpoints are defined as the points exactly halfway between the upper and lower limits and can be found for any interval by dividing the sum of the upper and lower limits by two. Table 2.11 displays midpoints for two different sets of intervals. *(For practice in finding midpoints, see Problems 2.8b and 2.9b.)*

**Real Limits.** For certain purposes, you must eliminate the "gap" between intervals and treat a distribution as a continuous series of categories that border each other. This is necessary, for example, in constructing some graphs, such as the histogram (see Section 2.6).

**TABLE 2.11   Midpoints**

| Interval Width = Three | |
| --- | --- |
| Interval | Midpoints |
| 0–2 | 1.0 |
| 3–5 | 4.0 |
| 6–8 | 7.0 |
| 9–11 | 10.0 |

| Interval Width = Six | |
| --- | --- |
| Interval | Midpoints |
| 100–105 | 102.5 |
| 106–111 | 108.5 |
| 112–117 | 114.5 |
| 118–123 | 120.5 |

**ONE STEP AT A TIME** Finding Midpoints

**1:** Find the upper and lower limits of the lowest interval in the frequency distribution. For any interval, the upper limit is the highest score included in the interval and the lower limit is the lowest score included in the interval. For example, for the top set of intervals in Table 2.11, the lowest interval (0–2) includes scores of 0, 1, and 2. The upper limit of this interval is 2 and the lower limit is 0.

**2:** Add the upper and lower limits and divide by 2. For the interval 0–2: (0 + 2)/2 = 1. The midpoint for this interval is 1.

**3:** Midpoints for other intervals can be found by repeating steps 1 and 2 for each interval. As an alternative, you can find the midpoint for any interval by adding the value of the interval width to the midpoint of the next lower interval. For example, the lowest interval in Table 2.11 is 0–2 and the midpoint is 1. Intervals are 3 units wide (i.e., they each include three scores), so the midpoint for the next higher interval (3–5) is 1 + 3, or 4. The midpoint for the interval 6–8 is 4 + 3, or 7, and so forth.

To illustrate, let's begin with Table 2.10. Note the "gap" of one year between intervals. As we saw before, the gap is only apparent: Scores are measured in whole years (i.e., 19, 21 vs. 19.5, or 21.3) and cannot fall between intervals. These types of intervals are called **stated limits** and they organize the scores of the variable into a series of discrete, non-overlapping intervals.

To treat the variable as continuous, we must use the **real limits**. To find the real limits of any interval, divide the distance between the stated limits (the "gap") in half, then add the result to all upper stated limits and subtract it from all lower stated limits. This process is illustrated below with the intervals stated in Table 2.10. The distance between intervals is one, so the real limits can be found by adding 0.5 to all upper limits and subtracting 0.5 from all lower limits.

| Stated Limits | Real Limits |
|---------------|-------------|
| 18–19 | 17.5–19.5 |
| 20–21 | 19.5–21.5 |
| 22–23 | 21.5–23.5 |
| 24–25 | 23.5–25.5 |
| 26–27 | 25.5–27.5 |

**ONE STEP AT A TIME** Finding Real Limits

**1:** Find the distance (the "gap") between the stated class A. In Table 2.10, for example, this value is 1.

**2:** Divide the value found in step 1 in half.

**3:** Add the value found in step 2 to all upper stated limits and subtract it from all lower stated limits.

**TABLE 2.12 Real Limits**

| Stated Limits | Real Limits |
|---|---|
| 3–5 | 2.5–5.5 |
| 6–8 | 5.5–8.5 |
| 9–11 | 8.5–11.5 |

| Stated Limits | Real Limits |
|---|---|
| 100–105 | 99.5–105.5 |
| 106–111 | 105.5–111.5 |
| 112–117 | 111.5–117.5 |
| 118–123 | 117.5–123.5 |

Note that when conceptualized with real limits, the intervals overlap with each other and the distribution can be seen as continuous. Table 2.12 presents additional illustrations of real limits for two different sets of intervals. In both cases, the "gap" between the stated limits is one. *(For practice in finding real limits, see Problems 2.7c and 2.8d.)*

**Cumulative Frequency and Cumulative Percentage.** Two commonly used adjuncts to the basic frequency distribution for interval-ratio-level and ordinal-level data are the **cumulative frequency** and **cumulative percentage** columns. Their primary purpose is to allow the researcher (and his or her audience) to tell at a glance how many cases fall below a given score or interval in the distribution.

To construct a cumulative frequency column, begin with the lowest interval (i.e., the interval with the lowest scores) in the distribution. The entry in the cumulative frequency columns for that interval will be the same as the number of cases in the interval. For the next higher interval, the cumulative frequency will be all cases in the interval plus all the cases in the first interval. For the third interval, the cumulative frequency will be all cases in the interval plus all cases in the first two intervals. Continue adding (or accumulating) cases until you reach the highest interval, which will have a cumulative frequency of all the cases in the interval plus all cases in all other intervals. For the highest interval, cumulative frequency equals the total number of cases. Table 2.13 shows a cumulative frequency column added to Table 2.10.

The cumulative percentage column is quite similar to the cumulative frequency column. Begin by adding a column to the basic frequency distribution for percentages as in Table 2.10. This column shows the percentage of all cases in each interval. To find cumulative percentages, follow the same addition pattern explained above for cumulative frequency. That is, the cumulative percentage for the lowest interval will be the same as the

**TABLE 2.13   Age of Respondents, Health and Counselling Services Survey**

| Interval | Frequency (f) | Cumulative Frequency |
|----------|---------------|----------------------|
| 18–19 | 11 | 11 |
| 20–21 | 5 | 16 |
| 22–23 | 2 | 18 |
| 24–25 | 1 | 19 |
| 26–27 | 1 | 20 |
| | $n = 20$ | |

percentage of cases in the interval. For the next higher interval, the cumulative percentage is the percentage of cases in the interval plus the percentage of cases in the first interval, and so on. Table 2.14 shows the age data with a cumulative percentage column added.

These cumulative columns are quite useful in situations where the researcher wants to make a point about how cases are spread across the range of scores. For example, Tables 2.13 and 2.14 show quite clearly that most students in the health and counselling services survey are 21 years of age or younger. If the researcher wishes to impress this feature of the age distribution on his or her audience, then these cumulative columns are quite handy. Most realistic research situations will be concerned with many more than 20 cases and/or many more categories than our tables have. Because the cumulative percentage column is clearer and easier to interpret in such cases, it is normally preferred to the cumulative frequencies column.

**Unequal Intervals.**   As a general rule, the intervals of frequency distributions should be equal in size in order to maximize clarity and ease of comprehension. For example, note that all of the intervals in Tables 2.13 and 2.14 are the same width (2 years). However, there are two other possibilities for stating intervals, and we will examine each situation separately.

**TABLE 2.14   Age of Respondents, Health and Counselling Services Survey**

| Interval | Frequency (f) | Cumulative Frequency | Percentage (%) | Cumulative Percentage (%) |
|----------|---------------|----------------------|----------------|---------------------------|
| 18–19 | 11 | 11 | 55 | 55 |
| 20–21 | 5 | 16 | 25 | 80 |
| 22–23 | 2 | 18 | 10 | 90 |
| 24–25 | 1 | 19 | 5 | 95 |
| 26–27 | 1 | 20 | 5 | 100 |
| | $n = 20$ | | 100 | |

---

**ONE STEP AT A TIME** Adding Cumulative Frequency and Percentage
Columns to Frequency Distributions

**To Add the Cumulative Frequency Column**

**1:** Begin with the lowest interval (the interval with the lowest scores). The entry in the cumulative frequency column will be the same as the number of cases in this interval.

**2:** Go to the next interval. The cumulative frequency for this interval is the number of cases in the interval plus the number of cases in the lower interval.

**3:** Continue adding (or accumulating) cases from interval to interval until you reach the interval with the highest scores, which will have a cumulative frequency equal to $n$.

**To Add the Cumulative Percentage Column**

**1:** Compute the percentage of cases in each category one at a time, then follow the pattern for the cumulative frequencies. The entry for the lowest interval will be the same as the percentage of cases in the interval.

**2:** For the next higher interval, the cumulative percentage is the percentage of cases in the interval plus the percentage of cases in the lower interval.

**3:** Continue adding (or accumulating) percentages from interval to interval until you reach the interval with the highest scores, which will have a cumulative percentage of 100%.

---

The first option is to use "open-ended" intervals. For instance, what would happen to the frequency distribution in Table 2.13 if we added one more student who was 47 years of age? We would now have 21 cases and there would be a large gap between the oldest respondent (now 47) and the second oldest (age 26). If we simply added the older student to the frequency distribution, we would have to include nine new intervals (28–29, 30–31, 32–33, etc.) with zero cases in them before we got to the 46–47 interval. This would waste space and probably be unclear and confusing. An alternative way to handle the situation where we have a few very high or low scores would be to add an open-ended interval to the frequency distribution, as in Table 2.15.

**TABLE 2.15** Age of Respondents, Health and Counselling Services Survey ($n = 21$)

| Intervals | Frequency ($f$) | Cumulative Frequency |
|---|---|---|
| 18–19 | 11 | 11 |
| 20–21 | 5 | 16 |
| 22–23 | 2 | 18 |
| 24–25 | 1 | 19 |
| 26–27 | 1 | 20 |
| 28 and older | 1 | 21 |
| | $n = 21$ | |

The open-ended interval in Table 2.15 allows us to present the information more compactly than listing all of the empty intervals between "28–29" and "46–47." We could handle an extremely low score by adding an open-ended interval as the lowest interval (e.g., "17 and younger"). There is a small price to pay for this efficiency, which is that there is no information in Table 2.15 about the exact scores included in the open-ended interval, so this technique should not be used indiscriminately.

The second option for stating intervals is to use intervals of "unequal size." On some variables, most scores are tightly clustered together but others are strewn across a broad range of scores. Consider, as an example, the distribution of income for individuals aged 15 years and over in Canada in 2010. According to the 2011 National Household Survey, most individuals (67.7%) reported annual incomes between $15,000 and $99,999, and a sizable grouping (26.5%) earned less than that. The problem (from a statistical point of view) comes with more affluent individuals, those with incomes of $100,000 and above. The number of these individuals is quite small, of course, but we must still account for these cases.

If we tried to use a frequency distribution with equal intervals of, say, $10,000, we would need 30 or 40 or more intervals to include all of the more affluent individuals, and many of our intervals in the higher income ranges—especially those over $150,000—would have few or zero cases. In situations such as this, we can use intervals of unequal size to summarize the variable more efficiently, as in Table 2.16.

Some of the intervals in Table 2.16 are $5,000 wide, others are $10,000, $20,000, or $25,000 wide, and two (the lowest and highest intervals) are

**TABLE 2.16   Distribution of Income by Individuals, Canada, 2010**

| Income | Frequency (f) | Percentage (%) |
|---|---|---|
| Less than $5,000 | 2,574,075 | 9.9 |
| $5,000 to $9,999 | 1,917,960 | 7.4 |
| $10,000 to $14,999 | 2,393,835 | 9.2 |
| $15,000 to $19,999 | 2,441,880 | 9.4 |
| $20,000 to $29,999 | 3,670,015 | 14.2 |
| $30,000 to $39,999 | 3,180,365 | 12.3 |
| $40,000 to $49,999 | 2,603,520 | 10.0 |
| $50,000 to $59,999 | 1,921,650 | 7.4 |
| $60,000 to $79,999 | 2,437,440 | 9.4 |
| $80,000 to $99,999 | 1,302,045 | 5.0 |
| $100,000 to $124,999 | 693,580 | 2.7 |
| $125,000 and above | 782,135 | 3.0 |
|  | 25,918,500 | 99.9* |

*As in this case, percentage columns will occasionally fail to total to 100.0% due to rounding error. If the percentage total is between 99.9% and 100.1%, ignore the discrepancy. Discrepancies greater than ±0.1% may indicate mathematical errors, and the entire column should be computed again.

Source: Data from Statistics Canada, 2011 *National Household Survey.*

open-ended. Tables that use intervals of mixed widths might be a little confusing for the reader, but the tradeoff in compactness and efficiency can be considerable.

**Procedures for Constructing Frequency Distributions for Interval-Ratio Variables.** We covered a lot of ground in the preceding section, so let's pause and review these principles by considering a specific research situation. Below are hypothetical data on the number of hours each student in an Introduction to Sociology course spent studying for the final exam ($n = 105$).

| | | | | | | | | | |
|----|----|----|----|----|----|----|----|----|----|
| 17 | 20 | 21 | 26 | 35 | 10 | 12 | 12 | 15 | 22 |
| 20 | 15 | 18 | 15 | 12 | 21 | 20 | 11 | 12 | 12 |
| 14 | 35 | 5  | 7  | 27 | 18 | 2  | 12 | 35 | 12 |
| 20 | 21 | 20 | 18 | 35 | 10 | 16 | 10 | 35 | 36 |
| 32 | 23 | 7  | 14 | 15 | 35 | 10 | 35 | 16 | 35 |
| 20 | 14 | 18 | 27 | 10 | 35 | 19 | 27 | 7  | 15 |
| 30 | 25 | 14 | 28 | 35 | 20 | 25 | 29 | 18 | 14 |
| 3  | 30 | 23 | 20 | 17 | 35 | 25 | 3  | 7  | 12 |
| 18 | 35 | 9  | 14 | 24 | 10 | 12 | 3  | 15 | 20 |
| 15 | 18 | 10 | 6  | 25 | 20 | 34 | 18 | 3  | 15 |
| 20 | 33 | 14 | 7  | 30 |    |    |    |    |    |

Listed in this format, the data are a hopeless jumble from which no one could derive much meaning. The function of the frequency distribution is to arrange and organize these data so that their meanings will be made obvious.

First, we must decide how many intervals to use in the frequency distribution. Following the guidelines presented in the One Step at a Time: Constructing Frequency Distributions for Interval-Ratio Variables box, let's use about 10 intervals ($k = 10$). By inspecting the data, we can see that the lowest score is 2 and the highest is 36. The range of these scores ($R$) is $36 - 2$, or 34. To find the approximate interval size ($i$), divide the range (34) by the number of intervals (10). Since $34/10 = 3.4$, we can set the interval size at 3.

The lowest score is 2, so the lowest interval will be 2–4. The highest interval will be 35–37, which will include the high score of 36. All that remains is to state the intervals in table format, count the number of scores that fall into each interval, and report the totals in a frequency column. These steps have been taken in Table 2.17, which also includes columns for the percentages and cumulative percentages. Note that this table is the product of several relatively arbitrary decisions. The researcher should remain aware of this fact and inspect the frequency distribution carefully. If the table is unsatisfactory for any reason, it can be reconstructed with a different number of categories and interval sizes.

**TABLE 2.17**  **Number of Hours Studied for Final Exam in Introduction to Sociology Course**

| Interval | Frequency (*f*) | Cumulative Frequency | Percentage (%) | Cumulative Percentage (%) |
|---|---|---|---|---|
| 2–4 | 5 | 5 | 4.76 | 4.76 |
| 5–7 | 7 | 12 | 6.67 | 11.43 |
| 8–10 | 8 | 20 | 7.62 | 19.05 |
| 11–13 | 10 | 30 | 9.52 | 28.57 |
| 14–16 | 17 | 47 | 16.19 | 44.76 |
| 17–19 | 11 | 58 | 10.48 | 55.24 |
| 20–22 | 15 | 73 | 14.29 | 69.53 |
| 23–25 | 7 | 80 | 6.67 | 76.20 |
| 26–28 | 5 | 85 | 4.76 | 80.96 |
| 29–31 | 4 | 89 | 3.81 | 84.77 |
| 32–34 | 3 | 92 | 2.86 | 87.63 |
| 35–37 | 13 | 105 | 12.38 | 100.01 |
| | *n* = 105 | | 100.01* | |

*Percentage column fails to total to 100% because of rounding error.

---

## ONE STEP AT A TIME  Constructing Frequency Distributions for Interval-Ratio Variables

**1:** Decide how many intervals (*k*) you wish to use. One reasonable convention suggests that the number of intervals should be about 10. Many research situations may require fewer than 10 intervals (*k* = 10), and it is common to find frequency distributions with as many as 15 intervals. Only rarely will more than 15 intervals be used, since the resultant frequency distribution would be too large for easy comprehension.

**2:** Find the range (*R*) of the scores by subtracting the low score from the high score.

**3:** Find the size of the intervals (*i*) by dividing *R* (from step 2) by *k* (from step 1):

$$i = R/k$$

Round the value of *i* to a convenient whole number. This will be the interval size or width.

**4:** State the lowest interval so that its lower limit is equal to or below the lowest score. By the same token, your highest interval will be the one that contains the highest score. Generally, intervals should be equal in size, but unequal and open-ended intervals may be used when convenient.

**5:** State the limits of the intervals at the same level of precision as you have used to measure the data. Do not overlap intervals. You will thereby define the intervals so that each case can be sorted into one and only one category.

**6:** Count the number of cases in each interval, and report these subtotals in a column labelled "Frequency." Report the total number of cases (*n*) at the bottom of this column. The table may also include a column for percentages, cumulative frequencies, and cumulative percentages.

**7:** Inspect the frequency distribution carefully. Has too much detail been lost? If so, reconstruct the table with a greater number of intervals (or use a smaller interval size). Is the table too detailed? If so, reconstruct the table with fewer intervals (or use wider intervals). Are there too many intervals with no cases in them? If so, consider using open-ended intervals or intervals of unequal size. Remember that the frequency distribution results from a number of decisions you make in a rather arbitrary manner. If the appearance of the table seems less than optimal given the purpose of the research, redo the table until you are satisfied that you have struck the best balance between detail and conciseness.

**8:** Give your table a clear, concise title, and number the table if your report contains more than one. All categories and columns must also be clearly labelled.

Now, with the aid of the frequency distribution, some patterns in the data can be discerned. There are three distinct clusterings of scores in the table. The single largest interval, with 17 cases, is 14–16. Nearly as many students, 15 cases, spent between 20 and 22 hours studying for the final exam. Combined with the interval between them (17–19 hours), this represents quite a sizable grouping of cases (43 out of 105, or 40.95% of all cases). The third grouping is in the 35–37 interval with 13 cases, showing that a rather large percentage of students (12.38%) spent relatively many hours studying for the final exam. The cumulative percentage column indicates that the majority of the students (55.24%) spent less than 20 hours studying for the exam. *(For practice in constructing and interpreting frequency distributions for interval-ratio-level variables, see Problems 2.5 to 2.9.)*

## 2.6 CHARTS AND GRAPHS

Researchers frequently use charts and graphs to present their data in ways that are visually more dramatic than frequency distributions. These devices are particularly useful for conveying an impression of the overall shape of a distribution and for highlighting any clustering of cases in a particular range of scores. Many graphing techniques are available, but we will examine just five. The first two, pie and bar charts, are appropriate for discrete variables at any level of measurement. The next two, histograms and frequency polygons, are used with both discrete and continuous interval-ratio variables but are particularly appropriate for the latter. The fifth, boxplots, will be examined in Chapter 3, after we have discussed central tendency and dispersion. Boxplots are appropriate for both discrete and continuous interval-ratio variables.

The sections that follow explain how to construct graphs and charts "by hand." These days, however, computer programs are almost always used to produce graphic displays. Graphing software is sophisticated and flexible but also relatively easy to use and, if such programs are available to you, you should familiarize yourself with them. The effort required to learn these programs will be repaid in the quality of the final product. The section on computer applications at the end of this chapter includes a demonstration of how to produce bar charts.

**Pie Charts.** To construct a **pie chart**, begin by computing the percentage of all cases that fall into each category of the variable. Then divide a circle (the pie) into segments (slices) proportional to the percentage distribution. Be sure that the chart and all segments are clearly labelled.

Figure 2.1 is a pie chart that displays the distribution of the "type of health professional seen" variable from the health and counselling services survey. The frequency distribution (see Table 2.6) is reproduced as

**TABLE 2.18   Type of Health Professional Seen by Respondents, Health and Counselling Services Survey**

| Health Professional | Frequency (f) | Percentage (%) |
|---|---|---|
| Medical Doctor | 10 | 50 |
| Counsellor | 7 | 35 |
| Other | 3 | 15 |
| | n = 20 | 100 |

Table 2.18, with a column added for the percentage distribution. Because a circle's circumference is 360°, we will apportion 180° (or 50%) for the first category, 126° (35%) for the second, and 54° (15%) for the last. The pie chart visually reinforces the relative preponderance of respondents who saw a medical doctor and the relative absence of respondents who saw other types of health professionals in the health and counselling services survey.

**Bar Charts.**   Like pie charts, **bar charts** are relatively straightforward. Conventionally, the categories of the variable are arrayed along the horizontal axis (or abscissa) and frequencies, or percentages if you prefer, along the vertical axis (or ordinate). For each category of the variable, construct (or draw) a rectangle of constant width and with a height that corresponds to the number of cases in the category. The bar chart in Figure 2.2 reproduces the data for the "type of health professional seen" variable from Figure 2.1 and Table 2.18.

This chart would be interpreted in exactly the same way as the pie chart in Figure 2.1, and researchers are free to choose between these two methods of displaying data. However, if a variable has more than four or five categories, the bar chart would be preferred. With too many categories, the pie chart gets very crowded and loses its visual clarity.

**FIGURE 2.1   Pie Chart: Type of Health Professional Seen by Respondents, Health and Counselling Services Survey**

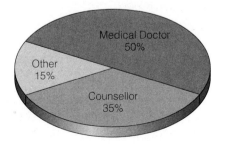

**FIGURE 2.2**  **Bar Chart: Type of Health Professional Seen by Respondents, Health and Counselling Services Survey (*n* = 20)**

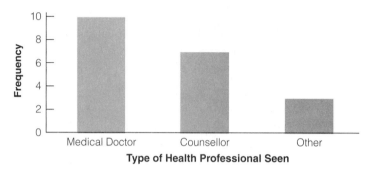

Bar charts are also particularly effective ways to display the relative frequencies for two or more categories of a variable when you want to emphasize some comparisons. Suppose, for example, that you wished to compare males and females on satisfaction with health and counselling services. Figure 2.3 displays these data, derived from Table 2.4, in an easily comprehensible way. The bar chart shows that satisfaction with services steadily increases for females, while it steadily decreases for males. Figure 2.3 also shows the special usefulness of bar charts for ordinal variables, since the placement of the variable values on the abscissa preserves the rank order of an ordinal variable's values. *(For practice in constructing and interpreting pie and bar charts, see Problems 2.5b and 2.10.)*

**Histograms.**  **Histograms** look a lot like bar charts and, in fact, are constructed in much the same way. However, histograms use real limits rather than stated limits; also, the categories or scores of the variables are contiguous, meaning that they border each other, as if they merged into each other in a continuous series. Therefore, these graphs are most appropriate

**FIGURE 2.3**  **Satisfaction with Services by Sex, Health and Counselling Services Survey (*n* = 20)**

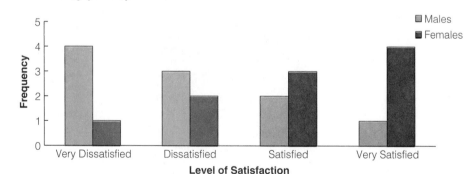

for continuous interval-ratio-level variables, although they are commonly used for discrete interval-ratio-level variables as well. To construct a histogram from a frequency distribution, follow these steps:

1. Array the real limits of the intervals or scores along the horizontal axis (abscissa).
2. Array frequencies along the vertical axis (ordinate).
3. For each category in the frequency distribution, construct a bar with height corresponding to the number of cases in the category and with width corresponding to the real limits of the intervals.
4. Label each axis of the graph.
5. Title the graph.

As an example, Table 2.19 presents the real limits, along with midpoints, of the intervals for the frequency distribution shown in Table 2.17. This information was used to construct a histogram of the distribution of study hours, as presented in Figure 2.4. Note that the edges of each bar correspond to the real limits and that the middle of each bar is directly over the midpoint of the interval. Overall, the histogram visually reinforces the relative concentration of students in the middle of the distribution, as well as the relatively large grouping of students who spent between 35 to 37 hours studying for the final exam in the Introduction to Sociology course.

**Frequency Polygons.**   Construction of a **frequency polygon** is similar to construction of a histogram. Instead of using bars to represent the frequencies, however, it uses dots at the midpoint of each interval. A straight line then connects the dots. Finally, to form a polygon, the line is dropped to the horizontal axis at the midpoint of the adjacent interval at the ends. Because

**TABLE 2.19   Real Limits and Midpoints of Intervals for Frequency Distribution Shown in Table 2.17**

| Interval (stated limits) | Real Limits | Midpoints | Frequency (f) |
|---|---|---|---|
| 2–4 | 1.5–4.5 | 3 | 5 |
| 5–7 | 4.5–7.5 | 6 | 7 |
| 8–10 | 7.5–10.5 | 9 | 8 |
| 11–13 | 10.5–13.5 | 12 | 10 |
| 14–16 | 13.5–16.5 | 15 | 17 |
| 17–19 | 16.5–19.5 | 18 | 11 |
| 20–22 | 19.5–22.5 | 21 | 15 |
| 23–25 | 22.5–25.5 | 24 | 7 |
| 26–28 | 25.5–28.5 | 27 | 5 |
| 29–31 | 28.5–31.5 | 30 | 4 |
| 32–34 | 31.5–3 4.5 | 33 | 3 |
| 35–37 | 34.5–37.5 | 36 | 13 |
|  |  |  | $n = 105$ |

**FIGURE 2.4 Histogram of Study Hours for Final Exam in Introduction to Sociology Course (*n* = 105)**

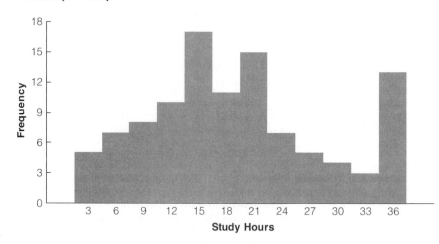

the line is continuous from highest to lowest score, these graphs are especially appropriate for continuous interval-ratio-level variables, although they are frequently used with discrete interval-ratio-level variables. Figure 2.5 displays a frequency polygon for the study hours data previously displayed in the histogram in Figure 2.4.

Histograms and frequency polygons are alternative ways of displaying essentially the same message. Thus, the choice between the two techniques is left to the aesthetic pleasures of the researcher. *(For practice in constructing and interpreting histograms and frequency polygons, see Problems 2.7b, 2.8e, and 2.9d.)*

**FIGURE 2.5 Frequency Polygon of Study Hours for Final Exam in Introduction to Sociology Course (*n* = 105)**

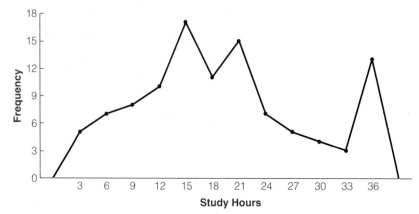

# READING STATISTICS 2: Percentages, Rates, Tables, and Graphs

The statistics covered in this chapter are frequently used in the research literature of the social sciences—as well as in the popular press and the media—and one of the goals of this text is to help you develop your ability to understand and critically analyze them. Fortunately, this task is usually quite straightforward, but these statistical tools are sometimes not as simple as they appear and they can be misused. Here are some ideas to keep in mind when reading research reports that use these statistics.

First, there are many different formats for presenting results, and the tables and graphs you find in the research literature will not necessarily follow the conventions used in this text. Second, because of space limitations, tables and graphs may be presented with minimum detail. For example, the researcher may present a frequency distribution with only a percentage column.

Begin your analysis by examining the statistics carefully. If you are reading a table or graph, first read the title, all labels (i.e., row and/or column headings), and any footnotes. These will tell you exactly what information is being presented. Inspect the body of the table or graph with the author's analysis in mind. See if you agree with the author's analysis. (You almost always will, but it never hurts to double-check and exercise your critical abilities.)

Finally, remember that most research projects analyze interrelationships among many variables. Because the tables and graphs covered in this chapter display variables one at a time, they are unlikely to be included in such research reports (or, perhaps, included only as background information). Even when they are not reported, you can be sure that the research began with an inspection of percentages, frequency distributions, or graphs for each variable. Univariate tables and graphs display a great deal of information about the variables in a compact, easily understood format and are almost universally used as descriptive devices.

## STATISTICS IN THE PROFESSIONAL LITERATURE

Social scientists in Canada rely considerably on the Canadian census for information about the characteristics and trends of change in Canadian society. Census data are readily available on Statistics Canada's website, but since they represent information about the entire population, the numbers are often large, cumbersome, and awkward to use or understand. Thus, percentages, rates, and graphs are extremely useful statistical devices when analyzing or presenting census information.

Consider, for example, a recent report on the changing Canadian family.* The purpose of the report was to present information regarding the structure of the Canadian family and to present and discuss recent changes and trends. Consider how this report might have read if the information had been given in words and raw numbers: The total number of families in Canada—married couples, common-law couples and lone-parent families—increased from 8,371,020 in 2001 to 9,389,700 in 2011. Among families in 2011, there were 6,293,950 married couple families, 1,567,910 common-law couple families, and 1,527,840 lone-parent families. Can you distil any meaningful understandings about Canadian family life from these sentences? Raw information simply does not speak for itself, and data have to be organized or placed in some context to reveal their meaning. Thus, social scientists almost always use percentages, rates, or graphs to present this kind of information so that they can understand it and convey their interpretations to others.

In contrast with raw information, consider the following table on family trends using percentages.

*(continued)*

### Canadian Families by Type, 2001 and 2011

| | Percent of All Families | |
|---|---|---|
| | 2001 | 2011 |
| *Couple Families:* | | |
| Married | 70.5% | 67.0% |
| Common-law | 13.8% | 16.7% |
| *Lone-Parent Families:* | | |
| Female parents | 12.7% | 12.8% |
| Male parents | 2.9% | 3.5% |
| Total Families | 100.0% | 100.0% |
| | (8,371,020) | (9,389,700) |

A quick comparison of the two years reveals a notable decrease in the percentage of Canadian families that consist of married couples and an increase in the percentages of common-law couples. What other trends can you see in the table?

*Source: Statistics Canada, 2012, *Portrait of Families and Living Arrangements in Canada.* Catalogue no. 98-312-X2011001.

## SUMMARY

1. We considered several different ways of summarizing the distribution of a single variable and, more generally, reporting the results of our research. Our emphasis throughout was on the need to communicate our results clearly and concisely. You will often find that, as you strive to communicate statistical information to others, the meanings of the information will become clearer to you as well.

2. Percentages, proportions, ratios, and rates represent several different techniques for enhancing clarity by expressing results in terms of relative frequency. Percentages and proportions report the relative occurrence of some category of a variable compared with the distribution as a whole. Ratios compare two categories with each other, and rates report the actual occurrences of some phenomenon compared with the number of possible occurrences per some unit of time.

3. Frequency distributions are tables that summarize the entire distribution of some variable. It is very common to construct these tables for each variable of interest as the first step in a statistical analysis. Columns for percentages, cumulative frequencies, and/or cumulative percentages often enhance the readability of frequency distributions.

4. Pie and bar charts, histograms, and frequency polygons are graphic devices used to express the basic information contained in the frequency distribution in a compact and visually dramatic way.

## SUMMARY OF FORMULAS

Proportions    2.1    $p = \dfrac{f}{n}$

Percentage    2.2    $\% = \left(\dfrac{f}{n}\right) \times 100$

| Ratios | 2.3 | $\text{Ratio} = \dfrac{f_1}{f_2}$ |
| --- | --- | --- |
| Rates | 2.4 | $\text{Rate} = \dfrac{f_{\text{actual}}}{f_{\text{possible}}}$ |

## GLOSSARY

**Bar chart.** A graphic display device for discrete variables. Response categories are represented by bars of equal width, the height of each corresponding to the number (or percentage) of cases in the response category.

**Cumulative frequency.** An optional column in a frequency distribution that displays the number of cases within an interval and all preceding intervals.

**Cumulative percentage.** An optional column in a frequency distribution that displays the percentage of cases within an interval and all preceding intervals.

**Frequency distribution.** A table that displays the number of cases in each response category of a variable.

**Frequency polygon.** A graphic display device for interval-ratio variables. Intervals are represented by dots placed over the midpoints, the height of each corresponding to the number (or percentage) of cases in the interval. All dots are connected by straight lines, and the line is dropped to the horizontal axis at the midpoint of the adjacent interval at the ends.

**Histogram.** A graphic display device for interval-ratio variables. Intervals are represented by contiguous bars of equal width (equal to the real limits), the height of each corresponding to the number (or percentage) of cases in the interval.

**Intervals.** The response categories created to produce frequency distributions for interval-ratio variables.

**Midpoint.** The point exactly halfway between the upper and lower limits of an interval.

**Percentage.** The number of cases in a response category of a variable divided by the number of cases in all response categories of the variable, with the entire quantity then multiplied by 100.

**Pie chart.** A graphic display device especially for discrete variables with only a few response categories. A circle (the pie) is divided into segments proportional in size to the percentage of cases in each response category of the variable.

**Proportion.** The number of cases in one response category of a variable divided by the number of cases in all response categories of the variable.

**Rate.** The number of actual occurrences of some phenomenon or trait divided by the number of possible occurrences per some unit of time.

**Ratio.** The number of cases in one response category divided by the number of cases in some other response category.

**Real limits.** The intervals of a frequency distribution when stated as continuous response categories.

**Stated limits.** The intervals of a frequency distribution when stated as discrete response categories.

## MULTIMEDIA RESOURCES

 nelson.com/student

Visit the companion website for the fourth Canadian edition of *Statistics: A Tool for Social Research* to access a wide range of student resources. Begin by clicking on the Student Resources section of the book's website to access online chapters and study tools.

## PROBLEMS

**2.1** SOC The tables that follow report the marital status of 20 respondents in two different apartment complexes. *(HINT: Make sure you have the correct numbers in the numerator and denominator before solving the following problems. For example, Problem 2.1a asks for "the percentage of the respondents who are married in each complex"; the denominators will be 20 for these two fractions. Problem 2.1d, however, asks for "the percentage of the single respondents who live in Complex B"; the denominator for this fraction will be 4 + 6, or 10.)*

| Status | Complex A | Complex B |
|---|---|---|
| Married | 5 | 10 |
| Common-law | 8 | 2 |
| Single | 4 | 6 |
| Separated | 2 | 1 |
| Widowed | 0 | 1 |
| Divorced | 1 | 0 |
| | 20 | 20 |

**a.** What percentage of the respondents in each complex are married?

**b.** What is the ratio of single to married respondents at each complex?

**c.** What proportion of each sample are widowed?

**d.** What percentage of the single respondents live in Complex B?

**e.** What is the ratio of the "unmarried/living together" to the married at each complex?

**2.2** At Algebra University, the numbers of males and females in the various major fields of study are as follows:

| Major | Males | Females | Totals |
|---|---|---|---|
| Humanities | 117 | 83 | 200 |
| Social sciences | 97 | 132 | 229 |
| Natural sciences | 72 | 20 | 92 |
| Business | 156 | 139 | 295 |
| Nursing | 3 | 35 | 38 |
| Education | 30 | 15 | 45 |
| Totals | 475 | 424 | 899 |

Read each of the following problems carefully before constructing the fraction and solving for the answer. *(HINT: Be sure you place the proper number in the denominator of the fractions. For example, some problems use the total number of males or females as the denominator, but others use the total number of majors.)*

**a.** What percentage of social science majors are male?

**b.** What proportion of business majors are female?

**c.** For the humanities, what is the ratio of males to females?

**d.** What percentage of the total student body are males?

**e.** What is the ratio of males to females for the entire sample?

**f.** What proportion of the nursing majors are male?

**g.** What percentage of the sample are social science majors?

**h.** What is the ratio of humanities majors to business majors?

**i.** What is the ratio of female business majors to female nursing majors?

**j.** What proportion of the males are education majors?

**2.3** CJ A city in Ontario had a population of 211,732 and experienced 47 bank robberies, 13 murders, and 23 auto thefts during a recent year. Compute a rate for each type of crime per 100,000 population. *(HINT: Make sure you set up the fraction with size of population in the denominator.)*

**2.4** CJ The numbers of homicides in five states and five Canadian provinces for the years 1997 and 2008 are as follows:

| State/Province | 1997 | | 2008 | |
| | Homicides | Population | Homicides | Population |
| --- | --- | --- | --- | --- |
| New Jersey | 338 | 8,053,000 | 376 | 8,883,000 |
| Iowa | 52 | 2,852,000 | 76 | 3,003,000 |
| Alabama | 426 | 4,139,000 | 353 | 4,882,000 |
| Texas | 1,327 | 19,439,000 | 1,374 | 24,327,000 |
| California | 2,579 | 32,268,000 | 2,142 | 36,757,000 |
| Nova Scotia | 24 | 936,100 | 12 | 936,600 |
| Quebec | 132 | 7,323,600 | 92 | 7,753,000 |
| Ontario | 178 | 11,387,400 | 176 | 12,936,300 |
| Manitoba | 31 | 1,137,900 | 54 | 1,206,000 |
| British Columbia | 116 | 3,997,100 | 117 | 4,383,800 |

Source: US Census Bureau and Statistics Canada.

Calculate the homicide rate per 100,000 population for each state and each province for each year. Relatively speaking, which state and which province had the highest homicide rates in each year? Which country seems to have the higher homicide rate? Write a paragraph describing these results.

**2.5** ⎡SOC⎤ The scores of 15 respondents on four variables are reported below. The numerical codes for the variables are as follows:

| Sex | Support for Legalization of Marijuana | Level of Education | Age |
| --- | --- | --- | --- |
| 1 = Male | 1 = In favour | 0 = Less than high school | Actual years |
| 2 = Female | 2 = Opposed | 1 = High school | |
| | | 2 = Community college | |
| | | 3 = Bachelor's | |
| | | 4 = Graduate | |

| Case Number | Sex | Support for Legalization of Marijuana | Level of Education | Age |
| --- | --- | --- | --- | --- |
| 1 | 2 | 1 | 1 | 45 |
| 2 | 1 | 2 | 1 | 48 |
| 3 | 2 | 1 | 3 | 55 |
| 4 | 1 | 1 | 2 | 32 |
| 5 | 2 | 1 | 3 | 33 |
| 6 | 1 | 1 | 1 | 28 |
| 7 | 2 | 2 | 0 | 77 |
| 8 | 1 | 1 | 1 | 50 |
| 9 | 1 | 2 | 0 | 43 |
| 10 | 2 | 1 | 1 | 48 |
| 11 | 1 | 1 | 4 | 33 |
| 12 | 1 | 1 | 4 | 35 |
| 13 | 1 | 1 | 0 | 39 |
| 14 | 2 | 1 | 1 | 25 |
| 15 | 1 | 1 | 1 | 23 |

**a.** Construct a frequency distribution for each variable. Include a column for percentages.

**b.** Construct pie and bar charts to display the distributions of sex, support for legalization of marijuana, and level of education.

**2.6** ⎡SW⎤ A local youth service agency has begun a sex education program for teenage girls who have been referred by the youth courts. The girls were given a 20-item test for general knowledge about sex, contraception, and anatomy and physiology upon admission to the program and again after completing the program. The scores for the first 15 girls to complete the program are listed on the next page.

| Case | Pretest | Post-Test | Case | Pretest | Post-Test |
|------|---------|-----------|------|---------|-----------|
| A | 8 | 12 | J | 15 | 12 |
| B | 7 | 13 | K | 13 | 20 |
| C | 10 | 12 | L | 4 | 5 |
| D | 15 | 19 | M | 10 | 15 |
| E | 10 | 8 | N | 8 | 11 |
| F | 10 | 17 | O | 12 | 20 |
| G | 3 | 12 | | | |
| H | 10 | 11 | | | |
| I | 5 | 7 | | | |

Construct frequency distributions for the pretest and post-test scores. Include a column for percentages. *(HINT: There were 20 items on the test, so the maximum range for these scores is 20. If you use 10 intervals to display these scores, the interval size will be 2. Because there are no scores of 0 or 1 for either test, you may state the first interval as 2–3. To make comparisons easier, both frequency distributions should have the same intervals.)*

**2.7** SOC Sixteen students in their final year of undergraduate studies completed a class to prepare them for the GRE (Graduate Record Examination). Their scores are reported below.

| | | | |
|-----|-----|-----|-----|
| 420 | 345 | 560 | 650 |
| 459 | 499 | 500 | 657 |
| 467 | 480 | 505 | 555 |
| 480 | 520 | 530 | 589 |

These same 16 students were given a test of math and verbal ability to measure their readiness for graduate-level work. The following scores are reported in terms of the percentage of correct answers for each test.

**Math Test**

| | | | |
|----|----|----|----|
| 67 | 45 | 68 | 70 |
| 72 | 85 | 90 | 99 |
| 50 | 73 | 77 | 78 |
| 52 | 66 | 89 | 75 |

**Verbal Test**

| | | | |
|----|----|----|----|
| 89 | 90 | 78 | 77 |
| 75 | 70 | 56 | 60 |
| 77 | 78 | 80 | 92 |
| 98 | 72 | 77 | 82 |

**a.** Display each of these variables in a frequency distribution with columns for percentages and cumulative percentages.
**b.** Construct a histogram and a frequency polygon for these data.
**c.** Find the upper and lower real limits for the intervals you established.

**2.8** GER Following are reported the number of times 25 residents of a community for senior citizens left their homes for any reason during the past week.

| | | | | |
|----|----|----|----|----|
| 0 | 2 | 1 | 7 | 3 |
| 7 | 0 | 2 | 3 | 17 |
| 14 | 15 | 5 | 0 | 7 |
| 5 | 21 | 4 | 7 | 6 |
| 2 | 0 | 10 | 5 | 7 |

**a.** Construct a frequency distribution to display these data.
**b.** What are the midpoints of the intervals?
**c.** Add columns to the table to display the percentage distribution, cumulative frequency, and cumulative percentages.
**d.** Find the real limits for the intervals you selected.
**e.** Construct a histogram and a frequency polygon to display these data.
**f.** Write a paragraph summarizing this distribution of scores.

**2.9** SOC Twenty-five students completed a questionnaire that measured their attitudes toward interpersonal violence. Respondents who scored high believed that in many situations a person could legitimately use physical force against another person. Respondents who scored low believed that in no situation (or very few situations) could the use of violence be justified.

| | | | | |
|----|----|----|----|----|
| 52 | 47 | 17 | 8 | 92 |
| 53 | 23 | 28 | 9 | 90 |
| 17 | 63 | 17 | 17 | 23 |
| 19 | 66 | 10 | 20 | 47 |
| 20 | 66 | 5 | 25 | 17 |

a. Construct a frequency distribution to display these data.
b. What are the midpoints of the intervals?
c. Add columns to the table to display the percentage distribution, cumulative frequency, and cumulative percentage.
d. Construct a histogram and a frequency polygon to display these data.
e. Write a paragraph summarizing this distribution of scores.

**2.10** PA/CJ As part of an evaluation of the efficiency of your local police force, you have gathered the following data on police response time to calls for assistance during two different years. (Response times were rounded off to whole

minutes.) Convert both frequency distributions into percentages and construct pie charts and bar charts to display the data. Write a paragraph comparing the changes in response time between the two years.

| Response Time, 2000 | $f$ | Response Time, 2010 | $f$ |
|---|---|---|---|
| 21 minutes or more | 35 | 21 minutes or more | 45 |
| 16–20 minutes | 75 | 16–20 minutes | 95 |
| 11–15 minutes | 180 | 11–15 minutes | 155 |
| 6–10 minutes | 375 | 6–10 minutes | 350 |
| Less than 6 minutes | 275 | Less than 6 minutes | 250 |
| | 940 | | 895 |

## Using SPSS to Produce Frequency Distributions and Graphs with the 2013 GSS

The demonstrations and exercises below use the shortened version of the 2013 GSS data set supplied with this textbook. Click the SPSS icon on your monitor screen to start SPSS. Load the 2013 GSS by clicking the file name (*2013_GSS_Shortened.sav*) on the first screen, or by clicking **File**, **Open**, and **Data** on the **SPSS Data Editor** window. In the **Open Data** dialog box, you may have to change the drive specification to locate the 2013 GSS data. Double-click the file name (*2013_GSS_Shortened.sav*) to open the data set. You are ready to proceed when you see the message "IBM SPSS Statistics Processor is ready" on the status bar at the bottom of the **SPSS Data Editor** window as shown in Figure 2.6.

The **SPSS Data Editor** window can actually be viewed in one of two unique modes. The **Data View** mode (Figure 2.6), which is the default mode when you start SPSS, displays the data in the data set. Each row represents a particular case and each column a particular variable. By contrast, the **Variable View** mode (Figure 2.7) shows the variables in that data set, where each row represents a particular variable and each column a particular piece of information (e.g., name, label) about the variable. When analyzing variables, be careful not to mix up the variable name and the variable label, or your analysis might not be performed by SPSS. To change from one mode to the other, click the appropriate tab located at the bottom of the **SPSS Data Editor** window.

Before we begin our demonstrations, it is important to note that SPSS provides the user with a variety of options for displaying information about the data file and output on the screen. We highly recommend that you tell SPSS to display lists of variables by name (e.g., *agegr10*) rather than labels (e.g., age group of respondent

**FIGURE 2.6 SPSS Data Editor Window: Data View**

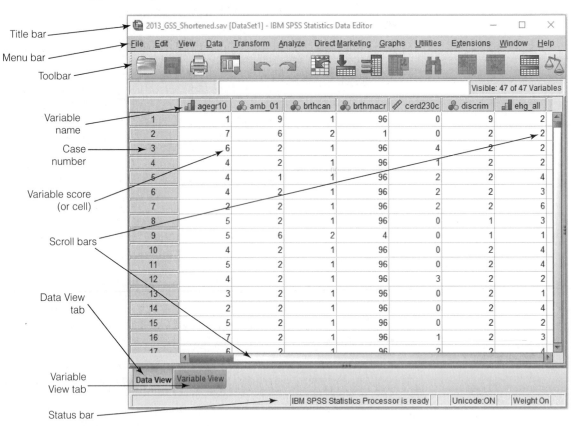

(groups of 10)). Lists displayed this way will be easier to read and to compare to the GSS and CCHS codebooks in Appendix G. To do this, click **Edit** on the main menu bar at the top of the **SPSS Data Editor** window, then click **Options** from the drop-down submenu. A dialog box labelled **Options** will appear with a series of tabs along the top. The **General** options should be displayed, but if not, click on the **General** tab. On the **General** screen, find the box labelled **Variable Lists**; if they are not already selected, click **Display names**, then **Alphabetical**, then click **OK**. If you make changes, a message may appear on the screen that tells you that changes will reset all dialogue box settings and close all open dialogue boxes. Click **OK**.

**FIGURE 2.7   SPSS Data Editor Window: Variable View**

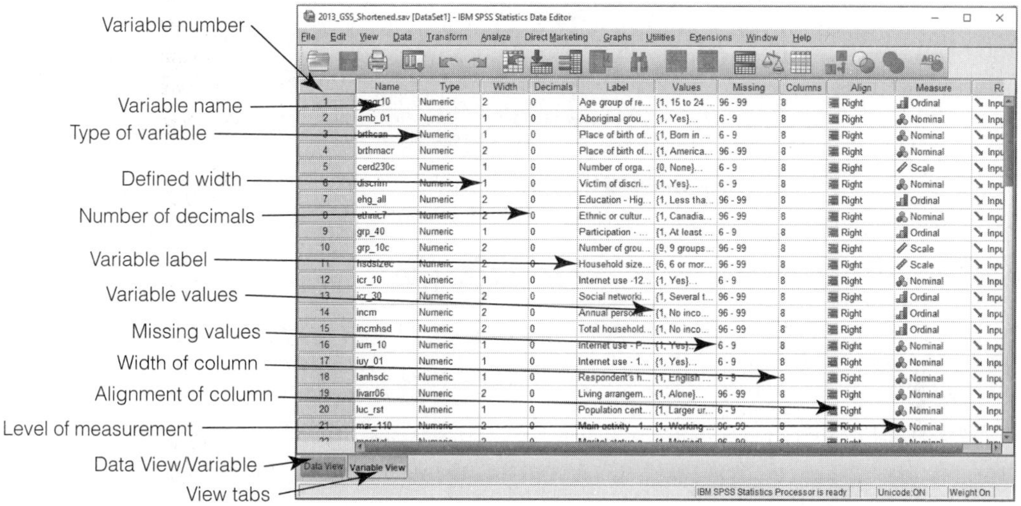

Variable number
Variable name
Type of variable
Defined width
Number of decimals
Variable label
Variable values
Missing values
Width of column
Alignment of column
Level of measurement
Data View/Variable View tabs

## SPSS DEMONSTRATION 2.1 Frequency Distributions

In this demonstration, we will use the **Frequencies** procedure to produce a frequency distribution for the variable *marstat* (marital status).

From the menu bar on the **SPSS Data Editor** window, click **Analyze**. From the menu that drops down, click **Descriptive Statistics** and then **Frequencies**. The **Frequencies** dialog box appears with the variables listed in alphabetical order in the left-hand box. Find *marstat* in the left-hand box by using the slider button or the arrow keys on the right-hand border to scroll through the variable list. As an alternative, type "m," and the cursor will move to the first variable name in the list that begins with the letter "m." In this case, the variable is *marstat,* the variable that we are interested in. Once *marstat* is highlighted, click the arrow button in the centre of the screen to move the variable name to the **Variable(s)** box. The variable name *marstat* should now appear in the box. Click the **OK** button at the bottom of the dialog box, and SPSS will rush off to create the frequency distribution you requested.

The output table (frequency distribution) will be in the **SPSS Output**, or **Viewer**, window, which will now be "closest" to you on the screen. As illustrated in Figure 2.8, the output table, along with other information, is in the right-hand box of the window, while the left-hand box contains an "outline" **log** of the entire output. To change the size of the **SPSS Output** window, click on the **Maximize** button, the middle symbol (shaped like either a square or two intersecting squares) in the upper-right-hand corner of the window. The actual output can also be edited by double-clicking on any part of the table. (See Appendix F.6 for more information on editing output.)

**FIGURE 2.8 SPSS Viewer (Output) Window**

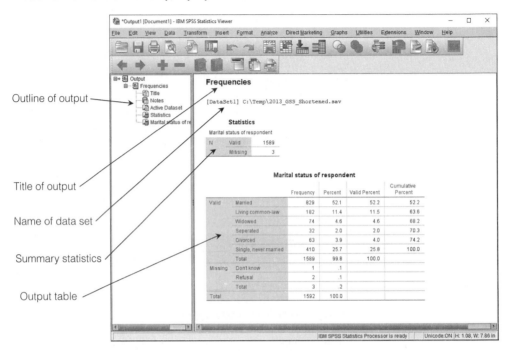

Let's briefly examine the elements of the output table in Figure 2.8. The variable description, or label, is printed at the top of the output ("Marital status"). The various categories are printed on the left. Moving one column to the right, we find the actual frequencies, or the number of times each score of the variable occurred. We see that 829 of the respondents were married, 182 had common-law status, and so forth.

Next are two columns that report percentages. The entries in the "Percent" column are based on all respondents in the sample. In this case, the denominator would include any respondents, even the ones coded as missing. The "Valid Percent" column eliminates all cases with missing values. Because we almost always ignore missing values, we will pay attention only to the "Valid Percent" column. The final column is a cumulative percentage column. For nominal-level variables like *marstat,* this information is not meaningful because the order in which the categories are stated is arbitrary.

The output table in the **SPSS Output** window can be printed or saved by selecting the appropriate command from the **File** menu. You can also transfer the table to a word processor document: Right-click on any part of the table, choose **Copy**, right-click on the spot in the word processor document where you want to place the table, and choose **Paste**. Appendix F.7 provides more information on these topics.

As a final note, the total number of cases in the GSS data set is 1,500. This can be verified by scrolling to the bottom of the **SPSS Data Editor** window, where you will find a total of 1,500 rows. However, the "total" number of cases in the output table above is 1,592. The reason for the difference is that the GSS data set is weighted to correct for sampling bias. Like many social surveys, the GSS under- and over-samples various groups of individuals—some individuals are more likely than others to be included in the sample. The weight variable included with the GSS, *wght_per*, corrects for this bias. Once you open the *2013_GSS_Shortened.sav* file, the weight variable is automatically turned on, as confirmed by the message "Weight On" on the status bar at the bottom of the **SPSS Data Editor** window. So, you are really analyzing 1,592, not 1,500, individuals when using this data file. (See Appendix G.4 for more information on this topic.)

## SPSS DEMONSTRATION 2.2 Graphs and Charts

SPSS can produce a variety of graphs and charts, and we will use the program to produce a bar chart in this demonstration. To conserve space, we will keep the choices as simple as possible, but you should explore the options for yourself. For any questions you might have that are not answered in this demonstration, click **Help** on the main menu bar.

To produce a bar chart, first click **Graphs** on the main menu bar, then **Legacy Dialogs**, then **Bar**. The **Bar Charts** dialog box will appear with three choices for the type of graph we want. The **Simple** option is already highlighted, and this is the one we want. Make sure that **Summaries for groups of cases** in the **Data in Chart Are** box is selected, then click **Define** at the bottom of the dialog box. The **Define Simple Bar** dialog box will appear with variable names listed on the left. Choose *ehg_all* (education—highest degree) from the variable list by moving the cursor to highlight this variable name. Click the arrow button in the middle of the screen to move *ehg_all* to the **Category Axis** text box.

Note that the **Bars Represent** box is above the **Category Axis** box. The options in this box give you control over the vertical axis of the graph, which can be calibrated in frequencies, percentages, or cumulative frequencies or percentages. Let's choose **N of cases** (frequencies), the option that is already selected. Click **OK** in the **Define Simple Bar** dialog box, and the following bar chart will be produced. (Note, to save space only the output graph, and not the whole **SPSS Output** window, is shown, which has been slightly edited for clarity and will not exactly match the output on your screen.)

The bar chart reveals that the most common levels of education for this sample are "High school diploma" and "College/CEGEP certificate/diploma." The least common level is "University certificate." Don't forget to **Save** or **Print** the chart if you wish.

**FIGURE 2.9** **Output Window is shown. (Also, this Output has been Slightly Edited for Clarity and will not Exactly Match the Output on Your Screen.)**

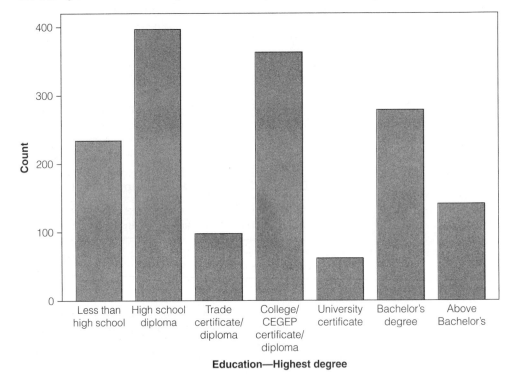

## Exercises (using *2013_GSS_Shortened.sav*)

**2.1** Get frequency distributions for five nominal or ordinal variables in the GSS data set. Write a sentence or two summarizing each frequency distribution. Your description should clearly identify the most and least common scores and any other noteworthy patterns you observe.

**2.2** Get a bar chart for *qin_50* (number of people known well enough to ask favour) and *hsdsizec* (household size). Write a sentence or two of interpretation for each chart.

# 3

# Measures of Central Tendency and Dispersion

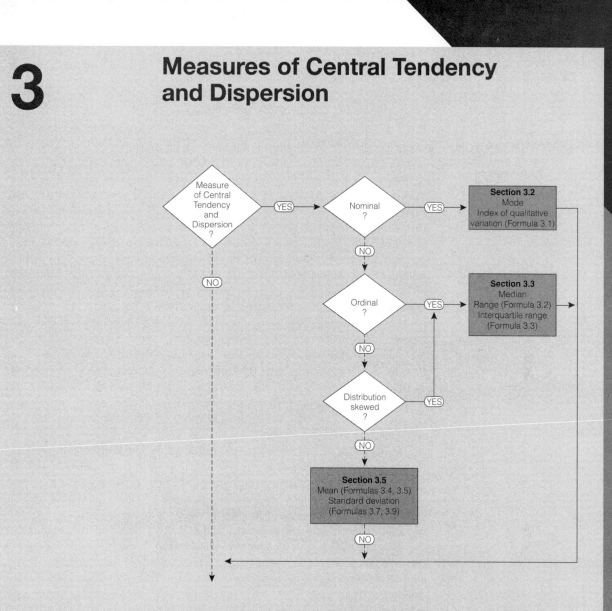

**LEARNING OBJECTIVES**

By the end of this chapter, you will be able to

1. Explain the purposes of measures of central tendency and dispersion and interpret the information they convey.

2. Calculate and explain the mode, median, and mean.

3. Calculate and explain the index of qualitative variation, the range, the interquartile range, and the standard deviation.

4. Analyze a boxplot.

5. Describe and explain the mathematical characteristics of the mean and the standard deviation.

6. Select an appropriate measure of central tendency and dispersion according to level of measurement and skew.

## 3.1 INTRODUCTION

One clear benefit of frequency distributions, graphs, and charts is that they summarize the overall shape of a distribution of scores in a way that can be quickly comprehended. Often, however, you will need to report more detailed information about the distribution. Specifically, two additional kinds of statistics are almost always useful: Some idea of the typical or average case in the distribution (e.g., "the average starting salary for social workers is $49,000 per year"), and some idea of how much variety or heterogeneity there is in the distribution ("In this province, starting salaries for social workers range from $43,000 per year to $55,000 per year"). These two kinds of statistics, the subjects of this chapter, are referred to as **measures of central tendency** and **measures of dispersion** respectively.

The three commonly used measures of central tendency—the mode, median, and mean—are all probably familiar to you. All three summarize an entire distribution of scores by describing the most common score (the mode), the middle case (the median), or the average of the scores of the cases (the mean) of that distribution. These statistics are powerful because they can reduce huge arrays of data to a single, easily understood number. Remember that the central purpose of descriptive statistics is to summarize or "reduce" data.

Nonetheless, measures of central tendency by themselves cannot summarize data completely. For a full description of a distribution of scores, measures of central tendency must be paired with measures of dispersion. While measures of central tendency are designed to locate the typical and/or central scores, measures of dispersion provide information about the amount of variety, diversity, or heterogeneity within a distribution of scores.

The importance of the concept of **dispersion** might be easier to grasp if we consider an example. Suppose that a sociology professor wants to evaluate the different styles of final exams that she administered last semester to students in the two sections of her Introduction to Sociology course. Students in Section A of the course received an essay-style final exam, while students in Section B received a multiple-choice final exam. As part of her investigation, she calculated that the mean exam score was 65% for students who wrote the essay-style exam and 65% for those who wrote the multiple-choice exam. The average exam score was the same, which provides no basis for judging if scores for one exam style were less or more diverse than scores for the other exam style. Measures of dispersion, however, can reveal substantial differences in the underlying distributions even when the measures of central tendency are equivalent. For example, consider Figure 3.1, which displays the distribution of exam scores for students in each section of the course in the form of frequency polygons (see Chapter 2).

Compare the shapes of these two figures. Note that the frequency polygon of exam scores for students who wrote the multiple-choice exam (Section B) is much flatter than the frequency polygon of exam scores for students who wrote the essay exam (Section A). This is because the

**FIGURE 3.1   Exams Scores for Two Styles of Exams**

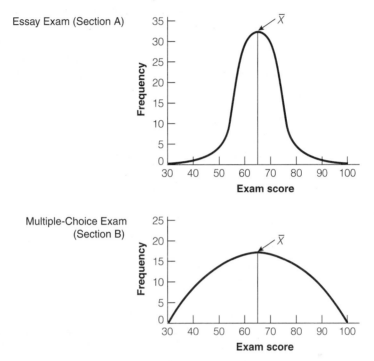

scores for students who wrote the multiple-choice exam are more spread out or more diverse than the scores for students who wrote the essay exam. In other words, the scores for the multiple-choice exam are much more variable and there are more scores in the high and low ranges and fewer in the middle, than there are on the essay exam. The essay exam scores are more similar to one another and are clustered around the mean. Both distributions have the same "average" score, but there is considerably more "variation" or dispersion in the scores for the multiple-choice exam. If you were the professor, would you be more likely to select an exam style for which students receive similar exam results (essay exam) or one for which some students receive very low scores and some other students very high scores (multiple-choice exam)? Note that if we had not considered disper-sion, a possibly important difference in the performance of students writing the two different types of exams might have gone unnoticed.

Keep the two shapes in Figure 3.1 in mind as visual representations of the concept of dispersion. The greater clustering of scores around the mean in the distribution in the upper part of the figure (essay exam distribu-tion) indicates *less* dispersion, and the flatter curve of the distribution in the lower part of the figure (multiple-choice exam distribution) indicates *more* variety or dispersion. Each of the measures of dispersion discussed in this chapter—index of qualitative variation, range, interquartile range, variance, and standard deviation—tends to increase in value as distributions become flatter (as the scores become more dispersed).

As with the three measures of central tendency, choosing which of the measures of dispersion to use depends on how the variables are measured. Indeed, the importance of variable level of measurement to the appropriate selection of measures of central tendency and dispersion cannot be underestimated. For this reason, our discussion of central tendency and dispersion in this chapter has been organized according to whether you are working with a nominal, ordinal, or interval-ratio variable. So, for example, the mode and index of qualitative variation are most appropriate for nominal-level variables. The median, range, and interquartile range can be used with variables measured at either the ordinal or interval-ratio level; however, the mean, variance, and standard deviation are more appropriate for interval-ratio-level variables. Finally, we will consider a visual representation of dispersion called a boxplot.

## 3.2 NOMINAL-LEVEL MEASURES

**Mode.** We begin our consideration of measures of central tendency with the **mode**. The mode of any distribution is the value that occurs most frequently. For example, in the set of scores 58, 82, 82, 90, 98, the mode is 82 because it occurs twice and the other scores occur only once.

The mode is, relatively speaking, a rather simple statistic, most useful when you want a "quick and easy" indicator of central tendency or when you are working with nominal-level variables. In fact, the mode is the only measure of central tendency that can be used with nominal-level variables. Such variables do not, of course, have numerical "scores" per se, and the mode of a nominally measured variable would be its largest category. For example, Table 3.1 reports the method of travel to work for a hypothetical sample of 100 workers. The mode of this distribution, the single largest category, is "Automobile."

If a researcher desires to report only the most popular or common value of a distribution, or if the variable under consideration is nominal, then the mode is the appropriate measure of central tendency. However, keep in mind that the mode does have limitations. First, some distributions have

**TABLE 3.1  Method of Travel to Work**

| Method | Frequency |
|---|---|
| Automobile | 50 |
| Public transportation | 30 |
| Walk | 10 |
| Bicycle | 5 |
| Other | 5 |
| | $n = 100$ |

**TABLE 3.2 A Distribution of Exam Scores**

| Scores | Frequency |
|--------|-----------|
| 58 | 2 |
| 60 | 2 |
| 62 | 3 |
| 64 | 2 |
| 66 | 3 |
| 67 | 4 |
| 68 | 1 |
| 69 | 1 |
| 70 | 2 |
| 93 | 5 |
| | $n = 25$ |

no mode at all (see Table 2.5) or so many modes that the statistic loses all meaning. Second, with ordinal and interval-ratio data, the modal score may not be central to the distribution as a whole. That is, *most common* does not necessarily mean "typical" in the sense of identifying the centre of the distribution. For example, consider the rather unusual (but not impossible) distribution of scores on an exam as illustrated in Table 3.2. The mode of the distribution is 93. Is this score very close to the majority of the scores? If the instructor summarized this distribution by reporting only the modal score, would he or she be conveying an accurate picture of the distribution as a whole?

**Index of Qualitative Variation.** We begin our consideration of measures of dispersion with the **index of qualitative variation (*IQV*)**. This statistic is the only measure of dispersion available for nominal-level variables (although it can also be used with ordinal-level variables). The *IQV* is the ratio of the amount of variation actually observed in a distribution of scores to the maximum variation that could exist in that distribution. The index varies from 0.00 (no variation) to 1.00 (maximum variation).

To illustrate the logic of this statistic, consider the idea that Canada will grow more ethnoculturally diverse in the future. Over the past few decades, Canada has experienced an increase in immigration from non-European countries. This has led to a change in the ethnocultural makeup of Canada. Will Canada continue to grow more diverse in the years to come?

Table 3.3 presents data on the size of visible and non-visible minority groups for 2006, 2011, and projections for 2031. (Note that the values in the table are percentages instead of frequencies, since this will greatly simplify computations.) If there were no diversity in Canada (e.g., if everyone were a non-visible minority, or alternatively, if everyone were a visible minority), the *IQV* would be 0.00. At the other extreme, if Canadians were distributed equally across the two groups (i.e., if each group comprised exactly 50% of the population), the *IQV* would achieve its maximum value (1.00).

**TABLE 3.3** **Visible Minority Status in Canada, 2006, 2011, 2031**

| | Percent of Total Population | | |
|---|---|---|---|
| Status* | 2006 | 2011 | 2031 |
| Visible minority | 16.25 | 19.07 | 30.55 |
| Non-visible minority | 83.75 | 80.93 | 69.45 |
| Total | 100.00 | 100.00 | 100.00 |

*In Canada, visible minorities, as defined by the *Employment Equity Act*, are persons, other than Aboriginal peoples, who are non-Caucasian in race or non-white in colour.

Sources: Statistics Canada. 2010. *Projections of the Diversity of the Canadian Population*, 2006 to 2031. Catalogue no. 91-551-X, Table 4, p. 23; Statistics Canada. 2011 National Household Survey: Data Tables: Visible Minority, Immigrant Status and Period of Immigration, Age Groups and Sex for the Population in Private Households of Canada, Provinces, Territories, Census Metropolitan Areas and Census Agglomerations, 2011 National Household Survey.

By inspection, you can see that Canada is becoming more ethnoculturally diverse over time. Visible minorities are projected to comprise 30.55% of the population in 2031 compared to 16.25% in 2006. Let's see how the *IQV* substantiates these observations.

The computational formula for the *IQV* is

**FORMULA 3.1**

$$IQV = \frac{k(100^2 - \Sigma Pct^2)}{100^2(k-1)}$$

where    $k$ = the number of variable response categories
$\Sigma Pct^2$ = the sum of the squared percentages of cases in the variable response categories

To use this formula, the sum of the squared percentages must first be computed. (This means, of course, that our frequency distribution must include a column of the valid percentages.) So we add a column for the squared percentages to our frequency distribution and we sum this column. This procedure is illustrated in Table 3.4.

**TABLE 3.4** **Finding the Sum of the Squared Percentages**

| | 2006 | | 2011 | | 2031 | |
|---|---|---|---|---|---|---|
| Status | % | %² | % | %² | % | %² |
| Visible minority | 16.25 | 264.06 | 19.07 | 363.66 | 30.55 | 933.30 |
| Non-visible minority | 83.75 | 7,014.06 | 80.93 | 6,549.66 | 69.45 | 4,823.30 |
| Total = | 100.00 | | 100.00 | | 100.00 | |
| $\Sigma Pct^2$ = | | 7,278.12 | | 6,913.32 | | 5,756.60 |

Statistics Canada. 2005. Population Projections of Visible Minority Groups, Canada, Provinces and Regions, 2001–2017. Catalogue no. 91-541-XIE.

For each year, the square of 100 is 10,000, and the sum of the squared percentages ($\Sigma Pct^2$) is the total of the second column. Substituting these values into Formula 3.1 for the year 2006, we have an *IQV* of 0.54:

$$IQV = \frac{2(10,000.00 - 7,278.12)}{10,000.00(1)} = \frac{2(2,721.88)}{10,000.00(1)} = 0.54$$

Because the value of $k$ square of 100 is the same for all three years, the *IQV* for the remaining years can be found by simply changing the values for $\Sigma Pct^2$. For 2011,

$$IQV = \frac{2(10,000.00 - 6,913.32)}{10,000.00(1)} = \frac{2(3,086.68)}{10,000.00(1)} = 0.62$$

and similarly, for 2031,

$$IQV = \frac{2(10,000.00 - 5,756.60)}{10,000.00(1)} = \frac{2(4,243.40)}{10,000.00(1)} = 0.85$$

Thus, the *IQV*, in a quantitative and precise way, substantiates our earlier impressions. Canada is growing more ethnoculturally diverse.

The *IQV* of 0.54 for the year 2006 means that the distribution of frequencies shows about 54% of the maximum variation possible. By 2031, the variation will increase to 85% of the maximum variation possible for the distribution of ethnocultural categories. Canadian society has grown increasingly diverse in its ethnocultural composition and will be quite heterogeneous by 2031.

In summary, the index of qualitative variation shows us that dispersion can be quantified even in nominal-level variables. The larger the index of qualitative variation, the more dispersed the data are for that variable; the smaller the index of qualitative variation, the more similar the data. *(For practice in calculating and interpreting the IQV, see Problems 3.2, 3.4, and 3.6.)*

---

**ONE STEP AT A TIME** **Finding the Index of Qualitative Variation (*IQV*)**

**1:** Ensure your frequency distribution table includes a valid percentage column.

**2:** Add a squared percentage column, and then square the valid percentage values and enter them into this column.

**3:** Sum the squared percentages ($Pct^2$).

**4:** Count the number of valid variable response categories ($k$).

**5:** Enter the $k$ and $Pct^2$ values into the *IQV* formula, and compute the *IQV*.

## 3.3 ORDINAL-LEVEL MEASURES

**Median.** The **median (***Md***)** is a measure of central tendency that represents the exact centre of a distribution of scores. The median is the score of the case that is in the exact middle of a distribution: Half the cases have scores higher and half the cases have scores lower than the case with the median score. Thus, if the median family income for a community is $35,000, half the families earn more than $35,000 and half earn less.

Before finding the median, the cases must be placed in order from the highest to the lowest score—or from the lowest to the highest. Once this is done, find the central or middle case. The median is the score associated with that case.

When the number of cases ($n$) is odd, the value of the median is unambiguous because there will always be a middle case. With an even number of cases, however, there will be two middle cases; in this situation, the median is defined as the score exactly halfway between the scores of the two middle cases.

To illustrate, assume that seven students were asked to indicate their level of support for the interuniversity athletic program at their universities on a scale ranging from 10 (indicating great support) to 0 (no support). After arranging their responses from high to low, you can find the median by locating the case that divides the distribution into two equal halves. With a total of seven cases, the middle case would be the fourth case, as there will be three cases above and three cases below the fourth case. If the seven scores were 10, 10, 8, 7, 5, 4, and 2, then the median is 7, the score of the fourth case.

To summarize: When $n$ is odd, find the middle case by adding 1 to $n$ and then dividing that sum by 2. With an $n$ of 7, the median is the score associated with the $(7 + 1)/2$, or fourth, case. If $n$ had been 21, the median would be the score associated with the $(21 + 1)/2$, or 11th, case.

Now, if we make $n$ an even number (8) by adding a student to the sample whose support for athletics was measured as a 1, we would no longer have a single middle case. The ordered distribution of scores would now be 10, 10, 8, 7, 5, 4, 2, 1; any value between 7 and 5 would technically satisfy the definition of a median (that is, would split the distribution into two equal halves of four cases each). This ambiguity is resolved by defining the median as the average of the scores of the two middle cases. In the example above, the median would be defined as $(7 + 5)/2$, or 6.

To summarize: To identify the two middle cases when $n$ is an even number, divide $n$ by 2 to find the first middle case and then increase that number by 1 to find the second middle case. In the example above with eight cases, the first middle case would be the fourth case ($n/2 = 4$) and the second middle case would be the $(n/2) + 1$, or fifth, case. If $n$ had been 142, the first middle case would have been the 71st case and the second middle case would have been the 72nd case. Remember that the median is defined as the average of the scores associated with the two middle cases.*

---

*If the middle cases have the same score, that score is defined as the median. In the distribution 10, 10, 8, 6, 6, 4, 2, and 1, the middle cases both have scores of 6 and, thus, the median would be defined as 6.

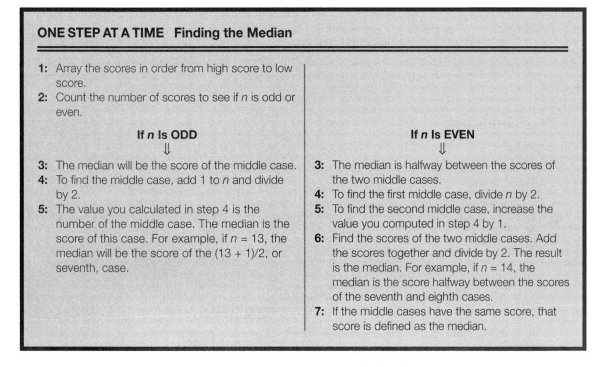

**ONE STEP AT A TIME**   **Finding the Median**

**1:** Array the scores in order from high score to low score.
**2:** Count the number of scores to see if $n$ is odd or even.

| **If $n$ Is ODD** | **If $n$ Is EVEN** |
|---|---|
| ⇓ | ⇓ |

**3:** The median will be the score of the middle case.
**4:** To find the middle case, add 1 to $n$ and divide by 2.
**5:** The value you calculated in step 4 is the number of the middle case. The median is the score of this case. For example, if $n = 13$, the median will be the score of the $(13 + 1)/2$, or seventh, case.

**3:** The median is halfway between the scores of the two middle cases.
**4:** To find the first middle case, divide $n$ by 2.
**5:** To find the second middle case, increase the value you computed in step 4 by 1.
**6:** Find the scores of the two middle cases. Add the scores together and divide by 2. The result is the median. For example, if $n = 14$, the median is the score halfway between the scores of the seventh and eighth cases.
**7:** If the middle cases have the same score, that score is defined as the median.

The procedures for finding the median are stated in general terms in the One Step at a Time box. It is important to emphasize that since the median requires that scores be ranked from high to low, it cannot be calculated for variables measured at the nominal level. Remember that the scores of nominal-level variables cannot be ordered or ranked: The scores are different from each other but do not form a mathematical scale of any sort. The median can be found for either ordinal or interval-ratio data but it is generally more appropriate for ordinal-level data.

**Range and Interquartile Range.**   The **range ($R$)**, defined as the difference or interval between the highest score ($H$) and lowest score ($L$) in a distribution, provides a quick and general notion of variability for variables measured at either the ordinal or interval-ratio level.

The mathematical formula for the range is:

**FORMULA 3.2**
$$R = H - L$$

where $R$ = the range
$H$ = the highest score
$L$ = the lowest score

Unfortunately, since it is based on only the two most extreme scores in a distribution, $R$ will be misleading as a measure of dispersion if just one of these scores is either exceptionally high or low. Such scores are often referred to as **outliers**.

The **interquartile range (*Q*)** is a type of range that avoids this problem. The interquartile range is the distance from the third quartile ($Q_3$) to the first quartile ($Q_1$) of a distribution of scores.*

The mathematical formula for the interquartile range is

**FORMULA 3.3**

$$Q = Q_3 - Q_1$$

where $Q$ = the interquartile range
$Q_3$ = the value of the third quartile
$Q_1$ = the value of the first quartile

The first quartile, $Q_1$, is the point below which 25% of the cases fall and above which 75% of the cases fall. The third quartile, $Q_3$, is the point below which 75% of the cases fall and above which 25% of the cases fall. If line *LH* represents a distribution of scores, the first and third quartiles and the interquartile range are located as shown:

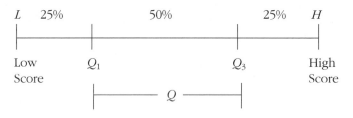

Thus, $Q$ is the range of the middle 50% of the cases in a distribution. Since it uses only the middle 50%, $Q$ is not influenced by outliers.

To illustrate the computation of the range and the interquartile range, let's consider the following set of eleven scores: 5, 8, 10, 12, 15, 18, 21, 22, 24, 26, and 99. These scores are ordered from low to high, though placing them in order from high to low will produce identical results. Either way, an ordered distribution of scores makes the range easy to calculate and is necessary for finding the interquartile range.

---

*A quartile is a member of a class of statistics called percentiles. A percentile identifies the point below which a specific percentage of cases fall (percentiles are further discussed in Chapter 4, in the context of what is called the "normal" curve). For example, if a score of 476 is reported as the 95th percentile, this means that 95% of the cases had scores lower than 476. Hence, the first quartile, $Q_1$, is simply the 25th percentile, second quartile, $Q_2$, the 50th percentile, which is the same as (you guessed it) the median, and third quartile, $Q_3$, the 75th percentile. Other commonly used percentiles are the decile and quintile. Deciles divide the distribution of scores into tenths. So, the first decile is the point below which 10% of the cases fall and is equivalent to the 10th percentile; the second decile is the same as the 20th percentile; and so on. Quintiles divide the distribution into fifths. The first quintile is the point below which 20% of the cases fall and is the same as the 20th percentile, the second quintile is the 40th percentile, etc.

To find the range, $R$, for this set of scores, the lowest score ($L$) is subtracted from the highest score ($H$). Therefore:

$$R = H - L$$
$$= 99 - 5$$
$$= 94$$

To calculate $Q$, we must locate the first and third quartiles ($Q_1$ and $Q_3$). To find the quartiles, first find the median for the ordered data (see the One Step at a Time: Finding the Median box). Next, divide the data so that there are an equal number of cases above and below the median. Finally, find the median of the lower and upper parts of the data. $Q_1$ is equal to the median of the lower half of the data and $Q_3$ to the median of the upper half. $Q$ equals the difference between $Q_3$ and $Q_1$. A step-by-step guide for finding the interquartile range is provided in the One Step at a Time box.

Continuing with the example above, we first divide the ordered data into two equal parts at the median ($Md = 18$). The scores in the lower half are 5, 8, 10, 12, and 15, and the scores in the upper half are 21, 22, 24, 26, and 99. We then find the median of the lower half of the data, or $Q_1$, which equals 10, and the median of the upper half of the data, or $Q_3$, which equals 24. We subtract $Q_1$ from $Q_3$ to find the interquartile range. Therefore:

$$Q = Q_3 - Q_1$$
$$= 24 - 10$$
$$= 14$$

Clearly, the interquartile range ($Q = 14$) is preferred to the range ($R = 94$) as a measure of dispersion for this example, because it eliminates the influence of outliers and provides more accurate information about the amount of diversity within the distribution.

---

**ONE STEP AT A TIME    Finding the Interquartile Range (Q)**

**1:** Array the scores in order from low to high scores. For example, 2, 4, 6, 8, 10, 12, 14, 16, 18, 20, 22, 24.

**2:** Find the median of the data (see the One Step at a Time: Finding the Median box). Continuing with the example data in step 1, $Md = (12 + 14)/2 = 13$.

**3:** Divide the ordered data into two equal parts at the median. Continuing this example, the lower half = 2, 4, 6, 8, 10, 12 and the upper half = 14, 16, 18, 20, 22, 24.

**4:** Find the median of the lower half of the data. (This value is equal to $Q_1$.) Continuing this example, $Md$ of 2, 4, 6, 8, 10, 12 = (6 + 8)/2 = 7.

**5:** Find the median of the upper half of the data. (This value is equal to $Q_3$.) Continuing this example, $Md$ of 14, 16, 18, 20, 22, 24 = (18 + 20)/2 = 19.

**6:** Subtract $Q_1$ from $Q_3$. (This value is equal to $Q$.) Finishing the example, $Q = 19 - 7 = 12$.

As another example, consider the following set of four scores: 2, 3, 8, and 9. $R$ for this data set is $9 - 2$, or 7. To calculate $Q$, the data set is divided into two equal parts at the median ($Md = 5.5$ or $[3 + 8]/2$), so scores 2 and 3 make up the lower half of the data set and scores 8 and 9 the upper half. The median of the lower half, $Q_1$, is 2.5, or $(2 + 3)/2$, and the median of the upper half, $Q_3$, is 8.5, or $(8 + 9)/2$. Hence, $Q$ equals $8.5 - 2.5$, or 6.

In conclusion, the range and interquartile range provide a measure of dispersion based on just two scores from a set of data. These statistics require that scores be ranked from low to high—or from high to low—so that they can be calculated for variables measured at either the ordinal or interval-ratio level. Since almost any sizable distribution will contain some atypically high and low scores, the interquartile range is a more useful measure of dispersion than the range because it is not affected by extreme scores or outliers. In the next section we will look at a graphical device used for displaying range and interquartile range information for ordinal and interval-ratio variables. *(The median, R, and Q may be found for any ordinal or interval-ratio variable in the problems at the end of this chapter.)*

**3.4 VISUALIZING DISPERSION: BOXPLOTS***

Together with the median, the range and interquartile range can be represented in a graph known as the **boxplot**, giving us a helpful way to visualize both central tendency and variability. It has the advantage of conveniently displaying the centre, spread, and overall range of scores in a distribution, and can be used with variables measured at either the ordinal or interval-ratio level.

The boxplot is based on information from a **five-number summary**, consisting of the lowest score, first quartile, second quartile (the median), third quartile, and highest score in a distribution. The construction of a boxplot requires a few steps. First, we calculate the first, second (the median), and third quartiles. Second, we draw a box between the first and third quartiles. (The width of the box is arbitrary, but should be reasonably proportional to the rest of the graph.) Third, we draw a line dividing the box at the median value. Fourth, we draw a vertical line (whisker) from the lowest score, indicated by a small horizontal line, to the box. Do the same for the highest score to the box.

To illustrate, Table 3.5 presents per capita (per person) health spending by governments in 2015 for OECD (Organisation for Economic Co-operation and Development) countries that spent at least $1,500 per person. Note that the scores have already been ordered from highest to lowest.

---

*This section is optional.

**TABLE 3.5 Total Government Health Expenditure per Capita (in US dollars), 2015**

| Rank | Country | Expenditure (US $) |
|---|---|---|
| 26 (highest) | Luxembourg | 5,590 |
| 25 | Norway | 5,286 |
| 24 | Switzerland | 4,821 |
| 23 | United States | 4,692 |
| 22 | Germany | 4,521 |
| 21 | Sweden | 4,406 |
| 20 | Netherlands | 4,275 |
| 19 | Denmark | 4,256 |
| 18 | Austria | 3,855 |
| 17 | Japan | 3,725 |
| 16 | Belgium | 3,702 |
| 15 | Ireland | 3,692 |
| 14 | France | 3,575 |
| 13 | Iceland | 3,345 |
| 12 | United Kingdom | 3,286 |
| 11 | Canada | 3,248 |
| 10 | Australia | 3,024 |
| 9 | Finland | 2,973 |
| 8 | New Zealand | 2,848 |
| 7 | Italy | 2,509 |
| 6 | Spain | 2,259 |
| 5 | Czech Republic | 2,031 |
| 4 | Slovenia | 1,958 |
| 3 | Portugal | 1,764 |
| 2 | Israel | 1,646 |
| 1 (lowest) | Slovak Republic | 1,642 |

Source: World Bank, World Development Indicators. http://databank.worldbank.org/data/reports.aspx?source=2&series=SH.XPD.PCAP&country=#

Since there is an even number of scores, the median ($Q_2$) is the score located halfway between the two middle cases, or between cases 13 (Iceland) and 14 (France). Given that the 2015 per capita health expenditures by the governments of Iceland and France were $3,345 and $3,575 respectively, the median is $\frac{\$3,345 + \$3,575}{2} = \frac{\$6,920}{2} = \$3,460$.

Next, we find the first quartile ($Q_1$) and the third quartile ($Q_3$). When we divide the ordered scores into two equal parts at the median ($Q_2$), there is an odd number of scores (13) below the median, and an odd number of scores (13) above the median. The median of each of these individual sets of scores is the score of the $\frac{13 + 1}{2}$, or seventh, case in each set. The seventh case below $Q_2$ is Italy, with a 2015 per capita health expenditure of $2,509, so $Q_1 = \$2,509$. The seventh case above $Q_2$ is Netherlands, with an expenditure of $4,275, so $Q_3 = \$4,275$. (We can easily calculate the interquartile range with this information: $Q = Q_3 - Q_1 = \$4,275 - \$2,509 = \$1,766$.)

We only still need the lowest $L$ and highest $H$ scores in order to construct our boxplot. It is of course easiest to recognize these scores in an ordered list. Of the 26 countries whose 2015 per capita government health spending was at least $1,500, Luxembourg spent the most ($5,590) and the Slovak Republic spent the least ($1,642). Thus, the highest and lowest scores in our boxplot, represented by the small horizontal lines, are $5,590 and $1,642, respectively. (We can now also easily calculate the range: $R = H - L = $5,590 - $1,642 = $3,948$.)

With the values of the five-number summary at hand ($L$, $Q_1$, $Q_2$, $Q_3$, and $H$), we are ready to construct our boxplot. We draw a box between the first and third quartiles (i.e., between $2,509 and $4,275), and a line dividing the box at the median value (i.e., at $3,460). Then we draw a vertical line (whisker) from the lowest score (i.e., $1,642), indicated by a small horizontal line, to the box, and a line from the largest score (i.e., $5,590), also indicated by a small horizontal line, to the box. Figure 3.2 displays a boxplot of the data provided in Table 3.5.

At a quick glance, the boxplot in Figure 3.2 shows us that the length of the box is shorter than the length of the whiskers. In other words, $Q$ (i.e., $1,766) is less than $R$ (i.e., $3,948). But beyond a simple comparison of $Q$ and $R$, the boxplot also shows us that the shaded box representing the middle 50% of the cases is closer to the end of the bottom whisker than it is to the end of the top whisker. This means that the middle 50% of the cases are somewhat concentrated in the lower range of scores, even though the distribution is otherwise quite spread out and extends quite high. Notably,

**FIGURE 3.2 Total Government Health Expenditure per Capita (in US dollars), 2015**

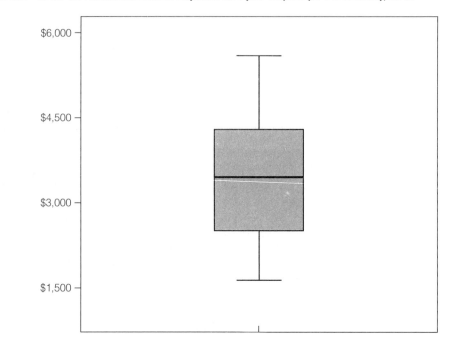

the greater length of the upper whisker, compared to the lower whisker, indicates a positive skew.

In addition, notice that the median line (in the middle of the box) is closer to the top of the box (i.e., to $Q_3$) than it is to the bottom of the box (i.e., to $Q_1$). This shows us that the 25% of cases located between $Q_2$ and $Q_3$ (represented by the top portion of the shaded box) are both less spread out and more concentrated in the higher score range than are the 25% of cases located between $Q_1$ and $Q_2$ (represented by the bottom portion of the shaded box). Thus, even though the annual per capita government health expenditures of the top spending countries varied considerably in 2015, more countries were represented in the top spending range than in the lower spending range. As you can see, the boxplot is a highly informative and very useful graph for ordinal-level and interval-ratio-level variables.

## 3.5 INTERVAL-RATIO-LEVEL MEASURES

**Mean.**   The **mean** ($\overline{X}$, read this as "ex-bar"), or arithmetic average, is by far the most commonly used measure of central tendency. It reports the average score of a distribution, and its calculation is straightforward: To compute the mean, add the scores and then divide by the number of scores ($n$). To illustrate: A family-planning clinic administered a 20-item test of general knowledge about contraception to 10 clients. The number of correct responses (the scores of the 10 clients) was 2, 10, 15, 11, 9, 16, 18, 10, 11, and 7. To find the mean of this distribution, add the scores (total = 109) and divide by the number of scores (10). The result (10.90) is the average number of correct responses on the test.

The mathematical formula for the mean is

**FORMULA 3.4**

$$\overline{X} = \frac{\Sigma(X_i)}{n}$$

where    $\overline{X}$ = the mean
$\Sigma(X_i)$ = the summation of the scores
$n$ = the number of cases in the sample

Since this formula introduces some new symbols, let us take a moment to consider it. First, the symbol $\Sigma$ (read this as "sum of") is a mathematical operator just like the plus sign ($+$) or divide sign ($\div$). It stands for "the summation of" and directs us to add whatever quantities are stated immediately following it.* The second new symbol is $X_i$ (read this as "$X$ sub $i$"), which refers to any single score—the "$i$th" score. If we wished to refer to a particular score in the distribution, the specific number of the score could replace the subscript. Thus, $X_1$ would refer to the first score, $X_2$ to the second, $X_{26}$ to the 26th, and so forth. The operation of adding all the scores is symbolized as $\Sigma(X_i)$.

---

*See the Prologue (Basic Mathematics Review) for further information on the summation sign and on summation operations.

---

**ONE STEP AT A TIME**   **Finding the Mean**

**1:**  Add up the scores ($X_i$).

**2:**  Divide the quantity you found in step 1 ($\Sigma X_i$) by $n$ (for a sample) or by $N$ (for a population).

---

This combination of symbols directs us to sum the scores, beginning with the first score and ending with the last score in the distribution. Thus, Formula 3.4 states in symbols what has already been stated in words (to calculate the mean, add the scores and divide by the number of scores), but in a very succinct and precise way.

Strictly speaking, the formula expressed in Formula 3.4 is for the mean of a sample. The mean of a population is calculated using exactly the same method as for calculating the sample mean; however, it is symbolized with the Greek letter mu, $\mu$ (pronounced "mew"), as shown in Formula 3.5.

**FORMULA 3.5**

$$\mu = \frac{\Sigma(X_i)}{N}$$

where $\Sigma(X_i)$ = the summation of the scores
$N$ = the number of cases in the population

Note that to differentiate between population measures, technically called population *parameters*, and sample measures, called sample *statistics*, it is common practice to use Greek letters for parameters and Roman letters for statistics. So, for example, the Greek letter $\mu$ represents the population mean and the Roman letter $\overline{X}$ represents the sample mean. Also note that it is customary to symbolize "number of cases" with the uppercase letter $N$ in formulas for population parameters (e.g., Formula 3.5) and the lowercase letter $n$ in formulas for sample statistics (e.g., Formula 3.4). These practices are followed throughout this textbook.

**Some Characteristics of the Mean.**   The mean is the most commonly used measure of central tendency, and we will consider its mathematical and statistical characteristics in some detail. First, the mean is always the centre of any distribution of scores in the sense that it is the point around which all of the scores cancel out. Symbolically:*

$$\Sigma(X_i - \overline{X}) = 0$$

Or, if we take each score in a distribution, subtract the mean from it, and add all of the differences, the resultant sum will always be 0. To illustrate, consider the following sample of scores: 10, 20, 30, 40, and 50. The mean of

*For the population, this characteristic is expressed symbolically as $\Sigma(X_i - \mu) = 0$.

**TABLE 3.6   A Demonstration Showing That All Scores on One Side of the Mean are Equally Weighted to All Scores on the Other Side of the Mean**

| $X_i$ | $(X_i - \bar{X})$ |
|---|---|
| 10 | $10 - 30 = -20$ |
| 20 | $20 - 30 = -10$ |
| 30 | $30 - 30 = 0$ |
| 40 | $40 - 30 = 10$ |
| 50 | $50 - 30 = 20$ |
| $\Sigma(X_i) = 150$ | $\Sigma(X_i - \bar{X}) = 0$ |

$$\bar{X} = \frac{\Sigma(X_i)}{n} = \frac{150}{5} = 30$$

these five scores is 150/5, or 30, and the sum of the differences is presented in Table 3.6.

The total of the negative differences ($-30$) is exactly equal to the total of the positive differences ($+30$), and this will always be the case. This algebraic relationship between the scores and the mean indicates that the mean is a good descriptive measure of the centrality of scores. You may think of the mean as a fulcrum on a seesaw that exactly balances all of the scores.

A second characteristic of the mean is called the *least-squares* principle, a characteristic that is expressed in this statement:*

$$\Sigma(X_i - \bar{X})^2 = \text{minimum}$$

This indicates that the mean is the point in a distribution around which the variation of the scores (as indicated by the squared differences) is minimized. If the differences between the scores and the mean are squared and then added, the resultant sum will be less than the sum of the squared differences between the scores and any other point in the distribution.

To illustrate this principle, consider the distribution of the five sample scores mentioned above: 10, 20, 30, 40, and 50. The differences between the scores and the mean have already been found. As illustrated in Table 3.7, if we square and sum these differences, we would get a total of 1,000. If we performed that same mathematical operation with any number other than the mean—say the value 31—the resultant sum would be greater than 1,000. Table 3.7 illustrates this point by showing that the sum of the squared differences around 31 is 1,005, a value greater than 1,000.

In a sense, the least-squares principle merely underlines the fact that the mean is closer to all of the scores than the other measures of central tendency. However, this characteristic of the mean is also the foundation of some of the most important techniques in statistics, including the variance and standard deviation.

---

*For the population, this characteristic is expressed symbolically as $\Sigma(X_i - \mu)^2 = \text{minimum}$.

**TABLE 3.7   A Demonstration That the Mean is the Point of Minimized Variation**

| $X_i$ | $(X_i - \bar{X})$ | $(X_i - \bar{X})^2$ | $(X_i - 31)^2$ |
|---|---|---|---|
| 10 | $10 - 30 = -20$ | $(-20)^2 = \quad 400$ | $(10 - 31)^2 = (-21)^2 = \quad 441$ |
| 20 | $20 - 30 = -10$ | $(-10)^2 = \quad 100$ | $(20 - 31)^2 = (-11)^2 = \quad 121$ |
| 30 | $30 - 30 = \quad 0$ | $(0)^2 = \quad 0$ | $(30 - 31)^2 = \quad (-1)^2 = \quad 1$ |
| 40 | $40 - 30 = \quad 10$ | $(10)^2 = \quad 100$ | $(40 - 31)^2 = \quad (9)^2 = \quad 81$ |
| 50 | $50 - 30 = \quad 20$ | $(20)^2 = \quad 400$ | $(50 - 31)^2 = \quad (19)^2 = \quad 361$ |
| $\Sigma(X_i) = 150$ | $\Sigma(X_i - \bar{X}) = \quad 0$ | $\Sigma(X_i - \bar{X})^2 = \quad 1{,}000$ | $\Sigma(X_i - 31)^2 = 1{,}005$ |

The final important characteristic of the mean is that every score in the distribution affects it. The mode (which is only the most common score) and the median (which deals only with the score of the middle case or cases) are not so affected. This quality is both an advantage and a disadvantage. On the one hand, the mean utilizes all the available information—every score in the distribution affects the mean. On the other hand, when a distribution has a few very high or very low scores (as noted in Section 3.3, these extreme scores are often referred to as outliers), the mean may become a very misleading measure of centrality.

To illustrate, consider again the sample of five scores mentioned above: 10, 20, 30, 40, and 50. Both the mean and the median of this distribution are 30. ($\bar{X} = 150/5 = 30$. $Md$ = score of third case = 30.) What will happen if we change the last score from 50 to 500? This change would not affect the median at all; it would remain at exactly 30. This is because the median is based only on the score of the middle case and is not affected by changes in the scores of other cases in the distribution.

The mean, in contrast, would be very much affected because it takes *all* scores into account. The mean would become 600/5, or 120. Clearly, the one extreme score in the data set disproportionately affects the mean. For a distribution that has a few scores much higher or lower than the other scores, the mean may present a very misleading picture of the typical or central score.

The general principle to remember is that, relative to the median, the mean is always pulled in the direction of extreme scores. The mean and the median will have the same value when and only when a distribution is symmetrical. When a distribution has some extremely high scores (this is called a positive **skew**), the mean will always have a greater numerical value than the median. If the distribution has some very low scores (a negative skew), the mean will be lower in value than the median. So, a quick comparison of the median and the mean will always tell you if a distribution is skewed and the direction of the skew. If the mean is less than the median, the distribution has a negative skew. If the mean is greater than the median, the distribution has a positive skew. Figures 3.3 to 3.5 depict three different frequency polygons that demonstrate these relationships. As you can see,

**FIGURE 3.3   A Positively Skewed Distribution**

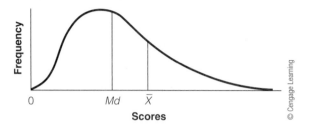

**FIGURE 3.4   A Negatively Skewed Distribution**

**FIGURE 3.5   An Unskewed, Symmetrical Distribution**

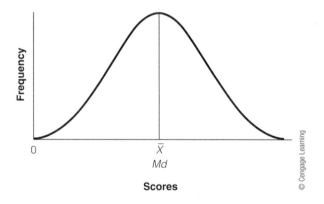

symmetry and skew are very important characteristics of distribution shape. More will be said about distribution shape in later chapters.

So, which measure is most appropriate for each distribution? If the distribution is highly skewed (as depicted in Figures 3.3 and 3.4), the mean no longer describes the typical or central score. Hence, the median should be used. If the distribution is unskewed, as shown in Figure 3.5, either measure can be used.

As a final note regarding the mean, since its computation requires addition and division, it should be used with variables measured at the interval-ratio level.

**Variance and Standard Deviation.**   In Section 3.3, we explored the range and interquartile range as measures of dispersion. A basic limitation of both statistics, however, is that they are based on only two scores. They do not use all the scores in the distribution, and in this sense, they do not capitalize on all the available information. Also, neither statistic provides any information on how far the scores are from one another or from some central point such as the mean. How can we design a measure of dispersion that would correct these faults? We can begin with some specifications: A good measure of dispersion should

1. Use all the scores in the distribution. The statistic should use all the information available.
2. Describe the average or typical deviation of the scores. The statistic should give us an idea of how far the scores are from one another or from the centre of the distribution.
3. Increase in value as the distribution of scores becomes more diverse. This would be a very handy feature because it would permit us to tell at a glance which distribution was more variable: The higher the numerical value of the statistic, the greater the dispersion.

One way to develop a statistic to meet these criteria would be to start with the distances between each score and the mean. The distances between the scores and the mean are technically called **deviations**, and this quantity will increase in value as the scores increase in their variety or heterogeneity. If the scores are more clustered around the mean (remember the graph for essay-style exam scores [Section A] in Figure 3.1), the deviations will be small. If the scores are more spread out or more varied (like the scores for multiple-choice exams [Section B] in Figure 3.1), the deviations will be greater in value. How can we use the deviations of the scores around the mean to develop a useful statistic?

One course of action would be to use the sum of the deviations as the basis for a statistic, but as we saw earlier in this section (see Table 3.6) the sum of deviations will always be zero. Still, the sum of the deviations is a logical basis for a statistic that measures the amount of variety in a set of scores, and statisticians have developed two ways around the fact that the positive deviations always equal the negative deviations. Both solutions eliminate the negative signs. The first does so by using the absolute values or by ignoring signs when summing the deviations. This is the basis for a statistic called the **mean deviation**, a measure of dispersion that is rarely used and will not be mentioned further.

The second solution squares each of the deviations. This makes all values positive because a negative number multiplied by a negative number becomes positive. For example, Table 3.8 lists the sample of five scores from Table 3.6, along with the deviations and the squared deviations. The sum of the squared deviations (400 + 100 + 0 + 100 + 400) equals 1,000. Thus, a

**TABLE 3.8  Computing the Standard Deviation**

| Scores<br>$(X_i)$ | Deviations<br>$(X_i - \overline{X})$ | Deviations Squared<br>$(X_i - \overline{X})^2$ |
|---|---|---|
| 10 | $(10 - 30) = -20$ | $(-20)^2 = 400$ |
| 20 | $(20 - 30) = -10$ | $(-10)^2 = 100$ |
| 30 | $(30 - 30) = 0$ | $(0)^2 = 0$ |
| 40 | $(40 - 30) = 10$ | $(10)^2 = 100$ |
| 50 | $(50 - 30) = 20$ | $(20)^2 = 400$ |
| $\Sigma(X_i) = 150$ | $\Sigma(X_i - \overline{X}) = 0$ | $\Sigma(X_i - \overline{X})^2 = 1{,}000$ |

$$\overline{X} = \frac{\Sigma(X_i)}{n} = \frac{150}{5} = 30$$

statistic based on the sum of the squared deviations will have many of the properties we want in a good measure of dispersion.

Before we finish designing our measure of dispersion, we must deal with another problem. The sum of the squared deviations will increase with the number of cases: the larger the number of cases, the greater the value of the measure. This would make it very difficult to compare the relative variability of distributions with different numbers of cases. We can solve this problem by dividing the sum of the squared deviations by the number of cases and thus standardizing for distributions of different sizes.

These procedures yield a statistic known as the **variance**, which is symbolized as $s^2$ for a sample and $\sigma^2$ for a population. The variance is used primarily in inferential statistics, although it is a central concept in the design of some measures of association. For purposes of describing the dispersion of a distribution, a closely related statistic called the **standard deviation** (symbolized as $s$ for a sample and $\sigma$ for a population) is typically used, and this statistic will be our focus for the remainder of this section.

Let's first look at the formulas for the sample variance and standard deviation:

**FORMULA 3.6**
$$s^2 = \frac{\Sigma(X_i - \overline{X})^2}{n}$$

**FORMULA 3.7**
$$s = \sqrt{\frac{\Sigma(X_i - \overline{X})^2}{n}}$$

where $X_i$ = the score
$\overline{X}$ = the sample mean
$n$ = the number of cases in the sample

To compute the standard deviation, it is advisable to construct a table such as Table 3.8 to organize computations. The five scores are listed in the left-hand column, the deviations are in the middle column, and the squared deviations are in the right-hand column.

The sum of the last column in Table 3.8 is the sum of the squared deviations and can be substituted into the numerator of the formula:

$$s = \sqrt{\frac{\Sigma(X_i - \overline{X})^2}{n}}$$

$$= \sqrt{\frac{1,000}{5}}$$

$$= \sqrt{200}$$

$$= 14.14$$

To finish solving the formula, divide the sum of the squared deviations by $n$ and take the square root of the result. To find the variance, square the standard deviation. For this problem, the variance is $s^2 = (14.14)^2 = 200$.

It is important to point out that some electronic calculators and statistical software packages (including SPSS) use slightly different formulas, with "$n - 1$" instead of "$n$" in the denominator to calculate the sample variance and standard deviation. This "$n - 1$" is called Bessel's correction, and it corrects for the underestimation of the population variance and standard deviation (that would occur if only $n$ were used) of $s_2$ and $s$. Instead, we choose to correct for this bias at later points in the textbook—for example, in Chapter 6 when calculating confidence

---

### Applying Statistics 3.1: The Mean and Standard Deviation

At a local preschool, 10 children were observed for 1 hour, and the number of aggressive acts committed by each was recorded in the following list. What are the mean and standard deviation of this distribution?

**Number of Aggressive Acts**

| $(X_i)$ | $(X_i - \overline{X})$ | $(X_i - \overline{X})^2$ |
|---|---|---|
| 1 | $1 - 4 = -3$ | 9 |
| 3 | $3 - 4 = -1$ | 1 |
| 5 | $5 - 4 = 1$ | 1 |
| 2 | $2 - 4 = -2$ | 4 |
| 7 | $7 - 4 = 3$ | 9 |
| 11 | $11 - 4 = 7$ | 49 |

| $(X_i)$ | $(X_i - \overline{X})$ | $(X_i - \overline{X})^2$ |
|---|---|---|
| 1 | $1 - 4 = -3$ | 9 |
| 8 | $8 - 4 = 4$ | 16 |
| 2 | $2 - 4 = -2$ | 4 |
| 0 | $0 - 4 = -4$ | 16 |
| $\Sigma(X_i) = 40$ | $\Sigma(X_i - \overline{X}) = 0$ | $\Sigma(X_i - \overline{X})^2 = 118$ |

$$\overline{X} = \frac{\Sigma(X_i)}{n} = \frac{40}{10} = 4.0$$

$$s = \sqrt{\frac{\Sigma(X_i - \overline{X})^2}{n}} = \sqrt{\frac{118}{10}} = \sqrt{11.8} = 3.44$$

During the study observation period, the children committed on average 4.0 aggressive acts with a standard deviation of 3.44.

intervals for sample means. Nevertheless, calculators and statistical software packages that use formulas with "$n - 1$" will produce results that are at least slightly different from results produced using Formulas 3.6 and 3.7. The size of the difference will decrease as sample size increases, but the problems and examples in this chapter use small samples, so the difference between using n and $n - 1$ in the denominator can be considerable. Some calculators offer the choice of "$n - 1$" or "$n$" in the denominator. If you use "$n$," the values calculated for the sample standard deviation will match the values in this textbook.

As a final point, like the mean, the variance and standard deviation for populations are calculated using exactly the same method as for samples, but population and sample measures are distinguished from each other using different symbols. The variance and standard deviation formulas for populations are shown in Formulas 3.8 and 3.9, respectively.

**FORMULA 3.8**
$$\sigma^2 = \frac{\Sigma(X_i - \mu)^2}{N}$$

**FORMULA 3.9**
$$\sigma = \sqrt{\frac{\Sigma(X_i - \mu)^2}{N}}$$

where $X_i$ = the score
$\mu$ = the population mean
$N$ = the number of cases in the population

**Interpreting the Standard Deviation.**   It is very possible that the meaning of the standard deviation (i.e., why we calculate it) is not completely obvious to you at this point. You might be asking: "Once I've gone to the trouble of calculating the standard deviation, what do I have?" The meaning of this measure of dispersion can be expressed in three ways. The first and most important involves the normal curve, and we will defer this interpretation until the next chapter.

A second way of thinking about the standard deviation is as an index of variability that increases in value as the distribution becomes more variable. In other words, the standard deviation is higher for more diverse distributions and lower for less diverse distributions. The lowest value the standard deviation can have is 0, and this would occur for distributions with no dispersion (i.e., if every single case in the distribution had exactly the same score). Thus, 0 is the lowest value possible for the standard deviation, but there is no upper limit.

A third way to get a feel for the meaning of the standard deviation is by comparing one distribution with another. You might do this when comparing one group against another (e.g., men vs. women) or the same variable at two different times or places. For example, according to data collected by

---

**ONE STEP AT A TIME** Finding the Standard Deviation (s) and the Variance ($s^2$) of a Sample

---

**To Begin**

1: Construct a computing table like Table 3.8, with columns for the scores ($X_i$), the deviations ($X_i - \bar{X}$), and the deviations squared ($X_i - \bar{X})^2$.
2: List the scores ($X_i$) in the left-hand column. Add up the scores and divide by $n$ to find the mean. As a rule, state the mean in two places of accuracy or two digits to the right of the decimal point.

**To Find the Values Needed to Solve Formula 3.7**

1: Find the deviations ($X_i - \bar{X}$) by subtracting the mean from each score, one at a time. List the deviations in the second column. Generally speaking, you should state the deviations at the same level of accuracy (two places to the right of the decimal point) as the mean.
2: Add up the deviations. The sum must equal zero (within rounding error). If the sum of the

deviations does not equal zero, you have made a computational error and need to repeat step 1, perhaps at a higher level of accuracy.
3: Square each deviation and list the result in the third column.
4: Add up the squared deviations listed in the third column.

**To Solve Formula 3.7**

1: Transfer the sum of the squared deviations column to the numerator in Formula 3.7.
2: Divide the sum of the squared deviations (the numerator of the formula) by $n$.
3: Take the square root of the quantity you computed in the previous step. This is the standard deviation.

**To Find the Variance ($s^2$)**

1: Square the value of the standard deviation (s).

---

Environment Canada over the period 1981–2010, Calgary, AB, and Gander, NL, had the same mean daily temperature in the month of January: −7.1 degrees Celsius (°C).

| Calgary | Gander |
|---|---|
| $\bar{X} = -7.1$ | $\bar{X} = -7.1$ |
| $s = 4.5$ | $s = 1.8$ |

Source: Environment Canada

While the cities have identical average daily temperatures, the standard deviation reveals that temperatures fluctuated much more during the month of January in Calgary. (This may partly reflect strong "chinook" winds, common to southern Alberta, that can dramatically raise the temperature for a few hours or days before it falls back to a normal level.) The higher standard deviation for Calgary (4.5°C) indicates a distribution of daily temperatures that is flatter and more spread out around the mean (remember the distribution for Section B in Figure 3.1), while the lower standard deviation for

Gander (1.8°C) reflects a distribution that is more clustered around the mean (like the distribution for Section A in Figure 3.1). So, compared to Calgary, daily temperatures in January in Gander are more similar to one another and more clustered in a narrower range of temperatures. The standard deviation is extremely useful for making comparisons of this sort between distributions of scores—in this example, for temperatures.

In conclusion, the standard deviation is the most important measure of dispersion because of its central role in many more advanced statistical applications. Since it is based on the mean, it should be used with variables measured at the interval-ratio level. Also, like the mean, the standard deviation uses all the scores in the distribution and thus is disproportionately influenced by outliers and extreme scores. When a distribution has outliers or extreme scores (a highly skewed distribution), the interquartile range should be used

---

### Applying Statistics 3.2: Describing Dispersion

The percent of persons in the labour force who work part-time in five cities in Western Canada and five cities in Eastern Canada is compared using data from the 2011 National Household Survey. Part-time workers are defined in the census as persons who work mainly part-time weeks (29 hours or less per week) on the basis of all jobs held during the year 2010. Columns for the computation of the standard deviation have already been added to the tables below. Which group of cities tends to have a higher percentage of part-time workers? Which group varies the most in terms of this variable? Computations for both the mean and standard deviation are shown below.

PERCENT OF LABOUR FORCE WITH PART-TIME JOBS, 2010, EASTERN CITIES

| City | Part-timers ($X_i$) | Deviations ($X_i - \overline{X}$) | Deviations Squared $(X_i - \overline{X})^2$ |
|---|---|---|---|
| Ottawa–Gatineau | 21.28 | $21.28 - 20.60 = 0.68$ | 0.4624 |
| Montreal | 21.28 | $21.28 - 20.60 = 0.68$ | 0.4624 |
| Quebec City | 20.54 | $20.54 - 20.60 = -0.06$ | 0.0036 |
| Toronto | 20.38 | $20.38 - 20.60 = -0.22$ | 0.0484 |
| Moncton–Saint John | 19.50 | $19.50 - 20.60 = -1.10$ | 1.2100 |
| | $\Sigma(X_i) = 102.98$ | $\Sigma(X_i - \overline{X}) = 0$ | $\Sigma(X_i - \overline{X})^2 = 2.1868$ |

$$\overline{X} = \frac{\Sigma(X_i)}{n} = \frac{102.98}{5} = 20.60$$

$$s = \sqrt{\frac{\Sigma(X_i - \overline{X})^2}{n}} = \sqrt{\frac{2.1868}{5}}$$

$$= \sqrt{0.4374} = 0.6614$$

*(continued)*

PERCENT OF LABOUR FORCE WITH PART-TIME JOBS, 2010, WESTERN CITIES

| City | Part-timers $(X_i)$ | Deviations $(X_i - \bar{X})$ | Deviations Squared $(X_i - \bar{X})^2$ |
|---|---|---|---|
| Victoria | 27.15 | $27.15 - 23.20 = \quad 3.95$ | 15.6025 |
| Vancouver | 24.29 | $24.29 - 23.20 = \quad 1.09$ | 1.1881 |
| Winnipeg | 23.50 | $23.50 - 23.20 = \quad 0.30$ | 0.0900 |
| Regina–Saskatoon | 20.99 | $20.99 - 23.20 = -2.21$ | 4.8841 |
| Calgary | 20.08 | $20.08 - 23.20 = -3.12$ | 9.7344 |
| | $\Sigma(X_i) = 116.01$ | $\Sigma(X_i - \bar{X}) = \quad 0$ | $\Sigma(X_i - \bar{X})^2 = 31.4991$ |

$$\bar{X} = \frac{\Sigma(X_i)}{n} = \frac{116.01}{5} = 23.20$$

$$s = \sqrt{\frac{\Sigma(X_i - \bar{X})^2}{n}} = \sqrt{\frac{31.4991}{5}}$$

$$= \sqrt{6.2998} = 2.5099$$

With such small groups, you can tell by simply inspecting the scores that the western cities have higher percentages of part-time workers in their labour forces. This impression is confirmed by both the median, which is 20.54 for the eastern cities (Quebec City is the middle case) and 23.50 for the western cities (Winnipeg is the middle case), and the mean (20.60 for the eastern cities and 23.20 for the western cities). For both groups, the mean is similar to the median, indicating an unskewed distribution of scores. Also, the five western cities are much more variable and diverse than the eastern cities. The range for the western cities is 7.07 ($R = 27.15 - 20.08 = 7.07$), much higher than the range for the eastern cities of 1.78 ($R = 21.28 - 19.50 = 1.78$). Similarly, the standard deviation for the western cities (2.51) is about four times greater in value than the standard deviation for the eastern cities (0.66). In summary, the five western cities average higher rates of part-time work and are also more variable than the five eastern cities.

Source: Statistics Canada, 2011 National Household Survey.

as the measure of dispersion. As noted in Section 3.3, the interquartile range uses only the middle 50% of the data in the distribution and thus is resistant to extreme scores. *(The mean and standard deviation may be found for any interval-ratio variable in the problems at the end of this chapter.)*

## 3.6 MEASURES OF CENTRAL TENDENCY AND DISPERSION FOR GROUPED DATA*

The techniques for ordinal and interval-ratio-level variables presented so far are used for ungrouped or raw data. These techniques can be readily extended to grouped, aggregate data in a frequency distribution. In this section, we will compute the median, mean, and standard deviation for sample data grouped in a frequency distribution.

Table 3.9 shows a frequency distribution of exam scores for a sample of 25 students. To more easily locate the median, cumulative frequencies have

*This section is optional.

**TABLE 3.9   Computing the Median for Aggregate Data in a Frequency Distribution**

| Score | Frequency | Cumulative Frequency |
|---|---|---|
| 58 | 2 | 2 |
| 60 | 2 | 4 |
| 62 | 3 | 7 |
| 64 | 2 | 9 |
| 66 | 3 | 12 |
| **67** | **4** | **16** |
| 68 | 1 | 17 |
| 69 | 1 | 18 |
| 70 | 2 | 20 |
| 93 | 5 | 25 |
| | $n = 25$ | |

been added to the table. Because the number of cases is odd, the median in this distribution is the score associated with the 13th case, or $(25 + 1)/2$. By adding frequencies, starting with the lowest score, we see that the 13th case is associated with the score 67.

We can also readily obtain the mean for aggregate data using a slightly modified version of the formula used to find the mean for ungrouped data (see Formula 3.4). The formula for aggregate data is

**FORMULA 3.10**
$$\overline{X} = \frac{\Sigma(fX_i)}{n}$$

where    $\overline{X}$ = the mean
$\Sigma(fX_i)$ = the summation of each score multiplied by its frequency
$n$ = the number of cases in the sample

Table 3.10 demonstrates the calculation of the mean for the distribution of exam scores described in the previous table.

**TABLE 3.10   Computing the Mean for Aggregate Data in a Frequency Distribution**

| Score ($X_i$) | Frequency ($f$) | Frequency × Score ($fX_i$) |
|---|---|---|
| 58 | 2 | 116 |
| 60 | 2 | 120 |
| 62 | 3 | 186 |
| 64 | 2 | 128 |
| 66 | 3 | 198 |
| 67 | 4 | 268 |
| 68 | 1 | 68 |
| 69 | 1 | 69 |
| 70 | 2 | 140 |
| 93 | 5 | 465 |
| | $n = 25$ | $\Sigma(fX_i) = 1{,}758$ |

The first ($X_i$) and second ($f$) columns in the distribution show each score and its frequency respectively. The third column ($fX_i$) displays the product of multiplying these numbers together. For example, the first score 58 is multiplied by its frequency 2, which equals 116. The mean of the frequency distribution is the sum of each score multiplied by its frequency, labelled $\Sigma(fX_i)$, divided by the number of cases in the sample ($n$).

$$\overline{X} = \frac{\Sigma(fX_i)}{n} = \frac{1758}{25} = 70.32$$

Thus, these 25 students have an average exam score of 70.32.

The formula for the standard deviation ($s$) for aggregate data in a frequency distribution is:

**FORMULA 3.11**

$$s = \sqrt{\frac{\Sigma f(X_i - \overline{X})^2}{n}}$$

where $f$ = the number of cases with a score
$X_i$ = the score
$\overline{X}$ = the mean
$n$ = the number of cases

Table 3.11 demonstrates the calculation of $s$.

The first ($X_i$) and second ($f$) columns in the distribution show each score and its frequency, respectively. The third column ($X_i-\overline{X}$) contains the deviations, and the fourth column ($X_i-\overline{X}$)$^2$ contains the squared deviations.

**TABLE 3.11  Computing the Standard Deviation for Aggregate Data in a Frequency Distribution**

| Score ($X_i$) | Frequency ($f$) | Deviations ($X_i - \overline{X}$) | Deviations Squared ($X_i - \overline{X}$)$^2$ | Deviations Squared Frequency $f(X_i-\overline{X})^2$ |
|---|---|---|---|---|
| 58 | 2 | −12.32 | 151.78 | 303.56 |
| 60 | 2 | −10.32 | 106.50 | 213.00 |
| 62 | 3 | −8.32 | 69.22 | 207.66 |
| 64 | 2 | −6.32 | 39.94 | 79.88 |
| 66 | 3 | −4.32 | 18.66 | 55.98 |
| 67 | 4 | −3.32 | 11.02 | 44.08 |
| 68 | 1 | −2.32 | 5.38 | 5.38 |
| 69 | 1 | −1.32 | 1.74 | 1.74 |
| 70 | 2 | −0.32 | 0.10 | 0.20 |
| 93 | 5 | 22.68 | 514.38 | 2,571.90 |
| | $n = 25$ | | | $\Sigma f(X_i - \overline{X})^2 = 3,483.38$ |

Recall from Table 3.10, $\overline{X} = 70.32$

The fifth column $f(X_i - \overline{X})^2$ displays the product of multiplying the frequencies and squared deviations together. Formula 3.11 is solved by taking the square root of the sum of these products $\Sigma f(X_i - \overline{X})^2$ divided by $n$.

$$s = \sqrt{\frac{\Sigma f(X_i - \overline{X})^2}{n}} = \sqrt{\frac{3{,}483.38}{25}} = \sqrt{139.34} = 11.80$$

Thus, the average deviation of these 25 exam scores from the mean, 70.32, is 11.8.

## 3.7 CHOOSING A MEASURE OF CENTRAL TENDENCY AND DISPERSION

Throughout this chapter, we have emphasized that the selection of a measure of central tendency or dispersion should, in general, be based on the level of measurement, meaning whether you are working with a nominal, ordinal, or interval-ratio variable. Table 3.12 summarizes the relation between the levels of measurement and the measures of central tendency and dispersion. The most appropriate measure of central tendency and dispersion for each level of measurement is in italics.

We have to keep in mind, however, that each measure of central tendency and dispersion is defined in a unique way. For example, even though they have a common purpose, the three measures of central tendency are quite different from one another and will have the same value only under certain, specific conditions (i.e., for symmetrical distributions). So, while your choice of an appropriate measure of central tendency or dispersion will generally depend on the way you measure the variable, you must also consider how the variable is distributed. The mean and standard deviation would be the most appropriate measures for a variable measured at the interval-ratio level; however, the median and interquartile range should be used if an interval-ratio variable has outliers or extreme scores (i.e., is highly skewed). Because of this, it is therefore also common to report more than just one measure of central tendency or dispersion whenever a variable's level of measurement permits more than one.

**TABLE 3.12   The Relation Between Level of Measurement and Measure of Central Tendency and Dispersion***

| Level of Measurement | Measure(s) of Central Tendency | Measure(s) of Dispersion |
|---|---|---|
| Nominal | *Mode* | *Index of Qualitative Variation* |
| Ordinal | Mode, *Median* | Index of Qualitative Variation, Range, *Interquartile Range* |
| Interval-ratio** | Mode, Median, *Mean* | Index of Qualitative Variation, Range, Interquartile Range, Variance, *Standard Deviation* |

*The most appropriate measure of central tendency and dispersion for each level of measurement is in italics.
**The median and interquartile range should be used for interval-ratio variables with highly skewed distributions.

## READING STATISTICS 3: Measures of Central Tendency and Dispersion

As was the case with frequency distributions, measures of central tendency and dispersion may not be presented in the professional research literature. These reports focus on the relationships between variables, not on describing them one by one. Univariate descriptive statistics are usually just the first step in the data analysis, not the ultimate concern, and probably will not be included in the final publication. On the other hand, some statistics (for example, the mean and standard deviation) serve a dual function. They not only are valuable descriptive statistics but also form the basis for many analytical techniques. Thus, they may be reported in the latter role if not in the former.

When included in research reports, measures of central tendency and dispersion will most often be presented in some summary form such as a table. A fragment of such a summary table might look like this:

| Variable | $\bar{X}$ | s | N |
|---|---|---|---|
| Age | 33.2 | 1.3 | 1078 |
| Number of children | 2.3 | 0.7 | 1078 |
| Years married | 7.8 | 1.5 | 1052 |
| Income | 55,786 | 1500 | 987 |

These tables describe the overall characteristics of the sample succinctly and, if you inspect the table carefully, you will have a good sense of the nature of the sample on the traits relevant to the project. Note that the number of cases varies from variable to variable in the preceding table. This is normal in social

science research and is caused by missing data or incomplete information on some of the cases.

### Statistics in the Professional Literature

Professors Fiona Kay and Jean Wallace were concerned with the effects of mentors on the careers of lawyers. Specifically, they wondered about the effects of specific types of mentoring relationships on career advancement and rewards. They also were concerned with gender differences: Do male and female lawyers benefit in different ways or at different levels from having a mentor? The researchers studied the careers of almost 1,600 lawyers in Ontario.

In this instalment of "Reading Statistics," we review some of the descriptive statistics reported by Kay and Wallace. As is usually the case, they reported these statistics as background information and to help identify differences and important patterns. The actual hypotheses are tested with more advanced statistics.

Kay and Wallace present means and standard deviations for about 25 different variables, six of which are reproduced here. These results show little difference between the genders on the variables measuring relationships with mentors and some of the variables measuring the progress of and respondents' satisfaction with their careers. While they did find large differences in earnings, there was little gender difference in other variables such as satisfaction with career.

Want to find out more? See the following source.

Source: F. Kay and J. Wallace, 2009, "Mentors as Social Capital: Gender, Mentors, and Career Rewards in Law Practice." *Sociological Inquiry*.

**Means and Standard Deviations for Selected Variables: Males vs. Females**

| Variable | Males | | Females | |
|---|---|---|---|---|
| | $\bar{X}$ | s | $\bar{X}$ | s |
| Closeness of relation with mentor | 2.85 | 0.69 | 2.85 | 0.73 |
| Quality of mentorship | 3.53 | 0.62 | 3.51 | 0.62 |
| Earnings | 205,502 | 143,417 | 134,577 | 109,730 |
| Progress toward meeting career goals | 3.41 | 1.01 | 3.25 | 0.96 |
| Value of work to respondent | 3.52 | 0.92 | 3.47 | 1.00 |
| Work satisfaction | 3.69 | 0.62 | 3.64 | 0.58 |

## 3.8 INTERPRETING STATISTICS: THE CENTRAL TENDENCY AND DISPERSION OF INCOME IN CANADA

A sizable volume of statistical material has been introduced in this chapter, so we will conclude by focusing on meaning and interpretation. What can you say after you have calculated, for example, means and standard deviations? Remember that statistics are tools to help us analyze information and answer questions. They never speak for themselves, and they always have to be understood in the context of some research question or test of a hypothesis. This section will provide an example of interpretation by posing and answering some questions about the changing distribution of income in Canada: "Is average income rising or falling?" "Does the average Canadian receive more or less income today than in the past?" "Is the distribution of income becoming more unequal (i.e., are the rich getting richer)?" The interpretation (words) will be explicitly linked to the statistics (numbers) so that you will be able to see how and why conclusions are developed.

We can answer these questions by looking at changes in measures of central tendency and dispersion. Changes in the mean and median will tell us, respectively, about changes in the average income for all Canadians (mean income) and income for the average Canadian (median income). The standard deviation would be the preferred measure of dispersion for an interval-ratio-level variable like income, but unfortunately, Statistics Canada does not provide this information. We will instead measure dispersion with a statistic called the Gini coefficient that is calculated by Statistics Canada.

The Gini coefficient measures the level of dispersion, or more specifically the level of inequality, in a given distribution. So, if everyone in Canada had the same income (i.e., no dispersion or inequality), the Gini coefficient would be 0; conversely, if just one individual held all income in Canada, it would be 1. Thus, the Gini coefficient ranges from 0 to 1. A decrease in the value of the Gini coefficient means a decrease in income inequality (less dispersion), and vice versa.

Before considering the data, we should keep in mind that virtually any distribution of income will be positively skewed (see Figure 3.3). That is, in any group, locality, province, or nation, the incomes of most people will be grouped around the mean or median, but some people—the wealthiest members of the group—will have incomes far higher than the average. Because the mean uses *all* the scores, it will be pulled in the direction of the extreme scores relative to the median. In a positively skewed distribution, the mean will be greater than the median.

Also, be aware that the values in Figure 3.6 are expressed in 2011 dollars. This eliminates any changes in the mean and median caused by inflation over the years. Without this adjustment, recent incomes would appear to be much higher than older incomes, not because of increased purchasing power and well-being, but rather because of the changing value of the dollar. Finally, Figure 3.6 is based on total income of Canadian households, not individual income.

Figure 3.6 shows that, expressed in 2011 dollars, the average Canadian household earned about $57,000 in 1980 (median = 57,000). By 2011, median

**FIGURE 3.6   Mean and Median Income of Households, 1980–2011, Canada**

Source: Data from Statistics Canada, CANSIM, Table 202–0705 (Gini coefficients)

income for the average Canadian household was again $57,000, after recovering from a period of overall decline that had indicated a marked decrease in standard of living. The intervening trend downward, between 1980 and 2011, has some noticeable declines in both the early 1980s and 1990s, both periods of recession. However, we also see periods of incline during the "boom economies" of the late 1980s and the late 1990s through the early 2000s.

The overall pattern of the mean income is almost identical to that of the median. It rises and falls in almost exactly the same ways and at the same times. Notice, however, that the mean is always higher than the median, a reflection of the characteristic positive skew of income data. In 1980, the mean income was 63,700, $6,700 higher than the median. By 2011, the mean was $75,000, $11,300 higher. What is this telling us? This increasingly positive skew means that the households with the highest incomes are becoming even more affluent relative to the bulk of the population. In other words, the growing distance between the mean and median suggests that in recent years, the wealthiest Canadians have been growing even wealthier relative to the rest of the population.

An increasing positive skew will be reflected by increases in the value of virtually any measure of dispersion. Although it does not supply information about the standard deviation, Statistics Canada calculates the Gini coefficient, reproduced in Figure 3.7. You can see by inspecting Figure 3.7 that the Gini coefficient is increasing, which indicates that incomes are growing in dispersion or variety. (Recall that the higher the Gini coefficient, the more dispersion or inequality that exists.) In 1980, the Gini coefficient was at 0.379. It rises to 0.431 by 2011, with most of the increase occurring in the 1990s. (To put this increase of 0.052, from 0.379 to 0.431, in the Gini coefficient in context, a difference of just 0.01 or more between two Gini coefficients is often considered to be meaningful and of consequence.) This trend would seem to indicate a growing income gap between less and more affluent Canadians over the time period and is very consistent with the positive skew in Figure 3.6.

In the end, the data show no increase in the income of the average Canadian (median) but an increase in the average income for all Canadians (mean). The increasing Gini coefficient indicates that incomes are growing in dispersion. Taken together, these findings would suggest that people with modest incomes continue to have modest incomes and, consistent with the ancient folk wisdom, the rich are getting richer.

**FIGURE 3.7**   **Dispersion of Household Income Measured by the Gini Coefficient, 1980–2011, Canada**

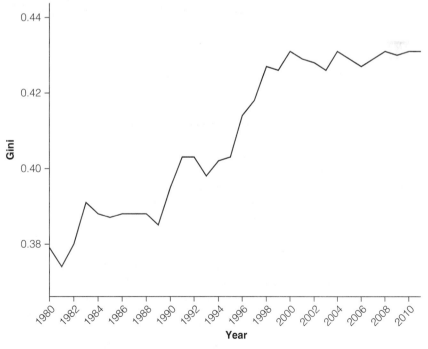

Source: Statistics Canada, CANSIM, Table 202-0705.

## SUMMARY

1. The three measures of central tendency presented in this chapter (mode, median, and mean) have a common purpose. Each reports some information about the most typical or representative value in a distribution. Appropriate use of these statistics permits the researcher to report important information about a distribution of scores in a single, easily understood number.

2. To provide a full description of a distribution of scores, measures of central tendency must be paired with measures of dispersion. Measures of dispersion, such as the index of qualitative variation, range and interquartile range, variance, and standard deviation, summarize information about the heterogeneity or variety in a distribution.

3. The mode reports the most common score and is used most appropriately with nominally measured variables. The median reports the score that is at the exact centre of the distribution and is most appropriately used with variables measured at the ordinal level and with highly skewed interval-ratio-level variables. The mean, the most frequently used of the three measures of central tendency, reports the most typical score. It is used most appropriately with

variables measured at the interval-ratio level (except when the distribution is highly skewed).

4. The index of qualitative variation is a measure of the dispersion of scores across variable response categories, and is most appropriate for variables measured at the nominal level. The range is the distance from the highest to the lowest score in the distribution. The interquartile range is the distance from the third to the first quartile. These two ranges are most appropriate for variables measured at the ordinal level. The standard deviation has a minimum value of zero (no variation) and increases in value as the variability of the distribution increases. It is used most appropriately with variables measured at the interval-ratio level; however, the interquartile range should be used if variables are highly skewed. The variance is used primarily in inferential statistics and in the design of some measures of association.

5. The boxplot is another graphic device used to express the distribution of ordinal-level and interval-ratio-level variable values in a compact and visually dramatic way. It is constructed from a five-number summary: the lowest score, first quartile, second quartile (the median), third quartile, and highest score in a distribution.

## SUMMARY OF FORMULAS

| | | |
|---|---|---|
| Index of qualitative variation | 3.1 | $IQV = \dfrac{k(100^2 - \Sigma Pct^2)}{100^2(k-1)}$ |
| Range | 3.2 | $R = H - L$ |
| Interquartile range | 3.3 | $Q = Q_3 - Q_1$ |
| Mean (sample) | 3.4 | $\bar{X} = \dfrac{\Sigma(X_i)}{n}$ |
| Mean (population) | 3.5 | $\mu = \dfrac{\Sigma(X_i)}{N}$ |
| Variance (sample) | 3.6 | $s^2 = \dfrac{\Sigma(X_i - \bar{X})^2}{n}$ |
| Standard deviation (sample) | 3.7 | $s = \sqrt{\dfrac{\Sigma(X_i - \bar{X})^2}{n}}$ |

| | | |
|---|---|---|
| Variance (population) | 3.8 | $\sigma^2 = \dfrac{\Sigma(X_i - \mu)^2}{N}$ |
| Standard deviation (population) | 3.9 | $\sigma = \sqrt{\dfrac{\Sigma(X_i - \mu)^2}{N}}$ |
| Mean (sample), aggregate data | 3.10 | $\overline{X} = \dfrac{\Sigma(fX_i)}{n}$ |
| Standard deviation (sample), aggregate data | 3.11 | $s = \sqrt{\dfrac{\Sigma f(X_i - \overline{X})^2}{n}}$ |

## GLOSSARY

**Boxplot.** A graphic device based on the median, interquartile range, and range. It is used to display the centre, dispersion, and overall range of scores in a distribution of ordinal-level or interval-ratio-level variable scores.

**Deviations.** The distances between the scores and the mean.

**Five-numbered summary.** A group of statistics consisting of the lowest score, first quartile, median, third quartile, and highest score of a distribution of scores, and the basis for the boxplot.

**Dispersion.** The amount of variety or heterogeneity in a distribution of scores.

**Index of qualitative variation.** The ratio of the amount of variation actually observed in a distribution of nominal- or ordinal-level variable scores to the maximum variation that could exist in that distribution.

**Interquartile range.** The distance from the third quartile to the first quartile.

**Mean.** The arithmetic average of the scores. $\overline{X}$ represents the mean of a sample, and $\mu$, the mean of a population.

**Mean deviation.** The average of the absolute deviations of the scores around the mean.

**Measures of central tendency.** Statistics that summarize a distribution of scores by reporting the most typical or representative value of the distribution.

**Measures of dispersion.** Statistics that indicate the amount of variety or heterogeneity in a distribution of scores.

**Median.** The point in a distribution of scores above and below which exactly half of the cases fall.

**Mode.** The most common value in a distribution, or the largest category of a variable.

**Outliers.** Extreme high or low scores in a distribution.

**Range.** The highest score minus the lowest score.

**Skew.** The extent to which a distribution of scores has a few scores that are extremely high (positive skew) or extremely low (negative skew). It is an important characteristic of distribution shape.

**Standard deviation.** The square root of the sum of the squared deviations of the scores around the mean, divided by the number of cases. The most important and useful descriptive measure of dispersion; $s$ represents the standard deviation of a sample; $\sigma$ the standard deviation of a population.

**Variance.** The sum of the squared deviations of the scores around the mean divided by the number of cases. A measure of dispersion used primarily in inferential statistics and also in correlation and regression techniques; $s^2$ represents the variance of a sample; $\sigma^2$, the variance of a population.

## MULTIMEDIA RESOURCES

 nelson.com/student

Visit the companion website for the fourth Canadian edition of *Statistics: A Tool for Social Research* to access a wide range of student resources. Begin by clicking on the Student Resources section of the book's website to access online chapters and study tools.

## PROBLEMS

**3.1** [SOC] A variety of information has been gathered from a sample of lower- and upper-year students living in residence at a large university, including their region of birth; the extent to which they support legalization of marijuana (measured on a scale on which 7 = strong support, 4 = neutral, and 1 = strong opposition); the amount of money they spend each week out-of-pocket for food, drinks, and entertainment; how many movies they watched in their residence rooms last week, and their opinion of cafeteria food (10 = excellent, 0 = very bad). Some results are presented below. Find the *most appropriate* measure of central tendency for each variable for lower-year students and then for upper-year students. Report the measure you selected as well as its value for each variable (e.g., "Mode = 3" or "Median = 3.5"). *(HINT: Determine the level of measurement for each variable first. In general, this will tell you which measure of central tendency is appropriate. See Section 3.6 to review the relationship between measure of central tendency and level of measurement. Also, remember that the mode is the most common score, and especially, remember to array scores from high to low before finding the median.)*

### LOWER-YEAR STUDENTS

| Student | Region of Birth | Legalization | Out-of-Pocket Expenses ($) | Movies | Cafeteria Food |
|---|---|---|---|---|---|
| A | Atlantic | 7 | 33 | 0 | 10 |
| B | Atlantic | 4 | 39 | 14 | 7 |
| C | Ontario | 3 | 45 | 10 | 2 |
| D | Prairies/West | 2 | 47 | 7 | 1 |
| E | Atlantic | 3 | 62 | 5 | 8 |
| F | Atlantic | 5 | 48 | 1 | 6 |
| G | Ontario | 1 | 52 | 0 | 10 |
| H | Ontario | 4 | 65 | 14 | 0 |
| I | Prairies/West | 1 | 51 | 3 | 5 |
| J | Quebec | 2 | 43 | 4 | 6 |

### UPPER-YEAR STUDENTS

| K | Atlantic | 7 | 65 | 0 | 1 |
|---|---|---|---|---|---|
| L | Prairies/West | 6 | 62 | 5 | 2 |
| M | Atlantic | 7 | 60 | 11 | 8 |
| N | Atlantic | 5 | 90 | 3 | 4 |
| O | Ontario | 1 | 62 | 4 | 3 |
| P | Ontario | 5 | 57 | 14 | 6 |
| Q | Quebec | 6 | 40 | 0 | 2 |
| R | Quebec | 7 | 49 | 7 | 9 |
| S | Atlantic | 3 | 45 | 5 | 4 |
| T | Quebec | 5 | 85 | 3 | 7 |
| U | Atlantic | 4 | 78 | 5 | 4 |

**3.2** The marital status of residents of four apartment complexes is reported below. Compute the index of qualitative variation for each neighbourhood. Which is the most heterogeneous of the four? Which is the least heterogeneous?

| Complex A Marital Status | Frequency | Complex B Marital Status | Frequency |
|---|---|---|---|
| Single | 26 | Single | 10 |
| Married | 31 | Married | 12 |
| Divorced | 12 | Divorced | 8 |
| Widowed | 5 | Widowed | 7 |
| | n = 74 | | n = 37 |

| Complex C | | Complex D | |
|---|---|---|---|
| **Marital Status** | **Frequency** | **Marital Status** | **Frequency** |
| Single | 20 | Single | 52 |
| Married | 30 | Married | 3 |
| Divorced | 2 | Divorced | 20 |
| Widowed | 1 | Widowed | 10 |
| | $n = 53$ | | $n = 85$ |

**3.3** PS You have been observing the local Liberal Party in a large city and have compiled some information about a small sample of party regulars.

Find the appropriate measure of central tendency for each variable.

| Respondent | Sex | Social Class | Number of Years in Party | Education | Marital Status | Number of Children |
|---|---|---|---|---|---|---|
| A | M | High | 32 | High school | Married | 5 |
| B | M | Medium | 17 | High school | Married | 0 |
| C | M | Low | 32 | High school | Single | 0 |
| D | M | Low | 50 | Grade 8 | Widowed | 7 |
| E | M | Low | 25 | Grade 4 | Married | 4 |
| F | M | Medium | 25 | High school | Divorced | 3 |
| G | F | High | 12 | College/University | Divorced | 3 |
| H | F | High | 10 | College/University | Separated | 2 |
| I | F | Medium | 21 | College/University | Married | 1 |
| J | F | Medium | 33 | College/University | Married | 5 |
| K | M | Low | 37 | High school | Single | 0 |
| L | F | Low | 15 | High school | Divorced | 0 |
| M | F | Low | 31 | Grade 8 | Widowed | 1 |

**3.4** SOC You have compiled the information below on each of the graduates voted "most likely to succeed" by a local high school for a 10-year period. For each variable, find the appropriate measure of dispersion. *(HINT: See Section 3.7 to review the relationship between measure of dispersion and level of measurement.)*

| Case | Present Income ($) | Marital Status | Owns a BMW? | Years of Education Post-High School |
|---|---|---|---|---|
| A | 24,000 | Single | No | 8 |
| B | 48,000 | Divorced | No | 4 |
| C | 54,000 | Married | Yes | 4 |
| D | 45,000 | Married | No | 4 |
| E | 30,000 | Single | No | 4 |
| F | 35,000 | Separated | Yes | 8 |
| G | 30,000 | Married | No | 3 |
| H | 17,000 | Married | No | 1 |
| I | 33,000 | Married | Yes | 6 |
| J | 48,000 | Single | Yes | 4 |

**3.5** SOC For 15 respondents, data have been gathered on four variables. Find and report the appropriate measure of central tendency for each variable.

| Respondent | Marital Status | Sex | Age | Attitude on Legalization of Marijuana Scale* |
|---|---|---|---|---|
| A | Single | Female | 18 | 10 |
| B | Single | Male | 20 | 9 |
| C | Widowed | Female | 21 | 8 |
| D | Married | Female | 30 | 10 |
| E | Married | Male | 25 | 7 |
| F | Married | Female | 26 | 7 |
| G | Divorced | Male | 19 | 9 |
| H | Widowed | Female | 29 | 6 |
| I | Divorced | Female | 31 | 10 |
| J | Married | Male | 55 | 5 |
| K | Widowed | Male | 32 | 4 |

| L | Married | Male | 28 | 3 |
|---|---------|--------|----|---|
| M | Divorced | Female | 23 | 2 |
| N | Married | Female | 24 | 1 |
| O | Divorced | Male | 32 | 9 |

*This scale is constructed so that a high score indicates strong opposition to legalization of marijuana.

**3.6** | SOC | Below are four variables for 30 cases taken from a national survey. Age is reported in years. The variable "happiness" consists of answers to the question "Taken all together, would you say that you are (1) very happy, (2) pretty happy, or (3) not too happy?" Respondents were asked how many sex partners they had over the past five years. Responses were measured on the following scale: 0–4 = actual numbers; 5 = 5–10 partners; 6 = 11–20 partners; 7 = 21–100 partners; and 8 = more than 100. For each variable, find the appropriate measure of dispersion.

| Respondent | Age | Happiness | Number of Partners | Sex |
|-----------|-----|-----------|---------|------|
| 1 | 20 | 1 | 2 | Male |
| 2 | 32 | 1 | 1 | Male |
| 3 | 31 | 1 | 1 | Female |
| 4 | 34 | 2 | 5 | Male |
| 5 | 34 | 2 | 3 | Male |
| 6 | 31 | 3 | 0 | Female |
| 7 | 35 | 1 | 4 | Male |
| 8 | 42 | 1 | 3 | Male |
| 9 | 48 | 1 | 1 | Female |
| 10 | 27 | 2 | 1 | Male |
| 11 | 41 | 1 | 1 | Male |
| 12 | 42 | 2 | 0 | Female |
| 13 | 29 | 1 | 8 | Male |
| 14 | 28 | 1 | 1 | Female |
| 15 | 47 | 2 | 1 | Male |
| 16 | 69 | 2 | 2 | Female |
| 17 | 44 | 1 | 4 | Female |
| 18 | 21 | 3 | 1 | Male |
| 19 | 33 | 2 | 1 | Male |
| 20 | 56 | 1 | 2 | Male |
| 21 | 73 | 2 | 0 | Female |
| 22 | 31 | 1 | 1 | Female |
| 23 | 53 | 2 | 3 | Male |
| 24 | 78 | 1 | 0 | Male |
| 25 | 47 | 2 | 3 | Male |
| 26 | 88 | 3 | 0 | Female |
| 27 | 43 | 1 | 2 | Male |
| 28 | 24 | 1 | 1 | Male |
| 29 | 24 | 2 | 3 | Male |
| 30 | 60 | 1 | 1 | Male |

**3.7** Compute the median, interquartile range, mean, and standard deviation of the 10 scores reported below.

10, 12, 15, 20, 25, 30, 32, 35, 40, 50

**3.8** | SOC | The table below lists the average weekly earnings for the 10 provinces in 2005 and 2010 (fictitious data). Compute the mean and median for each year and compare the two measures of central tendency. Which measure of central tendency is greater for each year? Are the distributions skewed? In which direction?

| Province | 2005 | 2010 |
|----------|------|------|
| Newfoundland and Labrador | 712 | 734 |
| Prince Edward Island | 667 | 709 |
| Nova Scotia | 570 | 697 |
| New Brunswick | 660 | 662 |
| Quebec | 648 | 745 |
| Ontario | 682 | 700 |
| Manitoba | 633 | 656 |
| Saskatchewan | 645 | 706 |
| Alberta | 617 | 680 |
| British Columbia | 712 | 741 |

**3.9** | SOC | In problem 3.8, you computed the mean and median weekly earnings for 10 Canadian provinces in two separate years. Now compute the standard deviation for each year. Did the average weekly earnings for the provinces become more or less variable over the period?

**3.10** | SW | As the head of a social services agency, you believe that your staff of 20 social workers is very much overworked compared to 10 years ago. The case loads for each worker are reported below for each of the two years in question. Has the average case load increased? What measure of central tendency is most appropriate to answer this question? Why?

| 2000 | | 2010 | |
|------|----|------|----|
| 52 | 55 | 42 | 82 |
| 50 | 49 | 75 | 50 |
| 57 | 50 | 69 | 52 |
| 49 | 52 | 65 | 50 |
| 45 | 59 | 58 | 55 |
| 65 | 60 | 64 | 65 |
| 60 | 65 | 69 | 60 |
| 55 | 68 | 60 | 60 |
| 42 | 60 | 50 | 60 |
| 50 | 42 | 60 | 60 |

**3.11** SOC The following table lists the approximate number of cars per 100 population for eight nations. Compute the mean and median for this data. Which is greater in value? Is there a positive skew in this data? How do you know?

| Nation | Number of Cars per 100 Population |
|---|---|
| United States | 50 |
| Canada | 45 |
| France | 46 |
| Germany | 51 |
| Japan | 39 |
| Mexico | 10 |
| Sweden | 44 |
| United Kingdom | 37 |

**3.12** SW For the test scores first presented in problem 2.6 and reproduced below, compute a mean and standard deviation for both the pretest and post-test. Based on these statistics, write a paragraph describing how the sample changed from test to test.

| Case | Pretest | Post-Test |
|---|---|---|
| A | 8 | 12 |
| B | 7 | 13 |
| C | 10 | 12 |
| D | 15 | 19 |
| E | 10 | 8 |
| F | 10 | 17 |
| G | 3 | 12 |
| H | 10 | 11 |
| I | 5 | 7 |
| J | 15 | 12 |
| K | 13 | 20 |
| L | 4 | 5 |
| M | 10 | 15 |
| N | 8 | 11 |
| O | 12 | 20 |

**3.13** SOC A sample of 25 first-year students at a university wrote a test that measured their literacy skills in reading and writing (their test scores were the number of incorrect answers, so the higher the score, the poorer the skills).

**a.** Compute the median and mean scores for these data.

| | | | | |
|---|---|---|---|---|
| 10 | 43 | 30 | 30 | 45 |
| 40 | 12 | 40 | 42 | 35 |
| 45 | 25 | 10 | 33 | 50 |
| 42 | 32 | 38 | 11 | 47 |
| 22 | 26 | 37 | 38 | 10 |

**b.** These same 25 students wrote the same test during their final year. Compute the median and mean for this second set of scores and compare them to the earlier set. What happened?

| | | | | |
|---|---|---|---|---|
| 10 | 45 | 35 | 27 | 50 |
| 35 | 10 | 50 | 40 | 30 |
| 40 | 10 | 10 | 37 | 10 |
| 40 | 15 | 30 | 20 | 43 |
| 23 | 25 | 30 | 40 | 10 |

**3.14** PA The data below represent the percentage of workers living in each city who used public transportation to commute to work in 2010 (fictitious data).

| City | Percent |
|---|---|
| Abbotsford | 20 |
| Barrie | 32 |
| Calgary | 26 |
| Dawson | 6 |
| Fredericton | 9 |
| Edmonton | 6 |
| Hamilton | 10 |
| Halifax | 11 |
| Kelowna | 15 |
| Mississauga | 14 |
| Montreal | 53 |
| Quebec City | 25 |
| Saskatoon | 3 |
| St. John's | 4 |
| Thunder Bay | 4 |
| Toronto | 31 |
| Vancouver | 18 |
| Winnipeg | 33 |

**a.** Calculate and compare the mean and median of this distribution. Summarize the results in a paragraph.

**b.** Compute and compare the standard deviation and interquartile range. Summarize the results in a paragraph.

**c.** If you removed Montreal from this distribution and recalculated, what would happen to the mean? To the median? Why?

**d.** What would happen to the value of the standard deviation if you removed Montreal from this distribution and recalculated? To the interquartile range? Why?

**3.15** At Algebra University the math department ran some special sections of the introductory math course using a variety of innovative teaching techniques. Students were randomly assigned to either the traditional sections or the experimental sections, and all students were given the same final exam. The results of the final are summarized below. What was the effect of the experimental course?

| Traditional | Experimental |
|---|---|
| $\overline{X} = 77.8$ | $\overline{X} = 76.8$ |
| $s = 12.3$ | $s = 6.2$ |
| $n = 478$ | $n = 465$ |

## You Are the Researcher

### Using SPSS to Compute Measures of Central Tendency and Dispersion with the 2012 CCHS

The demonstrations and exercises below use the shortened version of the 2012 CCHS data set (*CCHS_2012_Shortened.sav*) supplied with this textbook. Start SPSS by clicking the SPSS icon on your monitor screen. Load the 2012 CCHS. When you see the message "IBM SPSS Statistics Processor is ready" on the bottom of the "closest" screen, you are ready to proceed.

It is again important to note that SPSS displays information on variables by name (e.g., *dhh_sex*) or by label (e.g., sex). If labels are displayed, we highly recommend that you switch to variable names by clicking **Edit**, then **Options**, and then, on the **General** tab, select **Display names** and **Alphabetical**. Then click **OK**.

### SPSS DEMONSTRATION 3.1 Producing Measures of Central Tendency and Dispersion

Most of the statistics discussed in this chapter are available from either the **Frequencies** or **Descriptives** procedures. Here we will use **Frequencies**, which we used to produce a frequency distribution in Demonstration 2.1, to calculate measures of central tendency and dispersion for three variables: *geogprv* (province of residence), *gendmhi* (perceived mental health), and *alwdwky* (weekly alcohol consumption).

The three variables vary in level of measurement, and we could request only the appropriate measure of central tendency and dispersion for each variable. For example, we could request the mode for *geogprv* (nominal), the median for *gendmhi* (ordinal), and the mean for *alwdwky* (interval-ratio). While this would be reasonable, it's actually more convenient to get all measures of central tendency and dispersion for each variable and ignore the irrelevant output. Statistical packages typically generate more information than necessary, and it is common to disregard some of the output. Of course, if you decide to use the more convenient approach, then you need to make sure only to report the measures that are actually appropriate. For example, if you include an output table in a research study, you must edit your output table so that it only includes appropriate statistics.

To produce measures of central tendency and dispersion, begin by clicking **Analyze** from the menu bar; then click **Descriptive Statistics** and **Frequencies.** In the **Frequencies** dialog box, find the variable names in the list on the left and click the arrow button in the middle of the screen to move the names (*geogprv*, *gendmhi*, and *alwdwky*) to the **Variable(s)** box on the right.

To request specific statistics, click the **Statistics** button in the upper-right-hand corner of the **Frequencies** dialog box. The **Frequencies: Statistics** dialog box will open. Find the **Central Tendency** box on the right and click **Mean**, **Median**, and **Mode**. Next, find the **Dispersion** box on the left and click **Std. Deviation**, **Variance**, and **Range**. Then, in the **Percentile Values** section, click the checkbox next to **Quartiles**. Click **Continue**, and you will be returned to the **Frequencies** dialog box, where you might want to click the **Display Frequency Tables** box. The **Display Frequency Tables** box is checked by default, but when this box is *not* checked, SPSS will not produce frequency distribution tables and only the statistics we request will appear in the **Output** window. Next, click **OK**, and SPSS will produce the following output:

## Statistics

|  | | Province of Residence of Respondent | Perceived Mental Health | Weekly Consumption |
|---|---|---|---|---|
| *N* | Valid | 1,716 | 1,716 | 911 |
|  | Missing | 0 | 0 | 805 |
| Mean | | 37.17 | 2.99 | 4.46 |
| Median | | 35.00 | 3.00 | 2.00 |
| Mode | | 35 | 3 | 0 |
| Std. Deviation | | 13.609 | .948 | 6.134 |
| Variance | | 185.208 | .898 | 37.628 |
| Range | | 49 | 4 | 94 |
| Percentiles | 25 | 24.00 | 2.00 | .00 |
|  | 50 | 35.00 | 3.00 | 2.00 |
|  | 75 | 48.00 | 4.00 | 7.00 |

Looking only at the most appropriate measure of central tendency and dispersion for each variable, the mode for *geogprv* (province of residence) is "35." You can find out about the meaning or label of this value by consulting either the code book in Appendix G of the textbook or the online code book. To use the latter, click **Utilities** and then **Variables** and find *geogprv* in the variable list on the left. Either way, you will find that a score of 35 indicates "Ontario." This was the most common province of residence for persons in the sample and is thus the mode. (Note that the index of qualitative variation statistic is not available in the **Frequencies** command; however, it can easily be computed by producing a frequency distribution table, as illustrated in Demonstration 2.1, then inputting the appropriate information into Formula 3.1 as summarized in the One Step at a Time: Finding the Index of Qualitative Variation box. Also, note that, while the total number of cases in the CCHS data set appears to be 1,500, the total number of cases being analyzed is in fact 1,716. The reason for this difference is that, like the GSS, the CCHS data set is weighted to correct for sampling bias—some individuals are more likely than others to be included in the sample. The weight variable included with the CCHS, *wts_m*, corrects for this bias. Thus, you are really analyzing 1,716, not 1,500, individuals when using this data file.)

The median for *gendmhi* (perceived mental health) is a value of "3.00." Again, use either Appendix G or the online code book, and you will see that the category associated with this score is "very good." This means that the middle case in this distribution has a score of 3 (or that the middle case is in the interval "very good").

As for dispersion, the range for *gendmhi* is equal to 4. In other words, scores range from 0 (poor) to 4 (excellent). The interquartile range is the difference between the third quartile (labelled as "75" in the "Percentiles" row, meaning the 75th percentile) and the first quartile (labelled "25," or the 25th percentile). The score associated with the 75th percentile is 4, which indicates that 75% of the sample has a score below 4. Similarly, 25% has a score below 2. Hence the interquartile range is equal to $4 - 2$ or 2. (Note that the second quartile is labelled "50," or the 50th percentile, which is the same as the median.)

The output for *alwdwky* (weekly alcohol consumption) indicates that for the 911 respondents in the sample that consumed alcohol at some point during the past 12 months, the average number of drinks consumed in the week prior to the interview was 4.46. Since weekly alcohol consumption is an interval-ratio variable that has been measured in a defined unit (number of drinks), the value of the mean is numerically meaningful, and we do not need to consult the code book to interpret its meaning. The standard deviation for *alwdwky*, reported in the row labelled "Std. Deviation," is about 6.13, suggesting that Canadians are quite diverse in their weekly alcohol consumption. Remember, a standard deviation of zero indicates that every person has exactly the same score. So, with a standard deviation of over 6 drinks, there is plenty of diversity or heterogeneity in the distribution of alcohol consumption in Canada. The interquartile range can additionally be computed for *alwdwky*. Using the percentile information provided in the table, it is equal to 7.00 (the value of $Q_3$) minus 0.00 (the value of $Q_1$), which is 7.00. This large interquartile range thus shows us the same pattern of heterogeneity in Canadian weekly alcohol consumption that we found with the large standard deviation.

Note that SPSS used *"N"* in the output to refer to sample size (e.g., the "valid" number of cases in the sample for the variable *geogprv* is 1,716), rather than the standard notation of *"n"* used in the text of this textbook. Also note that SPSS did not hesitate to compute means and standard deviations for the two variables that were not interval-ratio. The program cannot distinguish between numerical codes (such as the scores for *geogprv*) and actual numbers—to SPSS, all numbers are the same. Also, SPSS cannot screen your commands to see if they are statistically appropriate. If you request nonsensical statistics (e.g., average sex or median province), SPSS will carry out your instructions without hesitation. The blind willingness of SPSS simply to obey commands makes it easy for you, the user, to request statistics that are completely meaningless. Computers don't care about meaning; they just crunch the numbers.

In this case, it was more convenient for us to produce statistics indiscriminately and then ignore the ones that were nonsensical. This will not always be the case, and the point of all this, of course, is to caution you to use SPSS wisely. As the manager of your local computer centre will be quick to remind you, computer resources (including paper) are not unlimited.

## SPSS DEMONSTRATION 3.2 The Descriptives Command

The **Descriptives** command in SPSS is designed to provide summary statistics for continuous interval-ratio-level variables. By default (i.e., unless you tell it otherwise), **Descriptives** produces the mean, the minimum and maximum scores (i.e., the lowest and highest scores), and the standard deviation. Unlike **Frequencies**, this procedure will not produce frequency distributions.

To illustrate the use of **Descriptives**, let's run the procedure for *alwdwky* (weekly alcohol consumption), *hwtgbmi* (BMI or body mass index, which is a measure of body fat), and *smk_204* (number of cigarettes smoked daily for daily smokers). Click **Analyze, Descriptive Statistics**, and **Descriptives**. The **Descriptives** dialog box will open. This dialog box looks just like the **Frequencies** dialog box and works in the same way. Find the variable names in the list on the left and, once they are highlighted, click the arrow button in the middle of the screen to transfer them to the **Variable(s)** box on the right. Click **OK** and the following output will be produced:

### Descriptive Statistics

|  | N | Minimum | Maximum | Mean | Std. Deviation |
|---|---|---|---|---|---|
| Weekly consumption | 911 | 0 | 94 | 4.46 | 6.134 |
| BMI | 1,716 | 13.47 | 54.34 | 25.9907 | 5.11195 |
| # of cigarettes smoked daily-daily smoker | 312 | 1 | 50 | 15.38 | 9.547 |
| Valid *N* (listwise) | 179 | | | | |

The sample, on the average, consumes 4.46 drinks per week with a standard deviation (reported in the column labelled "Std. Deviation") of about 6.13 drinks (this duplicates the frequencies output in Demonstration 3.1). The output also shows that people in the sample have, on average, a BMI score of about 25.99 with a standard deviation of about 5.11 (to put this in context, BMI scores over 25 indicate excessive weight). Finally, it reveals that for the 312 daily smokers in the sample, the average number of cigarettes smoked in a day is 15.38 with a standard deviation of about 9.55.

## SPSS DEMONSTRATION 3.3 Producing a Boxplot

In addition to the graphs generated in SPSS Demonstration 2.2, SPSS can also produce a boxplot of ordinal-level and interval-ratio-level variable scores. In this demonstration, we will use SPSS to generate a boxplot for *alwdwky* (weekly alcohol consumption).

Begin by clicking **Graphs** from the Menu bar; then click **Legacy Dialogs**; and from the list of graphs, click **Boxplot**. Next, click **Simple** and **Summaries of separate variables** in the **Boxplot** box (note that **Summaries of separate variables** is not the default setting in SPSS). In the **Define Simple Boxplot** dialog box, find the variable name in the list on the left and click the arrow button in the middle of the screen to move the name (*alwdwky)* to the **Variable(s)** box on the right. Finally, click **OK** and SPSS will produce the following output:

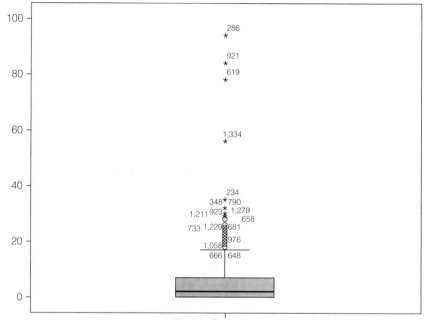

**Weekly Consumption**

Notice the substantial "clumping" of variable scores in the lower score range of this graph. This boxplot shows that even though there is substantial heterogeneity in weekly alcohol consumption patterns of Canadians, lower scores are much more typical than higher scores.

Notice, too, the circles and asterisks located above the top whisker. These symbols represent more extreme, outlying scores, and the numbers listed beside these symbols indicate, by default, the case numbers of the outlying scores. For example, the case number of the most extreme outlying score is 286, so it would be possible to look up case 286 in the data set in order to find out additional variable information about this extreme case. By contrast, there are no outlying scores below the minimum value; in fact, the minimum score and $Q_1$ are both 0, meaning that there is no dispersion between the minimum score and $Q_1$.

SPSS separates outlying scores into two categories: "apparent outliers," which are marked by circles, and "extreme outliers" which are marked by asterisks. Apparent outliers are those cases whose scores are between 1.5 and 3 times the interquartile range above $Q_3$ and/or below $Q_1$, and extreme outliers are those cases whose scores are more than 3 times the interquartile range above $Q_3$ and/or below $Q_1$. Outlying scores can thus occur above, below, or both above and below the boxplot. (It is also possible for a boxplot to have no outlying scores at all.) The use of circles and asterisks helps us to see at a glance both the density as well as the degree of atypicality of outlying scores, whenever any occur.

Whenever there are outliers, the top (and/or bottom) whisker is therefore not the same as the highest (and/or lowest) score, as is the case when there are no outliers. Instead, the top (and/or bottom) whisker is placed at the highest (and/or lowest) score that is less than or equal to 1.5 times the interquartile range above $Q_3$ (and/or 1.5 times the interquartile range below $Q_1$). When there are outliers, you will need to calculate the value of the top (and/or bottom) whisker by adding 1.5 times the interquartile range to the value of $Q_3$ (and/or subtracting 1.5 times the interquartile range from the value of $Q_1$). Since *alwdwky* has outliers only above the middle 50% box, we only need to calculate the value of the top whisker, using the Q value of 7 that we computed for *alwdwky* in SPSS Demonstration 3.1 With a $Q_3$ value of 7 and an interquartile range of 7, the value of the top whisker is 7 + (1.5)(7) or 17.5.

## Exercises (using *CCHS_2012_Shortened.sav*)

**3.1** Use the **Frequencies** command to get the most appropriate measure of central tendency and dispersion for any three nominal or ordinal variables of your own choosing. Remember that SPSS will not calculate the index of qualitative variation for you, but it will provide you with the basic frequency distribution information that you need in order to be able to calculate it yourself, using Formula 3.1. (*Hint: Use the level of measurement of the variable as your criteria for selecting the appropriate measure of central tendency.*) Write a sentence or two reporting each measure.

**3.2** Use the **Descriptives** command to get means, medians, and standard deviations for any two interval-ratio variables. Write a sentence or two reporting and explaining the mean, median, and standard deviation of each variable. Describe the nature of any skew you might detect in the distributions.

**3.3** Use the **Frequencies** command to find the interquartile range for each variable in Exercise 3.2. Write a few sentences summarizing these results.

**3.4** Use the **Graphs: Legacy Dialogs** command to create a boxplot for each variable in Exercise 3.2. Write a few sentences summarizing these results. Make sure to comment on any outliers that you may observe.

# 4

# The Normal Curve

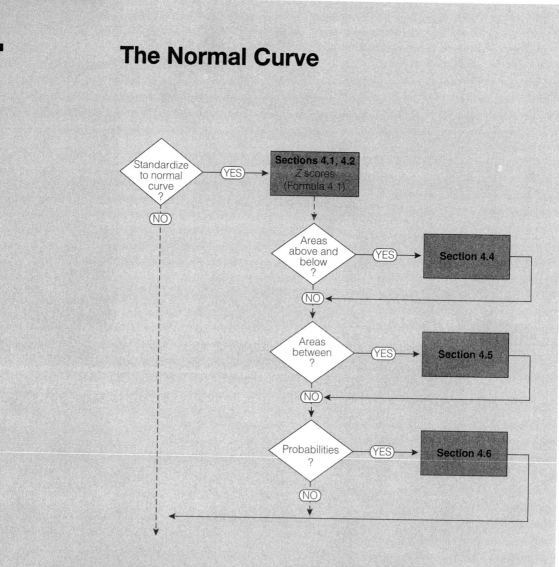

## LEARNING OBJECTIVES

By the end of this chapter, you will be able to

1. Define and explain the concept of the normal curve.
2. Convert raw (original) scores to $Z$ scores and use $Z$ scores and the normal curve table (Appendix A) to find areas above, below, and between points on the curve.
3. Express areas under the curve in terms of probabilities.

**4.1 INTRODUCTION**

The **normal curve** is a concept of great importance in statistics. In combination with the mean and standard deviation, the normal curve can be used to construct precise descriptive statements about empirical distributions. In addition, as we shall see in Part 2, it is also central to the theory that underlies inferential statistics. This chapter will conclude our treatment of descriptive statistics in Part 1 and lay important groundwork for Part 2.

The normal curve is a highly important theoretical model, a special kind of perfectly smooth frequency polygon that is unimodal (i.e., it has a single mode or peak) and symmetrical (unskewed) so that its mean, median, and mode are all exactly the same value. The normal curve is also bell-shaped, with its tails extending infinitely in both directions. Even though no empirical distribution has a shape that perfectly matches this ideal model, many variables (e.g., test results from large classes, test scores such as the GRE, people's height and weight) are close enough to permit the assumption of normality. In turn, this assumption makes possible one of the most important uses of the normal curve—the description of empirical distributions based on our knowledge of the theoretical normal curve.

The crucial point about the normal curve is that distances along the abscissa (horizontal axis) of the distribution, when measured in standard deviations from the mean, always encompass the *same* proportion of the total area under the curve. In other words, on any normal curve, the distance from any given point to the mean (when measured in standard deviations) will cut off exactly the *same* proportion of the total area.

To illustrate, Figures 4.1 and 4.2 present two hypothetical distributions of IQ scores, one for a sample of males and one for a sample of females, both normally distributed (or nearly so), such that:

| Males | Females |
|---|---|
| $\overline{X} = 100$ | $\overline{X} = 100$ |
| $s = 20$ | $s = 10$ |
| $n = 1,000$ | $n = 1,000$ |

Figures 4.1 and 4.2 are drawn with two scales on the horizontal axis or abscissa of the graph. The upper scale is stated in "IQ units" and the lower scale in standard deviations from the mean. These scales are interchangeable, and we can easily shift from one to the other. For example, for the males, an IQ score of 120 is one standard deviation (remember that, for the male group, $s = 20$) above the mean and an IQ of 140 is two standard deviations above (to the right of) the mean. Scores to the left of the mean are marked as negative values because they are less than the mean. An IQ of 80 is one standard deviation below the mean, an IQ score of 60 is two standard deviations less than the mean, and so forth. Figure 4.2 is marked in a similar way except that, because its standard deviation is a different value ($s = 10$), the markings occur at different points. For the female sample, one standard deviation above the mean is an IQ of 110, one standard deviation below the mean is an IQ of 90, and so forth.

**FIGURE 4.1** **IQ Scores for a Sample of Males**

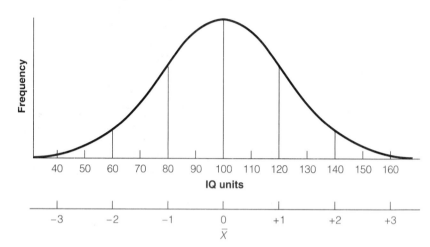

**FIGURE 4.2** **IQ Scores for a Sample of Females**

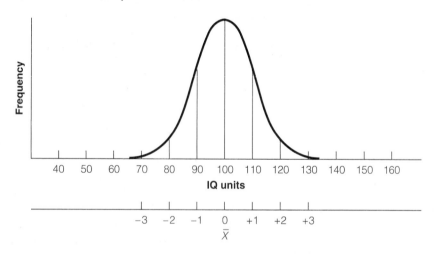

Recall that, on any normal curve, distances along the horizontal axis (or abscissa), when measured in standard deviations, always encompass exactly the same proportion of the total area under the curve. Specifically, the distance between one standard deviation above the mean and one standard deviation below the mean (or ±1 standard deviation) encompasses exactly 68.26% of the total area under the curve. This means that in Figure 4.1, 68.26% of the total area lies between the score of 80 (−1 standard deviation) and 120 (+1 standard deviation). The standard deviation for females is 10, so the same percentage of the area (68.26%) lies between the scores of 90 and 110. As long as an empirical distribution is normal, 68.26% of the total area will always be encompassed between ±1 standard deviation—regardless of the trait being measured and the number values of the mean and standard deviation.

Taking the normal curve's fixed relationship between the mean and standard deviation a little further, we see the following relationships between distances from the mean and areas under the curve:

| Between | Lies |
|---|---|
| ±1 standard deviation | 68.26% of the area |
| ±2 standard deviations | 95.44% of the area |
| ±3 standard deviations | 99.72% of the area |

These relationships are displayed graphically in Figure 4.3. Note that the relationships apply equally to normally distributed data in the population, but instead, Greek letters are used to represent the mean, $\mu$, and standard deviation, $\sigma$ (see Section 3.5). So, 68.26% of all cases in a normally distributed population are contained within $\pm 1\sigma$ of $\mu$; 95.44% of all cases in a normally distributed population are contained within $\pm 2\sigma$ of $\mu$; and 99.72% of all cases in a normally distributed population are contained within $\pm 3\sigma$ of $\mu$.* For the sake of brevity, we will refer to only sample data and symbols ($\overline{X}$ and $s$) for the remainder of this chapter.

**FIGURE 4.3   Areas Under the Theoretical Normal Curve**

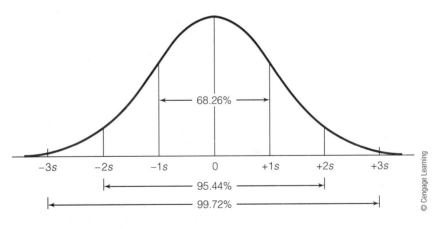

© Cengage Learning

*In the social sciences, we most commonly use the whole number area values of 90%, 95%, and 99%. These values correspond to the more precise standard deviation values of ±1.65, ±1.96, and ±2.58, respectively, as shown below.

| Between | Lies |
|---|---|
| ±1.65 standard deviations | 90% of the area |
| ±1.96 standard deviations | 95% of the area |
| ±2.58 standard deviations | 99% of the area |

We will have more to say about these precise values in Chapter 6, but for the sake of simplicity in this chapter, we will use only the whole number standard deviation values of ±1, ±2, and ±3.

The relationship between distance from the mean and area allows us to describe an empirical distribution of a variable in the sample (or population), provided that it is at least approximately normal. The position of individual scores can be described with respect to the mean, the distribution as a whole, or any other score in the distribution.

The areas between scores can also be expressed, if desired, in numbers of cases rather than percentage of total area. For example, a normal distribution of 1,000 cases will contain about 683 cases (68.26% of 1,000 cases) between ±1 standard deviation of the mean, about 954 cases (95.44% of 1,000 cases) between ±2 standard deviations, and about 997 cases (99.72% of 1,000 cases) between ±3 standard deviations. Thus, for any normal distribution, only a few cases will be farther away from the mean than ±3 standard deviations.

## 4.2 COMPUTING Z SCORES (STANDARD SCORES)

To find the percentage of the total area (or number of cases) above, below, or between scores in an empirical distribution, the original scores must first be expressed in units of the standard deviation or converted into **Z scores**, which are also called *standard scores*. The original scores could be in any unit of measurement (metres, IQ, dollars), but Z scores always have the same values for their mean (0) and standard deviation (1).

Think of converting the original scores into Z scores as a process of changing value scales—similar to changing from metres to yards, kilometres to miles, or gallons to litres. These units are different but equally valid ways of expressing distance, length, or volume. For example, a mile is equal to 1.61 kilometres, so two towns that are 10 miles apart are also 16.10 kilometres apart and a "5k" race covers 3.11 miles. Although you may be more familiar with kilometres than miles, either unit works perfectly well as a way of expressing distance.

In the same way, the original (or "raw") scores and Z scores are two equally valid but different ways of measuring distances under the normal curve. In Figure 4.1, for example, we could describe a particular score in terms of IQ units ("Amal's score was 120") or standard deviations ("Amal scored one standard deviation above the mean").

When we compute Z scores, we convert the original units of measurement (IQ units, centimetres, dollars, etc.) to Z scores and, thus, "standardize" the normal curve to a distribution that has a mean of 0 and a standard deviation of 1. The mean of the empirical normal distribution will be converted to 0, its standard deviation to 1, and all values will be expressed in Z-score form. The formula for converting original scores in a sample to Z scores is:*

**FORMULA 4.1**

$$Z = \frac{X_i - \overline{X}}{s}$$

---

*When converting original scores in a population, this formula is written as: $Z = \dfrac{X_i - \mu}{\sigma}$

**TABLE 4.1  Computing Z Scores for a Distribution of Original Scores**

| Score ($X_i$) | $Z \text{ Score} = \dfrac{X_i - \overline{X}}{s}$ |
|:---:|:---:|
| 10 | $\dfrac{10 - 30}{14.14} = -1.414$ |
| 20 | $\dfrac{20 - 30}{14.14} = -0.707$ |
| 30 | $\dfrac{30 - 30}{14.14} = 0.000$ |
| 40 | $\dfrac{40 - 30}{14.14} = 0.707$ |
| 50 | $\dfrac{50 - 30}{14.14} = 1.414$ |

Recall from Table 3.8: $\overline{X} = 30$, $s = 14.14$

Formula 4.1 will convert any score ($X_i$) from an empirical distribution into the equivalent Z score. To illustrate, consider the following sample of scores from Table 3.8: 10, 20, 30, 40, and 50. Their Z-score equivalents are presented in Table 4.1.

A Z score of positive 1.00 indicates that the original score lies one standard deviation unit above (to the right of) the mean. A negative Z score of 1.00 would fall one standard deviation unit below (to the left of) the mean. Thus, in the above example, the Z score of 1.414 indicates that the original score of 50 lies 1.414 standard deviation units above the mean, while −1.414 indicates that the original score of 10 lies 1.414 standard deviation units below the mean.

By inspection, you can see that the distribution of Z scores in Table 4.1 has a mean of 0 and a standard deviation of 1. To substantiate these observations, the mean and standard deviation of the Z distribution are computed using Formulas 3.4 and 3.7. The results are shown in Table 4.2. *(For practice in computing Z scores, see any of the problems at the end of this chapter.)*

## ONE STEP AT A TIME  Finding Z Scores

**1:** Subtract the value of the mean ($\overline{X}$) from the value of the score ($X_i$).

**2:** Divide the quantity found in step 1 by the value of the standard deviation ($s$). The result is the Z-score equivalent for this raw score.

**TABLE 4.2  Computing the Mean and Standard Deviation for a Distribution of $Z$ Scores**

| Scores ($X_i$) | Deviations ($X_i - \bar{X}$) | Deviations Squared ($X_i - \bar{X}$)$^2$ |
|---|---|---|
| −1.414 | −1.414 | 2.0 |
| −0.707 | −0.707 | 0.5 |
| 0.000 | 0.000 | 0.0 |
| 0.707 | 0.707 | 0.5 |
| 1.414 | 1.414 | 2.0 |
| $\Sigma(X_i) = 0.000$ | | $\Sigma(X_i - \bar{X})^2 = 5.0$ |

$$\bar{X} = \frac{\Sigma(X_i)}{n} = \frac{0}{5} = 0 \text{ (Formula 3.4)}$$

$$s = \sqrt{\frac{\Sigma(X_i - \bar{X})^2}{n}} = \sqrt{\frac{5}{5}} = \sqrt{1} = 1 \text{ (Formula 3.7)}$$

## 4.3 THE STANDARD NORMAL CURVE TABLE

The theoretical normal curve has been very thoroughly analyzed and described by statisticians. The areas related to any $Z$ score have been precisely determined and organized into a table format. This **standard normal curve table** or $Z$-score table is presented as Appendix A in this textbook, and a small portion of it is reproduced here for purposes of illustration as Table 4.3.

**TABLE 4.3  An Illustration of How to Find Areas Under the Normal Curve Using Appendix A**

| (a) $Z$ | (b) Area Between Mean and $Z$ | (c) Area Beyond $Z$ |
|---|---|---|
| 0.00 | 0.0000 | 0.5000 |
| 0.01 | 0.0040 | 0.4960 |
| 0.02 | 0.0080 | 0.4920 |
| 0.03 | 0.0120 | 0.4880 |
| ⋮ | ⋮ | ⋮ |
| 1.00 | 0.3413 | 0.1587 |
| 1.01 | 0.3438 | 0.1562 |
| 1.02 | 0.3461 | 0.1539 |
| 1.03 | 0.3485 | 0.1515 |
| ⋮ | ⋮ | ⋮ |
| 1.50 | 0.4332 | 0.0668 |
| 1.51 | 0.4345 | 0.0655 |
| 1.52 | 0.4357 | 0.0643 |
| 1.53 | 0.4370 | 0.0630 |
| ⋮ | ⋮ | ⋮ |

The standard normal curve table consists of three columns, with $Z$ scores in the left-hand column "a," area between the $Z$ score and the mean of the curve in the middle column "b," and area beyond the $Z$ score in the right-hand column "c." To find the area between any $Z$ score and the mean, go down the column labelled "$Z$" until you find the $Z$ score. For example, go down column "a" either in Appendix A or in Table 4.3 until you find a $Z$ score of $+1.00$. The entry in column "b" ("Area Between Mean and $Z$") is 0.3413. The table presents all areas in the form of proportions, but we can easily translate these into percentages by multiplying them by 100 (see Chapter 2). We could say either "a proportion of 0.3413 of the total area under the curve lies between a $Z$ score of 1.00 and the mean," or "34.13% of the total area lies between a score of 1.00 and the mean."

To illustrate further, find the $Z$ score of 1.50 either in column "a" of Appendix A or the abbreviated table presented in Table 4.3. This score is 1.5 standard deviations to the right of the mean and corresponds to an IQ of 130 for the men's IQ data (Figure 4.1). The area in column "b" for this score is 0.4332. This means that a proportion of 0.4332—or a percentage of 43.32%—of all the area under the curve lies between this score and the mean.

The third column in the table, column "c," presents "Area Beyond $Z$." These are areas above positive scores or below negative scores. This column will be used when we want to find an area above or below certain $Z$ scores, an application that will be explained in Section 4.4.

To conserve space, the standard normal curve table in Appendix A includes only positive $Z$ scores. Because the normal curve is perfectly symmetrical, however, the area between the score and the mean (column "b") for a negative score will be exactly the same as those for a positive score of the same numerical value. For example, the area between a $Z$ score of $-1.00$ and the mean will also be 34.13%, exactly the same as the area we found previously for a score of $+1.00$. Notice that areas are always positive values, regardless of whether a $Z$ score is positive or negative; however, as will be repeatedly demonstrated below, the sign of the $Z$ score is extremely important and should be carefully noted.

For practice in using Appendix A to describe areas under an empirical normal curve, verify that the $Z$ scores and areas given below are correct for the sample distribution of men's IQ. For each IQ score, the equivalent $Z$ score is computed using Formula 4.1, and then Appendix A is used to find areas between the score and the mean. ($\overline{X} = 100$, $s = 20$ throughout.)

| IQ Score | $Z$ Score | Area Between $Z$ and the Mean |
|---|---|---|
| 110 | $+0.50$ | 19.15% |
| 125 | $+1.25$ | 39.44% |
| 133 | $+1.65$ | 45.05% |
| 138 | $+1.90$ | 47.13% |

The same procedures apply when the $Z$-score equivalent of an actual score happens to be a minus value (i.e., when the raw score lies below the mean).

| IQ Score | $Z$ Score | Area Between $Z$ and the Mean |
|---|---|---|
| 93 | −0.35 | 13.68% |
| 85 | −0.75 | 27.34% |
| 67 | −1.65 | 45.05% |
| 62 | −1.90 | 47.13% |

Remember that the areas in Appendix A will be the same for $Z$ scores of the same numerical value regardless of sign. The area between the score of 138 (+1.90) and the mean is the same as the area between 62 (−1.90) and the mean. *(For practice in using the standard normal curve table, see any of the problems at the end of this chapter.)*

## 4.4 FINDING TOTAL AREA ABOVE AND BELOW A SCORE

To this point, we have seen how the normal curve table can be used to find areas between a $Z$ score and the mean. The information presented in the table can also be used to find other kinds of areas in an empirical distribution of a variable in the sample (or population), provided that it is at least approximately normal in shape. For example, suppose you need to determine the total area below the scores of two male subjects in the sample distribution described in Figure 4.1. The first subject has a score of 117 ($X_1 = 117$), which is equivalent to a $Z$ score of +0.85:

$$Z_1 = \frac{X_1 - \overline{X}}{s} = \frac{117 - 100}{20} = \frac{17}{20} = +0.85$$

The plus sign of the $Z$ score indicates that the score should be placed above (to the right of) the mean. To find the area below a positive $Z$ score, the area between the score and the mean (given in column "b") must be added to the area below the mean. As we noted earlier, the normal curve is symmetrical (unskewed), and its mean will be equal to its median. Therefore, the area below the mean (just like the median) will be 50%. Study Figure 4.4 carefully. We are interested in the shaded area.

By consulting the normal curve table, we find that the area between the score and the mean (see column "b") is 30.23% of the total area. The area below a $Z$ score of +0.85 is therefore 80.23% (50.00% + 30.23%). This subject scored higher than 80.23% of the persons tested.

The second subject has an IQ score of 73 ($X_2 = 73$), which is equivalent to a $Z$ score of −1.35:

$$Z_2 = \frac{X_2 - \overline{X}}{s} = \frac{73 - 100}{20} = \frac{-27}{20} = -1.35$$

**FIGURE 4.4   Finding the Area Below a Positive _Z_ Score**

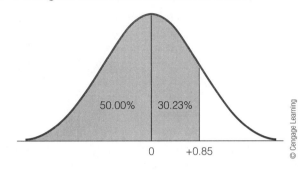

50.00%   30.23%

0        +0.85

© Cengage Learning

To find the area below a negative score, we use the column labelled "Area Beyond _Z_." The area of interest is depicted in Figure 4.5, and we must determine the size of the shaded area. The area beyond a score of $-1.35$ is given as 0.0885, which we can express as 8.85%. The second subject ($X_2 = 73$) scored higher than 8.85% of the tested group.

In these examples, we use the techniques for finding the area below a score. Essentially the same techniques are used to find the area above a score. If we need to determine the area above an IQ score of 108, for example, we would first convert to a _Z_ score

$$Z = \frac{X_i - \overline{X}}{s} = \frac{108 - 100}{20} = \frac{8}{20} = +0.40$$

and then proceed to Appendix A. The shaded area in Figure 4.6 represents the area in which we are interested. The area above a positive score is found in the "Area Beyond _Z_" column, and, in this case, the area is 0.3446, or 34.46%.

**FIGURE 4.5   Finding the Area Below a Negative _Z_ Score**

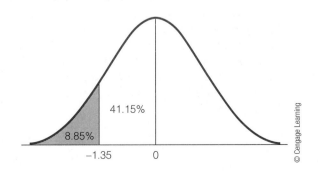

41.15%

8.85%

−1.35    0

© Cengage Learning

**FIGURE 4.6 Finding the Area Above a Positive *Z* Score**

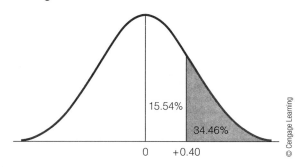

These procedures are summarized in Table 4.4 and in the One Step at a Time box. To find the total area above a positive *Z* score or below a negative *Z* score, go down the "*Z*" column of Appendix A until you find the standard score. The area you are seeking will be in the "Area Beyond *Z*" column (column "c"). To find the total area below a positive *Z* score or above a negative score, locate the standard score and then add the area in the "Area Between Mean and *Z*" (column "b") to either 0.5000 (for proportions) or 50.00 (for percentages). These techniques might be confusing at first, and you will find it helpful to draw the curve and shade in the areas in which you are interested.

**Finding Raw Scores.** Sometimes we want to work "backwards" and find a raw score when only a *percentile* has been reported. (Percentiles identify the point below which a specific percentage of cases fall. We first encountered them in Chapter 3 in calculating the interquartile range where we found three specific values: the first quartile, which is simply the 25th percentile; the second quartile, or 50th percentile; and the third quartile, or 75th percentile.) If a set of scores is normally distributed, we can use what we know about finding the area above (or below) a *Z* score to find the original, raw score.

**TABLE 4.4 Finding Areas Above and Below Positive and Negative *Z* Scores**

| To Find Area: | When the *Z* Score Is | |
| --- | --- | --- |
| | Positive | Negative |
| Above *Z* | Look in column "c" | Add column "b" area to 0.5000 or 50.00% |
| Below *Z* | Add column "b" area to 0.5000 or 50.00% | Look in column "c" |

**FIGURE 4.7**  **Finding the Raw Score of the 98.50th Percentile**

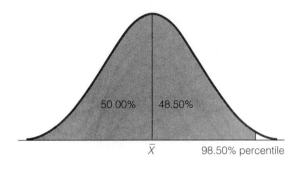

$\overline{X}$              98.50% percentile

For example, let's say that one of the females whose IQ data have been provided in Section 4.1 is told that her IQ is at the 98.5th percentile. In other words, 98.5% of all cases had a lower IQ score, as illustrated in Figure 4.7. She now wants to know her raw IQ score.

Since we know that the mean of the IQ data for females is 100 and the standard deviation is 10, we only need to find the $Z$ score of the 98.5th percentile to calculate her raw score, $X_i$. To do so, we must first find the area between the mean and $Z$ score. Scrolling down column "b" in Appendix A, we see that an area of 0.4850 (or 48.50%) corresponds to a $Z$ score value of 2.17. (We also know that the area below the mean contains 0.5000, or 50.00%, of all scores.)

Second, we insert the values of $Z$, $\overline{X}$, and $s$ into Formula 4.1 as follows:

$$Z = \frac{X_i - \overline{X}}{s} = 2.17 = \frac{X_i - 100}{10}$$

Then, through algebraic manipulation of this equation, we can find the raw score, $X_i$.

$$X_i = (2.17)(10) + 100 = 121.70$$

The female whose IQ is at the 98.50th percentile has a raw IQ score of 121.70. *(For practice in finding areas above or below Z scores, see Problems 4.1 to 4.7 at the end of this chapter. For practice in computing raw scores from percentiles, see Problems 4.8 to 4.11.)*

## 4.5 FINDING AREAS BETWEEN TWO SCORES

On occasion, you will need to determine the area between two scores rather than the total area above or below one score. In the case where the scores are on opposite sides of the mean, the area between the scores can be found by adding the areas between each score and the mean. Using the sample data of men's IQ as an example, if we wished to know the area between the IQ scores of 93 and 112, we would convert both scores to $Z$ scores, find the area between each score and the mean from Appendix A, and add these two areas together. The first IQ score of 93 converts to a $Z$ score of $-0.35$:

$$Z_1 = \frac{X_1 - \overline{X}}{s} = \frac{93 - 100}{20} = \frac{-7}{20} = -0.35$$

The second IQ score (112) converts to $+0.60$:

$$Z_2 = \frac{X_2 - \overline{X}}{s} = \frac{112 - 100}{20} = \frac{12}{20} = 0.60$$

Both scores are placed on Figure 4.8. We are interested in the total shaded area. The total area between these two scores is 13.68% + 22.57%, or 36.25%. Therefore, 36.25% of the total area (or about 363 of the 1,000 cases) lies between the IQ scores of 93 and 112.

When the scores of interest are on the same side of the mean, a different procedure must be followed to determine the area between them. For example, if we were interested in the area between the scores of 113 and 121, we would begin by converting these scores into $Z$ scores:

$$Z_1 = \frac{X_1 - \overline{X}}{s} = \frac{113 - 100}{20} = \frac{13}{20} = +0.65$$

$$Z_2 = \frac{X_2 - \overline{X}}{s} = \frac{121 - 100}{20} = \frac{21}{20} = +1.05$$

The scores are noted in Figure 4.9; we are interested in the shaded area. To find the area between two scores on the same side of the mean, find the area between each score and the mean (given in column "b" of Appendix A) and then subtract the smaller area from the larger. Between the $Z$ score of +0.65 and the mean lies 24.22% of the total area. Between +1.05 and the mean lies 35.31% of the total area. Therefore, the area between these two scores is 35.31% − 24.22%, or 11.09% of the total area (or about 111 of the 1,000 cases). The same technique would have been followed if both scores had been below the mean.

**FIGURE 4.8  Finding the Area Between Two Scores**

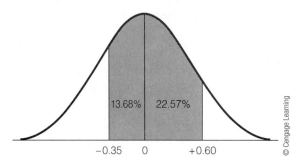

© Cengage Learning

**FIGURE 4.9   Finding the Area Between Two Scores**

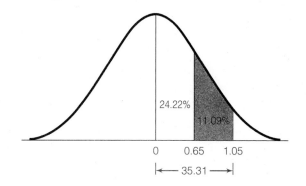

**TABLE 4.5   Finding Areas Between Scores**

| Situation | Procedure |
|---|---|
| Scores are on the SAME side of the mean | Find areas between each score and the mean in column "b." Subtract the smaller area from the larger area. |
| Scores are on OPPOSITE sides of the mean | Find areas between each score and the mean in column "b." Add the two areas together. |

The procedures for finding areas between two $Z$ scores are summarized in Table 4.5 and in the One Step at a Time box. *(For practice in finding areas between two scores, see Problems 4.3, 4.4, 4.6, 4.7, and 4.12 to 4.13.)*

## Applying Statistics 4.1: Finding the Area Below or Above a $Z$ Score

You have just received your score on a driver's licence test. If your score was 78 and you know that the mean score on the test was 67 with a standard deviation of 5, how does your score compare with the distribution of all test scores?

If you can assume that the test scores are normally distributed, you can compute a $Z$ score and find the area below or above your score. The $Z$-score equivalent of your raw score would be

$$Z = \frac{X_i - \overline{X}}{s} = \frac{78 - 67}{5} = \frac{11}{5} = +2.20$$

Turning to Appendix A, we find that the "Area Between Mean and $Z$" for a $Z$ score of 2.20 is 0.4861, which could also be expressed as 48.61%. Since this is a positive $Z$ score, we need to add this area to 50.00% to find the total area below. Your score is higher than 48.61 + 50.00, or 98.61%, of all the test scores. You did pretty well!

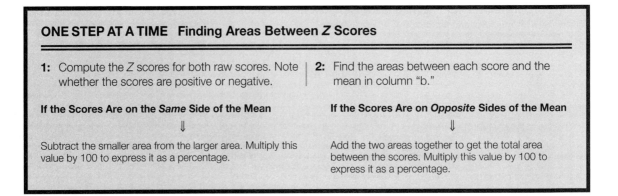

## ONE STEP AT A TIME   Finding Areas Between *Z* Scores

**1:** Compute the *Z* scores for both raw scores. Note whether the scores are positive or negative.

**2:** Find the areas between each score and the mean in column "b."

**If the Scores Are on the *Same* Side of the Mean**
⇓
Subtract the smaller area from the larger area. Multiply this value by 100 to express it as a percentage.

**If the Scores Are on *Opposite* Sides of the Mean**
⇓
Add the two areas together to get the total area between the scores. Multiply this value by 100 to express it as a percentage.

---

## Applying Statistics 4.2: Finding the Area Between *Z* Scores

All sections of Political Science 101 at a large university were given the same final exam. Test scores were distributed normally, with a mean of 72 and a standard deviation of 8. What percentage of students scored between 60 and 69 (a grade of C) and what percentage scored between 70 and 79 (a grade of B)? The first two scores are both below the mean. Using Table 4.4 as a guide, we must first compute *Z* scores, find areas between each score and the mean, and then subtract the smaller area from the larger.

$$Z_1 = \frac{X_i - \overline{X}}{s} = \frac{60 - 72}{8} = \frac{-12}{8} = -1.50$$

$$Z_2 = \frac{X_i - \overline{X}}{s} = \frac{69 - 72}{8} = \frac{-3}{8} = -0.38$$

Using column "b," we see that the area between $Z = -1.50$ and the mean is 0.4332 and the area between $Z = -0.38$ and the mean is 0.1480. Subtracting the smaller from the larger (0.4332 − 0.1480) gives 0.2852. Changing to percentage format, we can say that 28.52% of the students earned a C on the test. (Of course, since we do

not know the total number of students who wrote the final exam, we cannot calculate the exact number of students that this percentage represents.)

To find the percentage of students who earned a B, we must add the column "b" areas together, since the scores (70 and 79) are on opposite sides of the mean (see Table 4.4):

$$Z_1 = \frac{X_i - \overline{X}}{s} = \frac{70 - 72}{8} = \frac{-2}{8} = -0.25$$

$$Z_2 = \frac{X_i - \overline{X}}{s} = \frac{79 - 72}{8} = \frac{7}{8} = 0.88$$

Using column "b," we see that the area between $Z = -0.25$ and the mean is 0.0987 and that the area between $Z = 0.88$ and the mean is 0.3106. Therefore, the total area between these two scores is 0.0987 + 0.3106, or 0.4093. Translating to percentages again, we can say that 40.93% of the students earned a B on this test. (We can only calculate the exact number of students that this percentage represents if we know the total number of students who wrote the final exam.)

**4.6 USING THE NORMAL CURVE TO ESTIMATE PROBABILITIES**

To this point, we have thought of the theoretical normal curve as a way of describing the proportion or percentage of total area above, below, and between scores in an empirical distribution of interval-ratio variable scores. We have also seen that these areas can be converted into the number, proportion, or percentage of cases above, below, and between scores. In this section, we introduce the idea that the theoretical normal curve may also be thought of as a distribution of probabilities. Specifically, we may use the properties of the theoretical normal curve (Appendix A) to estimate the probability that a case randomly selected from an empirical normal distribution of interval-ratio variable scores will have a score that falls in a certain range. Very importantly, our use of the normal curve can also be extended to nominal and ordinal variable distributions, to estimate the probability that a randomly selected case will exhibit a particular characteristic such as having good health or poor health, having volunteered in the past 12 months or not having volunteered. This extended application will become clearer in Chapter 5. In terms of techniques, these probabilities will be found in exactly the same way as areas were found. Before we consider these mechanics, however, let us examine what is meant by the concept of **probability**.

Although we are rarely systematic or rigorous about it, we all attempt to deal with probabilities every day, and indeed, we base our behaviour on our estimates of the likelihood that certain events will occur. We constantly ask (and answer) questions such as: "What is the probability of rain?" "Of drawing to an inside straight in poker?" "Of the worn-out tires on my car going flat?" "Of passing a test if I don't study?"

To estimate the probability of an event, we must first be able to define what would constitute a "success." The examples above contain several different definitions of a success (i.e., rain, drawing a certain card, flat tires, and passing grades). To determine a probability, a fraction must be established, with the numerator equalling the number of events that would constitute a success and the denominator equalling the total number of possible events where a success could theoretically occur:

$$\text{Probability} = \frac{\#\,\text{successes}}{\#\,\text{events}}$$

To illustrate, assume that we wish to know the probability of selecting a specific card—say, the king of hearts—in one draw from a well-shuffled deck of cards. Our definition of a success is quite specific (drawing the king of hearts); and with the information given, we can establish a fraction. Only one card satisfies our definition of success, so the number of events that would constitute a success is 1; this value will be the numerator of the fraction. There are 52 possible events (i.e., 52 cards in the deck), so the denominator will be 52. The fraction is thus 1/52, which represents the probability of selecting the king of hearts on one draw from a well-shuffled deck of cards. Our probability of success is 1 out of 52.

We can leave the fraction established above as it is, or we can express it in several other ways. For example, we can express it as an odds ratio by inverting the fraction, showing that the odds of selecting the king of hearts on a single draw are 52:1 (or fifty-two to one). We can express the fraction as a proportion by dividing the numerator by the denominator. For our example above, the corresponding proportion is 0.0192, which is the proportion of all possible events that would satisfy our definition of a success. In the social sciences, probabilities are usually expressed as proportions, and we will follow this convention throughout the remainder of this section.* Using $p$ to represent "probability," the probability of drawing the king of hearts (or any specific card) can be expressed as

$$p \text{ (king of hearts)} = \frac{\#\,\text{successes}}{\#\,\text{events}} = \frac{1}{52} = 0.0192$$

As conceptualized here, probabilities have an exact meaning: over the long run, the events we define as successes will bear a certain proportional relationship to the total number of events. The probability of 0.0192 for selecting the king of hearts in a single draw really means that, over an infinite number of draws of one card at a time from a full deck of 52 cards, the proportion of successful draws will be 0.0192. Or, for every 10,000 draws, 192 will be the king of hearts, and the remaining 9,808 selections will be other cards. Thus, when we say that the probability of drawing the king of hearts in one draw is 0.0192, we are essentially applying our knowledge of what will happen over an infinite number of draws to a single draw.

Like proportions, probabilities range from 0.00 (meaning that the event has absolutely no chance of occurrence) to 1.00 (a certainty). As the value of the probability increases, the likelihood that the defined event will occur also increases. A probability of 0.0192 is close to zero, and this means that the event (drawing the king of hearts) is unlikely or improbable.

These techniques can be used to establish simple probabilities in any situation in which we can specify the number of successes and the total number of events. For example, a single die has six sides or faces, each with a different value ranging from 1 to 6. The probability of getting any specific number (say, a 4) in a single roll of a die is therefore

$$p \text{ (rolling a four)} = \frac{1}{6} = 0.1667$$

---

*This is also why it is reasonable for our purposes to use "$p$" to refer both to proportions as well as to probabilities.

Combining this way of thinking about probability with our knowledge of the theoretical normal curve allows us to estimate the likelihood of selecting a case that has a score within a certain range. For example, suppose we wished to estimate the probability that a randomly chosen subject from the distribution of men's IQ scores would have an IQ score between 95 and a mean score of 100. Our definition of a success would be the selection of any subject with a score in the specified range. Normally, we would next establish a fraction with the numerator equal to the number of subjects with scores in the defined range and the denominator equal to the total number of subjects. However, if the empirical distribution is normal in form, we can skip this step since the probabilities, in proportion form, are already stated in Appendix A. *That is, the areas in Appendix A can also be interpreted as probabilities.*

To determine the probability that a randomly selected case will have a score between 95 and the mean, we would convert the original score to a $Z$ score:

$$Z = \frac{X_i - \overline{X}}{s} = \frac{95 - 100}{20} = \frac{-5}{20} = -0.25$$

Using Appendix A, we see that the area between this score and the mean is 0.0987. This is the probability we are seeking. The probability that a randomly selected case will have a score between 95 and 100 is 0.0987 (or, rounded off, 0.10, or one out of 10). In the same fashion, the probability of selecting a subject from any range of scores can be estimated. Note that the techniques for estimating probabilities are exactly the same as those for finding areas. The only new information introduced in this section is the idea that the areas in the standard normal curve table can also be thought of as probabilities.

Consider an additional example: What is the probability that a randomly selected male will have an IQ less than 123? We will find probabilities in exactly the same way we found areas. The score ($X_i$) is above the mean, and, following the directions in Table 4.4, we will find the probability we are seeking by adding the area in column "b" to 0.5000. First, we find the $Z$ score:

$$Z = \frac{X_i - \overline{X}}{s} = \frac{123 - 100}{20} = \frac{23}{20} = +1.15$$

Next, look in column "b" of Appendix A to find the area between this score and the mean. Then add the area (0.3749) to 0.5000. The probability of selecting a male with an IQ of less than 123 is 0.3749 + 0.5000 or 0.8749. Rounding this value to 0.88, we can say that the odds are 0.88 (very high) that we will select a male with an IQ score in this range.

Technically, remember that this probability expresses what would happen over the long run: for every 100 males selected from this group over an infinite number of trials, 88 would have IQ scores less than 123 and 12 would not.

Let us close by stressing a very important point about probabilities and the normal curve. The probability is very high that any case randomly selected from a normal distribution will have a score close in value to that of the mean. The shape of the normal curve is such that most cases are clustered around the mean and decline in frequency as we move farther away—either to the right or to the left—from the mean value. In fact, given what we know about the normal curve, the probability that a randomly selected case will have a score within ±1 standard deviation of the mean is 0.6826. Rounding off, we can say that 68 out of 100 cases—or about two-thirds of all cases—selected over the long run will have a score between ±1 standard deviation or $Z$ score from the mean. The probabilities are higher that any randomly selected case will have a score close in value to the mean.

---

## Applying Statistics 4.3: Finding Probabilities

The distribution of scores on a political science final exam used in Applying Statistics 4.2 had a mean of 72 and a standard deviation of 8. What is the probability that a student selected at random will have a score less than 61? More than 80? Less than 98? To answer these questions, we must first calculate $Z$ scores and then consult Appendix A. We are looking for probabilities, so we will leave the areas in proportion form. The $Z$ score for a score of 61 is

$$Z_1 = \frac{X_i - \overline{X}}{s} = \frac{61 - 72}{8} = \frac{-11}{8} = -1.38$$

This score is a negative value (below, or to the left of, the mean), and we are looking for the area below. Using Table 4.3 as a guide, we see that we must use column "c" to find the area below a negative score. This area is 0.0838. Rounding off, we can say that the odds of selecting a student with a score less than 61 are only 8 out of 100. This low value tells us this would be an unlikely event.

The $Z$ score for the score of 80 is

$$Z_2 = \frac{X_i - \overline{X}}{s} = \frac{80 - 72}{8} = \frac{8}{8} = 1.00$$

The $Z$ score is positive, and to find the area above (greater than) 80, we look in column "c" (see Table 4.3). This value is 0.1587. The odds of selecting a student with a score greater than 80 are roughly 16 out of 100, about twice as likely as selecting a student with a score of less than 61.

The $Z$ score for the score of 98 is

$$Z_1 = \frac{X_i - \overline{X}}{s} = \frac{98 - 72}{8} = \frac{26}{8} = 3.25$$

To find the area below a positive $Z$ score, we add the area between the score and the mean (column "b") to 0.5000 (see Table 4.3). This value is 0.4994 + 0.5000, or 0.9994. It is extremely likely that a randomly selected student will have a score less than 98. Remember that scores more than ±3 standard deviations from the mean are very rare.

---

**ONE STEP AT A TIME**   **Finding Probabilities**

**1:** Compute the $Z$ score (or scores). Note whether the score is positive or negative.
**2:** Find the $Z$ score (or scores) in column "a" of the standard normal curve table (Appendix A).
**3:** Find the area above or below the score (or between the scores) as you would normally

(see the three previous One Step at a Time boxes in this chapter) and express the result as a proportion. Typically, probabilities are expressed as a value between 0.00 and 1.00 rounded to two digits beyond the decimal point.

---

In contrast, the probability of the case having a score beyond 3 standard deviations from the mean is very small. Look in column "c" ("Area Beyond $Z$") for a $Z$ score of 3.00 and you will find the value 0.0013. Adding the areas in the upper tail (beyond +3.00) to the area in the lower tail (beyond −3.00) gives us 0.0013 + 0.0013 for a total of 0.0026. The probability of selecting a case with a very high score or a very low score is 0.0026. If we randomly selected cases from a normally distributed variable, we would select cases with $Z$ scores beyond ±3.00 only 26 times out of every 10,000 trials.

The general point to remember is that cases with scores close to the mean are common and cases with scores far above or below the mean are rare. This relationship is central for an understanding of inferential statistics. As a final note, a supplement containing a more detailed and methodical discussion of probability has been added to our website. The supplement should be read in conjunction with Section 4.6, and not as a replacement for it. *(For practice in using the normal curve table to find probabilities, see problems 4.12 to 4.14 and 4.17.)*

## SUMMARY

**1.** The normal curve, in combination with the mean and standard deviation, can be used to construct precise descriptive statements about empirical distributions that are normally distributed. This chapter also lays some important groundwork for Part 2.

**2.** To work with the theoretical normal curve, raw scores must be transformed into their equivalent $Z$ scores. $Z$ scores allow us to find areas under the theoretical normal curve (Appendix A).

**3.** We considered three uses of the theoretical normal curve: finding total areas above and below a score, finding areas between two scores, and expressing these areas as probabilities. This last use of the normal curve is especially important because inferential statistics are centrally concerned with estimating the probabilities of defined events in a fashion very similar to the process introduced in Section 4.6.

**SUMMARY OF FORMULAS**

| | | |
|---|---|---|
| $Z$ scores | 4.1 | $Z = \dfrac{X_i - \overline{X}}{s}$ |

**GLOSSARY**

**Normal curve.** A bell-shaped theoretical distribution of scores that is unimodal and symmetrical. The standard normal curve always has a mean of 0 and a standard deviation of 1.

**Probability.** A ratio of the number of successes to the number of possible events.

**Standard normal curve table.** See Appendix A; a detailed description of the area between a $Z$ score and the mean of any standardized normal distribution.

**Z scores.** Standard scores; the way scores are expressed after they have been standardized to the theoretical normal curve.

**MULTIMEDIA RESOURCES**

nelson.com/student

Visit the companion website for the fourth Canadian edition of *Statistics: A Tool for Social Research* to access a wide range of student resources. Begin by clicking on the Student Resources section of the textbook's website to access online chapters and study tools.

**PROBLEMS**

**4.1** Scores on a quiz were normally distributed and had a mean of 10 and a standard deviation of 3. For each score below, find the $Z$ score and the percentage of area above and below the score.

| $X_i$ | $Z$ Score | % Area Above | % Area Below |
|---|---|---|---|
| 5 | | | |
| 6 | | | |
| 7 | | | |
| 8 | | | |
| 9 | | | |
| 11 | | | |
| 12 | | | |
| 14 | | | |
| 15 | | | |
| 16 | | | |
| 18 | | | |

**4.2** Assume that the distribution of a graduate-school entrance exam is normal with a mean of 500 and a standard deviation of 100. For each score below, find the equivalent $Z$ score, the percentage of the area above the score, and the percentage of the area below the score.

| $X_i$ | $Z$ Score | % Area Above | % Area Below |
|---|---|---|---|
| 650 | | | |
| 400 | | | |
| 375 | | | |
| 586 | | | |
| 437 | | | |
| 526 | | | |
| 621 | | | |
| 498 | | | |
| 517 | | | |
| 398 | | | |

**4.3** A class of final-year students at a university has been given a comprehensive examination to assess their educational experience. The mean on the test was 74 and the standard deviation was 10. What percentage of the students had scores

**a.** between 75 and 85? _____
**b.** between 80 and 85? _____
**c.** above 80? _____
**d.** above 83? _____
**e.** between 80 and 70? _____
**f.** between 75 and 70? _____
**g.** below 75? _____
**h.** below 77? _____
**i.** below 80? _____
**j.** below 85? _____

**4.4** For a normal distribution where the mean is 50 and the standard deviation is 10, what percentage of the area is

**a.** between the scores of 40 and 47? _____
**b.** above a score of 47? _____
**c.** below a score of 53? _____
**d.** between the scores of 35 and 65? _____
**e.** above a score of 72? _____
**f.** below a score of 31 and above a score of 69? _____
**g.** between the scores of 55 and 62? _____
**h.** between the scores of 32 and 47? _____

**4.5** At Algebra University the 200 students enrolled in Introductory Biology took a final exam on which their mean score was 72 and their standard deviation was 6. The table below presents the grades of 10 students. Convert each into a *Z* score and determine the *number of people* who scored higher or lower than each of the 10 students. *(HINT: Multiply the appropriate proportion by n and round the result.)*

| $X_i$ | Z Score | Number of Students Above | Number of Students Below |
|---|---|---|---|
| 60 | | | |
| 57 | | | |
| 55 | | | |
| 67 | | | |
| 70 | | | |
| 72 | | | |
| 78 | | | |
| 82 | | | |
| 90 | | | |
| 95 | | | |

**4.6** If a distribution of test scores is normal with a mean of 78 and a standard deviation of 11, what percentage of the area lies

**a.** below 60? _____
**b.** below 70? _____
**c.** below 80? _____
**d.** below 90? _____
**e.** between 60 and 65? _____
**f.** between 65 and 79? _____
**g.** between 70 and 95? _____
**h.** between 80 and 90? _____
**i.** above 99? _____
**j.** above 89? _____
**k.** above 75? _____
**l.** above 65? _____

**4.7** A scale measuring ageism (age discrimination) has been administered to a large sample of human resources managers at major corporations. The distribution of scores is approximately normal with a mean of 31 and a standard deviation of 5. What percentage of the sample had scores

**a.** below 20? _____
**b.** below 40? _____
**c.** between 30 and 40? _____
**d.** between 35 and 45? _____
**e.** above 25? _____
**f.** above 35? _____

**4.8** At Matrix University, second-year co-op students are asked how many days they were required to work off-site during a four-month period. If the number of days is normally distributed, with a mean of 18 and a standard deviation of 3, what is the raw score number of days of a student

**a.** whose *Z* score is 3? _____
**b.** whose *Z* score is 2? _____
**c.** whose *Z* score is 1? _____

**4.9** On a career preparation aptitude test, you are told that your score is at the 99th percentile in math and analytical reasoning. If the test scores are normally distributed, what is your raw score if

**a.** the mean is 1,000 and the standard deviation is 50? _____
**b.** the mean is 100 and the standard deviation is 10? _____

**4.10** On the same career preparation aptitude test, a second test writer's score is at the 35th percentile on mathematics and analytical reasoning. If the test scores are normally distributed, what is the second test writer's raw score if
  **a.** the mean is 1,000 and the standard deviation is 50? _____
  **b.** the mean is 100 and the standard deviation is 10? _____

**4.11** On the same career preparation aptitude test, a third test writer's score is at the 50th percentile on mathematics and analytical reasoning. If the test scores are normally distributed, what is the third test writer's raw score if
  **a.** the mean is 1,000 and the standard deviation is 50? _____
  **b.** the mean is 100 and the standard deviation is 10? _____

**4.12** The average burglary rate for a jurisdiction has been 311 per year with a standard deviation of 50. What is the probability that next year the number of burglaries will be
  **a.** less than 250? _____
  **b.** less than 300? _____
  **c.** more than 350? _____
  **d.** more than 400? _____
  **e.** between 250 and 350? _____
  **f.** between 300 and 350? _____
  **g.** between 350 and 375? _____

**4.13** For a math test on which the mean was 59 and the standard deviation was 4, what is the probability that a student randomly selected from this class will have a score
  **a.** between 55 and 65? _____
  **b.** between 60 and 65? _____
  **c.** above 65? _____
  **d.** between 60 and 50? _____

  **e.** between 55 and 50? _____
  **f.** below 55? _____

**4.14** On the scale mentioned in Problem 4.7, if a score of 40 or more is considered "highly discriminatory," what is the probability that a human resources manager selected at random will have a score in that range?

**4.15** The local police force gives all applicants an entrance exam and accepts only those applicants who score in the top 15% on the exam. If the mean score this year is 87 and the standard deviation is 8, would an individual with a score of 110 be accepted?

**4.16** After taking a city's merit examinations for the positions of social worker and employment counsellor you receive the following information on the tests and on your performance. On which of the tests did you do better?

| Social Worker | Employment Counsellor |
| --- | --- |
| $\overline{X} = 118$ | $\overline{X} = 27$ |
| $s = 17$ | $s = 3$ |
| Your score = 127 | Your score = 29 |

**4.17** In a distribution of scores with a mean of 35 and a standard deviation of 4, which event is more likely: that a randomly selected score will be between 29 and 31 or that a randomly selected score will be between 40 and 42?

**4.18** To be accepted into a university's co-op education program, students must have GPAs in the top 10% of the school. If the mean GPA is 2.78 and the standard deviation is 0.33, which of the following GPAs would qualify?
3.20, 3.21, 3.25, 3.30, 3.35

## Using SPSS to Produce Histograms and Compute *Z* Scores with the 2012 CCHS

The demonstrations and exercises below use the shortened version of the 2012 CCHS data set supplied with this textbook. Start SPSS and open the *CHS_2012_Shortened.sav* file.

### SPSS DEMONSTRATION 4.1 The Histogram

Before we can compute and use *Z* scores and the standard normal curve table (Appendix A), we need to find out if a variable has a normal, bell-shaped curve. The histogram, discussed in Chapter 2, provides a convenient method to display the distribution of a variable. Here we will use the **Histogram** command to show the distribution of *hwtgbmi* (BMI or body mass index). (BMI is a measure of body fat based on a person's weight and height. It is interpreted using a weight classification system that is the same for adult men and women as follows: less than 18.5 = underweight; 18.5–24.9 = normal; 25.0–29.9 = overweight; and 30.0 and over = obese.)

  The SPSS procedure for producing a histogram is very similar to that of the bar chart illustrated in Demonstration 2.2. Click **Graphs**, **Legacy Dialogs**, and then **Histogram**. The **Histogram** dialog box will appear. Select *hwtgbmi* from the variable list on the left, then click the arrow button at the top of the screen to move

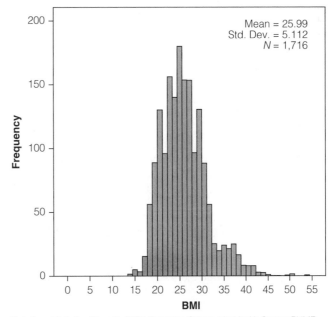

Data from Statistics Canada, 2005 Canadian Community Health Survey, PUMF

*hwtgbmi* to the **Variable** box. Click **OK** in the **Histogram** dialog box, and the histogram for *hwtgbmi* will be produced.

The distribution of *hwtgbmi* is approximately normal in shape. No empirical distribution is perfectly normal, but *hwtgbmi* is close enough to permit the assumption of normality. We can proceed to use the normal curve to convert the original scores of *hwtgbmi* into $Z$ scores.

## SPSS DEMONSTRATION 4.2 Computing $Z$ Scores

The **Descriptives** command introduced in Demonstration 3.2 can also be used to compute $Z$ scores for any variable. These $Z$ scores are then available for further operations and may be used in other tasks. SPSS will create a new variable consisting of the transformed scores of the original variable. The program uses the letter $Z$ with the letters of the variable name to designate the standardized scores of a variable.

In this demonstration, we will have SPSS compute $Z$ scores for *hwtgbmi*. First, click **Analyze**, **Descriptive Statistics**, and **Descriptives**. Find *hwtgbmi* in the variable list and click the arrow to move the variable to the **Variable(s)** box. Find the "**Save standardized values as variables**" option below the variable list and click the checkbox next to it. With this option selected for **Descriptives**, SPSS will compute $Z$ scores for all variables listed in the **Variable(s)** box. Click **OK**, and SPSS will produce the usual set of descriptive statistics for *hwtgbmi*. It will also add the new variable (called *Zhwtgbmi*), which contains the standardized scores for *hwtgbmi*, to the data set. To verify this, run the **Descriptives** command again and you will find *Zhwtgbmi* in the variable list. Transfer *Zhwtgbmi* to the **Variable(s)** box with *hwtgbmi*, then unclick the checkbox next to "**Save standardized values as variables**." Finally, click **OK**. The following output will be produced:

### Descriptive Statistics

|  | $N$ | Minimum | Maximum | Mean | Std. Deviation |
|---|---|---|---|---|---|
| BMI | 1,716 | 13.47 | 54.34 | 25.9907 | 5.11195 |
| $Z$ Score: BMI | 1,716 | −2.44930 | 5.54569 | .0000000 | 1.00000000 |
| Valid $N$ (listwise) | 1,716 |  |  |  |  |

Like any set of $Z$ scores, *Zhwtgbmi* has a mean of 0 and a standard deviation of 1. The new variable *Zhwtgbmi* can be treated just like any other variable and used in any SPSS procedure.

If you would like to inspect the scores of *Zhwtgbmi*, use the **Case Summaries** procedure. Click **Analyze**, **Reports**, and then **Case Summaries**. Move both *hwtgbmi* and *Zhwtgbmi* to the **Variable(s)** box. Be sure the "**Display cases**" checkbox at the bottom of the window is selected. Find the "**Limit cases to first**" option. This option can be used to set the number of cases included in the output. By default, the system lists only the first 100 cases in your file. You can raise or lower the value for "**Limit cases to first**" $n$ cases in your file or deselect this option to list all cases. For this exercise, let's set a limit of 20 cases. Make sure the checkbox to the left of the option is checked and type 20 in the textbox to the right. Click **OK**, and the following output will be produced (note that the output shows that "Total *N*" is 15. While the number of cases is set to 20, these 20 cases actually represent 15 cases. The reason for the difference is that the CCHS data set, as discussed in SPSS Demonstration 3.1, is weighted to correct for sampling bias):

**Case Summaries<sup>a</sup>**

| | BMI | Z Score: BMI |
|---|---|---|
| 1 | 19.70 | −1.23059 |
| 2 | 28.47 | .48500 |
| 3 | 27.05 | .20722 |
| 4 | 29.00 | .58868 |
| 5 | 21.63 | −.85304 |
| 6 | 22.13 | −.75523 |
| 7 | 42.55 | 3.23933 |
| 8 | 24.85 | −.22315 |
| 9 | 21.57 | −.86478 |
| 10 | 32.65 | 1.30269 |
| 11 | 24.92 | −.20945 |
| 12 | 32.04 | 1.18336 |
| 13 | 34.76 | 1.71545 |
| 14 | 27.24 | .24438 |
| 15 | 20.19 | −1.13474 |
| 16 | 27.76 | .34611 |
| 17 | 23.11 | −.56353 |
| 18 | 29.64 | .71387 |
| 19 | 17.87 | −1.58858 |
| 20 | 34.18 | 1.60199 |
| Total *N* | 15 | 15 |

<sup>a</sup>Limited to first 20 cases.

Scan the list of scores and note that the scores that are closer in value to the mean of *hwtgbmi* (25.99), are closer to the mean of *Zhwtgbmi* (.00), and the further away the score is from 25.99, the greater the numerical value of the *Z* score. Also note that, of course, scores below the mean (less than 25.99) have negative signs and scores above the mean (greater than 25.99) have positive signs.

## Exercises (using *CHS_2012_Shortened.sav*)

**4.1** Use the **Histogram** command to get a histogram of *smkdycs*. How close is this curve to a smooth, bell-shaped normal curve? Write a sentence or two of interpretation for the graph.

**4.2** Using Demonstration 4.2 as a guide, compute *Z* scores for *smkdycs*. Use the **Case Summaries** procedure to display the normalized and raw scores for each variable for 20 cases. Write a sentence or two summarizing these results.

## Cumulative Exercises

Cumulative exercises provide practice in choosing, computing, and analyzing statistics. These online exercises present only data sets and research questions. Students choose appropriate statistics as part of the exercise. Cumulative exercises can be found at nelson.com/students.

# Part 2

# From Description to Inference

The two chapters in this part of the textbook cover basic concepts and uses of inferential statistics. Inferential statistics allow us to learn about large groups (populations) from small, carefully selected subgroups (samples). These statistics are powerful and extremely useful. They are used to poll public opinion, research the potential market for new products, project the winners of elections, test the effects of new drugs, and in hundreds of other ways both inside and outside the social sciences.

Chapter 5 looks at the logic and theory behind inferential statistics. The chapter includes a brief description of the sampling technology used to select subgroups so as to justify making inferences to populations. This discussion is intended to give you a general overview of the process, rather than a comprehensive or detailed treatment of the subject. The most important part of this chapter, however, concerns the sampling distribution, the single most important concept in inferential statistics. The sampling distribution is the key link between populations and samples.

There are two main applications in inferential statistics, and Chapter 6 covers the first: using statistical information from a sample (e.g., a mean or a proportion) to estimate the characteristics of a population. The technique is called *estimation*, and it is commonly used in public opinion polling and election projection. Part 3 of the textbook covers the second application of inferential statistics: hypothesis testing.

# 5

# Introduction to Inferential Statistics
## Sampling and the Sampling Distribution

**LEARNING OBJECTIVES**

By the end of this chapter, you will be able to

1. Explain the purpose of inferential statistics in terms of generalizing from a sample to a population.
2. Explain the principle of random sampling and these key terms: population, sample, parameter, statistic, representative, and EPSEM.
3. Differentiate between the sampling distribution, the sample, and the population.
4. Explain the two theorems presented.

## 5.1 INTRODUCTION

One of the goals of social science research is to test our theories and hypotheses using many different populations of people, groups, societies, and historical eras. Obviously, we can have the greatest confidence in theories that have stood up to testing against the greatest variety of populations and social settings. A major problem we often face in social science research, however, is that the populations in which we are interested are too large to test. For example, a theory concerning political party preference among Canadian voters would be most suitably tested using the entire electorate, but it is impossible to interview every member of this group (more than 25 million people). Indeed, even for theories that could be reasonably tested with smaller populations—such as a local community or the student body at a university—the logistics of gathering data from every single case (entire populations) are staggering to contemplate.

If it is too difficult or expensive to do research with entire populations, how can we reasonably test our theories? To deal with this problem, social scientists select samples, or subsets of cases, from the populations of interest. Our goal in inferential statistics is to learn about the characteristics of a population (often called **parameters**), based on what we can learn from our samples. Two applications of inferential statistics are covered in this textbook. In estimation procedures, covered in Chapter 6, a "guess" of the population parameter is made, based on what is known about the sample. In hypothesis testing, covered in Chapters 7 through 13, the validity of a hypothesis about the population is tested against sample outcomes. This chapter looks at the theoretical foundations that underlie these inferential statistics. We begin by looking at the techniques used for selecting cases for a sample, then turn our attention to one of the most important concepts in inferential statistics: the sampling distribution.

## 5.2 PROBABILITY SAMPLING

In this chapter, we will review the basic procedures for selecting probability samples, the only type of sample that fully supports the use of inferential statistical techniques to generalize to populations. These types of samples are often described as "random," and you may be more familiar with this terminology. Because of its greater familiarity, we will often use the phrase "random sample" in the following chapters. The term "probability sample" is preferred, however, because in everyday language, "random" is often used to mean "by coincidence" or to give a connotation of unpredictability. As you will see, probability samples are selected by techniques that are careful and methodical and leave no room for haphazardness. Interviewing the people you happen to meet in a mall one afternoon may be "random" in some sense, but this technique will not result in a sample that could support inferential statistics. (In other words, if your sample is not a probability sample, you will be limited only to descriptive statistical techniques.)

Before considering probability sampling, let us point out that social scientists often use non-probability samples. For example, social scientists studying small group dynamics or the structure of attitudes or personal values might use the students enrolled in their classes as subjects. Such "convenience" samples are very useful for a number of purposes (e.g., exploring ideas or pretesting survey forms before embarking on a more ambitious project) and are typically less costly and easier to assemble. The major limitation of these samples is that results cannot be generalized beyond the group being tested. If a theory of ageism (prejudice, discrimination, and stereotyping of older people and old age), for example, has been tested only on the students who happen to have been enrolled in a particular section of an Introduction to Gerontology course (i.e., a course on the ageing process) at a particular university, we cannot conclude that the theory would be true for other types of people. Therefore, even when the evidence is very strong, we cannot place a lot of confidence in theories tested on nonprobability samples only.

The goal of probability sampling is to select cases so that the final sample is **representative** of the population from which it was drawn. A sample is representative if it reproduces the important characteristics of the population. For example, if the population consists of 60% females and 40% males, the sample should contain essentially the same proportions. In other words, a representative sample is very much like the population—only smaller. It is crucial for inferential statistics that samples be representative; if they are not, generalizing to the population becomes, at best, extremely hazardous.

How can we assure ourselves that our samples are representative? Unfortunately, it is not possible to guarantee that our samples will meet this crucial criterion. However, we can maximize the chances of a representative sample by following the principle of **EPSEM** (the "**E**qual **P**robability of **SE**lection **M**ethod"), the fundamental principle of probability sampling. To follow the EPSEM principle, we select the sample so that every element or case in the population has an equal probability of being selected. Our goal is to select a representative sample, and the technique we use to achieve it is to follow the rule of EPSEM.

The most basic EPSEM sampling technique produces a **simple random sample**. There are variations and refinements on this technique such as the systematic, stratified, and cluster sampling techniques, which are covered in a supplemental chapter on the website for this textbook. Here we will consider only simple random sampling.

To draw a simple random sample, we need a list of all elements or cases in the population and a system for selecting cases from the list that will guarantee that every case has an equal chance of being selected for the sample. The selection process could be based on a number of different kinds of operations such as drawing cards from a well-shuffled deck, flipping coins, throwing dice, or drawing numbers from a hat; however, cases are often selected by using tables of random numbers. These tables are lists of numbers that have no pattern to them (i.e., they are random). An example of such a table is available on the website for this textbook.

To use the table of random numbers, first assign each case on the population list a unique identification number. Then, select cases for the sample when their identification number corresponds to the number chosen from the table. This procedure will produce an EPSEM sample because the numbers in the table are in random order and any number is just as likely to be chosen as any other number. Stop selecting cases when you have reached your desired sample size and, if an identification number is selected more than once, ignore the repeats.*

Remember that the EPSEM selection technique and the representativeness of the final sample are two different things. In other words, the fact that a sample is selected according to EPSEM does not guarantee that the sample will be an exact representation or microcosm of the population. The probability is very high that an EPSEM sample will be representative, but just as a perfectly honest coin will sometimes show 10 heads in a row when flipped, an EPSEM sample will occasionally present an inaccurate picture of the population. One of the great strengths of inferential statistics is that they allow the researcher to estimate the probability of this type of error and interpret results accordingly.

To summarize, the purpose of inferential statistics is to acquire knowledge about populations, based on information derived from samples of that population. *Each of the statistics to be presented in the following chapters requires that samples be selected according to EPSEM.* While EPSEM

---

*Ignoring identification numbers when they are repeated is called "sampling without replacement." Technically, this practice compromises the randomness of the selection process. However, if the sample is a small fraction of the total population, we will be unlikely to select the same case twice and ignoring repeats will not bias our conclusions.

sampling techniques, of which simple random sampling is the most basic form, do not guarantee representativeness, the probability is high that EPSEM samples will be representative of the populations from which they are selected.

## 5.3 THE SAMPLING DISTRIBUTION

Once we have selected a probability sample, what do we know? On the one hand, we can gather a great deal of information from the cases in the sample. On the other, we know nothing about the population. Indeed, if we had information about the population, we probably wouldn't need the sample. Remember that we use inferential statistics to learn more about populations, and information from the sample is important primarily insofar as it allows us to generalize to the population.

When we use inferential statistics, we generally measure some variable (e.g., age, political party preference, or opinions about global warming) in the sample and then use the information from the sample to learn more about that variable in the population. In Part 2 of this textbook, you learned that three types of information are generally necessary to adequately characterize a variable: (1) the shape of its distribution, (2) some measure of central tendency, and (3) some measure of dispersion. Clearly, all three kinds of information can be gathered (or computed) on a variable from the cases in the sample. Just as clearly, none of the information is available for the population. Except in rare situations (e.g., IQ and height are thought to be approximately normal in distribution), nothing can be known about the exact shape of the distribution of a variable in the population. The means and standard deviations of variables in the population are also unknown. Let us remind you that if we had this information for the population, inferential statistics would be unnecessary.

In statistics, we link information from the sample to the population with a device known as the **sampling distribution**, the theoretical, probabilistic distribution of a statistic for all possible samples of a certain sample size ($n$). That is, the sampling distribution includes statistics that represent every conceivable combination of cases (i.e., every possible sample) from the population. A crucial point about the sampling distribution is that its characteristics are based on the laws of probability, not on empirical information, and are very well known. In fact, the sampling distribution is the central concept in inferential statistics, and a prolonged examination of its characteristics is certainly in order.

As illustrated by Figure 5.1, the general strategy of all applications of inferential statistics is to move between the sample and the population via the sampling distribution. Thus, three separate and distinct distributions are involved in every application of inferential statistics:

1. The sample distribution, which is empirical (i.e., it exists in reality) and known in the sense that the shape, central tendency, and dispersion

**FIGURE 5.1** **The Relationship Between the Sample, Sampling Distribution, and Population**

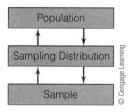

of any variable can be ascertained for the sample. Remember that the information from the sample is important primarily insofar as it allows the researcher to learn about the population.

2. The population distribution, which, while empirical, is unknown. Amassing information about or making inferences to the population is the sole purpose of inferential statistics.

3. The sampling distribution, which is non-empirical or theoretical. Because of the laws of probability, a great deal is known about this distribution. Specifically, the shape, central tendency, and dispersion of the distribution can be deduced and, therefore, the distribution can be adequately characterized.

The utility of the sampling distribution is implied by its definition. Because it encompasses all possible sample outcomes, the sampling distribution enables us to estimate the probability of any particular sample outcome, a process that will occupy our attention for the next five chapters.

The sampling distribution is theoretical, which means it is obtained hypothetically but not in practice. However, to understand better the structure and function of the distribution, let's consider an example of how one might be constructed. Suppose we wanted to gather some information about the age of a particular community of 10,000 individuals. We draw an EPSEM sample of 100 residents, ask all 100 respondents their age, and use those individual scores to compute a mean age of 27. This score is noted on the graph in Figure 5.2. Note that this sample is one of countless possible combinations of 100 people taken from this population of 10,000 and that the mean of 27 is one of millions of possible sample outcomes.

Now, replace the 100 respondents in the first sample, draw another sample of the same size ($n = 100$), and again compute the average age. Assume that the mean for the second sample is 30, and note this sample outcome on Figure 5.2. This second sample is another of the countless possible combinations of 100 people taken from this population of 10,000, and the sample mean of 30 is another of the millions of possible sample outcomes. Replace the respondents from the second sample and draw still another sample. Calculate and note the mean, replace this third sample,

**FIGURE 5.2   Constructing a Sampling Distribution**

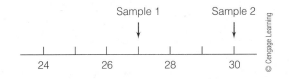

and draw a fourth sample, continuing these operations an infinite number of times, calculating and noting the mean of each sample. Now, try to imagine what Figure 5.2 would look like after tens of thousands of individual samples had been collected and the mean had been computed for each sample. What shape, mean, and standard deviation would this distribution of sample means have after we had collected all possible combinations of 100 respondents from the population of 10,000?

For one thing, we know that each sample will be at least slightly different from every other sample, because it is very unlikely that we will sample exactly the same 100 people twice. Because each sample will almost certainly be a unique combination of individuals, each sample mean will be at least slightly different in value. We also know that even though the samples are chosen according to EPSEM, they will not be representative of the population in every single case. For example, if we continue taking samples of 100 people long enough, we will eventually choose a sample that includes only the very youngest residents. Such a sample would have a mean much lower than the true population mean. Likewise, some of our samples will include only senior citizens and will have means that are much higher than the population mean. Common sense suggests, however, that such non-representative samples will be rare and that most sample means will cluster around the true population value.

To illustrate further, assume that we somehow come to know that the true mean age of the population is 30. As we have seen above, most of the sample means will also be approximately 30 and the sampling distribution of these sample means should peak at 30. Some of the sample means will "miss the mark," but the frequency of such misses should decline as we get farther away from 30. That is, the distribution should slope to the base as we get farther away from the population value—sample means of 29 or 31 should be common; means of 20 or 40 should be rare. Because the samples are random, the means should miss an equal number of times on either side of the population value, and the distribution itself should therefore be roughly symmetrical. In other words, the sampling distribution of all possible sample means should be approximately normal and will resemble the distribution presented in Figure 5.3. Recall from Chapter 4 that, on any normal curve, cases close to the mean (say, within $\pm 1$ standard deviation) are common and cases far from the mean (say, beyond $\pm 3$ standard deviations) are rare.

FIGURE 5.3   A Sampling Distribution of Sample Means

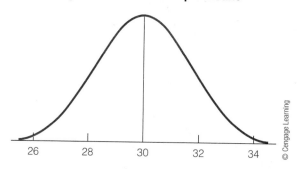

26    28    30    32    34

© Cengage Learning

These commonsense notions about the shape of the sampling distribution and other very important information about central tendency and dispersion are stated in two theorems. The first of these theorems states:

> If repeated random samples of size $n$ are drawn from a normal population with mean $\mu$ and standard deviation $\sigma$, then the sampling distribution of sample means will be normal with a mean $\mu$ and a standard deviation of $\sigma/\sqrt{n}$.

To translate: If we begin with a trait that is normally distributed across a population (IQ, height, or weight, for example) and take an infinite number of equally sized random samples from that population, then the sampling distribution of sample means will be normal. If it is known that the variable is distributed normally in the population, it can be assumed that the sampling distribution will be normal.

The theorem tells us more than the shape of the sampling distribution of all possible sample means, however. It also defines its mean and standard deviation. In fact, it says that the mean of the sampling distribution will be exactly the same value as the mean of the population. That is, if we know that the mean IQ of the entire population is 100, then we know that the mean of any sampling distribution of sample mean IQs will also be 100. Exactly why this should be so is explained and demonstrated in Section 5.4. Recall for now, however, that most sample means will cluster around the population value over the long run. Thus, the fact that these two values are equal should have intuitive appeal. As for dispersion, the theorem says that the standard deviation of the sampling distribution, also called the **standard error**, will be equal to the standard deviation of the population divided by the square root of $n$ (symbolically: $\sigma/\sqrt{n}$).

If the mean and standard deviation of a normally distributed population are known, the theorem allows us to compute the mean and standard deviation of the sampling distribution. Thus, we will know exactly as much about the sampling distribution (shape, central tendency, and dispersion) as we ever knew about any empirical distribution.

In the typical research situation, the values of the population mean and standard deviation are, of course, unknown. However, these values can nevertheless be estimated from sample statistics, as we shall see in the chapters that follow.

The first theorem requires a normal population distribution. What happens when the distribution of the variable in question is unknown or is known to not be normal in shape (such as income, which always has a positive skew)? These eventualities (very common, in fact) are covered by a second theorem, called the **Central Limit Theorem**:

> If repeated random samples of size $n$ are drawn from any population, with mean $\mu$ and standard deviation $\sigma$, then, as $n$ becomes large, the sampling distribution of sample means will approach normality, with mean $\mu$ and standard deviation $\sigma/\sqrt{n}$.

To translate: For *any* trait or variable, even those that are not normally distributed in the population, as sample size grows larger, the sampling distribution of sample means will become normal in shape.

The importance of the Central Limit Theorem is that it removes the constraint of normality in the population. Whenever the sample size is large, we can assume that the sampling distribution is normal, with a mean equal to the population mean and a standard deviation equal to $\sigma/\sqrt{n}$ regardless of the shape of the variable in the population. Thus, even if we are working with a variable that is known to have a skewed distribution (like income), we can still assume a normal sampling distribution.

The issue remaining, of course, is to define what is meant by a large sample. A good general rule is that if sample size ($n$) is 100 or more, the Central Limit Theorem applies, and you can assume that the sampling distribution is normal in shape. When $n$ is less than 100, you must have good evidence of a normal population distribution before you can assume that the sampling distribution is normal. Thus, a normal sampling distribution can be ensured by the expedient of using fairly large samples.

## 5.4 CONSTRUCTING THE SAMPLING DISTRIBUTION

Developing an understanding of the sampling distribution—what it is and why it's important—is often one of the more challenging tasks for beginning students of statistics. It may be helpful to briefly list the most important points about the sampling distribution:

1. Its definition: *The sampling distribution is the distribution of a statistic (like means or proportions) for all possible sample outcomes of a certain size.*
2. Its shape: *Normal* (see Appendix A).
3. Its central tendency and dispersion: *The mean of the sampling distribution is the same value as the mean of the population. The standard deviation of the sampling distribution—or the standard error—is equal to the population standard deviation divided by the square root of n. (See the previous theorems.)*

**TABLE 5.1  Calculating the Mean and Standard Deviation of the Population**

| Case | $(X_i)$ | Deviations $(X_i - \mu)$ | Deviations Squared $(X_i - \mu)^2$ |
|------|---------|--------------------------|-----------------------------------|
| 1 | 2 | $2 - 5 = -3.0$ | 9 |
| 2 | 4 | $4 - 5 = -1.0$ | 1 |
| 3 | 6 | $6 - 5 = 1.0$ | 1 |
| 4 | 8 | $8 - 5 = 3.0$ | 9 |
| | $\Sigma(X_i) = 20$ | $\Sigma(X_i - \mu) = 0.0$ | $\Sigma(X_i - \mu)^2 = 20$ |

$$\mu = \frac{\Sigma(X_i)}{N} = \frac{20}{4} = 5 \,(\text{Formula } 3.5)$$

$$\sigma = \sqrt{\frac{\Sigma(X_i - \mu)^2}{N}} = \sqrt{\frac{20}{4}} = \sqrt{5} = 2.236 \,(\text{Formula } 3.9)$$

To reinforce these points, we will construct a sampling distribution from hypothetical data. Suppose we have a population of four people and are interested in the amount of money each person has in his or her possession. (The number of cases in this problem is kept very small to simplify the computations.) We find that the first person in our population has $2, the second person has $4, the third person has $6, and the fourth person has $8. So this population has a mean, $\mu$, of $5 and a standard deviation, $\sigma$, of $2.236, as calculated in Table 5.1.

Recall that the sampling distribution of sample means is the theoretical distribution of the mean for all possible samples of a certain sample size ($n$), with a mean, $\mu$, and a standard deviation of $\sigma/\sqrt{n}$. So let us derive the sampling distribution of sample means for $n = 2$—that is, draw every conceivable combination (every possible sample) of two people from our population of four people. In order to draw every possible sample, sampling with replacement must be used; we randomly select a person from the population, replace that person back in the population, and then again randomly select a person from the population. Hence, we end up drawing several "odd"-looking samples as the same person can be selected twice into the same sample.

In a population of four people, there will be 16 theoretical samples of two people (i.e., when $n = 2$, there are only $4 \times 4$, or 16, possible samples). With 16 samples, there will be 16 sample means. Table 5.2 presents every possible sample of two people from our population of four people.

In the first sample, the person in our population with $2 in his or her possession was randomly selected twice—this is one of those "odd"-looking samples. The mean for this sample is $2, or $(2 + 2)/2 = 2$. In the second theoretical sample, the first person randomly selected from the population was again the person with $2. This person was replaced back in the population. Next, a second person was randomly selected from the population, which was the person with $4. The mean for this sample is $3, or $(2 + 4)/2 = 3$.

**TABLE 5.2**  **Calculating the Sampling Distribution of Sample Means ($n = 2$)**

|  | Sample Scores | Sample Mean |
|---|---|---|
| 1 | ($2, $2) | $2 |
| 2 | ($2, $4) | $3 |
| 3 | ($2, $6) | $4 |
| 4 | ($2, $8) | $5 |
| 5 | ($4, $2) | $3 |
| 6 | ($4, $4) | $4 |
| 7 | ($4, $6) | $5 |
| 8 | ($4, $8) | $6 |
| 9 | ($6, $2) | $4 |
| 10 | ($6, $4) | $5 |
| 11 | ($6, $6) | $6 |
| 12 | ($6, $8) | $7 |
| 13 | ($8, $2) | $5 |
| 14 | ($8, $4) | $6 |
| 15 | ($8, $6) | $7 |
| 16 | ($8, $8) | $8 |

This process continues until every possible sample of two people from our population of four people has been drawn, as shown in Table 5.2.

With all possible combinations of samples in hand (16 in total), we can build the sampling distribution of sample means. The histogram in Figure 5.4 displays this information. The histogram shows that the sample mean of 5 occurs four times, more than any other mean. We can confirm this by counting the number of times the mean of 5 occurs in Table 5.2. The means of 4 and 6 occur three times each, while the means of 3 and 7 occur twice, and the means of 2 and 8 occur once each. As per the theorems stated in the previous section, Figure 5.4 demonstrates that our sampling distribution of means is symmetrical and approximately normal in shape.

**FIGURE 5.4**  **Sampling Distribution of Sample Means ($n = 2$)**

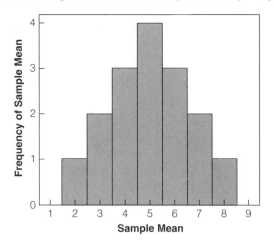

**TABLE 5.3   Calculating the Mean and Standard Deviation of the Sampling Distribution of Sample Means ($n = 2$)**

|  | Sample Mean ($X_i$) | Deviations ($X_i - \mu$) | Deviations Squared ($X_i - \mu)^2$ |
|---|---|---|---|
| 1 | 2 | $2 - 5 = -3.0$ | 9 |
| 2 | 3 | $3 - 5 = -2.0$ | 4 |
| 3 | 4 | $4 - 5 = -1.0$ | 1 |
| 4 | 5 | $5 - 5 = \phantom{-}0.0$ | 0 |
| 5 | 3 | $3 - 5 = -2.0$ | 4 |
| 6 | 4 | $4 - 5 = -1.0$ | 1 |
| 7 | 5 | $5 - 5 = \phantom{-}0.0$ | 0 |
| 8 | 6 | $6 - 5 = \phantom{-}1.0$ | 1 |
| 9 | 4 | $4 - 5 = -1.0$ | 1 |
| 10 | 5 | $5 - 5 = \phantom{-}0.0$ | 0 |
| 11 | 6 | $6 - 5 = \phantom{-}1.0$ | 1 |
| 12 | 7 | $7 - 5 = \phantom{-}2.0$ | 4 |
| 13 | 5 | $5 - 5 = \phantom{-}0.0$ | 0 |
| 14 | 6 | $6 - 5 = \phantom{-}1.0$ | 1 |
| 15 | 7 | $7 - 5 = \phantom{-}2.0$ | 4 |
| 16 | 8 | $8 - 5 = \phantom{-}3.0$ | 9 |
|  | $\Sigma(X_i) = \overline{80}$ | $\Sigma(X_i - \mu) = \overline{0.0}$ | $\Sigma(X_i - \mu)^2 = \overline{40}$ |

$$\mu = \frac{\Sigma(X_i)}{N} = \frac{80}{16} = 5 \text{ (Formula 3.5)}$$

$$\sigma = \sqrt{\frac{\Sigma(X_i - \mu)^2}{N}} = \sqrt{\frac{40}{16}} = \sqrt{2.5} = 1.581 \text{ (Formula 3.9)}$$

The theorems also tell us that the mean of the sampling distribution will be exactly the same value as the mean of the population and that the standard deviation of the sampling distribution will be equal to the standard deviation of the population divided by the square root of $n (\sigma/\sqrt{n})$. This is proved in Table 5.3.

Comparing Table 5.3 and Table 5.1, we see that the mean of the sampling distribution, 5, is exactly the same as the mean of the population, 5. We also see that the standard deviation of the sampling distribution, 1.581, is equal to the standard deviation of the population divided by the square root of $n$. That is, the population standard deviation, 2.236, divided by the square root of 2, or $2.236/\sqrt{2}$, is 1.581, which is identical to the standard deviation of the sampling distribution.

As further proof, Figure 5.5 shows the sampling distribution of sample means for $n = 3$. (Note that in a population of four people, when sample size equals three, there are $4 \times 4 \times 4$, or 64, possible samples.) We see that the mean of this sampling distribution is also 5 and that it is approximately normal in shape. However, in comparison to Figure 5.4, we see that the sampling distribution for $n = 3$ is less variable or spread out. That is, the standard deviation of this sampling distribution is equal to 1.291, or $2.236/\sqrt{3}$.

**FIGURE 5.5   Sampling Distribution of Sample Means ($n = 3$)**

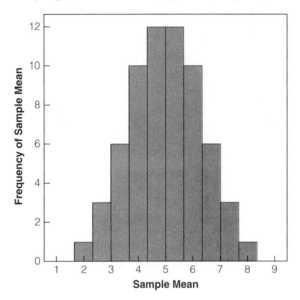

In conclusion, we have confirmed the three fundamental components of the theorems in Section 5.3. First, the sampling distribution is normal if either the sample size is large ($n = 100$ or more) or the shape of the distribution of the variable in the population is normal. We have seen that a sampling distribution will be approximately normal in shape even with a small sample size of $n = 2$ or 3 and a population of just four cases. Second, the sampling distribution has a mean, $\mu = 5$ in our example, that is identical to the mean of the population. Third, the standard deviation of the sampling distribution of sample means is equal to the standard deviation of the population divided by the square root of $n$.

## 5.5 LINKING THE POPULATION, SAMPLING DISTRIBUTION, AND SAMPLE

The role of the sampling distribution in inferential statistics is to link the sample with the population. In this section we look at how the sampling distribution works together with the sample and the population using the General Social Survey (GSS), the database used for SPSS exercises in this textbook.

We will start with the "population," or the group we are actually interested in and want to learn more about. In the case of the GSS, the population consists of all Canadians (aged 15 and older) living in private households in the 10 provinces. This includes about 29 million people. Clearly, we can never interview all of these people and learn what they are like or their views on various social issues.

What can be done to learn more about this huge population? This brings us to the concept of "sample," a carefully chosen subset of the population.

The GSS is administered to about 27,000 people, each of whom is chosen by a sophisticated technique that is ultimately based on the principle of EPSEM. The respondents are contacted at home and asked for background information (e.g., age, gender, years of education) as well as their behaviours, opinions, or attitudes regarding selected social issues. When all of this information is collated, the GSS database includes information on hundreds of variables for the people in the sample.

So we have a lot of information about the variables for the sample (the 27,000 or so people who actually respond to the survey), but no information about these variables for the population (the 29 million Canadians aged 15 and older living in private households in the 10 provinces). How do we go from the known characteristics of the sample to the unknown population?

This is the central question of inferential statistics, and the answer is "by using the sampling distribution." Remember that, unlike the sample and the population, the sampling distribution is a theoretical device. However, we can work with the sampling distribution because its shape, central tendency, and dispersion are defined by the theorems presented earlier in this chapter. First, for any variable from the GSS, we know that the sampling distribution will be normal in shape because the sample is "large" ($n$ is much greater than 100). Second, the theorems tell us that the mean of the sampling distribution will be the same value as the mean of the population. If all Canadians aged 15 and older living in private households in the 10 provinces met on average 3.29 people in the past month ($\mu = 3.29$), the mean of the sampling distribution will also be 3.29. Third, the theorems tell us that the standard deviation (or standard error) of the sampling distribution is equal to the population standard deviation ($\sigma$) divided by the square root of $n$. Therefore, the theorems tell us the statistical characteristics of this distribution (shape, central tendency, and dispersion), and this information allows us to link the sample to the population.

How does the sampling distribution link the sample to the population? It is crucial to know that the sampling distribution will be normal when $n$ is large. This means that more than two-thirds (68%) of all samples will be within $\pm 1$ standard deviation (i.e., standard error) of the mean (which is the same value as the population parameter), that about 95% are within $\pm 2$ standard deviations, and so forth. We do not (and cannot) know the actual value of the mean of the sampling distribution because it is impractical to draw every conceivable combination (i.e., every possible sample) of 27,000 Canadians from the population of 29 million Canadians living in private households in the 10 provinces. However, there is no need to draw all possible samples because the theorems give us crucial information about the mean and standard error of the sampling distribution that we can use to link the sample to the population. In practice, as you will see in the following chapters, we draw just one sample and use this information (i.e., that the sampling distribution of all possible sample means will be normal, with a mean equal to the population mean and a standard deviation equal to the population standard deviation divided by the square root of $n$) to link the sample to the population.

To summarize, we have focused on the GSS to see the roles played by the population, sample, and sampling distribution. Our goal is to infer information about the population (all Canadians aged 15 and older living in private households in the 10 provinces). When populations are too large to test (and contacting 29 million Canadians is far beyond the capacity of even the most energetic pollster), we use information from carefully drawn probability samples to estimate the characteristics of the population—the full sample of the GSS consists of about 27,000 Canadians aged 15 and older living in private households in the 10 provinces. The sampling distribution, the theoretical distribution whose characteristics are defined by the theorems, links the known sample to the unknown population.

## 5.6 SYMBOLS AND TERMINOLOGY

In the following chapters, we will be working with three entirely different distributions (i.e., the sample distribution, the population distribution, and the sampling distribution). The purpose of inferential statistics is to acquire knowledge of the population from information gathered from a sample by means of the sampling distribution. Furthermore, while we have focused on the sampling distribution of sample means, other statistics such as the sample proportion, which the Central Limit Theorem applies to, also have a sampling distribution.

To distinguish clearly among these various distributions, we will often use symbols. The symbols used for the means and standard deviations of samples and populations have already been introduced in Chapter 3. In this chapter, we have also used these population symbols for the sampling distribution for convenience. However, Table 5.4 provides new symbols for this distribution, denoted with Greek letter symbols that are subscripted according to the sample statistic of interest.

To read this table, note that the mean and standard deviation of a sample are denoted with Roman letters ($\overline{X}$ and $s$), while the mean and standard deviation of a population are denoted with the Greek letter equivalents ($\mu$ and $\sigma$). Proportions calculated on samples are symbolized as $P$-sub-$s$ ($s$ for sample),

**TABLE 5.4**  **Symbols for Means and Standard Deviations of Three Distributions**

|  | Mean | Standard Deviation | Proportion |
|---|---|---|---|
| 1. Samples | $\overline{X}$ | $s$ | $P_s$ |
| 2. Populations | $\mu$ | $\sigma$ | $P_u$ |
| 3. Sampling distributions |  |  |  |
| of means | $\mu_{\overline{X}}$ | $\sigma_{\overline{X}}$ |  |
| of proportions | $\mu_p$ | $\sigma_p$ |  |

© Cengage Learning

while population proportions are denoted as $P$-sub-$u$ ($u$ for the "universe" of the population). The symbols for the sampling distribution are Greek letters with Roman letter subscripts. The mean and standard deviation of a sampling distribution of sample means are "mu-sub-$x$-bar" and "sigma-sub-$x$-bar." The mean and standard deviation of a sampling distribution of sample proportions are "mu-sub-$p$" and "sigma-sub-$p$."

While only the mean and proportion have been mentioned here, the list of statistics which have a sampling distribution that the Central Limit Theorem applies to can be extended even further. Altogether, this textbook will examine four sampling distributions: the $Z$ distribution (also called the standard normal distribution), the Student's $t$ distribution, the chi-square distribution, and the $F$-ratio distribution.

## SUMMARY

1. Because populations are almost always too large to test, a fundamental strategy of social science research is to select a sample from the defined population and then use information from the sample to generalize to the population. This is done either by estimation or by hypothesis testing.

2. Researchers choose simple random samples by selecting cases from a list of the population following the rule of EPSEM (each case has an equal probability of being selected). Samples selected by the rule of EPSEM have a very high probability of being representative.

3. The sampling distribution, the central concept in inferential statistics, is a theoretical distribution of all possible sample outcomes. Because its overall shape, mean, and standard deviation are known (under the conditions specified in the two theorems), the sampling

distribution can be adequately characterized and utilized by researchers.

4. The two theorems that were introduced in this chapter state that when the variable of interest is normally distributed in the population or when sample size is large, the sampling distribution will be normal in shape, with its mean equal to the population mean and its standard deviation (or standard error) equal to the population standard deviation divided by the square root of $n$.

5. All applications of inferential statistics involve generalizing from the sample to the population by means of the sampling distribution. Both estimation procedures and hypothesis testing incorporate the three distributions, and it is crucial that you develop a clear understanding of each distribution and its role in inferential statistics.

## GLOSSARY

**Central Limit Theorem.** A theorem that specifies the mean, standard deviation, and shape of the sampling distribution, given that the sample is large.

**EPSEM.** The **E**qual **P**robability of **SE**lection **M**ethod for selecting samples. Every element or case in the population must have an equal probability of selection for the sample.

**Parameter.** A characteristic of a population.

**Representative.** The quality a sample is said to have if it reproduces the major characteristics of the population from which it was drawn.

**Sampling distribution.** The distribution of a statistic for all possible sample outcomes of a certain size. Under conditions specified in two theorems, the sampling distribution will be normal in shape with a mean equal to the population value and a standard deviation equal to the population standard deviation divided by the square root of $n$.

**Simple random sample.** A method for choosing cases from a population by which every case has an equal chance of being included.

**Standard error.** The standard deviation of a sampling distribution.

## MULTIMEDIA RESOURCES

  nelson.com/student

Visit the companion website for the fourth Canadian edition of *Statistics: A Tool for Social Research* to access a wide range of student resources. Begin by clicking on the Student Resources section of the textbook's website to access online chapters and study tools.

## PROBLEMS

**5.1** This exercise is extremely tedious and hardly ever works out the way it ought to (mostly because not many people have the patience to draw an "infinite" number of even very small samples). However, if you want a more concrete and tangible understanding of sampling distributions and the two theorems presented in this chapter, then this exercise may have a significant payoff. Below are listed the ages of a population of students at a very small community college ($N = 50$). By a random method (such as a table of random numbers), draw at least 50 samples of size 2 (i.e., 50 pairs of cases), compute a mean for each sample, and plot the means on a frequency polygon. (Incidentally, this exercise will work better if you draw 100 or 200 samples and/or use larger samples than $n = 2$.)

   **a.** The curve you've just produced is a sampling distribution. Observe its shape; after 50 samples, it should be approaching normality. What is your estimate of the population mean ($\mu$) based on the shape of the curve?

   **b.** Calculate the mean of the sampling distribution ($\mu_{\bar{X}}$). Be careful to do this by summing the sample means (not the scores) and dividing by the number of samples you've drawn. Now compute the population mean ($\mu$). These two means should be very close in value because ($\mu_{\bar{X}}$) $= \mu$ by the Central Limit Theorem.

   **c.** Calculate the standard deviation of the sampling distribution (use the means as scores)

and the standard deviation of the population. Compare these two values. You should find that the two standard deviations are very close in value because $\sigma_{\bar{X}} = \sigma/\sqrt{n}$.

   **d.** If none of the above exercises turned out as they should have, it is for one or more of the following reasons:

     **1.** You didn't take enough samples. You may need as many as 100 or 200 (or more) samples to see the curve begin to look "normal."

     **2.** Sample size (2) is too small. An $n$ of 5 or 10 would work much better.

     **3.** Your sampling method is not truly random and/or the population is not arranged in random fashion.

| | | | | |
|---|---|---|---|---|
| 17 | 20 | 20 | 19 | 20 |
| 18 | 21 | 19 | 20 | 19 |
| 19 | 22 | 19 | 23 | 19 |
| 20 | 23 | 18 | 20 | 20 |
| 22 | 19 | 19 | 20 | 20 |
| 23 | 17 | 18 | 21 | 20 |
| 20 | 18 | 20 | 19 | 20 |
| 22 | 17 | 21 | 21 | 21 |
| 21 | 20 | 20 | 20 | 22 |
| 18 | 21 | 20 | 22 | 21 |

## Using SPSS to Draw Random Samples with the 2012 CCHS

The demonstration and exercise below use the shortened version of the 2012 CCHS data. Start SPSS and open the *CCHS_2012_Shortened.sav* file.

### SPSS DEMONSTRATION 5.1 Estimating Average BMI

SPSS includes a procedure for drawing random samples from a database. We can use this procedure to illustrate some points about sampling and to convince the skeptics in the crowd that properly selected samples will produce statistics that are close approximations of the corresponding population values or parameters. For purposes of this demonstration, the CCHS sample will be treated as a population and its characteristics will be treated as parameters.

The instructions below will calculate a mean for *hwtgbmi* (BMI or body mass index) for three random samples of different sizes drawn from the CCHS sample. The actual average BMI score of the sample (which will be the parameter or $\mu$) is 25.99 (see Demonstration 3.2). The samples are roughly 10%, 25%, and 50% of the population size, and the program selects them by a process that is quite similar to a table of random numbers. Therefore, these samples may be considered "simple random samples."

As a part of this procedure we also request the "standard error of the mean" or S.E. mean. This is the standard deviation of the sampling distribution of sample means ($\sigma_{\bar{x}}$) for a sample of this size. This statistic will be of interest because we can expect our sample means to be within this distance of the population value or parameter.

With the *CCHS_2012_Shortened.sav* file loaded, click **Data** from the menu bar of the **Data Editor** window and then click **Select Cases**. The **Select Cases** window appears and presents a number of different options. To select random samples, check the circle next to "**Random sample of cases**" and then click on the **Sample** button. The **Select Cases: Random Sample** dialog box will open. We can specify the size of the sample in two different ways. If we use the first option, we can specify that the sample will include a certain percentage of cases in the database. The second option allows us to specify the exact number of cases in the sample. Let's use the first option and request a 10% sample by typing 10 into the box on the first line. Click **Continue**, and then click **OK** on the **Select Cases** window. The sample will be selected and can now be processed.

To find the mean income for the 10% sample, click **Analyze**, **Descriptive Statistics**, and then **Descriptives**. The **Descriptives** dialog box will be open. Find *hwtgbmi* in the variable list and transfer it to the **Variable(s)** box. On the **Descriptives** dialog box, click the **Options** button and select **S.E. mean** in addition to the usual statistics. Click **Continue** and then **OK**, and the requested statistics will appear in the output window.

Now, to produce a 25% sample, return to the **Select Cases** window by clicking **Data** and **Select Cases**. Click the **Reset** button at the bottom of the window and then click **OK** and the full data set ($N^* = 1,500$) will be restored. Repeat the

*Note that we are using upper-case $N$ here, instead of lower-case $n$, because we are treating the CCHS data set as a population in this exercise.

procedure we followed for selecting the 10% sample. Click the button next to "**Random sample of cases**" and then click on the **Sample** button. The **Select Cases: Random Sample** window will open. Request a 25% sample by typing 25 in the box, click **Continue** and **OK**, and the new sample will be selected.

Run the **Descriptives** procedure for the 25% sample (don't forget **S.E. mean**) and note the results. Finally, repeat these steps for a 50% sample. The results are summarized below:

| Sample % | Sample Size | Sample Mean | Standard Error | Sample Mean ± Standard Error |
|----------|-------------|-------------|----------------|------------------------------|
| 10       | 152         | 27.24       | 0.50           | 26.74 – 27.74                |
| 25       | 400         | 26.51       | 0.26           | 26.25 – 26.77                |
| 50       | 822         | 25.96       | 0.18           | 25.78 – 26.14                |

Notice that the standard error of the mean (i.e., the standard deviation of the sampling distribution of sample means) decreases as sample size increases. This should reinforce the commonsense notion that larger samples will provide more accurate estimates of population values. All three samples produced estimates (sample means) that are quite close in value to the population value of 25.99. However, the largest sample is the most accurate or closest to the true population value of 25.99, only 0.03 lower.

This demonstration should reinforce one of the main points of this chapter: Statistics calculated on samples that have been selected according to the principle of EPSEM will (almost always) be reasonable approximations of their population counterparts.

## Exercise (using *CCHS_2012_Shortened.sav*)

**5.1** Following the procedures in Demonstration 5.1, select three samples from the 2012 CCHS database (*CCHS_2012_Shortened.sav*): 15%, 30%, and 60%. Get descriptive statistics for *hwtgbmi* (don't forget to get the standard error), and use the results to complete the following table:

| Sample % | Sample Size | Sample Mean | Standard Error | Sample Mean ± Standard Error |
|----------|-------------|-------------|----------------|------------------------------|
| 15       | _____      | _____      | _____         | _____                       |
| 30       | _____      | _____      | _____         | _____                       |
| 60       | _____      | _____      | _____         | _____                       |

Summarize these results. What happens to standard error as sample size increases? Why? How accurate are the estimates (sample means)? Are all sample means within a standard error of 25.99? How does the accuracy of the estimates change as sample size changes?

# 6

# Estimation Procedures for Sample Means and Proportions

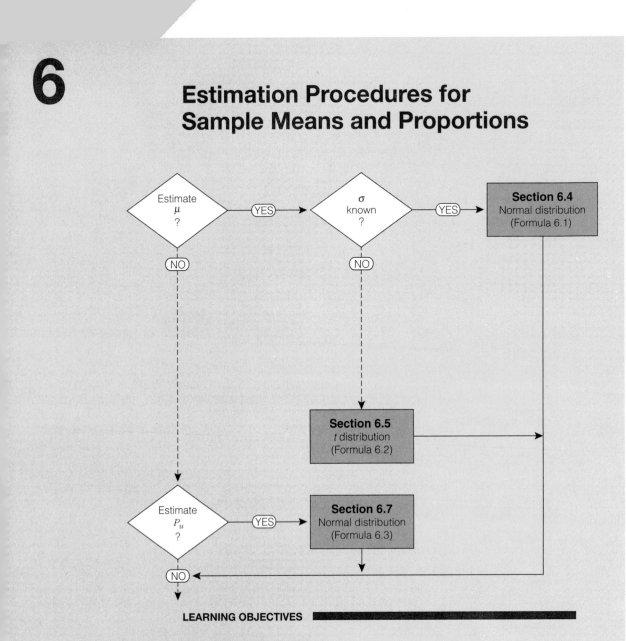

**LEARNING OBJECTIVES**

By the end of this chapter, you will be able to

1. Explain the logic of estimation and the role of the sample, sampling distribution, and population.

2. Define and explain the concepts of bias and efficiency.

3. Construct and interpret confidence intervals for sample means and sample proportions.

4. Use the error bar to graph a confidence interval.

5. Explain the relationships between confidence level, sample size, and the width of the confidence interval.

6. Determine the number of people needed in a sample to get a desired confidence interval.

## 6.1 INTRODUCTION

This chapter looks at estimation procedures. The  object of this branch of inferential statistics is to estimate population values or parameters from statistics computed from samples. Although the techniques presented in this chapter may be new to you, you are certainly familiar with their most common applications: public opinion polls and election projections. Polls and surveys on every conceivable issue—from the sublime to the trivial—have become a staple of the mass media and popular culture. The techniques you will learn in this chapter are essentially the same as those used by the most reputable, sophisticated, and scientific pollsters.

There are two kinds of estimation procedures. First, a **point estimate** is a sample statistic that is used to estimate a population value. For example, a newspaper story that reports that 50% of a sample of randomly selected Canadian drivers are driving less than usual due to high gas prices is reporting a point estimate. The second kind of estimation procedure involves **confidence intervals**, which consist of a range of values (an interval) instead of a single point. Rather than estimating a specific figure as in a point estimate, an interval estimate might be phrased as "between 47% and 53% of Canadian drivers report driving less than usual due to high gas prices." In this latter estimate, we are estimating that the population value falls between 47% and 53%, but we do not specify its exact value. Half the size (width) of the confidence interval, which in this example is half the percentage-point difference between 47% and 53%, or 3%, is called the radius of the confidence interval, or the **margin of error**, or simply sampling error.

## 6.2 BIAS AND EFFICIENCY

Both point and interval estimation procedures are based on sample statistics. Which of the many available sample statistics should be used? Estimators can be selected according to two criteria: **bias** and **efficiency**. Estimates should be based on sample statistics that are unbiased and relatively efficient. We will cover each of these criteria separately.

**Bias.**   An estimator is unbiased if, and only if, the mean of its sampling distribution is equal to the population value of interest. We know from the theorems presented in Chapter 5 that sample means conform to this criterion. The mean of the sampling distribution of sample means (which we note symbolically as $\mu_{\overline{X}}$) is the same as the population mean ($\mu$).

Sample proportions ($P_s$) are also unbiased. That is, if we calculate sample proportions from repeated random samples of size $n$ and then array them in a frequency polygon, the sampling distribution of sample proportions will have a mean ($\mu_p$) equal to the population proportion ($P_u$). Thus, if we are concerned with coin flips and sample honest coins 10 at a time ($n = 10$), the sampling distribution will have a mean equal to 0.5, which is the probability that an honest coin will be heads (or tails) when flipped.

However, other statistics are biased (i.e., have sampling distributions with means not equal to the population value).*

Knowing that sample means and proportions are unbiased allows us to determine the probability that they lie within a given distance of the population values we are trying to estimate. To illustrate, consider a specific problem. Assume that we wish to estimate the average household income of a community. A random sample of 500 households is taken ($n = 500$), and a sample mean of $75,000 is computed. In this example, the population mean is the average income of *all* households in the community and the sample mean is the average income for the 500 households that happened to be selected for our sample. Note that we do not know the value of the population mean ($\mu$)—if we did, we wouldn't need the sample—but it is $\mu$ that we are interested in. The sample mean of $75,000 is important and interesting primarily insofar as it can give us information about the population mean.

The two theorems presented in Chapter 5 give us a great deal of information about the sampling distribution of all possible sample means. Because $n$ is large, we know that the sampling distribution is normal and that its mean is equal to the population mean. We also know that all normal curves contain about 68% of the cases (the cases here are sample means) within $\pm 1$ $Z$ (i.e., $\pm 1$ standard deviation), 95% of the cases within $\pm 2$ $Z$'s ($\pm 2$ standard deviations), and more than 99% of the cases within $\pm 3$ $Z$'s ($\pm 3$ standard deviations) of the mean. Remember that we are discussing the sampling distribution here—the distribution of all possible sample outcomes or, in this instance, sample means. Thus, the probabilities are very good (approximately 68 out of 100 chances) that our sample mean of $75,000 is within $\pm 1$ $Z$, excellent (95 out of 100) that it is within $\pm 2$ $Z$'s, and overwhelming (99 out of 100) that it is within $\pm 3$ $Z$'s of the mean of the sampling distribution (which is the same value as the population mean). These relationships are graphically depicted in Figure 6.1.

If an estimator is unbiased, it is probably an accurate estimate of the population parameter ($\mu$ in this case). However, in less than 1% of the cases, a sample mean will be more than $\pm 3$ $Z$'s away from the mean of the sampling distribution (very inaccurate) by random chance alone. We literally have no idea if our particular sample mean of $75,000 is in this small minority. We do know, however, that the odds are high that our sample mean is considerably closer than $\pm 3$ $Z$'s to the mean of the sampling distribution and, thus, to the population mean.

*In particular, the sample standard deviation ($s$) is a biased estimator of the population standard deviation ($\sigma$). As you might expect, there is less dispersion in a sample than in a population and, as a consequence, $s$ will underestimate ($\sigma$). As we shall see, however, the sample standard deviation can be corrected for this bias and still serve as an estimate of the population standard deviation.

**FIGURE 6.1** **Areas Under the Sampling Distribution of Sample Means**

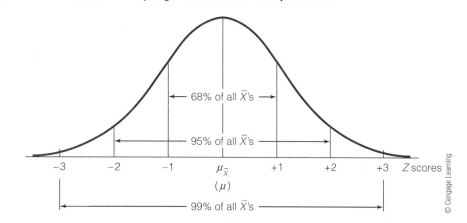

**Efficiency.** The second desirable characteristic of an estimator is efficiency, which is the extent to which the sampling distribution is clustered about its mean. Efficiency or clustering is essentially a matter of dispersion, as we saw in Chapter 3 (see Figure 3.1). The smaller the standard deviation of a sampling distribution, the greater the clustering and the higher the efficiency. Remember that the standard deviation of the sampling distribution of sample means, or the standard error of the mean, is equal to the population standard deviation divided by the square root of $n$. Therefore, the standard deviation of the sampling distribution is an inverse function of $n$ ($\sigma_{\overline{X}} = \sigma/\sqrt{n}$). As sample size increases, $\sigma_{\overline{X}}$ will decrease. We can improve the efficiency (or decrease the standard deviation of the sampling distribution) for any estimator by increasing sample size.

An example should make this clearer. Consider two samples of different sizes:

| Sample 1 | Sample 2 |
|---|---|
| $\overline{X}_1 = \$75,000$ | $\overline{X}_2 = \$75,000$ |
| $n_1 = 100$ | $n_2 = 1,000$ |

Both sample means are unbiased, but which is the more efficient estimator? Consider sample 1 and assume, for the sake of illustration, that the population standard deviation ($\sigma$) is \$5,000.* In this case, the standard deviation of the sampling distribution of all possible sample means with an $n$ of 100 would be or $\sigma/\sqrt{n}$ or $5000/\sqrt{100}$ or \$500.00. For sample 2, the standard deviation of all possible sample means with an $n$ of 1,000 would be much smaller. Specifically, it would be equal to $5000/\sqrt{1000}$ or \$158.11.

---

*In reality, of course, the value of the population standard deviation is rarely known.

**FIGURE 6.2** **A Sampling Distribution with $n = 100$ and $\sigma_{\bar{x}} = \$500.00$**

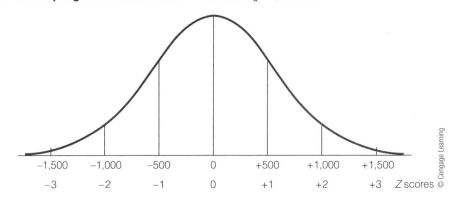

**FIGURE 6.3** **A Sampling Distribution with $n = 1,000$ and $\sigma_{\bar{x}} = \$158.11$**

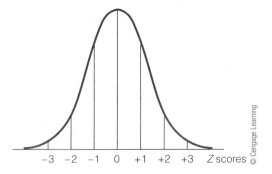

Sampling distribution 2 is much more clustered than sampling distribution 1. In fact, distribution 2 contains 68% of all possible sample means within $\pm 158.11$ of $\mu$ while distribution 1 requires a much broader interval of $\pm 500.00$ to do the same. The estimate based on a sample with 1,000 cases is much more likely to be close in value to the population parameter than is an estimate based on a sample of 100 cases. Figures 6.2 and 6.3 illustrate these relationships graphically.

To summarize: the standard deviation of all sampling distributions is an inverse function of $n$. Therefore, the larger the sample, the greater the clustering and the higher the efficiency. In part, these relationships between sample size and the standard deviation of the sampling distribution do nothing more than underscore our commonsense notion that much more confidence can be placed in large samples than in small (as long as both have been randomly selected).

## 6.3 ESTIMATION PROCEDURES: INTRODUCTION

The procedure for constructing a point estimate is straightforward. Draw an EPSEM sample, calculate either a proportion or a mean, and estimate that the population parameter is the same as the sample statistic. Remember that the larger the sample, the greater the efficiency and the more likely that the estimator is approximately the same as the population value. Also remember that, no matter how rigid the sampling procedure or how large the sample, there is always some chance that the estimator is very inaccurate.

Compared to point estimates, interval estimates are more complicated but safer because when we guess a range of values, we are more likely to include the population parameter. The first step in constructing an interval estimate is to decide on the risk you are willing to take of being wrong. An interval estimate is wrong if it does not include the population parameter. This probability of error is called **alpha** (symbolized as $\alpha$). The exact value of alpha will depend on the nature of the research situation, but a 0.05 probability is commonly used. Setting alpha equal to 0.05, also called using the 95% **confidence level**, means that over the long run the researcher is willing to be wrong only 5% of the time.* Or, to put it another way, if an infinite number of intervals were constructed at this alpha level (and with all other things being equal), 95% of them would contain the population value and 5% would not. In reality, of course, only one interval is constructed and, by setting the probability of error very low, we are setting the odds in our favour that the interval will include the population value.

The second step is to picture the sampling distribution, divide the probability of error equally into the upper and lower tails of the distribution, and then find the corresponding $Z$ score. For example, if we decided to set alpha equal to 0.05, we would place half (0.025) of this probability in the lower tail and half in the upper tail of the distribution. The sampling distribution would thus be divided as illustrated in Figure 6.4.

**FIGURE 6.4   The Sampling Distribution with Alpha ($\alpha$) Equal to 0.05**

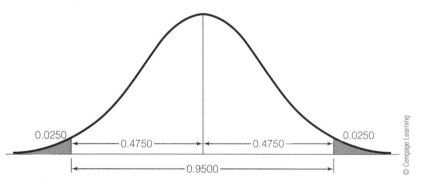

*Notice that the level of confidence is usually stated as a percentage, while the level of alpha is usually stated as a proportion.

**FIGURE 6.5**    Finding the *Z* Score That Corresponds to an Alpha (*α*) of 0.05

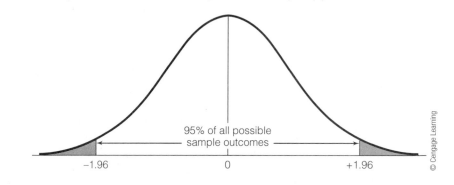

We need to find the *Z* score that marks the beginnings of the shaded areas. In Chapter 4, we learned how to calculate *Z* scores and find areas under the normal curve. Here, we will reverse that process. We need to find the *Z* score beyond which lies a proportion of 0.0250 of the total area. To do this, go down column "c" of Appendix A until you find this proportion (0.0250). The associated *Z* score is 1.96. Because the curve is symmetrical and we are interested in both the upper and lower tails, we designate the *Z* score that corresponds to an alpha of 0.05 as ±1.96 (see Figure 6.5).

We now know that 95% of all possible sample outcomes fall within ±1.96 *Z*-score units of the population value. In reality, of course, there is only one sample outcome, but if we construct an interval estimate based on +1.96 *Z*'s, the probabilities are that 95% of all such intervals will include or overlap the population value. Thus, we can be 95% confident that our interval contains the population value.

Besides the 95% level, there are three other commonly used confidence levels: the 90% level (*α* = 0.10), the 99% level (*α* = 0.01), and the 99.9% level (*α* = 0.001). To find the corresponding *Z* scores for these levels, follow the procedures outlined above for an alpha of 0.05. Table 6.1 summarizes all the information you will need.

**TABLE 6.1**    *Z* Scores for Various Levels of Alpha (*α*)

| Confidence Level (%) | Alpha | *α*/2 | *Z* Score |
| --- | --- | --- | --- |
| 90 | 0.10 | 0.0500 | ±1.65 |
| 95 | 0.05 | 0.0250 | ±1.96 |
| 99 | 0.01 | 0.0050 | ±2.58 |
| 99.9 | 0.001 | 0.0005 | ±3.29 |

You should turn to Appendix A and confirm for yourself that the $Z$ scores in Table 6.1 do indeed correspond to these alpha levels. As you do, note that, in the cases where alpha is set at 0.10 and 0.01, the precise areas we seek do not appear in the table. For example, with an alpha of 0.10, we would look in column "c" ("Area beyond") for the area 0.0500. Instead we find an area of 0.0505 ($Z = \pm1.64$) and an area of 0.0495 ($Z = \pm1.65$). The $Z$ score we are seeking is somewhere between these two other scores. When this condition occurs, take the larger of the two scores as $Z$. This will make the interval as wide as possible under the circumstances and is thus the most conservative course of action. In the case of an alpha of 0.01, we encounter the same problem (the exact area 0.0050 is not in the table), resolve it the same way, and take the larger score as $Z$. Finally, note that in the case where alpha is set at 0.001, we can choose from several $Z$ scores. Although our table is not detailed enough to show it, the closest $Z$ score to the exact area we want is $\pm3.291$, which we can round off to $\pm3.29$. *(For practice in finding $Z$ scores for various levels of confidence, see Problem 6.3.)*

The third step is to actually construct the confidence interval. In the following two sections, we illustrate how to construct an interval estimate with sample means; in Section 6.7, we show how to construct an interval estimate with sample proportions.

## 6.4 INTERVAL ESTIMATION PROCEDURES FOR SAMPLE MEANS ($\sigma$ KNOWN)

The formula for constructing a confidence interval based on sample means is given in Formula 6.1:

**FORMULA 6.1**

$$\text{c.i.} = \overline{X} \pm Z\left(\frac{\sigma}{\sqrt{n}}\right)$$

where c.i. = confidence interval

$\overline{X}$ = the sample mean

$Z$ = the $Z$ score as determined by the alpha level

$\dfrac{\sigma}{\sqrt{n}}$ = the standard deviation of the sampling distribution or the standard error of the mean

As an example, suppose you wanted to estimate the average IQ of a community and had randomly selected a sample of 200 residents, with a sample mean IQ of 105. Assume that the population standard deviation for IQ scores is 15, so we can set $\sigma$ equal to 15. If we are willing to run a 5%

chance of being wrong and set alpha at 0.05, the corresponding $Z$ score will be $\pm 1.96$. These values can be directly substituted into Formula 6.1, and an interval can be constructed

$$\text{c.i.} = \overline{X} \pm Z \left( \frac{\sigma}{\sqrt{n}} \right)$$

$$\text{c.i.} = 105 \pm 1.96 \left( \frac{15}{\sqrt{200}} \right)$$

$$\text{c.i.} = 105 \pm 1.96 \left( \frac{15}{14.14} \right)$$

$$\text{c.i.} = 105 \pm (1.96)(1.06)$$

$$\text{c.i.} = 105 \pm 2.08$$

That is, our estimate is that the average IQ for the population in question is somewhere between 102.92 (105 − 2.08) and 107.08 (105 + 2.08). Since 95% of all possible sample means are within $\pm 1.96$ $Z$'s (or 2.08 IQ units in this case) of the mean of the sampling distribution, the odds are very high that our interval will contain the population mean. In fact, even if the sample mean is as far off as $\pm 1.96$ $Z$'s (which is unlikely), our interval will still contain $\mu_{\overline{X}}$ and, thus, $\mu$. Only if our sample mean is one of the few that is more than $\pm 1.96$ $Z$'s from the mean of the sampling distribution will we have failed to include the population mean.

A word of caution is in order about sample size. Larger samples (i.e., samples with 100 or more cases) are large enough for the Central Limit Theorem to be applied. This is not the case for smaller samples (samples with fewer than 100 cases). To use the standardized normal ($Z$) distribution to construct confidence intervals for means based on small samples, we must assume that the population from which the sample is taken is normally distributed. Recall from Chapter 5 that we can assume that the sampling distribution is normal in shape if either the sample size is large—and the Central Limit Theorem is invoked—or the population is normally distributed. *(For practice with confidence intervals for sample means using the standard normal distribution, see Problems 6.1a –6.1c.)*

**6.5 INTERVAL ESTIMATION PROCEDURES FOR SAMPLE MEANS ($\sigma$ UNKNOWN)**

In the previous example, the value of the population standard deviation was known. Needless to say, it is unusual to have such information about a population. In the vast majority of cases, we will have no knowledge of $\sigma$. In these cases, however, we can estimate $\sigma$ with $s$, the sample standard deviation. Because $s$ is only an estimate of $\sigma$, the formula for constructing a confidence interval must be slightly revised. The revised formula for cases in which $\sigma$ is unknown is

**FORMULA 6.2**

$$\text{c.i.} = \overline{X} \pm t\left(\frac{s}{\sqrt{n-1}}\right)$$

where c.i. = confidence interval

$\overline{X}$ = the sample mean

$t$ = the $t$ score as determined by the alpha level and $n - 1$ degrees of freedom

$\dfrac{s}{\sqrt{n-1}}$ = the estimated standard error of the mean, when $\sigma$ is unknown

In comparing this formula with Formula 6.1, note that there are three changes. First, $\sigma$ is replaced by $s$. Second, the denominator of the last term is the square root of $n - 1$ rather than the square root of $n$, to correct for the fact that $s$ is biased estimator of $\sigma$ (see Section 6.2 for a discussion on bias). Third, to construct confidence intervals from sample means when $\sigma$ is unknown, we must use a different theoretical distribution, called the **Student's $t$ distribution**, to find areas under the sampling distribution.

The Student's $t$ distribution compensates for the fact that we are estimating the unknown $\sigma$ with $s$, and so its shape varies as a function of sample size—the larger the sample, the more accurate the estimate—or more specifically as a function of *degrees of freedom* (symbolized as $df$).* When we use the $t$ distribution to construct a confidence interval around a sample mean, the degrees of freedom are equal to $n - 1$. So, there is a "family" of $t$ sampling distributions, and the value of $df$ defines a specific "member" of this family (i.e., it defines the shape of the $t$ distribution).

**FIGURE 6.6    The $Z$ Distribution and the $t$ Distribution for Selected Degrees of Freedom ($df$)**

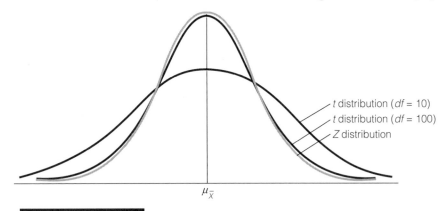

*Degrees of freedom are the number of values in a distribution that are free to vary. When constructing a confidence interval around a sample mean, a distribution has $n - 1$ degrees of freedom. This means that for a specific value of the mean, $n - 1$ scores are free to vary. For example, if the mean is 3 for a group of five scores, the distribution has $5 - 1$, or 4 degrees of freedom. When four of the scores are known, the fifth is fixed. If the four scores are 1, 2, 3, and 4, the fifth must be 5 and no other value.

The relative shapes of the $Z$ distribution and two specific $t$ distributions are depicted in Figure 6.6. For the smaller sample ($df = 10$), the $t$ distribution is flatter and has heavier tails (i.e., more area in the tails) than the $Z$ distribution, but, as sample size increases ($df = 100$), the $t$ distribution begins to resemble the $Z$ distribution. The $Z$ and $t$ distributions are essentially identical when sample size is greater than 100. As $n$ increases, the sample standard deviation becomes a more reliable estimator of the population standard deviation, and so the $t$ distribution becomes more like the $Z$ distribution.

The $t$ distribution is summarized in Appendix B. The $t$ table differs from the $Z$ table in several ways. First, there is a column on the left side of the table labelled "Degrees of Freedom" ($df$). As mentioned above, the exact shape of the $t$ distribution—and thus the exact location of the $t$ score corresponding to our chosen alpha level—varies as a function of sample size (degrees of freedom). Degrees of freedom must first be computed before the $t$ score for any alpha can be located. Second, alpha levels are arrayed across the top of Appendix B in two rows. When we are forming confidence intervals using $t$, we always use the row labelled "Level of Significance for Two-Tailed Test." Third, the entries in the table are actual $t$ scores, and not areas under the sampling distribution. *(For practice in finding t scores for various levels of confidence, see Problem 6.4.)*

To illustrate the use of this table, let's find the $t$ score for alpha $= 0.05$ and $n = 30$. First, we calculate the degrees of freedom ($df$), which are $n - 1$ or 29. Next, we scroll down the "Level of Significance for Two-Tailed Test" column at the 0.05 alpha level until we reach the appropriate row, or $df = 29$. This value, $\pm 2.045$, is the $t$ score.

Take a moment to notice an additional feature of the $t$ table. Scan the column for an alpha of 0.05, and note that, for one degree of freedom, the $t$ score is $\pm 12.706$ and that the value of the $t$ score decreases as degrees of freedom increase. For degrees of freedom greater than 120, the value of $t$ is the same as the comparable value of $Z$, or $\pm 1.96$. As sample size increases, the $t$ distribution comes to resemble the $Z$ distribution more and more until, with sample sizes greater than 120, the two distributions are essentially identical (see Figure 6.6).*

To demonstrate the construction of confidence intervals for sample means using the $t$ distribution, let's suppose you want to estimate the average IQ of a community using a randomly selected sample of 30 residents. From this sample, we find a mean IQ score of 105 and a standard deviation of 15, which we will use as an estimate of the population standard deviation. If we are willing to run a 5% chance of being wrong and set alpha at 0.05, the corresponding $t$ score

---

*Appendix B abbreviates the $t$ distribution by presenting a limited number of $t$ scores for degrees of freedom between 31 and 120. If the degrees of freedom for a specific problem equal 77 and alpha equals 0.05, two-tailed, we have a choice between a $t$ score of $\pm 2.000$ ($df = 60$) and a $t$ score of $\pm 1.980$ ($df = 120$). In situations such as these, take the larger table value as $t$. This will result in a wider confidence interval and is therefore the more conservative course of action.

will be 2.045, as we found previously. These values can be directly substituted into Formula 6.2, and an interval can be constructed.

$$\text{c.i.} = \overline{X} \pm t\left(\frac{s}{\sqrt{n-1}}\right)$$

$$\text{c.i.} = 105 \pm 2.045\left(\frac{15}{\sqrt{30-1}}\right)$$

$$\text{c.i.} = 105 \pm 2.045\left(\frac{15}{5.39}\right)$$

$$\text{c.i.} = 105 \pm 2.045(2.78)$$

$$\text{c.i.} = 105 \pm 5.69$$

---

### Applying Statistics 6.1: Estimating a Population Mean

Based on a random sample of 10,811 households, the 2009 Survey of Household Spending (SHS; a survey conducted by Statistics Canada to collect detailed information on the spending patterns of Canadian households) reveals that the average Canadian household spends a total of $70,961 annually. Total expenditure includes consumption of food, shelter, clothing, transportation, recreation, education, tobacco and alcohol products, and so on, as well as personal taxes, personal insurance payments, and pension and other contributions. Given the SHS sample reported a mean annual expenditure of $70,961, what is the estimate of the population mean? The information from the sample is

$$\overline{X} = 70,961$$
$$s = 60,805$$
$$n = 10,811$$

If we set alpha at 0.05, the corresponding $t$ score will be $\pm 1.98$,* and the 95% confidence interval will be

$$\text{c.i.} = \overline{X} \pm t\left(\frac{s}{\sqrt{n-1}}\right)$$

$$\text{c.i.} = 70,961 \pm 1.98\left(\frac{60,805}{\sqrt{10,811-1}}\right)$$

$$\text{c.i.} = 70,961 \pm 1.98\left(\frac{60,805}{103.97}\right)$$

$$\text{c.i.} = 70,961 \pm (1.98)(584.83)$$

$$\text{c.i.} = 70,961 \pm 1,157.96$$

Based on this result, we would estimate the population spends an average of $70,961 \pm $1,157.96 per year. The lower limit of our interval estimate (70,961 − 1,157.96) is 69,803.04, and the upper limit (70,961 + 1,157.96) is 72,118.96. Thus, another way to state the interval would be

$$69,803.04 \le \mu \le 72,118.96$$

The population mean is greater than or equal to $69,803.04 and less than or equal to $72,118.96. Because alpha was set at the 0.05 level, this estimate has a 5% chance of being wrong (i.e., of not containing the population mean).

*Appendix B presents a limited number of degrees of freedom. Because the degrees of freedom for this problem (10,810, or 10,811 − 1) are not shown, we use the next closest degrees of freedom ($df = 120$), which has a $t$ score of $\pm 1.980$ for an alpha level (two-tailed test) equal to 0.05.

Source: Statistics Canada, 2009 *Survey of Household Spending.*

---

**ONE STEP AT A TIME** **Constructing Confidence Intervals for Sample Means Using Formula 6.2**

**1:** Using the table in Appendix B, select an alpha level from the row labelled "Level of Significance for Two-Tailed Test." Next, find the row corresponding to the degrees of freedom $(n - 1)$ to locate the $t$ score.

**2:** Substitute the sample values into Formula 6.2 to construct the confidence interval.

**To Solve Formula 6.2**

**1:** Find the square root of $n - 1$.

**2:** Divide the value you found in step 1 into $s$, the sample standard deviation.

**3:** Multiply the value you found in step 2 by the value of $t$.

**4:** The value you found in step 3 is the radius of the confidence interval. To find the lower and upper limits of the interval, subtract and add this value to the sample mean.

**Interpreting the Confidence Interval**

**1:** Express the confidence interval in a sentence or two that identifies each of these elements:
a. The sample statistic (a mean in this case)
b. The confidence interval
c. Sample size $(n)$
d. The population to which you are estimating
e. The confidence level (e.g., 95%)

---

Based on the sample mean of 105, we would estimate the population mean to be located in the range from 99.31 to 110.69, with only a 5% chance that the actual population mean does not fall in this range.

As a final note, caution must be used when $n$ is less than 100 in constructing confidence intervals using the $t$ distribution. As with the standardized normal $(Z)$ distribution, samples with 100 or more cases are large enough for the Central Limit Theorem to be applied. Samples with fewer than 100 cases require us to assume that the population from which the sample is taken is normally distributed. So, in our example, we must assume that IQ scores are normally distributed in the entire population (community) because sample size is less than 100. Techniques used when this assumption cannot be met are beyond the scope of this text. (*For practice with confidence intervals for sample means using the t distribution, see Problems 6.1d–6.1f, 6.5–6.7, 6.18, and 6.19a–6.19c.*)

**6.6 GRAPHING A CONFIDENCE INTERVAL OF A SAMPLE MEAN**

A confidence interval of a sample mean can be depicted using a graph called the **error bar**. The error bar graph is based on the lower and upper limits of the confidence interval of a sample mean. The construction of an error bar requires a couple of steps. First, the sample mean is plotted with a symbol, such as a dot, at the centre of a graph. Second, a vertical line or "error bar" is drawn from the sample mean to the lower limit of its confidence interval, marked by a small horizontal line. The same is done between the sample mean and the upper limit of the confidence interval. The area bounded by the two error bars is equal to the width of the confidence interval of the sample mean.

Figure 6.7 displays the error bar graph for the 95% confidence interval of the mean IQ of a community, described in Section 6.5. Recall that the average IQ for the random sample of 30 residents is 105, with a standard deviation of 15. At the 95% confidence level, the average IQ for the community as a whole is between 99.31 (105 − 5.69) and 110.69 (105 + 5.69). Graphically, the dot in the middle of the error bar graph represents the sample mean and the vertical line above and below the sample mean represents the upper and lower limits of the confidence interval. *(For practice in constructing and interpreting error bars, see Problem 6.6.)*

**FIGURE 6.7**    **Error Bar Graph for the 95% Confidence Interval of the Mean IQ of a Community**

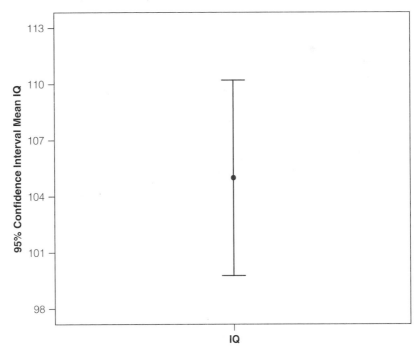

**6.7 INTERVAL ESTIMATION PROCEDURES FOR SAMPLE PROPORTIONS (LARGE SAMPLES)**

Estimation procedures for sample proportions are essentially the same as those for sample means. The major difference is that, because proportions are different statistics, we must use a different sampling distribution. In fact, again based on the Central Limit Theorem (if we have a large sample, $n \geq 100$), we know that sample proportions have sampling distributions that are normal in shape with means ($\mu_p$) equal to the population value ($P_u$) and standard deviations ($\sigma_p$) equal to $\sqrt{P_u( - P_u)/n}$.* The formula for constructing confidence intervals based on sample proportions is

**FORMULA 6.3**

$$\text{c.i.} = P_s \pm Z\sqrt{\frac{P_u(1 - P_u)}{n}}$$

The values for $P_s$ and $n$ come directly from the sample, and the value of $Z$ is determined by the confidence level, as was the case with sample means. This leaves one unknown in the formula, $P_u$—the same value we are trying to estimate. This dilemma can be resolved by setting the value of $P_u$ at 0.5. Because the second term in the numerator under the radical $(1 - P_u)$ is the reciprocal of $P_u$, the entire expression will always have a value of 0.5 × 0.5, or 0.25, which is the maximum value this expression can attain. That is, if we set $P_u$ at any value other than 0.5, the expression $P_u(1 - P_u)$ will decrease in value. If we set $P_u$ at 0.4, for example, the second term $(1 - P_u)$ would be 0.6, and the value of the entire expression would decrease to 0.24. Setting $P_u$ at 0.5 ensures that the expression $P_u(1 - P_u)$ will be at its maximum possible value and, consequently, the interval will be at maximum width. This is the most conservative possible solution to the dilemma posed by having to assign a value to $P_u$ in the estimation equation.

To illustrate these procedures, assume that you wish to estimate the proportion of students at your university who missed at least one day of classes because of illness last semester. Out of a random sample of 200 students, 60 reported that they had been sick enough to miss classes at least one day during the previous semester. The sample proportion upon which we will base our estimate is thus 60/200, or 0.30. At the 95% level of confidence, the interval estimate will be

$$\text{c.i.} = P_s \pm Z\sqrt{\frac{P_u(1 - P_u)}{n}}$$

$$\text{c.i.} = 0.30 \pm 1.96\sqrt{\frac{(0.5)(0.5)}{200}}$$

$$\text{c.i.} = 0.30 \pm 1.96\sqrt{\frac{0.25}{200}}$$

$$\text{c.i.} = 0.30 \pm (1.96)(0.035)$$

$$\text{c.i.} = 0.30 \pm 0.07$$

*We will not consider interval estimation for proportions based on small samples (fewer than 100 cases) in this textbook.

---

### Applying Statistics 6.2: Estimating Population Proportions

Canadians overwhelmingly believe that global warming, produced by greenhouse gases, is a real and major threat to future generations. According to a Leger Marketing survey, 81% of a random sample of 1,500 Canadians said "yes" to the question, "In your view, should the Government of Canada be tougher on Canadian citizens and corporations to ensure that collectively Canadians reduce greenhouse gas emissions?" Based on this finding, what is the estimate of the population value? The sample information is

$$P_s = 0.81$$
$$n = 1,500$$

Note that the percentage of those who said "yes" to the question has been stated as a proportion. If we set alpha at 0.05, the corresponding $Z$ score will be $\pm 1.96$, and the interval estimate of the population proportion will be

$$c.i. = P_s \pm Z\sqrt{\frac{P_u(1 - P_u)}{n}}$$

$$c.i. = 0.81 \pm 1.96\sqrt{\frac{(0.5)(0.5)}{1,500}}$$
$$c.i. = 0.81 \pm 1.96\sqrt{0.00017}$$
$$c.i. = 0.81 \pm (1.96)(0.013)$$
$$c.i. = 0.81 \pm 0.03$$

We can now estimate that the proportion of the population that believes the federal government needs to get tough on citizens and corporations to reduce greenhouse gas emissions is between 0.78 and 0.84. That is, the lower limit of the interval estimate is $(0.81 - 0.03)$ or 0.78, and the upper limit is $(0.81 + 0.03)$ or 0.84. We may also express this result in percentages and say that between 78% and 84% of the population is of the opinion that the government should be tougher on citizens and corporations in order to reduce greenhouse gas emissions. This interval has a 5% chance of not containing the population value.

Source: Leger Marketing, 2005, *Canadians and the Environmental Policies of Canada.*

---

Based on this sample proportion of 0.30, you would estimate that the proportion of students who missed at least one day of classes because of illness was between 0.23 and 0.37. The estimate could, of course, also be phrased in percentages by reporting that between 23% and 37% of the student body was affected by illness at least once during the past semester, at the 95% level of confidence. Additionally, as with the sample mean, the error bar can be used to graph the confidence interval of a sample proportion. *(For practice with confidence intervals for sample proportions, see Problems 6.2, 6.8–6.12, 6.15–6.17, and 6.19d–6.19g.)*

## 6.8 A SUMMARY OF THE COMPUTATION OF CONFIDENCE INTERVALS

To this point, we have covered the construction of confidence intervals using three different formulas. Table 6.2 presents these formulas organized by the situations in which they are used. For sample means with large samples ($n = 100$ or more) or normally distributed populations, when the population standard deviation is known, use

---

**ONE STEP AT A TIME**   **Constructing Confidence Intervals for Sample Proportions**

Begin by selecting an alpha level and finding the associated $Z$ score in Table 6.1. If you use the conventional alpha level of 0.05, the $Z$ score is $\pm 1.96$.

**To Solve Formula 6.3**

**1:** Substitute the value 0.25 for the expression $P_u(1 - P_u)$ in the numerator of the fraction under the square root sign.
**2:** Divide $n$ into 0.25.
**3:** Find the square root of the value you found in step 2.
**4:** Multiply the value you found in step 3 by the value of $Z$.

**5:** The value you found in step 4 is the radius of the confidence interval. To find the lower and upper limits of the interval, subtract and add this value to the sample proportion.

**Interpreting the Confidence Interval**

**1:** Express the confidence interval in a sentence or two that identifies each of these elements:
a. The sample statistic (a proportion in this case)
b. The confidence interval
c. Sample size ($n$)
d. The population to which you are estimating
e. The confidence level (e.g., 95%)

---

**TABLE 6.2   Choosing Formulas for Confidence Intervals**

| If the Sample Statistic Is a | and | | Use Formula | |
|---|---|---|---|---|
| mean | population standard deviation is known **and** $n \geq 100$ or population normally distributed | | 6.1 | c.i. $= \bar{X} \pm Z\left(\dfrac{\sigma}{\sqrt{n}}\right)$ |
| mean | population standard deviation is unknown **and** $n \geq 100$ or population normally distributed | | 6.2 | c.i. $= \bar{X} \pm t\left(\dfrac{s}{\sqrt{n-1}}\right)$ |
| proportion | large sample ($n \geq 100$) | | 6.3 | c.i. $= P_s \pm Z\sqrt{\dfrac{P_u(1 - P_u)}{n}}$ |

Formula 6.1. When the population standard deviation is unknown (which is the usual case), use Formula 6.2. For sample proportions with large samples, always use Formula 6.3.

**6.9 CONTROLLING THE WIDTH OF INTERVAL ESTIMATES**

The radius of a confidence interval for either sample means or sample proportions can be partly controlled by manipulating two terms in the equation. First, the confidence level can be raised or lowered, and second, the interval can be widened or narrowed by gathering samples of different sizes. The researcher alone determines the risk he or she is willing to take of being wrong (i.e., of not including the population value in the interval estimate). The exact confidence level (or alpha level) will depend, in part, on the purpose of the research. For example, if potentially harmful drugs were being tested, the researcher would naturally demand very high levels of confidence (99.99% or even 99.999%). On the other hand, if intervals are being constructed only for loose "guesstimates," then much lower confidence levels can be tolerated (such as 90%).

The relationship between interval size and confidence level is that intervals widen as confidence levels increase. This should make intuitive sense. Wider intervals are more likely to include or overlap the population value; hence, more confidence can be placed in them.

To illustrate this relationship, let us work through a hypothetical problem. The average salary for a random sample of 500 university professors in Canada is $115,000, with a known population standard deviation of $11,000. In constructing a 95% confidence interval, we find that it extends $964.22 above and below the sample mean (i.e., the interval is $115,000 ± $964.22).

If we had constructed the 90% confidence interval for these sample data (a lower confidence level), the $Z$ score in the formula would have decreased to ±1.65, and the interval would have been narrower:

$$\text{c.i.} = \overline{X} \pm Z \left( \frac{\sigma}{\sqrt{n}} \right)$$

$$\text{c.i.} = 115{,}000 \pm 1.65 \left( \frac{11{,}000}{\sqrt{500}} \right)$$

$$\text{c.i.} = 115{,}000 \pm (1.65)(491.95)$$

$$\text{c.i.} = 115{,}000 \pm 811.72$$

On the other hand, if we had constructed the 99% confidence interval, the $Z$ score would have increased to ±2.58, and the interval would have been wider:

$$\text{c.i.} = \overline{X} \pm Z \left( \frac{\sigma}{\sqrt{n}} \right)$$

$$\text{c.i.} = 115{,}000 \pm 2.58 \left( \frac{11{,}000}{\sqrt{500}} \right)$$

$$\text{c.i.} = 115{,}000 \pm (2.58)(491.95)$$

$$\text{c.i.} = 115{,}000 \pm 1{,}269.23$$

At the 99.9% confidence level, the $Z$ score would be $\pm 3.29$, and the interval would be wider still:

$$\text{c.i.} = \overline{X} \pm Z\left(\frac{\sigma}{\sqrt{n}}\right)$$

$$\text{c.i.} = 115{,}000 \pm 3.29\left(\frac{11{,}000}{\sqrt{500}}\right)$$

$$\text{c.i.} = 115{,}000 \pm (3.29)(491.95)$$

$$\text{c.i.} = 115{,}000 \pm 1{,}618.51$$

These four intervals are grouped together in Table 6.3, and the increase in interval size can be readily observed. Although sample means have been used to illustrate the relationship between interval width and confidence level, exactly the same relationships apply to sample proportions. *(To further explore the relationship between alpha and interval width, see Problem 6.13.)*

Sample size bears the opposite relationship to interval width. As sample size increases, interval width decreases. Larger samples give more precise (narrower) estimates. Again, an example should make this clearer. In Table 6.4, confidence intervals for four samples of various sizes are constructed and then grouped together for purposes of comparison. The sample data are the same as in Table 6.3, and the confidence level is 95% throughout. The relationships illustrated in Table 6.4 also hold true, of course, for sample proportions. *(To further explore the relationship between sample size and interval width, see Problem 6.14.)*

Notice that the decrease in interval width (or, increase in precision) does not bear a constant or linear relationship with sample size. With sample 2 as compared to sample 1, the sample size was increased by a factor of 5, but the interval is not five times as narrow. This is an important relationship because it means that $n$ might have to be increased many times to appreciably improve the accuracy of an estimate. Because the cost of a research project is a direct function of sample size, this relationship implies a point of diminishing returns in estimation procedures. A sample of 10,000 will cost about twice as much as a sample of 5,000, but estimates based on the larger sample will not be twice as precise. That having been said, Table 6.4 also

**TABLE 6.3 Interval Estimates for Four Confidence Levels**
**($\overline{X}$ = \$115,000, $\sigma$ = \$11,000, $n$ = 500 throughout)**

| Alpha | Confidence Level (%) | Interval | Interval Width |
|-------|----------------------|----------|----------------|
| 0.10 | 90 | \$115,000 ± 811.72 | \$1,623.44 |
| 0.05 | 95 | \$115,000 ± 964.22 | \$1,928.44 |
| 0.01 | 99 | \$115,000 ± 1,269.23 | \$2,538.46 |
| 0.001 | 99.9 | \$115,000 ± 1,618.51 | \$3,237.02 |

**TABLE 6.4   Interval Estimates for Four Different Samples**
**($\overline{X}$ = \$115,000, $\sigma$ = \$ 11,000, Alpha = 0.05 throughout)**

| Sample 1 ($n$ = 100) | | Sample 2 ($n$ = 500) | |
|---|---|---|---|
| c.i. = \$115,000 ± 1.96(11,000/$\sqrt{100}$)<br>c.i. = \$115,000 ± 2,156 | | c.i. = \$115,000 ± 1.96(11,000/$\sqrt{500}$)<br>c.i. = \$115,000 ± 964.22 | |
| **Sample 3 ($n$ = 1,000)** | | **Sample 4 ($n$ = 10,000)** | |
| c.i. = \$115,000 ± 1.96(11,000/$\sqrt{1,000}$)<br>c.i. = \$115,000 ± 681.85 | | c.i. = \$115,000 ± 1.96(11,000/$\sqrt{10,000}$)<br>c.i. = \$115,000 ± 215.60 | |
| **Sample** | **$n$** | **Interval Width** | |
| 1 | 100 | \$4,312.00 | |
| 2 | 500 | \$1,928.44 | |
| 3 | 1,000 | \$1,363.70 | |
| 4 | 10,000 | \$ 431.20 | |

shows that the largest relative benefit for narrowing a confidence interval can be obtained by increasing the size of a small sample even by a fairly modest (and therefore more affordable) amount.

## 6.10 DETERMINING SAMPLE SIZE

Have you ever wondered how researchers or pollsters decide how many people to include in a random sample when conducting a survey or poll? Well, they use a process similar to "reverse engineering." That is, they determine how many people are needed in a random sample to obtain a desired confidence interval. For instance, a gerontologist wants to estimate the mean income of senior citizens in Canada. How many seniors would she have to sample to be 99% confident that the sample mean is within plus or minus \$1,000 (margin of error) of the population mean, where previous research showed that the population standard deviation is \$5,000 (lacking knowledge of $\sigma$, she can replace it with $s$, the sample standard deviation, if available). Or, what sample size would a public opinion pollster need if she wanted to know what proportion of Canadians support reinstating the death penalty for murder within plus or minus 3% with a 95% certainty? We can solve these problems by simply rearranging the formulas for constructing a confidence interval.

For the mean, Formula 6.4 finds the minimum sample size needed in a simple random sample to get results with the desired level of precision:

**FORMULA 6.4**

$$n = \frac{Z^2 \times \sigma^2}{ME^2}$$

where $n$ = required sample size

$Z$ = Z score as determined by the alpha level

$\sigma$ = population standard deviation

$ME$ = margin of error

Using this formula the gerontologist can calculate the $n$ she needs for a 99% confidence interval, where $Z$ equals 2.58 and the margin of error is 1,000:

$$n = \frac{Z^2 \times \sigma^2}{ME^2}$$

$$n = \frac{2.58^2 \times 5,000^2}{1,000^2}$$

$$n = \frac{6.6564 \times 25,000,000}{1,000,000}$$

$$n = \frac{166,410,000}{1,000,000}$$

$$n = 166.41$$

The gerontologist needs to randomly sample, rounding up, at least 167 senior citizens to be 99% confident that the sample mean will be within plus or minus $1,000 of the population mean, that is, the mean income of all senior citizens in Canada.

For the proportion, Formula 6.5 finds the smallest sample size required to get the desired results in a simple random sample:

**FORMULA 6.5**

$$n = \frac{Z^2 \times (P_u \times (1 - P_u))}{ME^2}$$

where $n$ = required sample size

$Z$ = Z score as determined by the alpha level

$P_u$ = population proportion

$ME$ = margin of error

With this formula, the public opinion pollster can calculate the $n$ she needs for a 95% confidence interval, where $Z$ equals 1.96 and (expressed as proportions) a margin of error of 0.03 and $P_u$ set to 0.5:

$$n = \frac{Z^2 \times (P_u \times (1 - P_u))}{ME^2}$$

$$n = \frac{1.96^2 \times (0.5 \times 0.5)}{0.03^2}$$

$$n = \frac{3.8416 \times 0.25}{0.0009}$$

$$n = \frac{0.9604}{0.0009}$$

$$n = 1,067.11$$

So, at least 1,068 Canadians need to be randomly sampled for the pollster to be 95% confident that the sample proportion will be within plus or minus 0.03 of the population proportion.

The information in this example might sound familiar. Pollsters typically report their findings to the media with this information in a footnote, telling us that their estimate is "accurate within ±3%, 19 times out of 20" or that the "margin of error for a sample of 1,068 is ±3%, 19 times out of 20."

This example also reveals why political polls tend to randomly sample only 1,000 or so people—it is not necessary to have a sample much larger than around 1,000 because we are already 95% confident that our sample results will have a high level of precision, with a margin of error of just plus or minus 3%. Furthermore, and as noted in the previous section, the relationship between sample size and level of precision is not linear. That is to say that doubling the sample size, for instance, will not cut in half the margin of error. Doubling the sample size from 1,068 to 2,136 cuts the margin of error from ±3% to just ±2.1%. A relatively small increase in precision may not justify the cost associated with doubling sample size.

As a final note, Formulas 6.4 and 6.5 are used to determine sample size of a simple random sample when the population of interest is very large, typically a population size of 100,000 or more. Otherwise these formulas need to be slightly modified to correct for sampling design (when a simple random sample is not used) and/or population size (when the population size is less than 100,000).

## 6.11 INTERPRETING STATISTICS: PREDICTING THE ELECTION OF THE GOVERNMENT OF CANADA AND JUDGING ITS PERFORMANCE

The statistical techniques covered in this chapter have become a part of everyday life in Canada and elsewhere. In politics, for example, estimation techniques are used to track public sentiment, measure how citizens perceive the performance of political leaders, and project the likely winners of upcoming elections. We should acknowledge, nonetheless, that these applications of estimation techniques are also controversial. Many wonder if the easy availability of polls makes politicians overly sensitive to the whims of public sentiment. Others are concerned that election projections might work against people's readiness to participate fully in the democratic process and, in particular, cast their votes on election day. These are serious concerns but, in this textbook, we can do little more than acknowledge them and hope that you have the opportunity to pursue them in other, more appropriate settings.

In this instalment of Interpreting Statistics, we will examine the role of statistical estimation of voting intentions in the 2015 campaign for the federal election (election projections) that culminated in the election of Justin Trudeau and the Liberal Party. We will also examine trends in post-election polls on political party support. Both kinds of polls use the same formulas introduced in this chapter to construct confidence intervals (although the random samples were assembled according to a more complex technique that is beyond the scope of this textbook).

**Election Projections.** The federal election on October 19, 2015, among the Conservatives, the Liberals, the New Democratic Party (NDP), the Green Party, and the Bloc Québécois (BQ) was one of the most interesting and hotly contested elections in recent Canadian history, and one with a particularly high voter turnout—68.3%, the highest in 22 years. In this section, we will use our newly acquired knowledge of confidence intervals to explore how the popularity of the parties changed during the election campaign.

Table 6.5 presents the results of the last five surveys conducted before the 2015 federal election by EKOS Research Associates Inc., a Canadian public opinion research firm. The two left-hand columns show the dates of the polls and the sample size ($n$) for each poll. The five right-hand columns list the percentage of the sample that said, at the time the poll was conducted, that they intended to vote for each party. These are point estimates of the population parameters (which would be the actual percentage of the entire national electorate that would vote for the Conservatives, Liberals, NDP, Green Party, or BQ at that specific time). Table 6.5 expresses results in percentages for ease of communication, but actual estimates would be computed using sample proportions.

It can be seen from Table 6.5 that the Conservative Party had the lead for the entire length of the campaign, but the difference between the support for the Conservative Party and the Liberal Party was very small. This made it difficult to discern which of these two parties was probably going to win the election. It even prompted Ekos Research Associates to title two of their poll reports "Stalemate Continues" and "And the Winner is... We Don't Know."

Let us assume that one wanted to predict the election results based on the October 16–18, 2015, poll, when the Conservative Party has a lead of

**TABLE 6.5 EKOS Research Polling Results**

| Poll Date | Sample Size | Percentage of Sample for | | | | |
| | | Conservative | Liberal | NDP | Green | BQ |
|---|---|---|---|---|---|---|
| October 12–14, 2015 | 1,438 | 33.5 | 32.6 | 22.9 | 5.6 | 3.4 |
| October 13–15, 2015 | 1,813 | 34.0 | 32.8 | 22.7 | 5.1 | 3.4 |
| October 15–16, 2015 | 1,537 | 33.7 | 33.3 | 21.9 | 4.1 | 4.7 |
| October 16–17, 2015 | 1,621 | 34.3 | 32.6 | 21.0 | 5.4 | 5.4 |
| October 16–18, 2015 | 2,122 | 35.8 | 31.9 | 20.4 | 5.6 | 4.9 |

Source: EKOS Research Associates Inc. http://www.ekospolitics.com/index.php/category/national-results/

about 4 percentage points over the Liberal Party. Does this mean that the Conservatives were actually ahead of the Liberals in the popular vote? The percentages in Table 6.5 are point estimates, and these types of estimates are unlikely to match their respective parameters exactly. In other words, it is unlikely that the sample values in the table were exactly equal to the percentage of the electorate who were going to vote for each of the parties on that particular date. For this reason, confidence intervals would be safer to utilize because they use ranges of values, not single points, to estimate population values.

Table 6.6 displays the 95% confidence intervals for each party for these five polls, with the results again expressed as percentages rather than proportions. The dates and sample size of each poll are displayed in the left-most columns, followed by the 95% confidence intervals for each estimate and the width of the interval estimates. (Note that Table 6.6 underscores a very important point about estimation: As sample size increases, the width of the interval becomes narrower. For example, the first poll, taken on October 12–14, 2015, was based on a smaller sample, 1,438, and was 5.18 percentage points wide, compared with all the other polls, which were based on larger samples; as a result, all the other intervals were narrower (4.58%, 4.98%, 4.86%, and 4.28%, respectively).

The most important information in Table 6.6 is, of course, the intervals themselves, and it is an overlap in some intervals that can cause pollsters to declare a race "too close to call." So for example, the poll on October 16–18, 2015, showed that support for the Conservative Party was between 33.66% (35.8% − 2.14%) and 37.94% (35.8% + 2.14%), a width of 4.28 percentage points. Support for the Liberal Party in this poll was between 29.76% and 34.04%, again a width of 4.28 percentage points. (Note that the confidence intervals for each date have the same width because they are computed using the same sample size, or $n$, and the same confidence level, or 95%.)

**TABLE 6.6   Sample Size, Confidence Intervals, and Likely Winners**

| Poll Date | Sample Size | 95% Confidence Interval | | | | | Interval Width |
|---|---|---|---|---|---|---|---|
| | | Conservative | Liberal | NDP | Green | BQ | |
| October 12–14, 2015 | 1,438 | 33.5 ± 2.59 | 32.6 ± 2.59 | 22.9 ± 2.59 | 5.6 ± 2.59 | 3.4 ± 2.59 | 5.18 |
| October 13–15, 2015 | 1,813 | 34.0 ± 2.29 | 32.8 ± 2.29 | 22.7 ± 2.29 | 5.1 ± 2.29 | 3.4 ± 2.29 | 4.58 |
| October 15–16, 2015 | 1,537 | 33.7 ± 2.49 | 33.3 ± 2.49 | 21.9 ± 2.49 | 4.1 ± 2.49 | 4.7 ± 2.49 | 4.98 |
| October 16–17, 2015 | 1,621 | 34.3 ± 2.43 | 32.6 ± 2.43 | 21.0 ± 2.43 | 5.4 ± 2.43 | 5.4 ± 2.434 | 4.86 |
| October 16–18, 2015 | 2,122 | 35.8 ± 2.14 | 31.9 ± 2.14 | 20.4 ± 2.14 | 5.6 ± 2.14 | 4.9 ± 2.14 | 4.28 |

Source: EKOS Research Associates Inc. http://www.ekospolitics.com/index.php/category/national-results/

Remember that while we can be 95% sure that the parameter is in the interval, it may be *anywhere* between the upper and lower limits. Thus, this poll tells us that it was just as likely that the Liberal Party would win (e.g., support for the Liberals could have been as high as 34.04%, and support for the Conservatives could have been as low as 33.66%) as it was that the Conservatives would win (e.g., support for the Liberals could have been as low as 29.76%, and support for the Conservatives could have been as high as 37.94%). If the confidence intervals overlap, it is possible that the apparent losing party is actually ahead. In the end, when the intervals overlap—when the race is so close—the polls cannot identify a winner. Of course, we know that the Liberal Party went on to win a majority government in the 2015 federal election, while the Conservative Party formed the official opposition.

**Post-Election Party Support.** Once elected, a political party is not free of polls and confidence intervals. Since the federal election in October 2015, pollsters have tracked the parties' popularity by asking randomly selected samples of adult Canadians to choose their voting preferences, as illustrated in Figure 6.8. For purposes of clarity, only point estimates are shown, but you should remember that confidence interval estimates around these points would range about ±2% at the 95% confidence level (see Table 6.6).

As observed by the Canadian public opinion and research company Nanos Research, public opinion has shifted since the 2015 federal election (Figure 6.8). There are notable shifts in point estimates over the polling

**FIGURE 6.8   2015 Canadian Federal Election Results and Nanos Research Polling Data After the Election, October 10, 2015 to October 14, 2016**

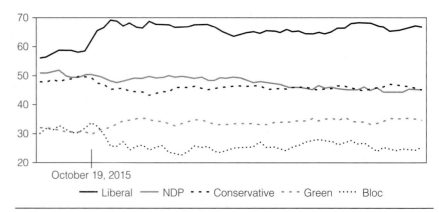

Source: Nanos Research. http://www.nanosresearch.com/tickers/Klipfolio/data.html

dates, such as a slight decrease in popularity of the Conservative Party and a marked increase for the Liberal Party. In this case, even when we interpret point estimates in the context of their confidence intervals, we observe that the Liberal Party has remained substantially ahead of the Conservative Party. For example, if the 95% confidence intervals around the point estimates were considered on the last polling date (October 14, 2016), we would see no overlap in the intervals for the Conservative and Liberal Parties. Thus, statistically speaking, there is a significant difference in popular support for the two leading parties on this particular date.

Returning to the many controversies surrounding public opinion polls, critics would argue that it is not a good thing to judge the government and its leader so continuously. To some extent, these approval ratings expose the prime minister and the governing party (and other political parties and leaders whose performance is similarly measured) to the whims of public sentiment and, at some level, could pressure them to cater to popular opinion and shape ("spin") their image to maintain support. However, information like that presented in Figure 6.8 supplies some interesting insights into the affairs not only of political institutions but also of society as a whole.

## READING STATISTICS 4: Polls

You are most likely to encounter the estimation techniques covered in this chapter in the mass media in the form of public opinion polls, election projections, and the like. Professional polling firms use interval estimates, and responsible reporting by the media will usually emphasize the estimate itself (e.g., "In a survey of the Canadian public, 57% of the respondents said that they approve of the prime minister's performance") but also will report the width of the interval ("This estimate is accurate to within ±3%," or "Figures from this poll are subject to a margin of error of ±3%"), the alpha level (usually as the confidence level of 95%), and the size of the sample ("1,458 households were surveyed").

Election projections and voter analyses have been common since the middle of the 20th century and are discussed further in Section 6.11. More recently, public opinion polling has been

increasingly used to gauge reactions to everything from the newest movies to the hottest gossip to the prime minister's conduct during the latest crisis. News magazines routinely report poll results as an adjunct to news stories, and similar stories are regular features of TV news and newspapers. We would include an example or two of these applications here, but polls have become so pervasive that you can choose your own example. Just pick up a news magazine or newspaper, leaf through it casually, and we bet that you'll find at least one poll. Read the story and try to identify the population, the confidence interval width, the sample size, and the confidence level. Bring the news item to class and dazzle your instructor.

As a citizen, as well as a social scientist, you should be extremely suspicious of polls that do not include such vital information as sample

*(continued)*

size or interval width. You should also check to find out how the sample was assembled. Samples selected in a non-random fashion cannot be regarded as representative of the Canadian public or, for that matter, of any population larger than the sample itself. Such non-scientific polls can be found when local TV news or sports programs ask viewers to call in and register their opinions about some current controversy. These polls are for entertainment only and must not be taken seriously. You should, of course, read all polls and surveys critically and analytically, but you should place confidence only in polls that are based on samples selected according to the rule of EPSEM (see Chapter 5) from some defined population.

In addition, ads, commercials, and reports published by partisan groups sometimes report statistics that seem to be estimates of the population. Often, such estimates are based on woefully inadequate sampling sizes and biased sampling procedures, and the data are collected under circumstances that evoke a desired response. "Person in the street" (or shopper in the grocery store) interviews have a certain folksy appeal but must not be accorded the same credibility as surveys conducted by reputable polling firms.

The social research industry in Canada, however, is regulated to some extent. By and large, the industry is self-regulated. The Marketing Research and Intelligence Association, representing most of the industry, has adopted codes of ethics and established standards for reporting and interpreting survey research results. Further, the reporting of election survey results during federal election campaigns is formally regulated by the *Canada Elections Act*. For instance, federal electoral legislation requires that published election period poll results contain basic methodological information such as margin of error and the date on which the poll was conducted.

## PUBLIC OPINION SURVEYS IN THE PROFESSIONAL LITERATURE

Thousands of political, social, and market research polls are conducted each year in Canada. For the social sciences, probably the single most important consequence of the growth in opinion polling is that many nationally representative databases are now available for research purposes. These high-quality databases are often available for free or for a nominal fee, and they make it possible to conduct "state of the art" research without the expense and difficulty of collecting data yourself. This is an important development because we can now easily test our theories against very high-quality data, and our conclusions will thus have a stronger empirical basis. Our research efforts will have greater credibility with our colleagues, with policy-makers, and with the public at large.

One of the more important and widely used databases of this sort is the General Social Survey (GSS). Since 1985, Statistics Canada has annually questioned a nationally representative sample of Canadians about a wide variety of issues and concerns. Because many of the questions are asked every five years or so, the GSS offers a longitudinal record of Canadian sentiment and opinion about a large variety of topics (e.g., see Reading Statistics 5). Each year, new topics of current concern are added and explored, and the variety of information available thus continues to expand. Like other nationally representative samples, the GSS sample is chosen by a probability design based on the principle of EPSEM (see Chapter 5). With a sample size of about 25,000, GSS estimates will be highly precise (see Table 6.4 and Section 6.9 for the discussion on the relationship between sample size and precision of estimates). The computer exercises in this textbook are based on the 2013 GSS. This database is described more fully in Appendix G.

## READING STATISTICS 5: Using Representative Samples to Track National Trends

Among other uses, the General Social Survey (GSS) can be used to track national trends and shifts in public opinion over time because many of the same questions are asked every few years. We demonstrate here how to assess trends in criminal victimization using the 1993, 1999, 2004, 2009, and 2014 GSS.

We considered two questions that measure perceptions of crime. The two questions, asked in the 1993, 1999, 2004, 2009, and 2014 GSS, are as follows:

Q1. Compared to other areas in Canada, do you think your neighbourhood has a higher amount of crime, about the same, or a lower amount of crime?

Q2. Do you feel very safe, reasonably safe, somewhat unsafe, or very unsafe from crime walking alone in your area after dark?

Over this period, respondents were less likely to say that their neighbourhood had above-average crime and that they feel unsafe from crime after dark. Figure 1 shows that the point estimate for the proportion of those who think their neighbourhood has higher-than-average crime fell from 0.116 (or 11.6%) in 1993 to 0.039 (3.9%) in 2014, as did the proportion who felt unsafe from crime while walking after dark: 0.273 in 1993 to 0.062 in 2014.

To estimate the population parameters or the proportions for all Canadians, interval estimates were calculated using Formula 6.3. The results, expressed this time in percentages, are shown in Table 1. For example, we can conclude that at the 95% confidence level, between 12.2% and 13.6% (12.9 ± 0.7) of Canadians felt unsafe

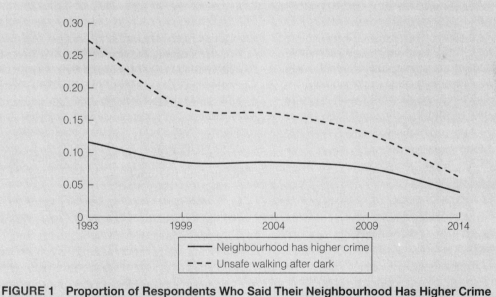

FIGURE 1  **Proportion of Respondents Who Said Their Neighbourhood Has Higher Crime and They Feel Unsafe Walking Alone After Dark, 1993 to 2014**

*(continued)*

walking alone after dark in 2014. In conclusion, the trends in these data suggest that Canadians' perception of crime has generally declined over the last 21 years.

**TABLE 1** **95% Confidence Interval of Percentage Who Said Neighbourhood Has Higher Crime and They Feel Unsafe Walking Alone After Dark, 1993, 1999, 2004, 2009, and 2014**

| Year | Sample Size | Neighbourhood Has Higher Crime | Unsafe Walking After Dark |
|------|-------------|-------------------------------|---------------------------|
| 1993 | 11,960 | 11.6 ± 0.90 | 27.3 ± 0.90 |
| 1999 | 25,876 | 8.5 ± 0.61 | 17.1 ± 0.61 |
| 2004 | 23,766 | 8.5 ± 0.63 | 16.0 ± 0.63 |
| 2009 | 19,422 | 7.6 ± 0.70 | 12.9 ± 0.70 |
| 2014 | 33,089 | 3.9 ± 0.54 | 6.2 ± 0.54 |

## SUMMARY

1. Population values can be estimated with sample values. With point estimates, a single sample statistic is used to estimate the corresponding population value. With confidence intervals, we estimate that the population value falls within a certain range of values.

2. Estimates based on sample statistics must be unbiased and relatively efficient. Of all the sample statistics, only means and proportions are unbiased. The means of the sampling distributions of these statistics are equal to the respective population values. Efficiency is largely a matter of sample size. The greater the sample size, the lower the value of the standard deviation of the sampling distribution, the more tightly clustered the sample outcomes will be around the mean of the sampling distribution, and the more efficient the estimate.

3. With point estimates, we estimate that the population value is the same as the sample statistic (either a mean or a proportion). With interval estimates, we construct a confidence interval, a range of values into which we estimate that the population value falls. The width of the interval is a function of the risk we are willing to take of being wrong (the alpha level) and the sample size. The interval widens as our probability of being wrong decreases and as sample size decreases.

4. A confidence interval can be depicted using an error bar graph. The middle of an error bar graph represents the sample statistic, and a vertical line above and below the sample statistic represents the upper and lower limits of the confidence interval.

5. The sample size needed to obtain a desired confidence interval can be determined prior to conducting a study. Sample size is determined by "rearranging" the formulas for confidence intervals.

6. To construct confidence intervals for sample means, use the standard normal distribution ($Z$) when the population standard deviation is known (and sample size is large or the population normally distributed); otherwise, use the Student's $t$ distribution. For sample proportions with large samples, use standard normal distribution ($Z$).

## SUMMARY OF FORMULAS

Confidence interval for a sample mean, large sample (or normally distributed population), population standard deviation known:

$$6.1 \quad \text{c.i.} = \overline{X} \pm Z\left(\frac{\sigma}{\sqrt{n}}\right)$$

Confidence interval for a sample mean, large sample (or normally distributed population), population standard deviation unknown:

$$6.2 \quad \text{c.i.} = \overline{X} \pm t\left(\frac{s}{\sqrt{n-1}}\right)$$

Confidence interval for a sample proportion, large samples:

$$6.3 \quad \text{c.i.} = P_s \pm Z\sqrt{\frac{P_u(1-P_u)}{n}}$$

Required sample size, for a mean:

$$6.4 \quad n = \frac{Z^2 \times \sigma^2}{ME^2}$$

Required sample size, for a proportion:

$$6.5 \quad n = \frac{Z^2 \times (P_u \times (1 - P_u))}{ME^2}$$

## GLOSSARY

**Alpha ($\alpha$).** The probability of error or the probability that a confidence interval does not contain the population value. Alpha levels are usually set at 0.10, 0.05, 0.01, or 0.001.

**Bias.** A criterion used to select sample statistics as estimators. A statistic is unbiased if the mean of its sampling distribution is equal to the population value of interest.

**Confidence interval.** An estimate of a population value in which a range of values is specified.

**Confidence level.** A frequently used alternative way of expressing alpha, the probability that an interval estimate will not contain the population value. Confidence levels of 90%, 95%, 99%, and 99.9% correspond to alphas of 0.10, 0.05, 0.01, and 0.001, respectively.

**Efficiency.** The extent to which the sample outcomes are clustered around the mean of the sampling distribution.

**Error bar.** A graphic display device used to illustrate the confidence interval of a sample statistic.

**Margin of error.** The radius (half the size) of a confidence interval for a sample mean or sample proportion. It is also called the margin of sampling error, or just sampling error.

**Point estimate.** An estimate of a population value where a single value is specified.

**Student's *t* distribution.** A distribution used in the construction of confidence intervals when the population standard deviation unknown.

## MULTIMEDIA RESOURCES

 nelson.com/student

Visit the companion website for the fourth Canadian edition of *Statistics: A Tool for Social Research* to access a wide range of student resources. Begin by clicking on the Student Resources section of the textbook's website to access online chapters and study tools.

## PROBLEMS

**6.1** For each sample mean below, construct the 95% confidence interval for estimating $\mu$, the population mean.

  **a.** $\bar{X} = 5.2$   **b.** $\bar{X} = 100$   **c.** $\bar{X} = 20$
      $\sigma = 0.7$       $\sigma = 9$        $\sigma = 3$
      $n = 157$       $n = 620$      $n = 220$
  **d.** $\bar{X} = 1{,}020$  **e.** $\bar{X} = 7.3$  **f.** $\bar{X} = 33$
      $s = 50$        $s = 1.2$      $s = 6$
      $n = 329$      $n = 105$    $n = 220$

**6.2** For each set of sample outcomes below, construct the 99% confidence interval for estimating $P_u$.

  **a.** $P_s = 0.14$  **b.** $P_s = 0.37$  **c.** $P_s = 0.79$
      $n = 100$      $n = 522$     $n = 121$
  **d.** $P_s = 0.43$  **e.** $P_s = 0.40$  **f.** $P_s = 0.63$
      $n = 1049$    $n = 548$    $n = 300$

**6.3** For each confidence level below, determine the corresponding $Z$ score.

| Confidence Level (%) | Alpha | Area Beyond $Z$ | $Z$ Score |
|---|---|---|---|
| 95% | 0.05 | 0.0250 | ±1.96 |
| 94% | | | |
| 92% | | | |
| 97% | | | |
| 98% | | | |
| 99.9% | | | |

**6.4** For each sample size and confidence level below, determine the corresponding $t$ score.

| Sample Size | Confidence Level (%) | Alpha | $t$ Score |
|---|---|---|---|
| 5 | 95 | 0.05 | 2.776 |
| 6 | 99 | | |
| 15 | 95 | | |
| 15 | 99 | | |
| 30 | 99 | | |
| 31 | 95 | | |
| 35 | 95 | | |
| 39 | 95 | | |
| 61 | 90 | | |

**6.5** SOC A researcher has gathered information from a random sample of 178 households. For each variable below, construct confidence intervals to estimate the population mean. Use the 90% level.

  **a.** An average of 2.3 people resides in each household. Standard deviation is 0.35.

  **b.** There was an average of 2.1 television sets ($s = 0.10$) and 0.78 telephones ($s = 0.55$) per household.

  **c.** The households averaged 6.0 hours of television viewing per day ($s = 3.0$).

**6.6** SOC A random sample of 100 television programs contained an average of 2.37 acts of physical violence per program. At the 99% level, what is your estimate of the population value? Construct an error bar to display your results.

$$\bar{X} = 2.37$$
$$s = 0.30$$
$$n = 100$$

**6.7** SOC A random sample of 429 university students was interviewed about a number of matters.

  **a.** They reported that they had spent an average of $178.23 on textbooks during the previous semester. If the sample standard deviation for these data is $15.78, construct an estimate of the population mean at the 99% level.

  **b.** They also reported that they had visited the health services clinic an average of 1.5 times a semester. If the sample standard deviation is 0.3, construct an estimate of the population mean at the 99% level.

  **c.** On the average, the sample had missed 2.8 days of classes per semester because of illness. If the sample standard deviation is 1.0, construct an estimate of the population mean at the 99% level.

  **d.** On the average, the sample had missed 3.5 days of classes per semester for reasons other than illness. If the sample standard deviation is 1.5, construct an estimate of the population mean at the 99% level.

**6.8** CJ A random sample of 500 residents of Pearson, Ontario, shows that exactly 50 of the respondents had been the victims of violent crime over the past year. Estimate the proportion of victims for the population as a whole, using the 90% confidence level. (*HINT: Calculate the sample proportion $P_s$ before using Formula 6.3. Remember that proportions are equal to frequency divided by n.*)

**6.9** [SOC] The survey mentioned in Problem 6.5 found that 25 of the 178 households consisted of unmarried couples who were living together. What is your estimate of the population proportion? Use the 95% level.

**6.10** [PA] A random sample of 324 residents of a community revealed that 30% were very satisfied with the quality of trash collection. At the 99% level, what is your estimate of the population value?

**6.11** [SOC] A random sample of 1,496 respondents of a major metropolitan area was questioned about a number of issues. Construct estimates for the population at the 90% level for each of the results reported below. Express the final confidence interval in percentages (e.g., "between 40 and 45% agreed that premarital sex was always wrong").

   **a.** When asked to agree or disagree with the statement "Explicit sexual books and magazines lead to rape and other sex crimes," 823 agreed.

   **b.** When asked to agree or disagree with the statement "Guns should be outlawed," 650 agreed.

   **c.** 375 of the sample agreed that marijuana should be legalized.

   **d.** 1,023 of the sample said that they had attended a religious service at least once within the past month.

   **e.** 800 agreed that public elementary schools should have sex education programs starting in grade 5.

**6.12** [SW] A random sample of 100 patients treated in a program for alcoholism and drug dependency over the past 10 years was selected. It was determined that 53 of the patients had been readmitted to the program at least once. At the 95% level, construct an estimate for the population proportion.

**6.13** For the sample data below, construct four different interval estimates of the population mean, one each for the 90%, 95%, 99%, and 99.9% level. What happens to the interval width as confidence level increases? Why?

$$\overline{X} = 100$$
$$s = 10$$
$$n = 500$$

**6.14** For each of the three sample sizes below, construct the 95% confidence interval. Use a sample proportion of 0.40 throughout. What happens to interval width as sample size increases? Why?

$$P_s = 0.40$$
$$\text{Sample A: } n = 100$$
$$\text{Sample B: } n = 1,000$$
$$\text{Sample C: } n = 10,000$$

**6.15** [PS] Two individuals are running for mayor of Pearson, Ontario. You conduct an election survey a week before the election and find that 51% of the respondents prefer candidate A. Can you predict a winner? Use the 99% level. *(HINT: In a two-candidate race, what percentage of the vote would the winner need? Does the confidence interval indicate that candidate A has a sure margin of victory? Remember that while the population parameter is probably ($\alpha = 0.01$) in the confidence interval, it may be anywhere in the interval.)*

$$P_s = 0.51$$
$$n = 578$$

**6.16** [SOC] The World Values Survey is administered periodically to random samples from societies around the globe. Below are listed the number of respondents in each nation who said that they are "very happy." Compute sample proportions and construct confidence interval estimates for each nation at the 95% level.

| Nation | Number "very happy" | Sample Size | Confidence Interval |
|---|---|---|---|
| United States | 805 | 2,232 | |
| Japan | 788 | 2,443 | |
| Brazil | 523 | 1,486 | |
| Nigeria | 977 | 1,759 | |
| China | 361 | 2,300 | |

Source: World Values Survey Association, *World Values Survey, Wave 5.*

**6.17** SOC The fraternities and sororities at Algebra University have been plagued by declining membership over the past several years and want to know if the incoming first-year students will be a fertile recruiting ground. Not having enough money to survey all 1,600 first-year students, they commission you to survey the interests of a random sample. You find that 35 of your 150 respondents are "extremely" interested in social clubs. At the 95% level, what is your estimate of the number of first-year students who would be extremely interested? *(HINT: The high and low values of your final confidence interval are proportions. How can proportions also be expressed as numbers?)*

**6.18** SOC You are the consumer affairs reporter for a daily newspaper. Part of your job is to investigate the claims of manufacturers, and you are particularly suspicious of a new economy car that the manufacturer claims will get 3.0 L/100 km. After checking the mileage figures for a random sample of 120 owners of this car, you find an average L/100 km of 3.1 with a standard deviation of 3.7. At the 99%

level, do your results tend to confirm or refute the manufacturer's claims?

**6.19** SOC The results listed below are from a survey given to a random sample of the Canadian public. For each sample statistic, construct a confidence interval estimate of the population parameter at the 95% confidence level. Sample size ($n$) is 2,987 throughout.

a. The average occupational prestige score was 43.87, with a standard deviation of 13.52.
b. The respondents reported watching an average of 2.86 hours of TV per day, with a standard deviation of 2.20.
c. The average number of children was 1.81, with a standard deviation of 1.67.
d. Of the 2,987 respondents, 876 identified themselves as Catholic.
e. Five hundred thirty-five of the respondents said that they had never married.
f. The proportion of respondents who said they voted for the Liberal Party in the 2015 federal election was 0.36.
g. When asked about capital punishment, 2,425 of the respondents said they opposed the death penalty for murder.

## You Are the Researcher

### Using SPSS to Produce Confidence Intervals with the 2012 CCHS

The demonstrations and exercises below use the shortened version of the 2012 CCHS data. Start SPSS and open the *CCHS_2012_Shortened.sav* file.

### SPSS DEMONSTRATION 6.1 Using the Explore Command for Constructing Confidence Intervals for Sample Means

The **Explore** procedure can be used to construct confidence intervals for the sample mean. The **Explore** command produces many of the same summary statistics and graphical displays produced by the **Frequencies** and **Descriptives** procedures but offers additional features. Here we will use **Explore** to compute the confidence interval for the mean of *smk_204* (number of cigarettes smoked per day for daily smokers).

From the main menu, click **Analyze, Descriptive Statistics**, and **Explore**. The **Explore** dialog box will open. Use the cursor to find *smk_204* in the list on the left and click the right-arrow button to transfer the variable to the **Dependent List** box. SPSS by default uses the 95% confidence level, which in fact we want to use for this demonstration. To request another level, you can click on the **Statistics button** at the top of the **Explore** dialog box. The **Explore: Statistics** dialog box will open. Type the desired level (e.g., 90%, 95%, or 99%) in the textbox next to "**Confidence Interval for Mean**," and click **Continue**. You will return to the **Explore** dialog box, where you might want to click the **Statistics** radio button within the **Display** section. Otherwise, SPSS will produce both summary statistics and plots (i.e., graphical displays).

Finally, click **OK,** and the output below will be produced:

**Descriptives**

| | | | Statistic | Std. Error |
|---|---|---|---|---|
| # of cigarettes smoked daily-daily smoker | Mean | | 15.38 | .541 |
| | 95% Confidence Interval for Mean | Lower Bound | 14.32 | |
| | | Upper Bound | 16.45 | |
| | 5% Trimmed Mean | | 14.79 | |
| | Median | | 13.68 | |
| | Variance | | 91.144 | |
| | Std. Deviation | | 9.547 | |
| | Minimum | | 1 | |
| | Maximum | | 50 | |
| | Range | | 49 | |
| | Interquartile Range | | 16 | |
| | Skewness | | 1.050 | .138 |
| | Kurtosis | | 1.857 | .275 |

The "Descriptives" output table contains a variety of statistics used to measure central tendency and dispersion. Some of these statistics are not covered in this textbook. If you wish to explore them, please use SPSS's online Help facility. In this section, we focus on parts of the table related to confidence intervals for the sample mean: the values for the "Lower Bound" and "Upper Bound" of the "95% Confidence Interval for Mean." The lower limit of our interval estimate is 14.32 and the upper limit is 16.45. Another way to state the interval would be

$$14.32 \le \mu \le 16.45$$

We estimate that daily smokers, on average, **smoke** between 14.32 and 16.45 **cigarettes per day**. Because alpha was set at the 0.05 level, this estimate has a 5% chance of being wrong (i.e., of not containing the population mean for number of cigarettes smoked).

## SPSS DEMONSTRATION 6.2 The Error Bar Graph

Here we'll produce an error bar graph for the confidence interval for the mean number of cigarettes smoked per day for daily smokers (*smk_204*). Click **Graphs, Legacy Dialogs**, and then **Error Bar**. The **Error Bars** dialog box will appear with two choices for the type of graph we want. The **Simple** option is already highlighted, and this is the one we want. At the bottom of the **Error Bars** dialog box, click the "**Summaries of separate variables**" radio button within the **Data in Chart Are** box, then click **Define**.

The **Define Simple Error Bar** dialog box appears with variable names listed on the left. Use the cursor to find *smk_204* in the list on the left and click the right-arrow button to transfer the variable to the **Error Bars** box. In the **Bars Represent** box, you have the option to select whether the error bar represents the confidence interval of the mean, the standard error of mean, or the standard deviation. Let's choose "**Confidence interval for mean**," the option that is already selected. You can also enter the desired confidence level into the **Level** box. We'll use 95% level, which is the default setting. Click **OK** and the following error bar graph will be produced:

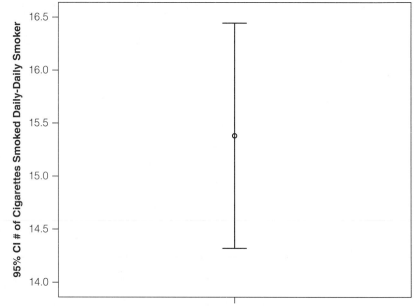

**# of Cigarettes Smoked Daily-Daily Smoker**

The error bar provides an illustration of the exact information given in the "Descriptives" output in Demonstration 6.1. The mean number of cigarettes smoked per day for daily smokers is 15.38 (marked by the small circle on the bar), and we estimate, at the 95% level of confidence (indicated by the length of the bar), that the mean number of cigarettes smoked for all daily smokers in Canada is somewhere between 14.32 (the small horizontal line at the bottom of the bar) and 16.45 (the small horizontal line at the top of the bar).

## DEMONSTRATION 6.3 Generating Statistical Information for Use in Constructing Confidence Intervals for Sample Proportions

Not all statistical techniques covered in this text are performed directly by SPSS. Unlike the **Explore** procedure for constructing confidence intervals for the sample mean, SPSS does not provide a program specifically for constructing intervals for the sample proportion. However, we can use SPSS to calculate the sample statistics, namely proportions, on which the interval estimates are based. Once you know these sample statistics, the confidence interval for the sample proportion is easily computed.

To illustrate this process, we'll construct a confidence interval for *flu_162* (when was your last seasonal flu shot). While we can estimate the population parameter for any or all of the categories of this variable, let's estimate the proportion of the population that has never had a flu shot.

First, calculate the sample proportion using the **Frequencies** command. From the menu bar, click **Analyze**, **Descriptive Statistics**, and **Frequencies**. Find *flu_162* in the left-hand box and move it to **Variable(s)** box. Click **OK**. The output for *flu_162* will look like this:

## When Was Your Last Seasonal Flu Shot?

|  | Frequency | Percent | Valid Percent | Cumulative Percent |
|---|---|---|---|---|
| Valid <1 YEAR | 516 | 30.1 | 30.1 | 30.1 |
| 1 TO <2 YEARS | 145 | 8.4 | 8.4 | 38.5 |
| 2 YEARS OR MORE | 279 | 16.3 | 16.3 | 54.8 |
| NEVER HAD A FLU SHOT | 776 | 45.2 | 45.2 | 100.0 |
| Total | 1716 | 100.0 | 100.0 | |

Second, substitute the values into Formula 6.3, not forgetting to change the percentages to proportions. Thus, using the 95% confidence level, we would have:

$$\text{c.i.} = P_s \pm Z \sqrt{\frac{P_u(1 - P_u)}{n}}$$

$$\text{c.i.} = 0.45 \pm 1.96 \sqrt{\frac{(0.5)(0.5)}{1,716}}$$

$$\text{c.i.} = 0.45 \pm (1.96)(0.012)$$

$$\text{c.i.} = 0.45 \pm 0.02$$

Changing back to percentages, we can estimate that between 43% (45% − 2%) and 47% (45% + 2%) of Canadians have never had a flu shot.

## Exercises (using *CCHS_2012_Shortened.sav*)

**6.1** Use the **Explore** command to get the 95% confidence interval for *hwtghtm* and *hwtgwtk*. Express the confidence intervals in words, as if you were reporting results in a newspaper story.

**6.2** Use the **Error Bar** command to get an error bar graph for each variable in Exercise 6.1. Write a sentence or two of interpretation for each graph.

**6.3** Use the **Frequencies** command to get sample proportions (convert the percentages in the frequency distributions) to estimate the population parameter for each of the following: proportion that drink alcohol "every day" (*alc_2*) and have "less than 5" servings of fruits and vegetables per day (*fvcgtot*). Use the 95% confidence level. Express the confidence intervals in words, as if you were reporting results in a newspaper story.

## Cumulative Exercises

Cumulative exercises provide practice in choosing, computing, and analyzing statistics. These online exercises present only data sets and research questions. Students choose appropriate statistics as part of the exercise. Cumulative exercises can be found at nelson.com/students.

# Part 3

# Bivariate Relationships: Tests of Significance and Measures of Association

The chapters in Part 3 of the textbook focus on three characteristics of the relationship between two variables: existence, strength, and direction. The first characteristic, existence, will be addressed with tests of statistical significance through a process called hypothesis testing. These tests are inferential statistics, and allow us to calculate whether a relationship between variables in a sample is likely to exist in the population. The characteristics of strength and direction will be addressed with the computation and analysis of a class of descriptive statistics known as measures of association. These statistics are extremely useful in scientific research and are commonly reported in the professional literature. They provide, in a single number, an indication of the strength and—if applicable—direction of a relationship between variables in a sample.

There is an important difference between statistical significance and association. Tests of statistical significance provide answers to certain questions: Is the relationship between variables found in the sample caused by mere random chance? What is the probability that the sample results reflect a real relationship in the population from which the sample was selected? Measures of association address a different set of questions: How strong is the relationship between the variables? What is the direction or pattern of the relationship? Thus, measures of association provide information complementary to tests of significance. Association and significance are two different things, and while the most satisfying results are those that are statistically significant *and* strong, it is common to find mixed results: relationships that are statistically significant but weak, not statistically significant but strong, and so forth.

Part 3 is organized according to the level of measurement of the variables whose relationship we are going to examine. We begin with a test of significance for relationships between nominal and/or ordinal variables (Chapter 7). Next, we look at measures of association designed for nominal variables in Chapter 8 and ordinal variables in Chapter 9. Before we move on to interval-ratio variables (Chapter 13), we consider hypothesis tests and measures of association for situations where we have a nominal or ordinal independent variable and an interval-ratio dependent variable in Chapters 11 and 12. Chapter 10 lays the groundwork for these chapters by introducing hypothesis testing for a single sample mean or sample proportion.

# 7 Hypothesis Testing with Nominal and Ordinal Variables
## Chi Square

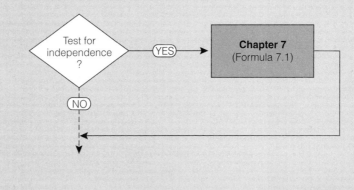

**LEARNING OBJECTIVES**

By the end of this chapter, you will be able to

1. Explain the logic of hypothesis testing.

2. Define and explain the conceptual elements involved in hypothesis testing, especially the null hypothesis (and research hypothesis), the sampling distribution, the alpha level, and the test statistic.

3. Explain what it means to "reject the null hypothesis" or "fail to reject the null hypothesis."

4. List and explain each of the factors (especially sample size) that affect the probability of rejecting the null hypothesis, and explain the differences between statistical significance and importance.

5. Identify and cite examples of situations in which the chi square test is appropriate.

6. Explain the structure of a bivariate table and the concept of independence as applied to expected and observed frequencies in a bivariate table.

7. Explain the logic of hypothesis testing as applied to a bivariate table.

8. Perform the chi square test using the five-step model and correctly interpret the results.

9. Explain the limitations of the chi square test.

**7.1 INTRODUCTION**

Chapter 6 introduced the techniques for estimating population parameters from sample statistics. Over the next few chapters, we will investigate a second application of inferential statistics called hypothesis testing. We will orient our discussion around level of measurement, as we did when we examined univariate descriptive statistics such as measures of central tendency and dispersion.

In this chapter, we will focus on hypothesis testing procedures when we have two "categorical" variables—two nominal variables, two ordinal variables, or one nominal and one ordinal variable. We also introduce the basic ideas behind the analysis of association in terms of bivariate tables and column percentages, with a more detailed discussion of bivariate descriptive statistics used to measure association between categorical variables to follow in Chapters 8 and 9. So, our approach will be first to test whether a statistically significant relationship exists between our variables, at our chosen level of confidence. If we detect such a relationship, we will then use special statistics, called measures of association, to assess additional characteristics of these relationships, namely their strength and direction.

Remember that the use of inferential procedures is only justified when we are using a randomly drawn sample. While it would of course be better if we had access to the full population rather than a sample of it, researchers usually do not have the resources necessary to test everyone in a large group and must instead use random samples. Thanks to the theorems discussed in Chapter 5, we can infer a lot about the population on the basis of the information obtained from our randomly drawn sample. Yet, remember that the EPSEM procedure for drawing random samples does not guarantee representativeness; there will always be a small amount of uncertainty in our conclusions. One of the great advantages of inferential statistics is that we will be able to estimate the probability of error and evaluate our decisions accordingly.

**7.2 AN OVERVIEW OF HYPOTHESIS TESTING**

**Hypothesis testing**, also known as significance testing, is an inferential statistical procedure designed to test for the existence of a relationship between variables, or a difference between groups of cases, at the level of the population. The testing method comprises a distinctive logic based on a comparison of the empirical reality of our actual random sample data, against a standard of what we would expect to observe in our sample if there were no relationship between our variables or if there were no difference between groups of cases. Remember that we are interested in the actual situation in the population; however, since we must work with a sample, it will often be the case that our sample will not resemble the population perfectly. The relationship or difference that we observe in our sample might therefore be due to random sampling error.

So, our attention turns to the question of the size of the observed difference between groups of cases or relationship between variables. For example, the size of the difference in poverty rates of males and females (i.e., the relationship between sex and poverty) in a random sample of 1,000 people. If the size is very small, we would be more inclined to attribute it to random sampling error, and to conclude "no difference" or "no relationship" however, if the size is very large, we would regard a conclusion of "no difference" or "no relationship" as unlikely. Instead, in such a case, we would be more likely to interpret a large discrepancy as pointing toward a real difference between groups or relationship between variables in the population.

## 7.3 THE FIVE-STEP MODEL FOR HYPOTHESIS TESTING

Even though every test of significance is logically unique, all tests of significance follow the same systematic five-step process:

Step 1. Make assumptions and meet test requirements.
Step 2. State the null hypothesis.
Step 3. Select the sampling distribution and establish the critical region.
Step 4. Compute the test (obtained) statistic.
Step 5. Make a decision and interpret the results of the test.

These distinctive steps will be followed in every test of significance that we will undertake in this and later chapters. Let's take a closer look at each of the steps.

**Step 1. Make Assumptions and Meet Test Requirements.** Any application of statistics requires that certain assumptions be made, and all tests of hypotheses similarly have certain requirements that must be met. First, all tests of hypothesis must be based on a random sample that has been selected according to the rules of EPSEM (see Chapter 5). Most tests of hypothesis also have additional requirements pertaining to such considerations as the shape of the population distribution and the level of measurement of the included variables.

**Step 2. State the Null Hypothesis ($H_0$).** The **null hypothesis ($H_0$)** is the formal name for the statement of "no difference" or "no relationship," and its exact formulation will vary depending on the specific test being conducted. Usually, however, the researcher believes that a difference between groups, or a relationship between variables actually does exist, and therefore wants to reject the null hypothesis. At this point in the five-step model, the researcher's belief is stated in the **research hypothesis ($H_1$)**. $H_1$ always directly contradicts $H_0$. Thus, the researcher's goal in hypothesis testing is often to gather evidence for the research hypothesis by rejecting the null hypothesis.

**Step 3. Select the Sampling Distribution and Establish the Critical Region.** The sampling distribution is the probabilistic yardstick against which a particular sample outcome is measured. Specifically, by assuming that the null hypothesis is true (and only by this assumption), we can measure the probability of any specific sample outcome using the sampling distribution. There are several different sampling distributions, and we choose the distribution that is appropriate for our particular hypothesis test. The sampling distributions that we will use for significance testing in this textbook are standard normal ($Z$) distribution, Student's $t$ distribution, chi square distribution, and $F$ distribution. You are already familiar with $Z$ and $t$ distributions, which we used to construct confidence intervals to estimate population means and proportions.

The critical region consists of the areas under the sampling distribution that include unlikely sample outcomes. Before conducting the test of hypothesis, we must define what we mean by "unlikely." This decision rule will establish the **critical region** or **region of rejection**. The word *region* is used because, essentially, we are describing those areas under the sampling distribution that contain the unlikely sample outcomes. In other words, we must specify in advance those sample outcomes that are so unlikely that they will lead us to reject the null hypothesis, thus lending credibility to our research hypothesis. Conversely, if our sample does not have a value in the critical region, then we would fail to reject the null hypothesis—a decision that makes our research hypothesis seem less likely to be true.

By convention, the size of the critical region is reported as the **alpha level** ($\alpha$), the proportion of all of the area included in the critical region. One very commonly used alpha level is 0.05. Other commonly used alphas are 0.10, 0.01, and 0.001.

**Step 4. Compute the Test Statistic.** To evaluate the probability of any given sample outcome, the sample value must be converted into an **obtained** score. Test (obtained) statistic values are calculated differently, depending on the logic of the specific hypothesis test. Notably, just as alpha refers to the amount of area/probability located in the critical region in the tails, beyond the critical statistic score, *p* (not to be confused with a proportion) refers to the exact amount of area/probability located in the tails, beyond the test (obtained) statistic score. Thus, if $p$ is less than alpha, then the obtained statistic has exceeded the critical statistic in magnitude. $p$ is also the exact amount of risk, in our own test, of rejecting the null hypothesis when it is true.

**Step 5. Make a Decision and Interpret the Results of the Test.** As the last step in the hypothesis-testing process, the test (obtained) statistic is compared with the critical region. If the test statistic falls in the critical region, our decision will be to reject the null hypothesis. If the test statistic does not fall in the critical region, we fail to reject the null hypothesis.

**TABLE 7.1** **Making a Decision in Step 5 and Interpreting the Results of the Test**

| Situation | Decision | Interpretation |
|---|---|---|
| The test statistic is in the critical region | Reject the null hypothesis ($H_0$) | The difference is statistically significant |
| The test statistic is not in the critical region | Fail to reject the null hypothesis ($H_0$) | The difference is not statistically significant |

Note that there are two parts to step 5. First, you make a decision about the null hypothesis: If the test statistic falls in the critical region, we reject $H_0$. If the test statistic does not fall in the critical region, we fail to reject the $H_0$. Second, and just as importantly, you need to interpret the results of the test and say what your decision means. The procedures for making a decision about the null hypothesis and interpreting the results of the test are summarized in Table 7.1.

This five-step model will serve us as a framework for decision making throughout the hypothesis-testing chapters. The exact nature and method of expression for our decisions will be different for different situations. However, familiarity with the five-step model will help you master this material by providing a common frame of reference for all significance testing.

## 7.4 SELECTING AN ALPHA LEVEL

In order to determine the critical region, the researcher must select an alpha level, as mentioned in step 3. The alpha level plays a crucial role in hypothesis testing, as it is our selection of alpha that determines exactly what we mean by an "unlikely" sample outcome. If the probability of the observed sample outcome is lower than the alpha level (i.e., if the test statistic falls into the critical region), we reject the null hypothesis as unlikely to be true. Thus, the alpha level will have important consequences for our decision in step 5.

How can reasonable decisions be made with respect to the value of alpha? Recall that the alpha level defines what will be meant by "unlikely." The alpha level also tells us the probability that the decision to reject the null hypothesis, if the test statistic falls into the critical region, will be incorrect. In hypothesis testing, the error of incorrectly rejecting the null hypothesis, or rejecting a null hypothesis that is actually true, is called a **Type I error**, or **alpha error**. A Type I error can be thought of as a "false positive" outcome of a criminal trial, such that a jury finds the accused guilty of the crime despite actually being not guilty. The null hypothesis in this example is that the person is *not guilty*, and the research hypothesis is that the person is *guilty*. To minimize Type I errors, use very small values for alpha.

To elaborate, when an alpha level is specified, the sampling distribution is divided into two sets of possible sample outcomes. The critical region includes all unlikely or rare sample outcomes. Outcomes in this region will cause us to reject the null hypothesis. The remainder of the area consists of all sample outcomes that are "non-rare." The lower the level of alpha, the smaller the critical region and the greater the distance between the mean of the sampling distribution and the beginnings of the critical region. Thus, the lower the alpha level, the harder it will be to reject the null hypothesis and, because a Type I error can be made only if our decision in step 5 is to reject the null hypothesis, the lower the probability of a Type I error.

However, there is a complication. As the critical region decreases in size (i.e., as alpha levels decrease), the non-critical region must become larger. All other things being equal, the lower the alpha level, the less likely that the sample outcome will fall into the critical region. This raises the possibility of a second type of incorrect decision, called a **Type II error**, or **beta ($\beta$) error**: failing to reject a null hypothesis that is, in fact, false. A Type II error is thus analogous to a "false negative" outcome of a criminal trial, such that a jury finds a person *not guilty* of the crime despite actually being *guilty*.

In sum, the probability of a Type I error decreases as the alpha level decreases, but the probability of a Type II error increases. The two types of error are inversely related, and it is not possible to minimize both in the same test. In conducting a hypothesis test, we calculate the probability of committing a Type I error (which we control by adjusting the alpha level), but not the probability of committing a Type II error—this remains unknown. Through additional computation, however, we can calculate the probability of not committing a Type II error—in other words, the probability of correctly rejecting the null hypothesis, or making the right decision!

This is referred to as the "power" of a hypothesis test. The routines for computing the power of a hypothesis test will not be considered in this textbook. We must also be aware that there are different consequences associated with making each type of error. For example, in determining guilt during a criminal trial, sending an innocent person to jail (Type I error) has far different consequences than those that result from setting a guilty person free (Type II error). Which of these errors is more serious depends on the social costs related to them. Canadians tend to be distressed when Type II errors occur in the justice system, but outraged by Type I errors. The Canadian justice system, therefore, places great importance on decreasing Type I errors (sending innocent people to jail) at the expense of increasing Type II errors (letting guilty people go free).

It may be helpful to clarify the relationships between decision making and errors in table format. Table 7.2 lists the two decisions we can make in step 5 of the five-step model: We either reject or fail to reject the null hypothesis. The other dimension of Table 7.2 lists the two possible conditions of

**TABLE 7.2  Decision Making and the Null Hypothesis**

| The $H_0$ Is Actually | Decision | |
|---|---|---|
| | Reject | Fail to Reject |
| True | Type I or $\alpha$ error | OK |
| False | OK | Type II or $\beta$ error |

the null hypothesis: It is either actually true or actually false. The table combines these possibilities into a total of four possible combinations, two of which are desirable ("OK") and two of which are errors. The two desirable outcomes are rejecting null hypotheses that are actually false and failing to reject null hypotheses that are actually true. The goal of any scientific investigation is to verify true statements and reject false statements.

The remaining two combinations are errors or situations that, naturally, we wish to avoid. If we reject a null hypothesis that is in fact true, we are saying that a true statement is false. Likewise, if we fail to reject a null hypothesis that is in fact false, we are saying that a false statement is true. We want to wind up in one of the boxes labelled "OK" in Table 7.2—to always reject false statements and accept the truth when we find it. Remember, however, that hypothesis testing always carries an element of risk and that it is not possible to minimize the chances of both Type I and Type II errors simultaneously.

What all of this means, finally, is that you must think of selecting an alpha level as an attempt to balance the two types of error. Higher alpha levels will minimize the probability of Type II error (saying that false statements are true), and lower alpha levels will minimize the probability of Type I error (saying that true statements are false). Normally, in social science research, we will want to minimize Type I errors, and lower alpha levels (0.05, 0.01, 0.001, or lower) will be used. The 0.05 level in particular has emerged as a generally recognized indicator of a significant result. However, the widespread use of the 0.05 level is simply a convention, and there is no reason that alpha cannot be set at virtually any sensible level (such as 0.04, 0.027, 0.083). The researcher has the responsibility of selecting the alpha level that seems most reasonable in terms of the goals of the research project.

## 7.5 INTRODUCTION TO CHI SQUARE

The **chi square ($\chi^2$) test** has probably been the most frequently used test of hypothesis in the social sciences, a popularity that is due largely to the fact that the assumptions and requirements in step 1 of the five-step model are easy to satisfy. Specifically, the test can be conducted with variables measured at any level of measurement, and because it is a **non-parametric** or "distribution-free" test, it requires no assumptions at all about the shape of the population distribution. While the website for this textbook provides discussion of other non-parametric tests of significance such as the Mann–Whitney U test and the Wald–Wolfowitz runs test, the chi square test is the focus of this chapter.

Why is it an advantage to have assumptions and requirements that are easy to satisfy? The decision to reject the null hypothesis (step 5) is not specific: It means only that one statement in the model (step 1) *or* the null hypothesis (step 2) is wrong. Usually, of course, we single out the null hypothesis for rejection. The more certain we are of the model, the greater our confidence that the null hypothesis is the faulty assumption. A "weak" or easily satisfied model means that our decision to reject the null hypothesis can be made with even greater certainty.

Chi square has also been popular for its flexibility. It can be used not only with variables at any level of measurement but also with variables that have many categories or scores. However, while chi square can be used at any level of measurement, it is most appropriate for categorical—i.e., nominal and ordinal—variables.

## 7.6 BIVARIATE TABLES

Chi square is computed from **bivariate tables**, so called because they display the scores of cases on two different variables at the same time. Bivariate tables are used to ascertain whether there is a significant relationship between the variables and for other purposes that we will investigate in later chapters. In fact, these tables are very commonly used in research, and a detailed examination of them is in order.

First of all, bivariate tables have (of course) two dimensions. The horizontal (across) dimension is referred to in terms of **rows**, and the vertical dimension (up and down) is referred to in terms of **columns**. Each column or row represents a score on a variable, and the intersections of the rows and columns **(cells)** represent the various combined scores on both variables.

Let's use an example to clarify. Suppose a researcher is interested in the relationship between sex and volunteering. Is there a difference in the level of involvement in volunteering between the sexes? For the sake of simplicity, let us assume that level of involvement has only two response categories. That is, people have been classified as either male or female and as either high or low in their level of involvement in voluntary associations.

By convention, the independent variable (the variable taken to be the cause) is placed in the columns and the dependent variable (the variable taken to be the effect) is placed in the rows. In the example at hand, sex is the causal variable (the question was, "Is membership *affected by sex*?"), and each column will represent a score on this variable. Each row, on the other hand, will represent a score on level of membership (high or low). Table 7.3 displays the outline of the bivariate table for a sample of 100 people.

Note some further details of the table. First, subtotals have been added to each column and row. These are called the row or column **marginals**, and in this case, they tell us that 50 members of the sample were male and 50 were female (the column marginals) and 50 were rated as high in

**TABLE 7.3  Level of Participation in Voluntary Associations by Sex for 100 Citizens**

| Participation Level | Sex | | |
|---|---|---|---|
| | Male | Female | |
| High | | | 50 |
| Low | | | 50 |
| | 50 | 50 | 100 |

participation and 50 were rated as low (the row marginals). Second, the total number of cases in the sample ($n = 100$) is reported at the intersection of the row and column marginals. Finally, take careful note of the labelling of the table: Each row and column is identified, and the table has a descriptive title that includes the names of the variables, with the dependent variable listed first. Clear, complete labels and concise titles should be included in *all* tables, graphs, and charts.

As you probably noticed, Table 7.3 lacks one piece of crucial information: the frequencies of each sex that rated high or low on the dependent variable. To finish the table, we need to classify each member of the sample in terms of both their sex and their level of participation, keep count of how often each combination of scores occurs, and record these numbers in the appropriate cell of the table. Because each of our variables (sex and participation level) has two scores, there are four possible combinations of scores, each corresponding to a cell in the table. For example, males with high levels of participation would be counted in the upper-left-hand cell, females with low levels of participation would be counted in the lower-right-hand cell, and so forth. When we are finished counting, each cell will display the number of times each combination of scores occurred.

Finally, note how the bivariate table can be expanded to accommodate variables with more than just two scores. For instance, if we have measured participation level with three categories (e.g., high, moderate, and low) rather than two, we will simply add an additional row to the table.

**7.7 THE LOGIC OF CHI SQUARE**

The chi square test has several different uses. This chapter will deal with an application called the chi square test for **independence**. In the context of chi square, the concept of independence refers to the relationship between the variables. Specifically, two variables are independent if the classification of a case into a particular category of one variable has no effect on the probability that the case will fall into any particular category of the second variable. For example, sex and participation in voluntary associations will be

**TABLE 7.4**  **The Cell Frequencies That Would Be Expected if Levels of Participation and Sex Were Independent**

| Participation Levels | Sex | | |
|---|---|---|---|
| | Male | Female | |
| High | 25 | 25 | 50 |
| Low | 25 | 25 | 50 |
| | 50 | 50 | 100 |

independent of each other if the classification of a case as male or female has no effect on the classification of the case as high or low on participation. In other words, the variables are independent if level of participation and sex are completely unrelated to each other.

Consider Table 7.3 again. If these two variables are truly independent, the cell frequencies will be determined solely by random chance and we will find that, just as an honest coin will show heads about 50% of the time when flipped, about half the male respondents will rank high on participation and half will rank low. The same pattern holds for the 50 female respondents; therefore, each of the four cells will have about 25 cases in it, as illustrated in Table 7.4. This pattern of cell frequencies indicates that the sex of the subjects has no effect on the probability that they will be either high or low in participation. The probability of being classified as high or low will be 0.5 for both males and females, and the variables will therefore be independent.

The null hypothesis for chi square is that the variables are independent. Under the assumption that the null hypothesis is true, the cell frequencies we would expect to find if only random chance were operating are computed. These frequencies, called **expected frequencies** (symbolized $f_e$), are then compared, cell by cell, with the frequencies actually observed (**observed frequencies**, symbolized $f_o$) and recorded in a table. If the null hypothesis is true and the variables are independent, then there should be little difference between the expected and observed frequencies. If the null is false, however, there should be large differences between the two. The greater the differences between expected ($f_e$) and observed ($f_o$) frequencies, the less likely the variables are independent and the more likely we will be able to reject the null hypothesis.

**7.8 THE COMPUTATION OF CHI SQUARE**

As with all tests of hypothesis, with chi square we compute a test statistic, $\chi^2$ **(obtained)**, from the sample data and then place that value on the sampling distribution of all possible sample outcomes. Specifically, the value of $\chi^2$ (obtained) will be compared with the value of $\chi^2$ **(critical)**, which will be determined by consulting a chi square table (Appendix C) for a particular alpha level and number of degrees of freedom. Before conducting the formal test of hypothesis, let us take a moment to consider the calculation of chi square, as defined by Formula 7.1.

**FORMULA 7.1**

$$\chi^2(\text{obtained}) = \sum \frac{(f_o - f_e)^2}{f_e}$$

where $f_o$ = the cell frequencies observed in the bivariate table
$f_e$ = the cell frequencies that would be expected if the variables were independent

We must work on a cell-by-cell basis to solve this formula. To compute chi square, subtract the expected frequency from the observed frequency for each cell, square the result, divide by the expected frequency for that cell, and then sum the resultant values for all cells.

This formula requires an expected frequency for each cell in the table. In Table 7.4, the marginals are the same value for all rows and columns, and the expected frequencies are obvious by intuition: $f_e$ = 25 for all four cells. In the more usual case, the expected frequencies will not be obvious because the marginals will be unequal, and we must use Formula 7.2 to find the expected frequency for each cell:

**FORMULA 7.2**

$$f_e = \frac{\text{Row marginal} \times \text{Column marginal}}{n}$$

That is, the expected frequency for any cell is equal to the total number of cases in the row (the row marginal) times the total number of cases in the column (the column marginal) divided by the total number of cases in the table ($n$).

An example using Table 7.5 should clarify these procedures. A random sample of 100 social work graduates has been classified in terms of whether the Canadian Association of Schools of Social Work (CASSW) has accredited their undergraduate programs (the column or independent variable), and

**TABLE 7.5  Employment of 100 Social Work Graduates by CASSW Accreditation Status of Undergraduate Program (fictitious data)**

| | Accreditation Status | | |
|---|---|---|---|
| Employment Status | Accredited | Not Accredited | Totals |
| Working as a social worker | 30 | 10 | 40 |
| Not working as a social worker | 25 | 35 | 60 |
| Totals | 55 | 45 | 100 |

**TABLE 7.6  Expected Frequencies for Table 7.5**

| Employment Status | Accreditation Status | | Totals |
|---|---|---|---|
| | Accredited | Not Accredited | |
| Working as a social worker | 22 | 18 | 40 |
| Not working as a social worker | 33 | 27 | 60 |
| Totals | 55 | 45 | 100 |

whether these graduates were hired in social work positions within three months of graduation (the row or dependent variable).

Beginning with the upper-left-hand cell (graduates of CASSW-accredited programs who are working as social workers), the expected frequency for this cell, using Formula 7.2, is (40)(55)/100, or 22. For the other cell in this row (graduates of non-accredited programs who are working as social workers), the expected frequency is (40)(45)/100, or 18. For the two cells in the bottom row, the expected frequencies are (60)(55)/100, or 33, and (60)(45)/100, or 27, respectively. The expected frequencies for all four cells are displayed in Table 7.6.

Note that the row and column marginals as well as the total number of cases in Table 7.6 are exactly the same as those in Table 7.5. The row and column marginals for the expected frequencies must *always* equal those of the observed frequencies, a relationship that provides a convenient way of checking your arithmetic to this point.

The value for chi square for these data can now be found by solving Formula 7.1. It will be helpful to use a computing table, such as Table 7.7, to organize the several steps required to compute chi square. The table lists the observed frequencies ($f_o$) in column 1 in order from the upper-left-hand cell to the lower-right-hand cell, moving left to right across the table and top to bottom. Column 2 lists the expected frequencies ($f_e$) in exactly the same order. Double-check to make sure you have listed the cell frequencies in the same order for both these columns.

**TABLE 7.7  Computational Table for Table 7.5**

| (1) | (2) | (3) | (4) | (5) |
|---|---|---|---|---|
| $f_o$ | $f_e$ | $f_o - f_e$ | $(f_o - f_e)^2$ | $(f_o - f_e)^2/f_e$ |
| 30 | 22 | 8 | 64 | 2.91 |
| 10 | 18 | −8 | 64 | 3.56 |
| 25 | 33 | −8 | 64 | 1.94 |
| 35 | 27 | 8 | 64 | 2.37 |
| $n = 100$ | $n = 100$ | 0 | $\chi^2$(obtained) $= 10.78$ | |

The next step is to subtract the expected frequency from the observed frequency for each cell and list these values in column 3. To complete column 4, square the value in column 3, and then, in column 5, divide the column 4 value by the expected frequency for that cell. Finally, add up column 5. The sum of this column is $\chi^2$ (obtained).

$$\chi^2(\text{obtained}) = 10.78$$

Note that the totals for columns 1 and 2 ($f_o$ and $f_e$) are exactly the same. This will always be the case, and if the totals do not match, you have probably made a mistake in the calculation of the expected frequencies. Also note that the sum of column 3 will always be zero, another convenient way to check your math to this point.

This sample value for chi square must still be tested for its significance. *(For practice in computing chi square, see any of the end-of-chapter problems.)*

---

**ONE STEP AT A TIME   Computing Chi Square**

Begin by preparing a computing table similar to Table 7.7. List the observed frequencies ($f_o$) in column 1. The total for column 1 is the number of cases ($n$).

**To Find the Expected Frequencies ($f_e$) Using Formula 7.2**

**1:** Start with the upper-left-hand cell and multiply the row marginal by the column marginal for that cell.

**2:** Divide the quantity you found in step 1 by $n$. The result is the expected frequency ($f_e$) for that cell. Record this value in the second column of the computing table. Make sure you place the value of $f_e$ in the same row as the observed frequency for that cell.

**3:** Repeat steps 1 and 2 for each cell in the table. Double-check to make sure you are using the correct row and column marginals. Record each $f_e$ in the second column of the computational table.

**4:** Find the total of the expected frequencies column. This total *must* equal the total of the observed frequencies column (which is the same as $n$). If the two totals do not match (within rounding error), recompute the expected frequencies.

**To Find Chi Square Using Formula 7.1**

**1:** For each cell, subtract the expected frequency ($f_e$) from the observed frequency ($f_o$); then list these values in the third column of the computational table ($f_o - f_e$). Find the total for this column. If this total is not zero, you have made a mistake and need to check your computations.

**2:** Square each of the values in the third column of the table and record the result in the fourth column, labelled $(f_o - f_e)^2$.

**3:** Divide each value in column 4 by the expected frequency for that cell; then record the result in the fifth column, labelled $(f_o - f_e)^2/f_e$.

**4:** Find the total for the fifth column. This value is $\chi^2$ (obtained).

## 7.9 THE CHI SQUARE TEST FOR INDEPENDENCE

As always, the five-step model for significance testing will provide the framework for organizing our decision making. The data presented in Table 7.5 will serve as our example.

**Step 1. Make Assumptions and Meet Test Requirements.** First, the sample must be selected according to the rules of EPSEM. Second, the variables must be measured at the nominal or ordinal level. Note that we make no assumptions about the shape of the sampling distribution.

Model: Random sampling
Level of measurement is nominal or ordinal

**Step 2. State the Null Hypothesis.** As stated previously, the null hypothesis in the case of chi square states that the two variables are independent. If the null is true, the differences between the observed and expected frequencies will be small. As usual, the research hypothesis directly contradicts the null. Thus, if we reject $H_0$, the research hypothesis will be supported.

$H_0$: The two variables are independent.
($H_1$: The two variables are dependent.)

**Step 3. Select the Sampling Distribution and Establish the Critical Region.** The sampling distribution of sample chi squares, unlike the $Z$ and $t$ distributions, is positively skewed, with higher values of sample chi squares in the upper tail of the distribution (to the right). Thus, with the chi square test, the critical region is established in the upper tail of the sampling distribution.

Values for $\chi^2$ (critical) are given in Appendix C. This table is similar to the $t$ table, with alpha levels arrayed across the top and degrees of freedom down the side. A major difference, however, is that degrees of freedom ($df$) for chi square are found by the following formula:

**FORMULA 7.3**

$$df = (r - 1)(c - 1)$$

where $(r - 1)(c - 1)$ = the value of $r - 1$ (number of rows minus 1)
multiplied by $c - 1$ (number of columns minus 1)

A table with two rows and two columns (a $2 \times 2$ table) has one degree of freedom regardless of the number of cases in the sample.* A table with

---

*As noted in Chapter 6, degrees of freedom are the number of values in a distribution that are free to vary for any particular statistic. In bivariate tables, the degrees of freedom are determined by cell size rather than sample size. For example, a $2 \times 2$ table has one degree of freedom because, for a given set of marginals, once one cell frequency is determined, all other cell frequencies are fixed (i.e., they are no longer free to vary). In Table 7.5, for example, if any cell frequency is known, all others are determined. If the upper-left-hand cell is known to be 30, the remaining cell in that row must be 10, because there are 40 cases total in the row and $40 - 30 = 10$. Once the frequencies of the cells in the top row are established, cell frequencies for the bottom row are determined by subtraction from the column marginals. Incidentally, this relationship can be used to good advantage when computing expected frequencies. For example, in a $2 \times 2$ table, only one expected frequency needs to be computed. The $f_e$'s for all other cells can then be found by subtraction.

two rows and three columns would have $(2 - 1)(3 - 1)$, or two degrees of freedom. Our sample problem involves a $2 \times 2$ table with $df = 1$, so if we set alpha at 0.05, the critical chi square score will be 3.841. Summarizing these decisions, we have

$$\text{Sampling distribution} = \chi^2 \text{distribution}$$
$$\text{Alpha} = 0.05$$
$$\text{Degrees of freedom} = 1$$
$$\chi^2 (\text{critical}) = 3.841$$

**Step 4. Compute the Test Statistic.** The mechanics of these computations were introduced in Section 7.8. As you recall, we had

$$\chi^2 (\text{obtained}) = \sum \frac{(f_o - f_e)^2}{f_e}$$

$$\chi^2 (\text{obtained}) = 10.78$$

**Step 5. Make a Decision and Interpret the Results of the Test.** Comparing the test statistic with the critical region,

$$\chi^2 (\text{obtained}) = 10.78$$

$$\chi^2 (\text{critical}) = 3.841$$

we see that the test statistic falls into the critical region, and therefore, we reject the null hypothesis of independence. The pattern of cell frequencies observed in Table 7.5 is unlikely to have occurred by chance alone. The variables are dependent. Specifically, based on these sample data, the probability of securing employment in the field of social work is dependent on the CASSW accreditation status of the program. *(For practice in conducting and interpreting the chi square test for independence, see Problems 7.3 to 7.15.)*

Let's take a moment to stress exactly what the chi square test does and does not tell us. A significant chi square means that the variables are (probably) dependent on each other in the population: CASSW accreditation status makes a difference in whether or not a person is working as a social worker. Chi square does not give us any detail about the relationship, however. In our example, it does not tell us if it's the graduates of the accredited programs or the non-accredited programs that are more likely to be working as social workers. To compare these two groups, we must perform some additional calculations. We can figure out how the independent variable (CASSW accreditation status) is affecting the dependent variable (employment as a social worker) by computing **column percentages**, which is done by calculating percentages within each column of the bivariate table. This procedure is analogous to calculating percentages for frequency distributions (see Chapter 2).

**TABLE 7.8  Column Percentages for Table 7.5**

| Employment Status | Accreditation Status | | Totals (%) |
| --- | --- | --- | --- |
| | Accredited (%) | Not Accredited (%) | |
| Working as a social worker | 54.55 | 22.22 | 40.00 |
| Not working as a social worker | 45.45 | 77.78 | 60.00 |
| Totals | 100.00 | 100.00 | 100.00 |
| | (55) | (45) | |

To calculate column percentages, divide each cell frequency by the total number of cases in the column (the column marginal). For Table 7.5, starting in the upper-left-hand cell, we see that there are 30 cases in this cell and 55 cases in the column. In other words, 30 of the 55 graduates of CASSW-accredited programs are working as social workers. The column percentage for this cell is therefore $(30/55) \times 100 = 54.55\%$. For the lower-left-hand cell, the column percentage is $(25/55) \times 100 = 45.45\%$. For the two cells in the right-hand column (graduates of non-accredited programs), the column percentages are $(10/45) \times 100 = 22.22\%$ and $(35/45) \times 100 = 77.78\%$. All column percentages are displayed in Table 7.8.

Column percentages help make the relationship between the two variables more obvious. We can see easily from Table 7.8 that students from CASSW-accredited programs are more likely to be working as social workers. Nearly 55% of these students are working as social workers versus less than 25% of the students from non-accredited programs. We already knew that this relationship is significant (unlikely to be caused by random chance), and now, with the aid of column percentages, we know how the two variables are related. According to these results, graduating from a

---

### ONE STEP AT A TIME  Computing Column Percentages

**1:** Start with the upper-left-hand cell. Divide the cell frequency (the number of cases in the cell) by the total number of cases in that column (or the column marginal). Multiply the result by 100 to convert to a percentage.

**2:** Move down one cell and repeat step 1. Continue moving down the column, cell by cell, until you have converted all cell frequencies to percentages.

**3:** Move to the next column. Start with the cell in the top row and repeat step 1 (making sure you use the correct column total in the denominator of the fraction).

**4:** Continue moving down the second column until you have converted all cell frequencies to percentages.

**5:** Continue these operations, moving from column to column, one at a time, until you have converted all cell frequencies to percentages.

CASSW-accredited program is a decided advantage for people seeking to enter the social work profession.

Let's highlight two points in summary:

1. Chi square is a test of statistical significance. It tests the null hypothesis that the variables are independent in the population. If we reject the null hypothesis, we are concluding, with a known probability of error (determined by the alpha level), that the variables are dependent on each other in the population. In the terms of our example, this means that CASSW-accreditation status makes a difference in the likelihood of finding work as a social worker. By itself, however, chi square does not tell us the exact nature of the relationship.
2. Computing column percentages allows us to examine the bivariate relationship in more detail. By comparing the column percentages for the various scores of the independent variable, we can see exactly how the independent variable affects the dependent variable. In this case, the column percentages reveal that graduates of CASSW-accredited programs are more likely to find work as social workers. We will explore column percentages more extensively when we discuss bivariate association in Chapters 8 and 9.

## 7.10 THE LIMITATIONS OF HYPOTHESIS TESTING: SIGNIFICANCE VERSUS IMPORTANCE

Given that we are usually interested in rejecting the null hypothesis, we should take a moment to consider systematically the factors that affect our decision in step 5. Generally speaking, the probability of rejecting the null hypothesis is a function of several independent factors:

1. The size of the observed difference between groups or relationship between variables
2. The alpha level
3. The size of the sample

Only the first of these is not under the direct control of the researcher. The relationship between the alpha level and the probability of rejection is straightforward: The higher the alpha level, the larger the critical region, the higher the percentage of all possible sample outcomes that fall in the critical region, and the greater the probability of rejection. Thus, it is easier to reject the $H_0$ at the 0.05 level than at the 0.01 level, and easier still at the 0.10 level. The danger here, of course, is that higher alpha levels will lead to more frequent Type I errors, and we might find ourselves declaring small differences to be statistically significant.

The other factor is sample size: With all other factors constant, the probability of rejecting $H_0$ increases with sample size. In other words, the larger the sample, the more likely we are to reject the null hypothesis, and with very large samples (say, samples with thousands of cases), we may declare small differences to be statistically significant. This pattern of higher probabilities for rejecting $H_0$ with larger samples holds for all tests of significance.

On the one hand, the relationship between sample size and the probability of rejecting the null hypothesis should not alarm us unduly. Larger samples are, after all, better approximations of the populations they represent. Thus, decisions based on larger samples can be trusted more than decisions based on small samples.

On the other hand, this relationship clearly underlines what is perhaps the most significant limitation of hypothesis testing. Simply because a difference is statistically significant does not guarantee that it is important in any other sense. Particularly with very large samples, relatively small differences may be statistically significant. Even with small samples, of course, differences that are otherwise trivial or uninteresting may be statistically significant. In these situations, when it is clear that the research results were not produced by random chance, the researcher must still assess their importance. Do they firmly support a theory or hypothesis? Are they clearly consistent with a prediction or analysis? Do they strongly indicate a line of action in solving some problem? These are the kinds of questions a researcher must ask when assessing the importance of the results of a statistical test. Also, we should note that researchers have access to some very powerful ways of analyzing the importance (versus the statistical significance) of research results. These statistics, including bivariate measures of association and multivariate statistical techniques, will be introduced in later chapters, following the presentation of each test of significance.

Furthermore, it can also happen that a finding of no statistical importance may nevertheless be very interesting and theoretically important. An assessment of the importance of the result of a significance test is therefore not limited only to situations of statistical significance. For example, although measures of association are not needed in these circumstances, non-significant results can help us to identify weaknesses or limitations in our theoretical models, or can show us when programs meant to achieve particular outcomes are not effective and need to be revised.

The crucial point is that statistical significance and theoretical or practical importance can be two very different things. In other words, an observed result could therefore be

- statistically significant and important; or
- statistically significant but unimportant; or
- not statistically significant and yet important; or
- not statistically significant and unimportant.

## Applying Statistics 7.1: The Chi Square Test

Do men and women vary in their opinions about cohabitation? A random sample of 47 males and females has been rated as high or low in their support for "living together." The results are as follows:

| Support for Cohabitation | Group | | Totals |
|---|---|---|---|
| | Males | Females | |
| High | 15 | 5 | 20 |
| Low | 10 | 17 | 27 |
| Totals | 25 | 22 | 47 |

The frequencies we would expect to find if the null hypothesis ($H_0$: The variables are independent) were true are as follows:

| Support for Cohabitation | Group | | Totals |
|---|---|---|---|
| | Males | Females | |
| High | 10.64 | 9.36 | 20.00 |
| Low | 14.36 | 12.64 | 27.00 |
| Totals | 25.00 | 22.00 | 47.00 |

Expected frequencies are found on a cell-by-cell basis by means of the formula

$$f_e = \frac{\text{Row marginal} \times \text{Column marginal}}{n}$$

The calculation of chi square will be organized into a computational table.

| (1) | (2) | (3) | (4) | (5) |
|---|---|---|---|---|
| $f_o$ | $f_e$ | $f_o - f_e$ | $(f_o - f_e)^2$ | $(f_o - f_e)^2/f_e$ |
| 15 | 10.64 | 4.36 | 19.01 | 1.79 |
| 5 | 9.36 | −4.36 | 19.01 | 2.03 |
| 10 | 14.36 | −4.36 | 19.01 | 1.32 |
| 17 | 12.64 | 4.36 | 19.01 | 1.50 |
| $n = 47$ | $n = 47.00$ | | 0.00 | $\chi^2$ (obtained) = 6.64 |

$$\chi^2 \text{(obtained)} = 6.64$$

### Step 1. Make Assumptions and Meet Test Requirements.

Model: Random sampling
Level of measurement is nominal or ordinal

### Step 2. State the Null Hypothesis.

$H_0$: The two variables are independent.
($H_1$: The two variables are dependent.)

### Step 3. Select the Sampling Distribution and Establish the Critical Region.

Sampling distribution = $\chi^2$ distribution
Alpha = 0.05
Degrees of freedom = 1
$\chi^2$ (critical) = 3.841

### Step 4. Compute the Test Statistic.

$$\chi^2 \text{(obtained)} = \sum \frac{(f_o - f_e)^2}{f_e}$$

$$\chi^2 \text{(obtained)} = 6.64$$

### Step 5. Make a Decision and Interpret the Results of the Test.
With an obtained $\chi^2$ of 6.64, we would reject the null hypothesis of independence. For this sample, there is a statistically significant relationship between gender and support for cohabitation.

To complete the analysis, it would be useful to know exactly how the two variables are related. We can determine this by computing and analyzing column percentages:

| Support for Cohabitation | Group | | |
|---|---|---|---|
| | Males (%) | Females (%) | Totals (%) |
| High | 60.00 | 22.73 | 42.55 |
| Low | 40.00 | 77.27 | 57.45 |
| Totals | 100.00 | 100.00 | 100.00 |

The column percentages show that 60% of males in this sample are highly supportive versus 23% of females. We have already concluded that the relationship is significant, and now we know the pattern of the relationship: males are more supportive.

## READING STATISTICS 6: Hypothesis Testing

Professional researchers use a vocabulary that is much terser than our everyday language when presenting the results of tests of significance. This is partly because space limitations in scientific journals require conciseness and partly because professional researchers can assume a certain level of statistical literacy in their audiences. Thus, they omit many of the elements—such as the null hypothesis or the critical region—that we have been so careful to state.

Instead, researchers report only the sample values (e.g., observed frequencies), the value of the test statistic (e.g., chi square), the alpha level, the degrees of freedom (when applicable), and sample size. The results of a study on region and political party affiliation might be reported as "the relation between these variables was found to be significant, $\chi^2$ (16, $n = 3,454$) = 86.14, $p < 0.05$." Note that the alpha level is reported as "$p < 0.05$." This is shorthand for "the probability of a difference of this magnitude occurring by chance alone, if the null hypothesis of independence is true, is less than 0.05" and is a good illustration of how researchers can convey a great deal of information in just a few symbols. In a similar fashion, our somewhat long-winded phrase, "the test statistic falls in the critical region and, therefore, the null hypothesis is rejected," is rendered tersely and simply: "the relationship ... was ... found to be significant."

When researchers need to report the results of many tests of significance, they often use a summary table to report the sample information and whether the difference is significant at a certain alpha level. If you read the researcher's description and analysis of such tables, you should have little difficulty interpreting and understanding them. As a final note, these comments about how significance tests are reported in the literature apply to all of the tests of hypotheses covered in this textbook.

## 7.11 THE CHI SQUARE TEST: AN EXAMPLE

To this point, we have confined our attention to 2 × 2 tables, that is, tables with two rows and two columns. For purposes of illustration, we will work through the computational routines and decision-making process for a larger (3 × 2) table. As you will see, larger tables require more computations (because they have more cells), but in all other essentials they are dealt with in the same way as the 2 × 2 table.

Let's consider the case where a researcher is concerned with the possible effects of working at a paid job on academic progress of university students. Do students who work while studying, with their extra work responsibilities, suffer academically as compared to students who do not work while studying? Is academic performance dependent on working while studying? A random sample of 453 students is gathered, and each student is classified as either working while studying (Yes) or not working while studying (No) and—using grade-point average (GPA) as a measure—as a good, average, or poor student. Results are presented in Table 7.9.

For the top-left-hand cell (students who work while studying with good GPAs) the expected frequency would be (160 × 175)/453, or 61.81. For the other cell in this row, expected frequency is (160 × 278)/453, or 98.19. In similar fashion, all expected frequencies are computed (being very careful to use the correct row and column marginals) and displayed in Table 7.10.

**TABLE 7.9** **Grade-Point Average (GPA) by Working While Studying for 453 University Students**

|  | Working While Studying | | |
| --- | --- | --- | --- |
| GPA | Yes | No | Totals |
| Good | 70 | 90 | 160 |
| Average | 60 | 110 | 170 |
| Poor | 45 | 78 | 123 |
| Totals | 175 | 278 | 453 |

**TABLE 7.10** **Expected Frequencies for Table 7.9**

|  | Working While Studying | | |
| --- | --- | --- | --- |
| GPA | Yes | No | Totals |
| Good | 61.81 | 98.19 | 160.00 |
| Average | 65.67 | 104.33 | 170.00 |
| Poor | 47.52 | 75.48 | 123.00 |
| Totals | 175.00 | 278.00 | 453.00 |

The next step is to solve the formula for $\chi^2$ (obtained), being very careful to be certain that we are using the proper $f_o$'s and $f_e$'s for each cell. Once again, we will use a computational table (Table 7.11) to organize the calculations and then test the obtained chi square for its statistical significance. Remember that obtained chi square is equal to the total of column 5.

The value of the obtained chi square (2.78) can now be tested for its significance.

**Step 1. Make Assumptions and Meet Test Requirements.**

> Model: Random sampling
> Level of measurement is nominal

**TABLE 7.11** **Computational Table for Table 7.9**

| (1) | (2) | (3) | (4) | (5) |
| --- | --- | --- | --- | --- |
| $f_o$ | $f_e$ | $f_o - f_e$ | $(f_o - f_e)^2$ | $(f_o - f_e)^2/f_e$ |
| 70 | 61.81 | 8.19 | 67.08 | 1.09 |
| 90 | 98.19 | −8.19 | 67.08 | 0.68 |
| 60 | 65.67 | −5.67 | 32.15 | 0.49 |
| 110 | 104.33 | 5.67 | 32.15 | 0.31 |
| 45 | 47.52 | −2.50 | 6.25 | 0.13 |
| 78 | 75.48 | 2.50 | 6.25 | 0.08 |
| $n = 453$ | $n = 453.00$ | 0.00 | $\chi^2$ (obtained) = 2.78 | |

**Step 2. State the Null Hypothesis.**

$H_0$: The two variables are independent.
($H_1$: The two variables are dependent.)

**Step 3. Select the Sampling Distribution and Establish the Critical Region.**

Sampling distribution $= \chi^2$ distribution
Alpha $= 0.05$
Degrees of freedom $= (r - 1)(c - 1) = (3 - 1)(2 - 1) = 2$
$\chi^2$ (critical) $= 5.991$

**Step 4. Compute the Test Statistic.**

$$\chi^2(\text{obtained}) = \sum \frac{(f_o - f_e)^2}{f_e}$$

$$\chi^2(\text{obtained}) = 2.78$$

**Step 5. Make a Decision and Interpret the Results of the Test.** The test statistic, $\chi^2$ (obtained) $= 2.78$, does not fall into the critical region, which, for alpha $= 0.05$, $df = 2$, begins at the $\chi^2$ (critical) of 5.991. Therefore, we fail to reject the null hypothesis. The observed frequencies are not significantly different from the frequencies we would expect to find if the variables were independent and only random chance were operating. Based on these sample results, we can conclude that the academic performance of university students is not dependent on their work status. Since we failed to reject the null hypothesis, we will not examine column percentages as we did for Table 7.5.

## 7.12 THE LIMITATIONS OF THE CHI SQUARE TEST

Like any other test, chi square has limits, and you should be aware of several potential difficulties. First, even though chi square is very flexible and handles many different types of variables, it becomes difficult to interpret when the variables have many categories. For example, two variables with five categories each would generate a 5 × 5 table with 25 cells—far too many combinations of scores to be easily absorbed or understood. As a very rough rule of thumb, the chi square test is easiest to interpret and understand when both variables have four or fewer scores.

Two further limitations of the test are related to sample size. When sample size is small, it can no longer be assumed that the sampling distribution of all possible sample outcomes is accurately described by the chi square distribution. For chi square, a small sample is defined as one where a high percentage of the cells have expected frequencies ($f_e$) of 5 or less. Various rules of thumb have been developed to help the researcher decide what constitutes a "high percentage of cells." Probably the safest course is to take corrective action whenever *any* of the cells have expected frequencies of 5 or less.

## Applying Statistics 7.2: The Chi Square Test in a Larger (2 × 4) Table

There has been a good deal of public debate, particularly in the last decade, over privatization of the Canadian health care system. Do attitudes toward privatization of health care vary by region of residence? Is attitude on privatization dependent on region? We will examine this issue with an actual random sample of 369 Canadians from the 2006 Canadian Election Study, and classify respondents by their region of residence— Atlantic Canada, Quebec, Ontario, and Western Canada—and, as a measure of privatization, by whether they favour or oppose having some private hospitals in Canada. (The Canadian Election Study surveyed adults in the 10 provinces only, thus excluding the territories.) The 2 × 4 table below shows these results:

| | Region | | | | |
|---|---|---|---|---|---|
| Attitude | Atlantic | Quebec | Ontario | Western | Totals |
| Favour | 15 | 58 | 46 | 69 | 188 |
| Oppose | 21 | 38 | 65 | 57 | 181 |
| Totals | 36 | 96 | 111 | 126 | 369 |

The frequencies we would expect to find if the null hypothesis ($H_0$: The variables are independent) were true are

| | Region | | | | |
|---|---|---|---|---|---|
| Attitude | Atlantic | Quebec | Ontario | Western | Totals |
| Favour | 18.34 | 48.91 | 56.55 | 64.19 | 188.00 |
| Oppose | 17.66 | 47.09 | 54.45 | 61.81 | 181.00 |
| Totals | 36.00 | 96.00 | 111.00 | 126.00 | 369.00 |

Expected frequencies are found on a cell-by-cell basis by the formula

$$\frac{\text{Row marginal} \times \text{Column marginal}}{n}$$

The calculation of chi square will be organized into a computational table.

| (1) | (2) | (3) | (4) | (5) |
|---|---|---|---|---|
| $f_o$ | $f_e$ | $f_o - f_e$ | $(f_o - f_e)^2$ | $(f_o - f_e)^2/f_e$ |
| 15 | 18.34 | −3.34 | 11.15 | 0.61 |
| 58 | 48.91 | 9.09 | 82.63 | 1.69 |
| 46 | 56.55 | −10.55 | 111.30 | 1.97 |
| 69 | 64.19 | 4.81 | 23.14 | 0.36 |
| 21 | 17.66 | 3.34 | 11.15 | 0.63 |
| 38 | 47.09 | −9.09 | 82.63 | 1.75 |
| 65 | 54.45 | 10.55 | 111.30 | 2.04 |
| 57 | 61.81 | −4.81 | 23.14 | 0.37 |
| $n = 369$ | $n = 369.00$ | 0.00 | | $\chi^2$ (obtained) = 9.42 |

### Step 1. Make Assumptions and Meet Test Requirements.

Model: Random sampling
Level of measurement is nominal or ordinal

### Step 2. State the Null Hypothesis.

$H_0$: The two variables are independent.
($H_1$: The two variables are dependent.)

### Step 3. Select the Sampling Distribution and Establish the Critical Region.

Sampling distribution = $\chi^2$ distribution
Alpha = 0.05
Degrees of freedom = $(r - 1)(c - 1)$
$= (2 - 1)(4 - 1) = 3$
$\chi^2$(critical) = 7.815

### Step 4. Compute the Test Statistic.

$$\chi^2(\text{obtained}) = \sum \frac{(f_o - f_e)^2}{f_e}$$

$$\chi^2 (\text{obtained}) = 9.42$$

### Step 5. Make a Decision and Interpret the Results of the Test.
With an obtained $\chi^2$ of 9.42, we would reject the null hypothesis of independence. For this sample, there is

a statistically significant relationship between region of residence and attitude toward health care privatization.

To omplete the analysis, it would be useful to know exactly how the two variables are related. We can determine this by computing and analyzing column percentages:

| | | | Region | | |
|---|---|---|---|---|---|
| Attitude | Atlantic | Quebec | Ontario | Western | Totals |
| Favour | 41.67 | 60.42 | 41.44 | 54.76 | 50.95 |
| Oppose | 58.33 | 39.58 | 58.56 | 45.24 | 49.05 |
| Totals | 100.00% | 100.00% | 100.00% | 100.00% | 100.00% |

The column percentages show that just 41% of persons from the Atlantic provinces and Ontario favour having some private hospitals in Canada. By comparison, about 55% and 60% of persons from Western Canada and Quebec, respectively, favour the privatization of some hospitals. We have already concluded that the relationship is significant, and now we know the pattern of the relationship.

Source: Canadian Election Study, *2006 Canadian Election Study.*

---

## READING STATISTICS 7: Gender Differences in Health

In this section, we will examine a study on gender and health among Canadian university students. The research was conducted by a group of scholars in the Department of Kinesiology and Physical Education at Wilfrid Laurier University.

The research team selected a sample of 166 male and 472 female undergraduate students. Each student answered questions about their overall health and health-related behaviours during the current school year. The bivariate tables below show relationship between gender and participation in physical activity, hours per day engaged in social activities, and general state of health. Chi square was used to assess each relationship for statistical significance at the 0.05 alpha level. Significant relationships are symbolized as $p < 0.05$ in the tables. This tells us that the relationship would occur by chance alone less than 1 in 20 times, or 5% of the time (see the discussion of the "$p$" format in Section 7.3).

The first and second bivariate tables reveal that gender is significantly related to both physical and social activity at the 0.05 level. Looking at the column percentages, we see how these variables are related. Almost 3 out of 10 (27%) male respondents participated five or more times per week in physical activity. The comparable figure for females

is about 2 out of 10 (19%). Males are also more socially active: about 21% spent five to six hours per day in social activity compared to less than 15% of female respondents.

HEALTH BEHAVIOURS AND HEALTH STATUS BY GENDER: Frequencies and Percentages[*]

| 1. Participation in physical activity | Gender | |
|---|---|---|
| | Male | Female |
| Never | 6 (3.6%) | 28 (5.9%) |
| 1–2 times/week | 48 (29.1%) | 198 (41.9%) |
| 3–4 times/week | 66 (40.0%) | 155 (32.8%) |
| 5+ times/week | 45 (27.3%) | 91 (19.3%) |
| Totals | 165 (100.0%) | 472 (99.9%) |

$$\chi^2 = 11.9, p < 0.05$$

| 2. Hours/day engaged in social activities | Gender | |
|---|---|---|
| | Male | Female |
| 0–2 | 25 (15.2%) | 108 (23.0%) |
| 3–4 | 92 (55.8%) | 273 (58.2%) |
| 5–6 | 35 (21.2%) | 67 (14.3%) |
| 6+ | 13 (7.9%) | 21 (4.5%) |
| Totals | 165 (100.1%) | 469 (100.0%) |

$$\chi^2 = 10.0, p < 0.05$$

*(continued)*

| 3. General state of health | Gender | |
|---|---|---|
| | Male | Female |
| Excellent | 53 (32.5%) | 104 (22.2%) |
| Good | 96 (58.9%) | 320 (68.2%) |
| Poor/Fair | 14 (8.6%) | 45 (9.5%) |
| Totals | 163 (100.0%) | 469 (99.9%) |

$$\chi^2 = 6.9, p < 0.05$$

*Percentages may not total to 100% because of rounding error.

Turning to the third bivariate table, we see that the relationship between gender and general health state is statistically significant at the 0.05 level. Furthermore, almost 33% of males in the sample have excellent health compared to 22% of females. According to the authors, the relationship between gender and general health among Canadian university students reflects differences in disease prevention and health promotion between males and females:

> Although Canadian male university students engaged in negative health-related behaviors more frequently than females, this study also revealed that male students were engaging in two key positive and preventive health measures more than their female counterparts. First, male students were engaging more frequently than female students in physical activity. ... This is important as regular exercise has been identified by numerous health organizations as reducing the risk of cardiovascular illnesses and various cancers, as well as increasing quality of life. ... [Second], male students also engaged in significantly greater amounts of social activity per day than females. ... Social activity may serve as a buffer for college life stress for Canadian male students and therefore act as a health promoting behavior. (pp. 40–41)

Source: K. dawson, m. schneider, p. fletcher, and p. bryden, 2007, "examining gender differences in the health behaviors of Canadian university students," *Journal of the Royal Society for the Promotion of Health*.

In the case of 2 × 2 tables, the value of $\chi^2$ (obtained) can be adjusted by applying Yates's correction for continuity, the formula for which is

**FORMULA 7.4**

$$\chi_c^2 = \sum \frac{(|f_o - f_e| - 0.5)^2}{f_e}$$

where $\chi_c^2$ = corrected chi square
$|f_o - f_e|$ = the absolute values of the difference between the observed and expected frequency for each cell

The correction factor is applied by reducing the absolute value* of the term $(f_o - f_e)$ by 0.5 before squaring the difference and dividing by the expected frequency for the cell.

For tables larger than 2 × 2, there is no correction formula for computing $\chi^2$(obtained) for small samples. It may be possible to combine some of the categories of the variables and thereby increase cell sizes. Obviously, however, this course of action should be taken only when it is sensible to do so. In other words, distinctions that have clear theoretical justifications should not be erased merely to conform to the requirements

---

*Absolute values ignore plus and minus signs.

of a statistical test. When you feel that categories cannot be combined to build up cell frequencies, and the percentage of cells with expected frequencies of 5 or less is small, it is probably justifiable to continue with the uncorrected chi square test as long as the results are regarded with a suitable amount of caution.

A second potential problem related to sample size occurs with large samples. As we noted earlier in the chapter, all tests of hypothesis are sensitive to sample size. That is, the probability of rejecting the null hypothesis increases as the number of cases increases, regardless of any other factor. It turns out that chi square is especially sensitive to sample size and that larger samples may lead to the decision to reject the null hypothesis when the actual relationship is trivial. In fact, chi square is more responsive to changes in sample size than other test statistics, because the value of $\chi^2$ (obtained) will increase at the same rate as sample size. That is, if sample size is doubled, the value of $\chi^2$(obtained) will be doubled. *(For an illustration of this principle, see Problem 7.14.)*

Our major purpose in stressing the relationship between sample size and the value of chi square is really to point out, once again, the distinction between statistical significance and theoretical importance. On the one hand, tests of significance play a crucial role in research. As long as we are working with random samples, we must know whether our research results could have been produced by mere random chance.

On the other hand, like any other statistical technique, tests of hypothesis are limited in the range of questions they can answer. Specifically, these tests will tell us whether our results are statistically significant or not. They will not necessarily tell us if the results are important in any other sense. To deal more directly with questions of importance, we must use an additional set of statistical techniques called measures of association. We previewed these techniques in this chapter when we used column percentages. In Chapters 8 and 9, we will take a more in-depth look at measures of association for nominal and ordinal variables, respectively.

## SUMMARY

1. All the basic concepts and techniques for testing hypotheses were presented in this chapter. We saw how to test the null hypothesis of "independence" of variables. The central question is whether variables are independent in the population represented by the sample.

2. All tests of a hypothesis involve finding the probability of the observed sample outcome, given that the null hypothesis is true. If the outcome has a low probability, we reject the

null hypothesis. In the usual research situation, we will wish to reject the null hypothesis and thereby support the research hypothesis.

3. The five-step model will be our framework for decision making throughout the chapters on hypothesis testing. What we do during each step, however, will vary, depending on the specific test being conducted.

4. There are two kinds of errors in hypothesis testing. A Type I, or alpha, error is rejecting a

true null hypothesis; a Type II, or beta, error is failing to reject a false null hypothesis. The probabilities of committing these two types of error are inversely related and cannot be simultaneously minimized in the same test. By selecting an alpha level, we try to balance the probability of these two kinds of error.

5. The chi square test for independence is appropriate for situations in which the variables of interest have been organized into table format. The null hypothesis is that the variables are independent or that the classification of a case into a particular category on one variable has no effect on the probability that the case will be classified into any particular category of the second variable.

6. Because chi square is non-parametric and requires only categorical (i.e., nominal or ordinal) variables, its model assumptions are easily satisfied. Furthermore, because it is computed from bivariate tables, in which the number of rows and columns can be easily expanded, the chi square test can be used in many situations in which other tests are inapplicable.

7. In the chi square test, we first find the frequencies that would appear in the cells if the variables were independent ($f_e$) and then compare those frequencies, cell by cell, with the frequencies actually observed in the cells ($f_o$). If the null hypothesis is true, expected and observed frequencies should be quite close in value. The greater the difference between the observed and expected frequencies, the greater the possibility of rejecting the null hypothesis.

8. The chi square test has several important limitations. It is often difficult to interpret when tables have many (more than four or five) dimensions. Also, as sample size ($n$) decreases, the chi square test becomes less trustworthy, and corrective action may be required. Finally, with very large samples, we might declare relatively trivial relationships to be statistically significant. As is the case with all tests of hypothesis, statistical significance is not the same thing as "importance" in any other sense.

9. If you are still confused about the uses of inferential statistics described in this chapter, don't be alarmed or discouraged. A sizable volume of rather complex material has been presented, and only rarely will a beginning student fully comprehend the unique logic of hypothesis testing on the first exposure. After all, it is not every day that you learn how to test a statement you don't believe (the null hypothesis) against a distribution that doesn't exist (the sampling distribution)!

10. In all tests of hypothesis, a number of factors affect the probability of rejecting the null hypothesis: the size of the difference, the alpha level, and sample size. Statistical significance is not the same thing as theoretical or practical importance. Even after a difference is found to be statistically significant, researchers must still demonstrate the relevance or importance of their findings. The statistics presented in later chapters of this textbook will give us some of the tools we need to deal directly with issues beyond statistical significance.

## SUMMARY OF FORMULAS

Chi square (obtained):

7.1 $\quad \chi^2 \text{ (obtained)} = \sum \dfrac{(f_o - f_e)^2}{f_e}$

Expected frequencies:

7.2 $\quad f_e = \dfrac{\text{Row marginal} \times \text{Column marginal}}{n}$

Degrees of freedom, bivariate tables:

7.3 $\quad df = (r - 1)(c - 1)$

Yates's correction for continuity:

7.4 $\quad \chi_c^2 = \sum \dfrac{(|f_o - f_e| - 0.5)^2}{f_e}$

## GLOSSARY

**Alpha level (α).** The proportion of area under the sampling distribution that contains unlikely sample outcomes, given that the null hypothesis is true. Also, the probability of Type I error. Alpha is associated with the critical statistic score.

**Bivariate table.** A table that displays the joint frequency distributions of two variables.

**Cells.** The cross-classification categories of the variables in a bivariate table.

**$\chi^2$ (critical).** The score on the sampling distribution of all possible sample chi squares that marks the beginning of the critical region.

**$\chi^2$ (obtained).** The test statistic as computed from sample results.

**Chi square test.** A non-parametric test of hypothesis for variables that have been organized into a bivariate table.

**Column.** The vertical dimension of a bivariate table. By convention, each column represents a score on the independent variable.

**Column percentages.** Percentages computed within each column of a bivariate table.

**Critical region (region of rejection).** The area under the sampling distribution that, in advance of the test itself, is defined as including unlikely sample outcomes, given that the null hypothesis is true.

**Expected frequency ( $f_e$ ).** The cell frequencies that would be expected in a bivariate table if the variables were independent.

**Five-step model.** A step-by-step guideline for conducting tests of hypotheses. A framework that organizes decisions and computations for all tests of significance.

**Hypothesis testing (significance testing).** Statistical tests that estimate the probability of sample outcomes if assumptions about the population (the null hypothesis) are true.

**Independence.** The null hypothesis in the chi square test. Two variables are independent if, for all cases, the classification of a case on one variable has no effect on the probability that the case will be classified in any particular category of the second variable.

**Marginals.** The row and column subtotals in a bivariate table.

**Non-parametric.** A "distribution-free" test. These tests do not assume a normal sampling distribution.

**Null hypothesis ($H_0$).** A statement of "no difference" or "no relationship." In the context of the chi square test of independence, the variables are assumed to be independent in the population.

**Observed frequency ( $f_o$ ).** The cell frequencies actually observed and recorded in a bivariate table.

**$p$.** The area under the sampling distribution that indicates the exact likelihood of rejecting the null hypothesis when it is true (i.e., the exact risk of a Type I error). $p$ is associated with the test (obtained) statistic.

**Research hypothesis ($H_1$).** A statement that contradicts the null hypothesis. In the context of the chi square test of independence, the research hypothesis says that the variables are dependent in the population.

**Row.** The horizontal dimension of a bivariate table, conventionally representing a score on the dependent variable.

**Test statistic.** The obtained statistic. The value computed in step 4 of the five-step model that converts the sample outcome into a chi square score.

**Type I error (alpha error).** The probability of rejecting a null hypothesis that is, in fact, true.

**Type II error (beta error).** The probability of failing to reject a null hypothesis that is, in fact, false.

## MULTIMEDIA RESOURCES

 nelson.com/student

Visit the companion website for the fourth Canadian edition of *Statistics: A Tool for Social Research* to access a wide range of student resources. Begin by clicking on the Student Resources section of the textbook's website to access online chapters and study tools.

**PROBLEMS**

**7.1** For each table below, calculate the obtained chi square. *(HINT: Calculate the expected frequencies for each cell with Formula 7.2. Double-check to make sure you are using the correct row and column marginals for each cell. It may be helpful to record the expected frequencies in table format as well—see Tables 7.4, 7.6, and 7.10. Next, use a computational table to organize the calculation for Formula 7.1—see Tables 7.7 and 7.11. For each cell, subtract expected frequency from observed frequency, and record the result in column 3. Square the value in column 3 and record the result in column 4, then divide the value in column 4 by the expected frequency for that cell and record the result in column 5. Remember that the sum of column 5 in the computational table is the obtained chi square. As you proceed, check to make sure you are using the correct values for each cell.)*

**a.**

| 20 | 25 | 45 |
|----|----|----|
| 25 | 20 | 45 |
| 45 | 45 | 90 |

**b.**

| 10 | 15 | 25 |
|----|----|----|
| 20 | 30 | 50 |
| 30 | 45 | 75 |

**c.**

| 25 | 15 | 40 |
|----|----|-----|
| 30 | 30 | 60 |
| 55 | 45 | 100 |

**d.**

| 20 | 45 | 65 |
|----|----|-----|
| 15 | 20 | 35 |
| 35 | 65 | 100 |

**7.2** SOC Twenty-five cities have been classified as high or low on their homicide rates and on the number of guns sold within city limits. Calculate the obtained chi square for these data.

| Volume of Gun Sales | Homicide Rate Low | High | Totals |
|---------------------|-----|------|--------|
| High | 8 | 5 | 13 |
| Low | 4 | 8 | 12 |
| Totals | 12 | 13 | 25 |

**7.3** SW A local politician is concerned that a program for the homeless in her city is discriminating against women. The data below were taken from random samples of female and male homeless people.

| Received Services? | Sex Female | Male | Totals |
|--------------------|------------|------|--------|
| Yes | 6 | 7 | 13 |
| No | 4 | 9 | 13 |
| Totals | 10 | 16 | 26 |

**a.** Is there a statistically significant relationship between sex and whether the person has received services from the program?

**b.** Compute column percentages for the table to determine the pattern of the relationship. Which group is more likely to get services?

**7.4** Is there a "gender gap" in support of the Liberal Party of Canada among university faculty? To answer this question, a sample of university faculty has been asked about their political party preference.

| Party Preference | Sex Male | Female | Totals |
|------------------|----------|--------|--------|
| Liberal | 10 | 15 | 25 |
| Other | 15 | 10 | 25 |
| Totals | 25 | 25 | 50 |

**a.** Is there a statistically significant relationship between sex and party preference?

**b.** Compute column percentages for the table to determine the pattern of the relationship. Which sex is more likely to prefer the Liberals?

**7.5** PA Is there a relationship between salary levels and unionization for public employees? The data below represent this relationship for fire departments in a random sample of 100 cities of roughly the same size. Salary data have been dichotomized at the median. Summarize your findings.

| Salary | Status Union | Non-union | Totals |
|--------|--------------|-----------|--------|
| High | 21 | 29 | 50 |
| Low | 14 | 36 | 50 |
| Totals | 35 | 65 | 100 |

**a.** Is there a statistically significant relationship between these variables?

**b.** Compute column percentages for the table to determine the pattern of the relationship. Which group is more likely to get high salaries?

**7.6** SOC A program of pet therapy has been running at a local nursing home. Are the participants in the program more alert and responsive than non-participants? The results, drawn from a random sample of residents, are reported below.

| | Status | | |
| | Participants | Non-participants | Totals |
| Alertness | | | |
|---|---|---|---|
| High | 23 | 15 | 38 |
| Low | 11 | 18 | 29 |
| Totals | 34 | 33 | 67 |

**a.** Is there a statistically significant relationship between participation and alertness?

**b.** Compute column percentages for the table to determine the pattern of the relationship. Which group is more likely to be alert?

**7.7** SOC The provincial Ministry of Education has rated a sample of local school boards for compliance with province-mandated guidelines for quality. Is the quality of a school board significantly related to the affluence of the community as measured by per capita income?

| | Per Capita Income | | |
| Quality | Low | High | Totals |
|---|---|---|---|
| Low | 16 | 8 | 24 |
| High | 9 | 17 | 26 |
| Totals | 25 | 25 | 50 |

**a.** Is there a statistically significant relationship between these variables?

**b.** Compute column percentages for the table to determine the pattern of the relationship. Are high- or low-income communities more likely to have high-quality schools?

**7.8** CJ A local judge has been allowing some individuals convicted of "driving under the influence"

to work in a hospital emergency room as an alternative to fines, suspensions, and other penalties. A random sample of offenders has been drawn. Do participants in this program have lower rates of recidivism for this offence?

| | Status | | |
| | Participants | Non-participants | Totals |
| Recidivist? | | | |
|---|---|---|---|
| Yes | 60 | 123 | 183 |
| No | 55 | 108 | 163 |
| Totals | 115 | 231 | 346 |

**a.** Is there a statistically significant relationship between these variables?

**b.** Compute column percentages for the table to determine the pattern of the relationship. Which group is more likely to be arrested again for driving under the influence?

**7.9** SOC Is there a relationship between length of marriage and satisfaction with marriage? The necessary information has been collected from a random sample of 100 respondents drawn from a local community.

| | Length of Marriage (in years) | | | |
| | Less than 5 | 5–10 | More than 10 | Totals |
| Satisfaction | | | | |
|---|---|---|---|---|
| Low | 10 | 20 | 20 | 50 |
| High | 20 | 20 | 10 | 50 |
| Totals | 30 | 40 | 30 | 100 |

**a.** Is there a statistically significant relationship between these variables? Write a sentence or two explaining your decision.

**b.** Compute column percentages for the table to determine the pattern of the relationship. Which group is more likely to be highly satisfied?

**7.10** PS Is there a relationship between political ideology and class standing? Are upper-class persons significantly different from lower-class individuals on this variable? The table below reports the relationship between these two variables for a random sample of 267 adult Canadians.

|  | Class Standing | | |
|---|---|---|---|
| Political Ideology | Lower-Class | Upper-Class | Totals |
| Liberal | 43 | 40 | 83 |
| Moderate | 50 | 50 | 100 |
| Conservative | 40 | 44 | 84 |
| Totals | 133 | 134 | 267 |

**a.** Is there a statistically significant relationship between these variables?
**b.** Compute column percentages for the table to determine the pattern of the relationship. Which group is more likely to be conservative?

**7.11** |SOC| At a large urban university, about half of the students live off campus in various arrangements, and the other half live in residence on campus. Is academic performance dependent on living arrangements? The results based on a random sample of 300 students are presented below.

|  | Residential Status | | | |
|---|---|---|---|---|
| GPA | Off Campus with Roommates | Off Campus with Parent | On Campus | Totals |
| Low | 22 | 20 | 48 | 90 |
| Moderate | 36 | 40 | 54 | 130 |
| High | 32 | 10 | 38 | 80 |
| Totals | 90 | 70 | 140 | 300 |

**a.** Is there a statistically significant relationship between these variables?
**b.** Compute column percentages for the table to determine the pattern of the relationship. Which group is more likely to have a high GPA?

**7.12** |SOC| An urban sociologist has built up a database describing a sample of the neighbourhoods in her city and has developed a scale by which each area can be rated for "quality of life" (this includes measures of pollution, noise, open space, services available, etc.). She has also asked samples of residents of these areas about their level of satisfaction with their neighbourhoods.

|  | Quality of Life | | | |
|---|---|---|---|---|
| Satisfaction | Low | Moderate | High | Totals |
| Low | 21 | 15 | 6 | 42 |
| Moderate | 12 | 25 | 21 | 58 |
| High | 8 | 17 | 32 | 57 |
| Totals | 41 | 57 | 59 | 157 |

**a.** Is there significant agreement between the sociologist's objective ratings of quality of life and the respondents' self-reports of satisfaction?
**b.** Compute column percentages for the table to determine the pattern of the relationship. Which group is most likely to say that their satisfaction is high?

**7.13** |SOC| Does support for the legalization of marijuana vary by region of Canada? The table displays the relationship between the two variables for a random sample of 1,020 adult Canadians.

|  | Region | | | | |
|---|---|---|---|---|---|
| Legalize? | Atlantic | Central | Western | Northern | Totals |
| Yes | 60 | 65 | 42 | 78 | 245 |
| No | 245 | 200 | 180 | 150 | 775 |
| Totals | 305 | 265 | 222 | 228 | 1,020 |

**a.** Is there a statistically significant relationship between these variables?
**b.** Compute column percentages for the table to determine the pattern of the relationship. Which region is most likely to favour the legalization of marijuana?

**7.14** |SOC| A researcher is concerned with the relationship between attitudes toward violence and violent behaviour. If attitudes "cause" behaviour (a very debatable proposition), then people who have positive attitudes toward violence should have high rates of violent behaviour. A pretest was conducted on 70 respondents. Among other things, the respondents were asked, "Have you been involved in a violent incident of any kind over the past six months?" The researcher established the following relationship:

| | Attitude Toward Violence | | |
|---|---|---|---|
| Involvement | Favourable | Unfavourable | Totals |
| Yes | 16 | 19 | 35 |
| No | 14 | 21 | 35 |
| Totals | 30 | 40 | 70 |

The chi square calculated on these data is 0.23, which is not significant at the 0.05 level (confirm this conclusion with your own calculations). Undeterred by this result, the researcher proceeded with the project and gathered a random sample of 7,000. In terms of percentage distributions, the results for the full sample were exactly the same as for the pretest:

| | Attitude Toward Violence | | |
|---|---|---|---|
| Involvement | Favourable | Unfavourable | Totals |
| Yes | 1,600 | 1,900 | 3,500 |
| No | 1,400 | 2,100 | 3,500 |
| Totals | 3,000 | 4,000 | 7,000 |

However, the chi square obtained is a very healthy 23.4 (confirm with your own calculations). Why is the full-sample chi square significant when the pretest was not? What happened? Do you think the second result is important?

**7.15** SOC Some results from a survey given to a random sample of Canadians are presented below. For each table, conduct the chi square test of significance and compute column percentages. Write a sentence or two of interpretation for each test.

**a.** Support for same-sex marriage by age:

| | Age | | | |
|---|---|---|---|---|
| Support? | Younger than 30 | 30–49 | 50 and Older | Totals |
| Yes | 154 | 360 | 213 | 727 |
| No | 179 | 441 | 429 | 1,049 |
| Totals | 333 | 801 | 642 | 1,776 |

**b.** Support for gun control by age:

| | Age | | | |
|---|---|---|---|---|
| Support? | Younger than 30 | 30–49 | 50 and Older | Totals |
| Favour | 361 | 867 | 675 | 1,903 |
| Oppose | 144 | 297 | 252 | 693 |
| Totals | 505 | 1,164 | 927 | 2,596 |

**c.** Fear of walking alone at night by age:

| | Age | | | |
|---|---|---|---|---|
| Fear? | Younger than 30 | 30–49 | 50 and Older | Totals |
| Yes | 147 | 325 | 300 | 772 |
| No | 202 | 507 | 368 | 1,077 |
| Totals | 349 | 832 | 668 | 1,849 |

**d.** Support for legalizing marijuana by age:

| | Age | | | |
|---|---|---|---|---|
| Legalize? | Younger than 30 | 30–49 | 50 and Older | Totals |
| Should | 128 | 254 | 142 | 524 |
| Should not | 224 | 534 | 504 | 1,262 |
| Totals | 352 | 788 | 646 | 1,786 |

**e.** Support for suicide when a person has an incurable disease by age:

| | Age | | | |
|---|---|---|---|---|
| Support? | Younger than 30 | 30–49 | 50 and Older | Totals |
| Yes | 225 | 537 | 367 | 1,129 |
| No | 107 | 270 | 266 | 643 |
| Totals | 332 | 807 | 633 | 1,772 |

**You Are the Researcher**

## Using SPSS to Conduct the Chi Square Test with the 2013 GSS

The demonstrations and exercises below use the shortened version of the 2013 GSS data set supplied with this textbook.

## SPSS DEMONSTRATION 7.1 Does Volunteering Behaviour Vary by Sex?

The **Crosstabs** procedure in SPSS produces bivariate tables and a wide variety of statistics. This procedure is commonly used in social science research at all levels, and you will see many references to **Crosstabs** in chapters to come. We will introduce the command here, and we will return to it often in later sessions.

In this demonstration, we ask two questions: "Is sex significantly related to volunteering behaviour?" And if so, "Are females more likely to be volunteers?" We can answer these questions, at least for the 2013 GSS sample, by constructing a bivariate table to display the relationship between *vcg_300* (volunteering indicator) and *sex* (sex). We will also request a chi square test for the table.

Start SPSS and load the 2013 GSS database (*GSS_2013_Shortened.sav*). From the main menu bar, click **Analyze, Descriptive Statistics**, then **Crosstabs**. The **Crosstabs** dialog box will appear with the variables listed in a box on the left. Highlight *vcg_300* and click the arrow to move the variable name into the **Row(s)** box, then highlight *sex* and move it into the **Column(s)** box. Click the **Statistics** button at the top of the window, then click the box next to **Chi-square**. Click **Continue**. Then, click the **Cells** button and check the boxes next to "**Expected**" in the **Counts** box and "**Column**" in the **Percentages** box. This will generate the expected frequencies and column percentages, respectively, for the table. Click **Continue** and **OK**, and the output below will be produced. (Note that the output has been slightly edited for clarity and will not exactly match the output on your screen.)

### Volunteer Work—12 Months* Sex of Respondent Cross-tabulation

| | | | Sex of Respondent | | |
| | | | Male | Female | Total |
|---|---|---|---|---|---|
| Volunteer work—12 months | Yes | Count | 249 | 310 | 559 |
| | | % within sex of respondent | 31.2% | 39.4% | 35.2% |
| | No | Count | 550 | 477 | 1027 |
| | | % within sex of respondent | 68.8% | 60.6% | 64.8% |
| Total | | Count | 799 | 787 | 1586 |
| | | % within sex of respondent | 100.0% | 100.0% | 100.0% |

### Chi Square Tests

| | Value | df | Asymptotic Significance (2-sided) | Exact Sig. (2-sided) | Exact Sig. (1-sided) |
|---|---|---|---|---|---|
| Pearson chi-square | 11.755[a] | 1 | .001 | | |
| Continuity correction[b] | 11.398 | 1 | .001 | | |
| Likelihood ratio | 11.772 | 1 | .001 | | |
| Fisher's exact test | | | | .001 | .000 |
| Linear-by-linear association | 11.748 | 1 | .001 | | |
| N of valid cases | 1586 | | | | |

[a] 0 cells (0.0%) have expected count less than 5. The minimum expected count is 277.39.

[b] Computed only for a 2 × 2 table.

The cross-tabulation table is small (2 × 2), and the information is straightforward. Let's begin with the cells. Each cell displays the observed frequency or the number of cases in the cell ("Count") and the column percentage for that cell ("% within Sex"). For example, there were 249 males who volunteered, and these were 31.2% of all males. By contrast, there were 310 females who volunteered or 39.4%, who reported having volunteered. Females are generally more likely than males to have volunteered.

The table also displays the expected frequency for each cell. The greater the differences between expected frequencies ("Expected Count") and observed frequencies ("Count"), the less likely the variables are independent and the more likely we will be able to reject the null hypothesis. The results of the chi square test are formally reported in the output block that follows the cross-tabulation table.

The value of $\chi^2$ (obtained) is found in the row "Pearson Chi-Square." The value of the obtained chi square is 11.775, the degree of freedom is 1, and the exact significance of the chi square is 0.001. (The value of 0.001 is the exact *probability* of getting the pattern observed in the cell frequencies if only chance is operating, and is often called the "*p*" value.)

To test whether there is a significant relationship between the variables we can manually compare the value of $\chi^2$ (obtained) to the value of $\chi^2$ (critical), determined by consulting the chi square table in Appendix C for a particular alpha level and degrees of freedom as we have practised throughout this chapter. The test statistic, $\chi^2$ (obtained), of 11.775 falls into the critical region (i.e., 11.775 is greater than 3.841). So, we reject the null hypothesis. However, because SPSS provides the exact probability, there is no need to look up the test statistic in the chi square table. The exact probability value, 0.001, is well below the standard indicator of a significant result (alpha = 0.05), so we reject the null hypothesis that the variables are independent and conclude that there is a statistically significant relationship between sex and volunteering behaviour. Being a volunteer is dependent on sex, with females being more likely to volunteer. In Exercise 7.1, you will have the opportunity to investigate other variables that might be significantly related to volunteering behaviour.

As a final note, the number of the cells with expected frequencies less than five is provided at the bottom of the "Chi-Square Tests" output box. Yates's correction for continuity, labelled "Continuity Correction," should be used in any 2 × 2 table where one or more cells have expected counts of less than five. When this is the case for tables larger than 2 × 2, consider collapsing categories of the variables to increase cell sizes.

### SPSS DEMONSTRATION 7.2 Does Religious Participation Vary by Canadian Birth Status?

In this demonstration we will examine the relationship between Canadian birth status and the frequency of religious participation. Specifically, "Is religious participation higher for people born in Canada or people not born in Canada?" Run the **Crosstabs** procedure again with *ree_02* (frequency of religious participation in the past 12 months) as the row variable and *brthcan* as the column variable. Don't forget to request chi square, expected frequencies, and column percentages. The output, slightly edited for clarity, is shown below.

**Frequency of Religious Participation—12 Months\* Place of Birth of Respondent—Canada Cross-tabulation**

| | | | Place of Birth of Respondent—Canada | | |
| --- | --- | --- | --- | --- | --- |
| | | | Born in Canada | Born Out-side Canada | Total |
| Frequency of religious participation—12 months | At least once a week | Count | 153 | 107 | 260 |
| | | % within place of birth of respondent—Canada | 12.9% | 29.4% | 16.7% |
| | At least once a month | Count | 125 | 40 | 165 |
| | | % within place of birth of respondent—Canada | 10.5% | 11.0% | 10.6% |
| | At least 3 times a year | Count | 119 | 45 | 164 |
| | | % within place of birth of respondent—Canada | 10.0% | 12.4% | 10.6% |
| | Once or twice a year | Count | 199 | 45 | 244 |
| | | % within place of birth of respondent—Canada | 16.7% | 12.4% | 15.7% |
| | Not at all | Count | 593 | 127 | 720 |
| | | % within place of birth of respondent—Canada | 49.9% | 34.9% | 46.4% |
| Total | | Count | 1189 | 364 | 1553 |
| | | % within place of birth of respondent—Canada | 100.0% | 100.0% | 100.0% |

**Chi Square Tests**

| | Value | df | Asymptotic Significance (2-sided) |
| --- | --- | --- | --- |
| Pearson chi-square | 63.882[a] | 4 | .000 |
| Likelihood ratio | 59.387 | 4 | .000 |
| Linear-by-linear association | 54.050 | 1 | .000 |
| N of valid cases | 1553 | | |

[a] 0 cells (0.0%) have expected count less than 5. The minimum expected count is 38.44.

Chi square is 63.882, degrees of freedom is 4, and the exact probability of getting this pattern of cell frequencies by random chance alone is .000. Note that when the exact probability value is less than .0005, SPSS cuts it off at three decimal places, or .000, to save space. Therefore, there is a significant relationship between the variables. The column percentages show that religious participation increases from people born in Canada to people not born in Canada. Focusing on the top row, for example, we see that 29.4% of people not born in Canada participated in religious services at least once a week in the past 12 months, while only 12.9% of people born in Canada did so. Looking at the bottom row, we see that 49.9% of people born in Canada did not participation in religious services at all in the past 12 months, while 34.9% of people not born in Canada followed this pattern. Exercise 7.2 provides an opportunity to look at other variables that might be significantly related to *ree_02*.

## Exercises (using *GSS_2013_Shortened.sav*)

**7.1.** For a follow-up to Demonstration 7.1, find two more variables that might be related to *vcg_300*. Run the **Crosstabs** procedure with *vcg_300* as the row variable and your other variables as the column variables.* Write a paragraph summarizing the results of these two tests. Which relationships are significant at the 0.05 alpha level?

**7.2.** As a follow-up to Demonstration 7.2, find two more variables that might be related to *ree_02*. Use the **Crosstabs** procedure to see if any of your variables have a significant relationship with *ree_02*.* Which of the variables had the most significant relationship?

---

*If necessary, use the recode procedure shown in Appendix F.5 to reduce the number of categories in the independent (column) variables.

# 8 Measures of Association for Variables Measured at the Nominal Level

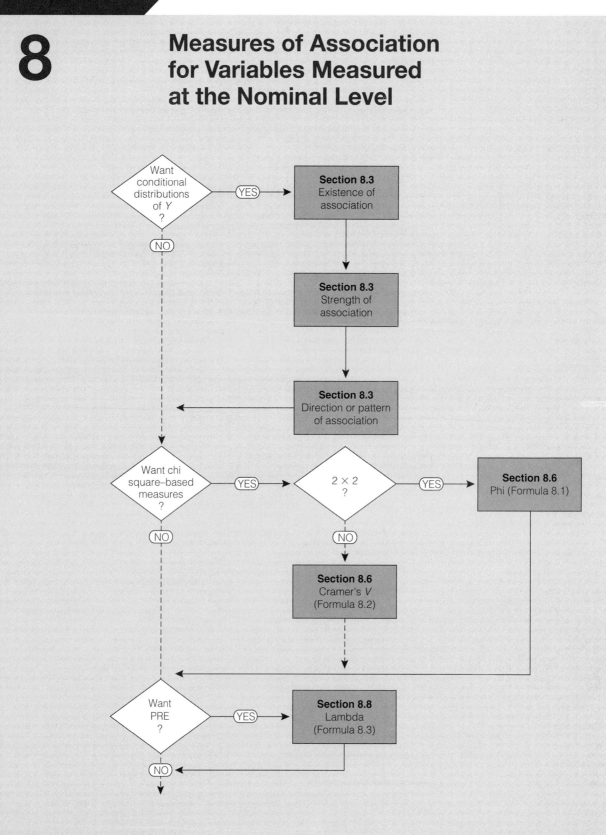

**LEARNING OBJECTIVES** ▰▰▰▰▰▰▰▰▰▰▰▰▰▰

By the end of this chapter, you will be able to

1. Explain how we can use measures of association to describe and analyze the importance of relationships (versus their statistical significance).

2. Define "association" in the context of bivariate tables and in terms of changing conditional distributions.

3. List and explain the three characteristics of a bivariate relationship: existence, strength, and pattern or direction.

4. Investigate a bivariate association by properly calculating percentages for a bivariate table and interpreting the results.

5. Compute and interpret three measures of association for variables measured at the nominal level: phi, Cramer's $V$, and lambda.

## 8.1 INTRODUCTION

As we saw in Chapter 7, tests of statistical significance are extremely important in social science research. As long as social scientists must work with samples rather than populations, these tests are indispensable for dealing with the possibility that our research results are the products of mere random chance. However, tests of significance are often merely the first step in the analysis of research results. These tests do have limitations, and statistical significance is not necessarily the same thing as relevance or importance. Furthermore, all tests of significance are affected by sample size; tests performed on large samples may result in decisions to reject the null hypothesis when, in fact, the observed relationship between variables is quite weak.

Beginning with this chapter, we will be working with a class of descriptive statistics called **measures of association**. Whereas tests of significance detect non-random relationships, measures of association provide information about the strength and, where appropriate, the direction of relationships—information that is more directly relevant for assessing the importance of relationships and testing the power and validity of our theories. The theories that guide scientific research are almost always stated in cause-and-effect terms (e.g., "variable $X$ causes variable $Y$"). As an example, recall our discussion of the materialistic hypothesis in Chapter 1. In that theory, the causal (or independent) variable was social class and the effect (or dependent) variable was health status. The theory asserts that social class *causes* health. Measures of association help us trace causal relationships among variables, and they are our most important and powerful statistical tools for documenting, measuring, and analyzing cause-and-effect relationships.

As useful as they are, measures of association, like any class of statistics, do have their limitations. Most importantly, these statistics cannot *prove* that two variables are causally related. Even if there is a strong (and significant) statistical association between two variables, we cannot necessarily conclude that one variable is a cause of the other. We will explore causation in more detail in Part 4, but for now you should keep in mind that causation and association are two different things. We can use a statistical association between variables as evidence for a causal relationship, but association by itself is not proof that a causal relationship exists.

Another important use for measures of association is prediction. If two variables are associated, we can predict the score of a case on one variable from the score of that case on the other variable. For example, if social class and health are associated, we can predict that people who have high social class will be healthier than those with low social class. Note that prediction and causation can be two separate matters. If variables are associated, we can predict from one to the other even if the variables are not causally related.

In conclusion, this chapter begins by introducing the concept of **association** between variables in the context of bivariate tables and will stress the use of percentages to analyze associations between variables, as introduced in Chapter 7. We will then proceed to the logic, calculation, and interpretation of some widely used measures of association. By the end of the chapter, you will have an array of statistical tools you can use to analyze the strength and direction of associations between variables.

## 8.2 ASSOCIATION BETWEEN VARIABLES AND THE BIVARIATE TABLE

Most generally, two variables are said to be associated if the distribution of one of them changes under the various categories or scores of the other. For example, suppose that an industrial sociologist was concerned with the relationship between job satisfaction and productivity for assembly-line workers. If these two variables are associated, then scores on productivity will change under the different conditions of satisfaction. Highly satisfied workers will have different scores on productivity than workers who are low on satisfaction, and levels of productivity will vary by levels of satisfaction.

This relationship will become clearer with the use of bivariate tables. As we discussed in Chapter 7, bivariate tables display the scores of cases on two different variables. By convention, the **independent** or **X variable** (i.e., the variable taken as causal) is arrayed in the columns, and the **dependent** or **Y variable** in the rows (for the sake of brevity, we will often refer to the independent variable as $X$ and the dependent variable as $Y$ in the material that follows). Each non-marginal column of the table (the vertical dimension) represents a score or category of the independent variable ($X$), and each non-marginal row (the horizontal dimension) represents a score or category of the dependent variable ($Y$).*

---

*While it is conventional to construct a bivariate table in this format, the opposite is also acceptable where the columns are scores of the dependent variable and rows are scores of the independent variable.

**TABLE 8.1  Productivity by Job Satisfaction (frequencies)**

|  | Job Satisfaction ($X$) | | | |
|---|---|---|---|---|
| Productivity ($Y$) | Low | Moderate | High | Totals |
| Low | 30 | 21 | 7 | 58 |
| Moderate | 20 | 25 | 18 | 63 |
| High | 10 | 15 | 27 | 52 |
| Totals | 60 | 61 | 52 | 173 |

Table 8.1 displays a relationship between productivity and job satisfaction for a fictitious sample of 173 factory workers. We focus on the columns to detect the presence of an association between variables displayed in table format. Each column shows the pattern of scores on the dependent variable for each score on the independent variable. For example, the left-hand column indicates that 30 of the 60 workers who were low on job satisfaction were low on productivity, 20 were moderate on productivity, and 10 were high on productivity. The middle column shows that 21 of the 61 moderately satisfied workers were low on productivity, 25 were moderate on productivity, and 15 were high on productivity. Of the 52 workers who are highly satisfied (the right-hand column), 7 were low on productivity, 18 were moderate, and 27 were high.

By inspecting the table from column to column we can observe the effects of the independent variable on the dependent variable (provided, of course, that the table is constructed with the independent variable in the columns). These "within-column" frequency distributions are called the **conditional distributions of $Y$**; they display the distribution of scores on the dependent variable for each condition (or score) of the independent variable.

Table 8.1 indicates that productivity and satisfaction are associated: The distribution of scores on $Y$ (productivity) changes across the various conditions of $X$ (satisfaction). For example, half of the workers who were low on satisfaction were also low on productivity (30 out of 60), and over half of the workers who were high on satisfaction were high on productivity (27 out of 52).

Although it is intended to be a test of significance, the chi square statistic provides another way to detect the existence of an association between two variables that have been organized into table format. Any non-zero value for obtained chi square indicates that the variables are associated. For example, the obtained chi square for Table 8.1 is 24.2, a value that affirms our previous conclusion, based on the conditional distributions of $Y$, that an association of some sort exists between job satisfaction and productivity.

Often, the researcher will have already conducted a chi square test before considering matters of association. In such cases, it will not be necessary to inspect the conditional distributions of $Y$ to ascertain whether the two variables are associated. If the obtained chi square is zero, the two variables are independent and not associated. Any value other than zero indicates some association between the variables. Remember, however, that statistical significance (inferential statistics) and association (descriptive statistics) are two different things. It is perfectly possible for two variables to be associated (as indicated by a non-zero chi square) but still independent in the population (if we fail to reject the null hypothesis).

In this section we have defined, in a general way, the concept of association between two variables. We have also shown two different ways to detect the presence of an association. In the next section, we will extend the analysis beyond questions of the mere presence or absence of an association and, in a systematic way, see how we can develop additional, very useful information about the relationship between two variables.

## 8.3 THREE CHARACTERISTICS OF BIVARIATE ASSOCIATIONS

Bivariate associations possess three different characteristics, each of which must be analyzed for a full investigation of the relationship. Investigating these characteristics may be thought of as a process of finding answers to three questions:

**1.** Does an association exist?
**2.** If an association does exist, how strong is it?
**3.** If an association does exist, what is the pattern and/or the direction of the association?

We will consider each of these questions separately.

**Does an Association Exist?**   We have already discussed the general definition of association, and we have seen that we can detect an association by observing the conditional distributions of $Y$ in a table or by using chi square. In Table 8.1, we know that the two variables are associated to some extent because the conditional distributions of productivity ($Y$) are different across the various categories of satisfaction ($X$) and because the chi square statistic is a non-zero value.

Comparisons from column to column in Table 8.1 are relatively easy to make because the column totals are roughly equal. This will not usually be the case, and it is helpful to compute percentages to control for varying column totals. These column percentages, introduced in Chapter 7, are computed within each column separately and make the pattern of association more visible.

The general procedure for detecting association with bivariate tables is to compute percentages within the columns (vertically or down each

**TABLE 8.2 Productivity by Job Satisfaction (percentages)**

| Productivity (Y) | Job Satisfaction (X) | | | Totals (%) |
|---|---|---|---|---|
| | Low (%) | Moderate (%) | High (%) | |
| Low | 50.00 | 34.43 | 13.46 | 33.53 |
| Moderate | 33.33 | 40.98 | 34.62 | 36.42 |
| High | 16.67 | 24.59 | 51.92 | 30.05 |
| Totals | 100.00 | 100.00 | 100.00 | 100.00 |
| | (60) | (61) | (52) | (173) |

column) and then compare column to column across the table (horizontally or across the rows). We can conveniently remember this procedure with the following statement: "Percentage Down, Compare Across." Table 8.2 presents column percentages calculated from the data in Table 8.1. Besides controlling for any differences in column totals, tables in percentage form are usually easier to read because changes in the conditional distributions of Y are easier to detect.

In Table 8.2, we can see that the largest cell changes position from column to column. For workers who are low on satisfaction, the single largest cell is in the top row (low on productivity). For the middle column (moderate on satisfaction), the largest cell is in the middle row (moderate on productivity), and for the right-hand column (high on satisfaction), it is in the bottom row (high on productivity). Even a cursory glance at the conditional distributions of Y in Table 8.2 reinforces our conclusion that an association does exist between these two variables.

If two variables are not associated, then the conditional distributions of Y will not change across the columns. The distribution of Y would be the same for each condition of X. Table 8.3 illustrates a "perfect non-association" between age and productivity. Table 8.3 is only one of many patterns that indicate "no association." The important point is that the conditional distributions of Y are the same. Levels of productivity do not change at all for the various age groups and, therefore, no

**TABLE 8.3 Productivity by Age (an illustration of no association)**

| Productivity (Y) | Age (X) | | |
|---|---|---|---|
| | 25–34 (%) | 35–44 (%) | 45+ (%) |
| Low | 33.33 | 33.33 | 33.33 |
| Moderate | 33.33 | 33.33 | 33.33 |
| High | 33.33 | 33.33 | 33.33 |
| Totals | 100.00 | 100.00 | 100.00 |

association exists between these variables. Also, the obtained chi square computed from this table would have a value of zero, again indicating no association.

The use of **panelled pie charts** and **clustered bar charts** can also help us to recognize association between variables. Both these bivariate graphs are visual representations of the conditional distributions of $Y$ shown in the bivariate table. As we saw with the univariate pie and bar charts in Chapter 2, pie charts are especially useful for nominal and ordinal variables that do not have many response categories; and bar charts are very useful for nominal and ordinal variables with many response categories, and when we want to preserve the ranked order of ordinal variable response categories in the chart.

To construct a panelled pie chart, begin by computing the column percentages. Then draw a circle (a pie) for each response category of the independent variable. Each pie thus represents 100% of the cases in its respective response category. Next, divide each circle (each pie) into segments (slices) proportional to the percentages shown in its respective response category's distribution of $Y$. Be sure that the chart and all segments are clearly labelled. Figure 8.1 shows the panelled pie chart for the conditional distributions of $Y$ of Table 8.2.

To detect variable relationships with the panelled pie chart, look for changes in the size of each dependent variable (productivity) slice from one pie to the next, across all the values of the independent variable (job satisfaction). As shown in Figure 8.1, the high productivity slice increases in size as job satisfaction increases, while the low productivity slice decreases in size.

**FIGURE 8.1   Panelled Pie Chart of Productivity by Job Satisfaction (percentages)**

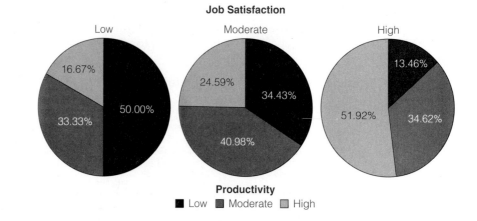

**FIGURE 8.2 Clustered Bar Chart of Productivity by Job Satisfaction (percentages)**

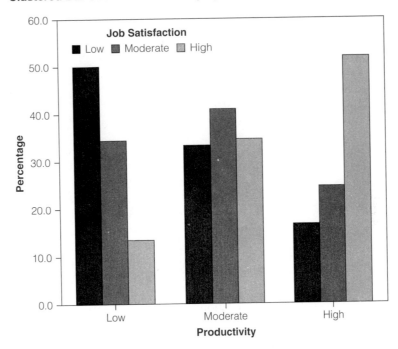

The construction of a clustered bar chart uses a somewhat similar approach as we used for the panelled pie chart. To construct a clustered bar chart, begin by computing the column percentages. Then place the dependent variable response categories along the horizontal axis (i.e., abscissa) and percentages on the vertical axis (i.e., ordinate). Above each dependent variable response category, construct a rectangle of constant width for every independent variable response category. The height of each independent variable response category should correspond to its conditional distribution of $Y$. Be sure that the chart and all bars are clearly labelled. Figure 8.2 shows the clustered bar chart for the conditional distributions of $Y$ of Table 8.2.

To detect variable relationships with the clustered bar chart, look for changes in the height of each independent variable (job satisfaction) value bar from one set of clustered bars to the next, across all values of the dependent variable (productivity). As shown in Figure 8.2, as the high job satisfaction bar increases in height, productivity increases, while the low productivity bar decreases in height.

**How Strong Is the Association?**   Once we establish the existence of the association, we need to develop some idea of how strong the association is. This is essentially a matter of determining the amount of change in

**TABLE 8.4   Productivity by Age (an illustration of perfect association)**

| Productivity (Y) | Age (X) | | |
|---|---|---|---|
| | 25-34 (%) | 35-44 (%) | 45+ (%) |
| Low | 0 | 0 | 100 |
| Moderate | 0 | 100 | 0 |
| High | 100 | 0 | 0 |
| | 100 | 100 | 100 |

the conditional distributions of Y. At one extreme, of course, there is the case of "no association," where the conditional distributions of Y do not change at all (see Table 8.3). At the other extreme is a perfect association, the strongest possible relationship. In general, a perfect association exists between two variables if each value of the dependent variable is associated with one and only one value of the independent variable. In a bivariate table, all cases in each column would be located in a single cell and there would be no variation in Y for a given value of X (see Table 8.4).

A perfect relationship would be taken as very strong evidence of a causal relationship between the variables, at least for the sample at hand. In fact, the results presented in Table 8.4 would indicate that, for this sample, age is the sole cause of productivity. Also, in the case of a perfect relationship, predictions from one variable to the other could be made without error. If we knew that a particular worker was between the ages of 25 and 34, for example, we could be sure that he or she was highly productive.

Of course, the huge majority of relationships fall somewhere between the two extremes of no association and perfect association. We need to develop some way of describing these intermediate relationships consistently and meaningfully. For example, Tables 8.1 and 8.2 show that there is an association between productivity and job satisfaction. How could this relationship be described in terms of strength? How close is the relationship to perfect? How far away from no association?

To answer these questions, researchers rely on statistics called measures of association, a variety of which are presented later in this chapter and in the chapters to follow. Measures of association provide precise, objective indicators of the strength of a relationship. Virtually all of these statistics are designed so that they have a lower limit of 0.00 and an upper limit of 1.00 ($\pm$1.00 for ordinal and interval-ratio measures of association). A measure that equals 0.00 indicates no association between the variables (the conditional distributions of Y do not vary), and a measure of 1.00 ($\pm$1.00 in the case of ordinal and interval-ratio measures) indicates a perfect relationship. The exact meaning of values between 0.00 and 1.00 varies from measure to measure, but for all measures, the closer the value is to 1.00, the stronger the relationship (the greater the change in the conditional distributions of Y).

We will begin to consider measures of association used in social research later in this chapter. At this point, let's consider the **maximum difference**, a less formal way of assessing the strength of a relationship based on comparing column percentages across the rows. This technique is "quick and easy": easy to apply (at least for small tables) but limited in its usefulness. To calculate the maximum difference, compute the column percentages as usual and then skim the table across *each* of the rows to find the largest difference in *any* row between column percentages. For example, the largest difference in column percentages in Table 8.2 is in the top row between the "Low" column and the "High" column: 50.00% − 13.46% = 36.54%. The maximum difference in the middle row is between "moderates" and "lows" (40.98% − 33.33% = 7.65%), and in the bottom row, it is between "highs" and "lows" (51.92% − 16.67% = 35.25%). Both of the latter values are less than the maximum difference in the top row.

Once you have found the maximum difference in the table, you can use the scale presented in Table 8.5 to describe the strength of the relationship. Using this scale, we can describe the relationship between productivity and job satisfaction in Table 8.2 as strong.

You should be aware that the relationships between the size of the maximum difference and the descriptive terms (weak, moderate, and strong) in Table 8.5 are arbitrary and approximate. We will get more precise and useful information when we compute and analyze measures of association, beginning later in this chapter. Also, maximum differences are easiest to find and most useful for smaller tables. In large tables, with many (say, more than three) columns and rows, it can be cumbersome to find the high and low percentages and it is advisable to consider only measures of association as indicators of the strength of relationships for these tables. Finally, note that the maximum difference is based on only two values (the high and low column percentages within any row). Like the range (see Chapter 3), this statistic can give a misleading impression of the overall strength of the relationship. Within these limits, however, the maximum difference can provide a useful, quick, and easy way of characterizing the strength of relationships (at least for smaller tables).

As a final caution, do not mistake chi square as an indicator of the strength of a relationship. Even very large values for chi square do not

**TABLE 8.5  The Relationship Between the Maximum Difference and the Strength of the Relationship**

| Maximum Difference | Strength |
|---|---|
| *If the maximum difference is* | *The strength of the relationship is* |
| between 0 and 10 percentage points | weak |
| between 11 and 30 percentage points | moderate |
| more than 30 percentage points | strong |

necessarily mean that the relationship is strong. Remember that significance and association are two separate matters and that chi square, by itself, is not a measure of association. While a non-zero value indicates that there is some association between the variables, the magnitude of chi square bears no particular relationship to the strength of the association. However, as we will see later in this chapter, there are ways to transform chi square into other statistics that do measure the strength of the association between two variables. *(For practice in computing percentages and judging the existence and strength of an association, see any of the problems at the end of this chapter.)*

**What Is the Pattern and/or the Direction of the Association?**    Investigating the pattern of the association requires that we ascertain which values or categories of one variable are associated with which values or categories of the other. We have already remarked on the pattern of the relationship between productivity and satisfaction. Table 8.2 indicates that low scores on satisfaction are associated with low scores on productivity, moderate satisfaction with moderate productivity, and high satisfaction with high productivity.

When both variables are at least ordinal in level of measurement, the association between the variables may also be described in terms of direction.* The direction of the association can be positive or negative. An association is positive if the variables vary in the same direction. That is, in a **positive association**, high scores on one variable are associated with high scores on the other variable, and low scores on one variable are associated with low scores on the other. In a positive association, as one variable increases in value, the other also increases; and as one variable decreases, the other also decreases. Table 8.6 displays, with fictitious data, a positive relationship between education and use of public libraries. As education increases (as you move from left to right across the table), library use also increases (the percentage of "high" users increases). The association between job satisfaction and productivity, as displayed in Tables 8.1 and 8.2, is also a positive association.

In a **negative association**, the variables vary in opposite directions. High scores on one variable are associated with low scores on the other, and increases in one variable are accompanied by decreases in the other. Table 8.7 displays a negative relationship, again with fictitious data, between education and television viewing. The amount of television viewing decreases as education increases. In other words, as you move from left to right across the top of the table (as education increases), the percentage of heavy viewers decreases.

---

*Variables measured at the nominal level have no numerical order to them (by definition). Therefore, associations including nominal-level variables, while they may have a pattern, cannot be said to have a direction.

**TABLE 8.6   Library Use by Education (an illustration of a positive relationship)**

| Library Use | Education | | |
|---|---|---|---|
| | Low | Moderate | High |
| Low | 60% | 20% | 10% |
| Moderate | 30 | 60 | 30 |
| High | 10 | 20 | 60 |
| Totals | 100% | 100% | 100% |

**TABLE 8.7   Amount of Television Viewing by Education (an illustration of a negative relationship)**

| Television Viewing | Education | | |
|---|---|---|---|
| | Low | Moderate | High |
| Low | 10% | 20% | 60% |
| Moderate | 30 | 60 | 30 |
| High | 60 | 20 | 10 |
| Totals | 100% | 100% | 100% |

Measures of association for ordinal and interval-ratio variables are designed so that they will take on positive values for positive associations and negative values for negative associations. Thus, a measure of association preceded by a plus sign indicates a positive relationship between the two variables, with the value +1.00 indicating a perfect positive relationship. A negative sign indicates a negative relationship, with −1.00 indicating a perfect negative relationship. We will consider the direction of relationships in more detail in Chapters 9 and 13. *(For practice in determining the pattern of an association, see any of the end-of-chapter problems. For practice in determining the direction of a relationship, see Problems 8.1 and 8.7.)*

**8.4 THE IMPORTANCE OF PERCENTAGES AND SOME ERRORS OF INTERPRETATION**

We have seen how percentages can be used to analyze associations between variables. While they are among the humblest of statistics, percentages can provide important information about the relationship between two variables. Of course, this information will be clear and accurate only when bivariate tables are properly constructed, percentages are computed within columns, and comparisons are made from column to column. Errors and misunderstandings can occur when there is confusion about which variable is the cause (or independent variable) and which is the effect (or dependent variable), or when the researcher asks the wrong questions about the relationship.

To illustrate these problems, let's review the process by which we analyze bivariate tables. When we compare column percentages across the table, we are asking: "Does $Y$ (the dependent variable) vary by $X$ (the independent variable)?" We conclude that there is evidence for a causal relationship if the values of $Y$ change under the different values of $X$.

To illustrate further, consider Table 8.8, which shows the relationship between age—15 to 44, 45 to 64, and 65 and older—and the importance of religion in people's lives. The data are taken from the Canadian sample of the World Values Survey (Wave 5)—a global survey on people's values,

**TABLE 8.8**   Importance of Religion in Life by Age Group (frequencies and percentages)

| Importance of Religion | Age Group | | |
|---|---|---|---|
| | 15–44 | 45–64 | 65+ |
| Important | 515 (50.84%) | 449 (60.43%) | 291 (77.60%) |
| Not important | 498 (49.16%) | 294 (39.57%) | 84 (22.40%) |
| | 1,013 (100.00%) | 743 (100.00%) | 375 (100.00%) |

Source: World Values Survey Association, *World Values Survey, Wave 5.*

beliefs, and well-being. Age must be the independent or causal variable in this relationship, since it may shape people's attitudes and opinions. The reverse cannot be true: a person's opinion cannot cause their age. Age is the column variable in the table, and the percentages are computed in the proper direction. A quick inspection shows that importance of religion varies by age group, indicating that there may be a causal relationship between these variables. The maximum difference between the columns is about 27 percentage points, indicating that the relationship is moderate to strong.

What if we had misunderstood this causal relationship? If we had computed percentages within each row, for example, age would become the dependent variable. We would be asking "Does age vary by the importance of religion in peoples' lives?" Table 8.9 shows the results of asking this incorrect question.

A casual glance at the top row of the table seems to indicate a causal relationship since 41.03% of the respondents who said that religion is important in their lives are younger (15–44) adults, while 35.78% are middle-aged (44–64) adults, and just 23.19% are older (65+) adults. If we looked *only* at the top row of the table (as people sometimes do), we would conclude that younger persons attach more importance to religion than older persons. But the second row shows that younger adults are also the majority (56.85%) of those who said that religion is *not* important in their lives. How can this be? The row percentages in this table simply reflect the fact that younger adults out-number the other age groups, especially elderly persons: for example,

**TABLE 8.9**   Row Percentages

| Importance of Religion | Age Group | | | |
|---|---|---|---|---|
| | 15–44 | 45–64 | 65+ | |
| Important | 41.03% | 35.78% | 23.19% | 100.00% |
| Not important | 56.85% | 33.56% | 9.59% | 100.00% |

there are almost three times as many young adults as older adults in the sample. Computing percentages within the rows would make sense only if age could vary by attitude or opinion, and Table 8.9 could easily lead to false conclusions about this relationship.

Professional researchers sometimes compute percentages in the wrong direction or ask a question about the relationship incorrectly, and you should always check bivariate tables to make sure that the analysis agrees with the patterns in the table.

## 8.5 INTRODUCTION TO MEASURES OF ASSOCIATION

Conditional distributions, column percentages, and the maximum difference provide very useful information about the bivariate association and should always be computed and analyzed. However, they can be awkward and cumbersome to use, especially for larger tables. Measures of association, on the other hand, characterize the strength (and for ordinal- and interval-ratio-level variables, also the direction) of bivariate relationships in a single number—a more compact and convenient format for interpretation and discussion.

There are many measures of association, but we will confine our attention to a few of those most widely used. We will cover these statistics by the level of measurement for which they are most appropriate. In this chapter, we will consider measures appropriate for nominally measured variables. In the next chapter, we will cover measures of association for ordinal-level variables, and in Chapter 13, we will consider Pearson's $r$, a measure of association or correlation for interval-ratio-level variables. You will note that several of the research situations used as examples involve variables measured at different levels (e.g., one nominal-level variable and one ordinal-level variable). The general procedure in the situation of "mixed levels" is to be conservative and select measures of association appropriate for the lower of the two levels of measurement. However, special measures of association are sometimes available for special situations. For example, Chapter 12 will include measures of association for variables with mixed levels of measurement, when the independent variable is either nominal or ordinal and the dependent variable is interval-ratio.

## 8.6 CHI SQUARE– BASED MEASURES OF ASSOCIATION

When working with nominal-level variables, social science researchers rely heavily on measures of association based on the value of chi square. While chi square per se is a test of statistical significance, it can be transformed into other statistics that measure the strength of the association between two variables. When the value of chi square is already known, these measures are easy to calculate. To illustrate, let us reconsider Table 7.5, which displayed, with fictitious data, a relationship between CASSW (Canadian

**TABLE 8.10 Employment Status of 100 Social Work Graduates by CASSW-Accreditation Status of Undergraduate Program**

| Employment Status | Accreditation Status | | Totals |
|---|---|---|---|
| | Accredited | Not Accredited | |
| Working as a social worker | 30 | 10 | 40 |
| Not working as a social worker | 25 | 35 | 60 |
| Totals | 55 | 45 | 100 |

Association of Schools of Social Work) accreditation and employment for social work graduates. For the sake of convenience, this table is reproduced here as Table 8.10.

We saw in Chapter 7 that this relationship is statistically significant ($\chi^2 = 10.78$, which is significant at the 0.05 alpha level), but the question now concerns the *strength* of the association. A brief glance at Table 8.10 shows that the conditional distributions of employment status do change, so the variables are associated. To emphasize this point, it is always helpful to calculate column percentages, as in Table 8.11.

So far, we know that the relationship between these two variables is statistically significant and that there is an association of some kind between CASSW accreditation and employment. To assess the strength of the association, we will compute **phi ($\phi$)**. This statistic is a frequently used chi square–based measure of association appropriate for 2 × 2 tables (i.e., tables with two rows and two columns).

**Calculating Phi.** One attraction of phi is that it is easy to calculate. Simply divide the value of the obtained chi square by the total number of cases in the sample ($n$) and take the square root of the result. Expressed in symbols, the formula for phi is

**FORMULA 8.1**

$$\phi = \sqrt{\frac{\chi^2}{n}}$$

**TABLE 8.11 Employment Status by CASSW-Accreditation Status (percentages)**

| Employment Status | Accreditation Status | | Totals (%) |
|---|---|---|---|
| | Accredited (%) | Not Accredited (%) | |
| Working as a social worker | 54.55 | 22.22 | 40.00 |
| Not working as a social worker | 45.45 | 77.78 | 60.00 |
| | 100.00 | 100.00 | 100.00 |

For the data displayed in Table 8.10, the chi square is 10.78. Therefore, phi is

$$\phi = \sqrt{\frac{\chi^2}{n}}$$

$$\phi = \sqrt{\frac{10.78}{100}}$$

$$\phi = 0.33$$

For a 2 × 2 table, phi ranges in value from 0 (no association) to 1.00 (perfect association). The closer to 1.00, the stronger the relationship; the closer to 0.00, the weaker the relationship. For Table 8.10, we already knew that the relationship was statistically significant at the 0.05 level. Phi, as a measure of association, adds information about the strength of the relationship. As for the pattern of the association, the column percentages in Table 8.11 show that graduates of CASSW-accredited programs were more often employed as social workers.

**Calculating Cramer's V.**   For tables larger than 2 × 2 (specifically, for tables with more than two columns and more than two rows), the upper limit of phi can exceed 1.00. This makes phi difficult to interpret, and a more general form of the statistic called **Cramer's V** must be used for larger tables. The formula for Cramer's V is

**FORMULA 8.2**

$$V = \sqrt{\frac{\chi^2}{(n)(\min\ r - 1, c - 1)}}$$

where (min $r - 1, c - 1$) = the minimum value of $r - 1$ (number of rows minus 1) or $c - 1$ (number of columns minus 1)

In words: To calculate $V$, find the lesser of the number of rows minus 1 ($r - 1$) or the number of columns minus 1 ($c - 1$), multiply this value by $n$, divide the result into the value of chi square, and then find the square root. Cramer's $V$ has an upper limit of 1.00 for any size table and will be the same value as phi if the table has either two rows or two columns. Like phi, Cramer's $V$ can be interpreted as an index that measures the strength of the association between two variables.

To illustrate the computation of $V$, suppose you had gathered the data displayed in Table 8.12, which shows the relationship between membership in student clubs or organizations and academic achievement for a sample of

**TABLE 8.12  Academic Achievement by Student-Club Membership (fictitious data)**

| Academic Achievement | Club Membership | | | |
|---|---|---|---|---|
| | Varsity or Intramural Sports Club | Non-sports Club | No Membership | Totals |
| Low | 4 | 4 | 17 | 25 |
| Moderate | 15 | 6 | 4 | 25 |
| High | 4 | 16 | 5 | 25 |
| Totals | 23 | 26 | 26 | 75 |

university students. The obtained chi square for this table is 32.14, a value that is significant at the 0.05 level. Cramer's $V$ is

$$V = \sqrt{\frac{\chi^2}{(n)(\min r - 1, c - 1)}}$$

$$V = \sqrt{\frac{32.14}{(75)(2)}}$$

$$V = \sqrt{\frac{32.14}{150}}$$

$$V = \sqrt{0.21}$$

$$V = 0.46$$

Because Table 8.12 has the same number of rows and columns, we may use either $(r - 1)$ or $(c - 1)$ in the denominator. In either case, the value of the denominator is $n$ multiplied by $(3 - 1)$, or $n$ multiplied by 2. Column percentages are presented in Table 8.13 to help identify the pattern of this relationship. Members of sports clubs tend to be moderate, members of non-sports clubs tend to be high, and non-members tend to be low in academic achievement.

**TABLE 8.13  Academic Achievement by Student-Club Membership (percentages)**

| Academic Achievement | Club Membership | | | |
|---|---|---|---|---|
| | Varsity or Intramural Sports Club | Non-sports Club | No Membership | Totals |
| Low | 17.39 | 15.38 | 65.38 | 33.33 |
| Moderate | 65.22 | 23.08 | 15.39 | 33.33 |
| High | 17.39 | 61.54 | 19.23 | 33.33 |
| Totals | 100.00 | 100.00 | 100.00 | 100.00 |

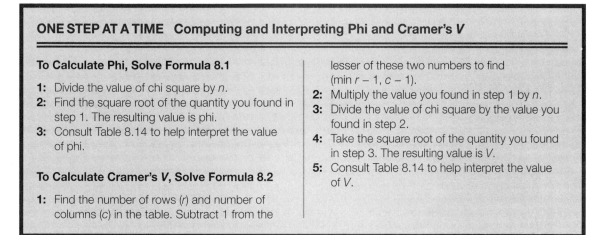

**ONE STEP AT A TIME** Computing and Interpreting Phi and Cramer's *V*

**To Calculate Phi, Solve Formula 8.1**

**1:** Divide the value of chi square by *n*.
**2:** Find the square root of the quantity you found in step 1. The resulting value is phi.
**3:** Consult Table 8.14 to help interpret the value of phi.

**To Calculate Cramer's *V*, Solve Formula 8.2**

**1:** Find the number of rows (*r*) and number of columns (*c*) in the table. Subtract 1 from the lesser of these two numbers to find (min *r* − 1, *c* − 1).
**2:** Multiply the value you found in step 1 by *n*.
**3:** Divide the value of chi square by the value you found in step 2.
**4:** Take the square root of the quantity you found in step 3. The resulting value is *V*.
**5:** Consult Table 8.14 to help interpret the value of *V*.

**Interpreting Phi and Cramer's *V*.** It will be helpful to have some general guidelines for interpreting the value of measures of association for nominal variables, similar to the guidelines we used for interpreting the maximum difference in column percentages. Table 8.14 presents the general relationship between the value of the statistic and the strength of the relationship for phi and Cramer's *V*. As was the case with Table 8.5, the relationships in Table 8.14 are arbitrary and meant as general guidelines only. Using these guidelines, we can characterize the relationship in Table 8.10 (phi = 0.33) and Table 8.12 (Cramer's *V* = 0.46) as strong.

**Limitations of Phi and Cramer's *V*.** One limitation of phi and Cramer's *V* is that they are only general indicators of the strength of the relationship. Of course, the closer these measures are to 0.00, the weaker the relationship, and the closer to 1.00, the stronger the relationship. Values between 0.00 and 1.00 can be described as weak, moderate, or strong according to the general guidelines presented in Table 8.14 but have no direct or meaningful interpretation. On the other hand, phi and *V* are easy to calculate (once the value of chi square has been obtained) and are commonly used indicators of the

**TABLE 8.14** **The Relationship Between the Value of Nominal-Level Measures of Association and the Strength of the Relationship**

| Value | Strength |
|---|---|
| *If the value is* | *The strength of the relationship is* |
| between 0.00 and 0.10 | weak |
| between 0.11 and 0.30 | moderate |
| greater than 0.30 | strong |

importance of an association. *(For practice in computing phi and Cramer's V, see any of the problems at the end of this chapter. Problems with 2 × 2 tables will minimize computations. Remember that for tables with either two rows or two columns, phi and Cramer's V will have the same value.)*

## 8.7 PROPORTIONAL REDUCTION IN ERROR MEASURES OF ASSOCIATION

In recent years, measures based on a logic known as **proportional reduction in error (PRE)** have been developed to complement the older chi square–based measures of association. Unlike their chi square–based counterparts, PRE-based measures of association provide a direct, meaningful interpretation.

Most generally stated, the logic of PRE measures requires us to make two different predictions about the scores of cases. In the first prediction, we ignore information about the independent variable and, therefore, make many errors in predicting the score on the dependent variable. In the second prediction, we take account of the score of the case on the independent variable to help predict the score on the dependent variable. If there is an association between the variables, we will make fewer errors when taking the independent variable into account. The value of a PRE-based measure of association therefore has a precise, meaningful interpretation in the sense that it quantitatively measures the proportional reduction in errors between the two predictions. Applying these general thoughts to the case of nominal-level variables will make the logic clearer.

## 8.8 LAMBDA: A PRE MEASURE OF ASSOCIATION

For nominal-level variables, we first predict the category into which each case will fall on the dependent variable ($Y$) while ignoring the independent variable ($X$). Because we would, in effect, be predicting blindly in this case, we would make many errors (i.e., we would often incorrectly predict the category of a case on the dependent variable).

The second prediction allows us to take the independent variable into account. If the two variables are associated, the additional information supplied by the independent variable will reduce our errors of prediction (i.e., we should misclassify fewer cases). The stronger the association between the variables, the greater the reduction in errors. In the case of a perfect association, we would make no errors at all when predicting the score on $Y$ from the score on $X$. But when there is no association between the variables, knowledge of the independent variable will not improve the accuracy of our predictions. We would make just as many errors of prediction with knowledge of the independent variable as we would without knowledge of it.

An illustration should make these principles clearer. Suppose you were placed in the rather unusual position of having to predict whether each of the next 100 people you meet will be shorter or taller than 174 centimetres under the condition that you would have no knowledge of these people at all. With absolutely no information about these people, your predictions will be wrong quite often (you will often misclassify a tall person as short, and vice versa).

Now assume that you must go through this ordeal twice, but on the second round, you know the sex of the person whose height you must predict. Because height is associated with sex and females are, on the average, shorter than males, the optimal strategy would be to predict that all females are short and that all males are tall. Of course, you will still make errors on this second round, but if the variables are associated, the number of errors on the second round will be less than the number of errors on the first. That is, using information about the independent variable will reduce the number of errors (if, of course, the two variables are related). How can these unusual thoughts be translated into a useful statistic?

**Lambda.**   One hundred individuals have been categorized by sex and height, and the data are displayed in Table 8.15. It is clear, even without percentages, that the two variables are associated. To measure the strength of this association, a PRE measure called **lambda** (symbolized by the Greek letter $\lambda$) will be calculated. Following the logic introduced above, we must find two quantities. First, we find the number of prediction errors made while ignoring the independent variable (sex). Then, we find the number of prediction errors made while taking sex into account. These two sums will then be compared to derive the statistic.

First, the information given by the independent variable (sex) can be ignored, in effect, by working only with the row marginals. Two different predictions can be made about height (the dependent variable) by using these marginals. We can predict either that all subjects are tall *or* that all subjects are short.* For the first prediction (all subjects are tall), 48 errors will be made. That is, for this prediction, all 100 cases would be placed in the first row. Because only 52 of the cases actually belong in this row, this prediction would result in $(100 - 52)$, or 48, errors. If we had predicted that all subjects were short, on the other hand, we would have made 52 errors $(100 - 48 = 52)$. We will take the *lesser* of these two numbers and refer

**TABLE 8.15   Height by Sex**

| Height | Sex | | Totals |
|---|---|---|---|
| | Male | Female | |
| Tall | 44 | 8 | 52 |
| Short | 6 | 42 | 48 |
| Totals | 50 | 50 | 100 |

*Other predictions are, of course, possible, but these are the only two permitted by lambda.

to this quantity as "$E_1$" for the number of errors made while ignoring the independent variable. So, $E_1 = 48$.

In the second step in the computation of lambda, we predict the score on $Y$ (height) again, but this time we take $X$ (sex) into account. To do this, follow the same procedure as in the first step but this time move from column to column. Because each column is a category of $X$, we thus take $X$ into account in making our predictions. For the left-hand column (males), we predict that all 50 cases will be tall and make 6 errors ($50 - 44 = 6$). For the second column (females), our prediction is that all females are short, and 8 errors will be made. By moving from column to column, we have taken $X$ into account and have made a total of 14 errors of prediction, a quantity we refer to as "$E_2$" ($E_2 = 6 + 8 = 14$).

If the variables are associated, we will make fewer errors under the second procedure than under the first. In other words, $E_2$ will be smaller than $E_1$. In this case, we made fewer errors of prediction while taking sex into account ($E_2 = 14$) than while ignoring sex ($E_1 = 48$), so sex and height are clearly associated. Our errors were reduced from 48 to only 14. To find the *proportional* reduction in error, use Formula 8.3:

**FORMULA 8.3**
$$\lambda = \frac{E_1 - E_2}{E_1}$$

where $E_1$ = the total number of cases minus the largest row total
$E_2$ = the sum of the following: for each column, the column total minus the largest cell frequency

For the sample problem, the value of lambda would be

$$\lambda = \frac{E_1 - E_2}{E_1}$$
$$\lambda = \frac{48 - 14}{48}$$
$$\lambda = \frac{34}{48}$$
$$\lambda = 0.7083$$

The value of lambda ranges from 0.00 to 1.00. Of course, a value of 0.00 means that the variables are not associated at all ($E_1$ is the same as $E_2$), and a value of 1.00 means that the association is perfect ($E_2$ is zero and scores on the dependent variable can be predicted without error from the independent variable). Unlike phi or $V$, however, the numerical value of lambda between the extremes of 0.00 and 1.00 has a precise meaning: It is an index of the extent to which the independent variable ($X$) helps us predict (or, more loosely, understand) the dependent variable ($Y$). When multiplied by

100, the value of lambda indicates the strength of the association in terms of the percentage reduction in error. Thus, the lambda above would be interpreted by concluding that knowledge of sex improves our ability to predict height by 70.83%. Or, we are 70.83% better off knowing sex when attempting to predict height.

**Calculating Lambda: Another Example.**   In this section, we will work through another example, based on actual data, to state the computational routine for lambda in more general terms. Implemented in 1994, the North American Free Trade Agreement (NAFTA) removed most barriers to trade and increased cross-border trade among the United States, Canada, and

---

### Applying Statistics 8.1: Measures of Association

A random sample of students from the Canadian Internet Use Survey, conducted by Statistics Canada to measure the extent and scope to which Canadians use the Internet, was asked about using the Internet to play games in the last year. The table below displays the actual data for this variable by sex of respondent. Is online gaming related to sex?

|                | Sex   |        |        |
|----------------|-------|--------|--------|
| Online Gaming  | Male  | Female | Totals |
| Yes            | 399   | 332    | 731    |
| No             | 255   | 538    | 793    |
| Totals         | 654   | 870    | 1,524  |

Because this is a 2 × 2 table, we can compute phi as a measure of association. The chi square for the table is 78.09, so phi is

$$\phi = \sqrt{\frac{\chi^2}{n}}$$

$$\phi = \sqrt{\frac{78.09}{1,524}}$$

$$\phi = \sqrt{0.038}$$

$$\phi = 0.19$$

which indicates a moderate relationship between the two variables.

A lambda can also be computed as an additional measure of association:

$$E_1 = 1,524 + 793 = 731$$

$$E_2 = (654 - 399) + (870 - 538)$$
$$= 255 + 332 = 587$$

$$\lambda = \frac{E_1 - E_2}{E_1}$$

$$\lambda = \frac{731 - 587}{731}$$

$$\lambda = \frac{144}{731}$$

$$\lambda = 0.1970$$

A lambda of 0.1970 indicates that we would make 19.70% fewer errors in predicting use of the Internet to play games ($Y$) from sex ($X$), as opposed to predicting use of the Internet to play games while ignoring sex. The association is moderate and, by inspection of the table, we can see that male students are more likely to play games online (61.01%) and that female students are more likely not to use the Internet to play games (61.84%).

Source: Statistics Canada, *2012 Canadian Internet Use Survey.*

**TABLE 8.16  Opinion Toward Free Trade\* by Region**

|  | Region | | | | |
|---|---|---|---|---|---|
| Opinion on Free Trade | Atlantic | Quebec | Ontario | Western | Totals |
| Somewhat/Strongly Disagree | 10 | 40 | 29 | 60 | 139 |
| Somewhat Agree | 21 | 33 | 48 | 43 | 145 |
| Strongly Agree | 10 | 19 | 40 | 26 | 95 |
| Totals | 41 | 92 | 117 | 129 | 379 |

\*Based on the question, "Do you strongly agree, somewhat agree, somewhat disagree, or strongly disagree that, overall, free trade with the U.S. has been good for the Canadian economy?"

Source: Data from Canadian Election Study, *2006 Canadian Election Study*.

Mexico. Since that time, public opinion on NAFTA in Canada has been mixed. We will use data from the 2006 Canadian Election Study, shown in Table 8.16, to examine whether public opinion toward free trade at that time varied by region. (The Canadian Election Study surveyed adults in the 10 provinces only, thus excluding the territories.) To make the number of cases in this example more manageable, yet still representative, we randomly selected about 10% of cases (or 379 respondents) from the full sample of about 4,000 respondents.

**Step 1.** To find $E_1$, the number of errors made while ignoring $X$ (region, in this case), subtract the largest row total from $n$. For Table 8.16, $E_1$ will be

$$E_1 = n - \text{(Largest row total)}$$
$$E_1 = 379 - 145$$
$$E_1 = 234$$

Thus, we will misclassify 234 cases on opinion toward free trade while ignoring region.

**Step 2.** Next, $E_2$—the number of errors made when taking the independent variable into account—must be found. For each column, subtract the largest cell frequency from the column total and then add the subtotals together. For the data presented in Table 8.16:

$$\text{For Atlantic Canada:  } 41 - 21 = 20$$
$$\text{For Quebec:  } 92 - 40 = 52$$
$$\text{For Ontario: } 117 - 48 = 69$$
$$\text{For Western Canada: } 129 - 60 = 69$$
$$E_2 = 210$$

A total of 210 errors are made when predicting opinion toward free trade while taking region into account.

**Step 3.** In step 1, 234 errors of prediction were made as compared to 210 errors in step 2. Because the number of errors has been reduced, the variables are associated. To find the proportional reduction in error, the values for $E_1$ and $E_2$ can be directly substituted into Formula 8.3:

$$\lambda = \frac{234 - 210}{234}$$

$$\lambda = \frac{24}{234}$$

$$\lambda = 0.1026$$

Using our conventional labels (see Table 8.14), we would call this a weak relationship. Using PRE logic, we can add more detail to the characterization: When attempting to predict opinion toward free trade, we would make 10.26% fewer errors by taking region into account. Knowledge of a respondent's region of residence improves the accuracy of our predictions by a factor of 10.26%. The weak strength of lambda indicates that factors other than region are associated with the dependent variable.

**Limitations of Lambda.**  As a measure of association, lambda has two characteristics that should be stressed. First, lambda is asymmetric. This means that the value of the statistic will vary depending on which variable is taken as dependent. For example, in Table 8.16, the value of lambda would be about 0.07 if region had been taken as the dependent variable (verify this with your own computation). Thus, you should exercise some caution when designating a dependent variable. If you consistently follow the convention of arraying the independent variable in the columns and the dependent variable in the rows and compute lambda as outlined previously, the asymmetry of the statistic should not be confusing.

---

### ONE STEP AT A TIME    Computing and Interpreting Lambda

**To Calculate Lambda, Solve Formula 8.3**

**1:** To find $E_1$, subtract the largest row subtotal (marginal) from $n$.

**2:** Starting with the far left-hand column, subtract the largest cell frequency in the column from the column total. Repeat this step for all columns in the table.

**3:** Add up all the values you found in step 2. The result is $E_2$.

**4:** Subtract $E_2$ from $E_1$.

**5:** Divide the quantity you found in step 4 by $E_1$. The result is lambda.

**To Interpret Lambda**

**1:** Multiply the value of lambda by 100. This percentage tells us the extent to which our predictions of the dependent variable are improved by taking the independent variable into account. Also, lambda may be interpreted using the descriptive terms in Table 8.14.

Second, when one of the row totals is much larger than the others, lambda can be misleading. It can be 0.00 even when other measures of association are greater than 0.00 and the conditional distributions for the table indicate there is an association between the variables. This anomaly is a function of the way lambda is calculated and suggests that great caution should be exercised in the interpretation of lambda when the row marginals are very unequal. In fact, in these situations, a chi square–based measure of association would be the preferred measure of association. *(For practice in computing lambda, see any of the problems at the end of this chapter. As with phi and Cramer's V, it's probably a good idea to start with small samples and 2 × 2 tables.)*

## SUMMARY

1. Analyzing the association between variables provides information that is complementary to tests of significance. The latter are designed to detect non-random relationships, whereas measures of association are designed to quantify the importance or strength of a relationship.

2. Relationships between variables have three characteristics: the existence of an association, the strength of the association, and the direction or pattern of the association. These three characteristics can be investigated by calculating percentages for a bivariate table in the direction of the independent variable (vertically) and then comparing in the other direction (horizontally). This procedure can be summarized in the following statement: "Percentage Down, Compare Across." It is often useful (as well as quick and easy) to assess the strength of a relationship by finding the maximum difference in column percentages in any row of the table. The panelled pie chart and clustered bar chart make the "Percentage Down, Compare Across" procedure graphically visible.

3. Tables 8.1 and 8.2 can be analyzed in terms of these three characteristics. Clearly, a relationship does exist between job satisfaction and productivity, because the conditional distributions of the dependent variable (productivity) are different for the three different conditions of the independent variable (job satisfaction). Even without a measure of association, we can see that the association is substantial in that the change in Y (productivity) across the three categories of X (satisfaction) is marked. The maximum difference of 36.54% confirms that the relationship is substantial (strong). Furthermore, the relationship is positive in direction: Productivity increases as job satisfaction rises, and workers who report high job satisfaction tend also to be high on productivity. Workers with little job satisfaction tend to be low on productivity.

4. Given the nature and strength of the relationship, it could be predicted with fair accuracy that highly satisfied workers tend to be highly productive ("happy workers are busy workers"). These results might be taken as evidence of a causal relationship between these two variables, but they cannot, by themselves, prove that a causal relationship exists—association is not the same thing as causation. In fact, although we have presumed that job satisfaction is the independent variable, we could have argued the reverse causal sequence ("busy workers are happy workers"). The results presented in Tables 8.1 and 8.2 are consistent with both causal arguments.

5. Phi, Cramer's V, and lambda are measures of association, and each is appropriate for a

specific situation. We use phi for $2 \times 2$ tables and Cramer's $V$ for tables larger than $2 \times 2$. While phi and Cramer's $V$ are chi square–based measures, lambda is a PRE-based measure and provides a more direct interpretation for values between the extremes of 0.00 and 1.00. These statistics express information about the strength of relationship *only*. In all cases, be sure to analyze the column percentages as well as the measures of association to maximize the information you have about the relationship.

## SUMMARY OF FORMULAS

| | | |
|---|---|---|
| Phi | 8.1 | $\phi = \sqrt{\dfrac{\chi^2}{n}}$ |
| Cramer's $V$ | 8.2 | $V = \sqrt{\dfrac{\chi^2}{(n)(\min r - 1, c - 1)}}$ |
| Lambda | 8.3 | $\lambda = \dfrac{E_1 - E_2}{E_1}$ |

## GLOSSARY

**Association.** The relationship between two (or more) variables. Two variables are said to be associated if the distribution of one variable changes for the various categories or scores of the other variable.

**Clustered bar chart.** A bivariate (or multivariate) bar chart that displays the conditional distributions of $Y$ of a contingency table.

**Conditional distribution of $Y$.** The distribution of scores on the dependent variable for a specific score or category of the independent variable when the variables have been organized into table format.

**Cramer's $V$.** A chi square–based measure of association. Appropriate for nominally measured variables that have been organized into a bivariate table of any number of rows and columns.

**Dependent variable.** In a bivariate relationship, the variable that is taken as the effect.

**Independent variable.** In a bivariate relationship, the variable that is taken as the cause.

**Lambda ($\lambda$).** A measure of association appropriate for nominally measured variables that have been organized into a bivariate table. Lambda is based on the logic of proportional reduction in error (PRE).

**Maximum difference.** A way to assess the strength of an association between variables that have been organized into a bivariate table. The maximum difference is the largest difference between column percentages for any row of the table.

**Measures of association.** Statistic that quantifies the strength of the association between variables. For ordinal-level and interval-ratio-level variables, this statistic also indicates the direction of the relationship.

**Negative association.** A bivariate relationship where the variables vary in opposite directions. As one variable increases, the other decreases, and high scores on one variable are associated with low scores on the other.

**Panelled pie chart.** A bivariate (or multivariate) pie chart that displays the conditional distributions of $Y$ of a contingency table.

**Phi ($\phi$).** A chi square–based measure of association. Appropriate for nominally measured variables that have been organized into a $2 \times 2$ bivariate table.

**Positive association.** A bivariate relationship where the variables vary in the same direction. As one variable increases, the other also increases, and high scores on one variable are associated with high scores on the other.

**Proportional reduction in error (PRE).** The logic that underlies the definition and computation of statistics such as lambda. All PRE statistics compare the number of errors made when predicting the dependent variable while ignoring the independent variable ($E_1$) with the number of errors made while taking the independent variable into account ($E_2$).

**X.** Symbol used for any independent variable.

**Y.** Symbol used for any dependent variable.

## MULTIMEDIA RESOURCES

 nelson.com/student

Visit the companion website for the fourth Canadian edition of *Statistics: A Tool for Social Research* to access a wide range of student resources. Begin by clicking on the Student Resources section of the textbook's website to access online chapters and study tools.

## PROBLEMS

**8.1** PA Various supervisors in the municipal government of Pearson, Ontario, have been rated on the extent to which they practise authoritarian styles of leadership and decision making. The efficiency of each department has also been rated, and the results are summarized below. Calculate percentages for the table so that it shows the effect of leadership style on efficiency. Is there an association between these two variables? Describe the strength and direction of the relationship.

| | Authoritarianism | | |
|---|---|---|---|
| Efficiency | Low | High | Totals |
| Low | 10 | 12 | 22 |
| High | 17 | 5 | 22 |
| Totals | 27 | 17 | 44 |

**8.2** SOC The administration of a university has proposed an increase in the mandatory student fee in order to finance an upgrading of the varsity football program. A sample of the faculty has completed a survey on the issue. Is there any association between support for raising fees and the sex, discipline, or tenured status of the faculty?

Calculate percentages for each table, then describe the strength and pattern of the association.

**a.** Support for raising fees by sex:

| | Sex | | |
|---|---|---|---|
| Support | Male | Female | Totals |
| For | 12 | 8 | 20 |
| Against | 15 | 12 | 27 |
| Totals | 27 | 20 | 47 |

**b.** Support for raising fees by discipline:

| | Discipline | | |
|---|---|---|---|
| Support | Social Sciences & Arts | Science & Business | Totals |
| For | 6 | 13 | 19 |
| Against | 14 | 14 | 28 |
| Totals | 20 | 27 | 47 |

**c.** Support for raising fees by tenured status:

| | Status | | |
|---|---|---|---|
| Support | Tenured | Non-tenured | Total |
| For | 15 | 4 | 19 |
| Against | 18 | 10 | 28 |
| Total | 33 | 14 | 47 |

**8.3** | PS | How consistent are people in their voting habits? Do the same people vote from election to election? Below are the results of a poll in which people were asked if they had voted in each of the last two federal elections. Calculate percentages for the table, and assess the strength and pattern of this relationship.

|  | 2011 Election | | |
| --- | --- | --- | --- |
| 2015 Election | Voted | Didn't Vote | Totals |
| Voted | 117 | 23 | 140 |
| Didn't Vote | 17 | 178 | 195 |
| Totals | 134 | 201 | 335 |

**8.4** | SOC | A needs assessment survey has been distributed in a large retirement community. Residents were asked to check off the services or programs they thought should be added. Is there any association between sex and the perception of a need for more social occasions? Calculate percentages for the table, and assess the strength and pattern of this relationship.

|  | Sex | | |
| --- | --- | --- | --- |
| More Parties? | Male | Female | Totals |
| Yes | 321 | 426 | 747 |
| No | 175 | 251 | 426 |
| Totals | 496 | 677 | 1,173 |

**8.5** Compute a phi and a lambda for Problems 8.1–8.4. Compare the value of the measure of association with your impressions of the strength of the relationships based solely on the percentages you calculated for those problems.

**8.6** In any social science journal, find an article that includes a bivariate table. Inspect the table and the related text carefully and answer the following questions:
  **a.** Identify the variables in the table. What values (categories) does each possess? What is the level of measurement for each variable?
  **b.** Is the table in percentage form? In what direction are the percentages calculated? Are comparisons made between columns or rows?
  **c.** Is one of the variables identified by the author as independent?

  **d.** How is the relationship characterized by the author in terms of the strength of the association? In terms of the direction (if any) of the association?
  **e.** Find the measure of association (if any) calculated for the table. What is the numerical value of the measure? What is the sign (if any) of the measure?

**8.7** If a person's political ideology (liberal, moderate, or conservative) is known, can we predict their position on issues? If liberals are generally progressive and conservatives are generally traditional (with moderates in between), what relationships would you expect to find between political ideology and these issues?
  **a.** Support for same-sex marriage
  **b.** The death penalty
  **c.** The legal right to commit suicide for people with incurable diseases
  **d.** Support for traditional gender roles
  **e.** Support for the legalization of marijuana

The tables below show the results of a recent public opinion survey. For each table, compute column percentages and the maximum difference. Summarize the strength and direction of each relationship in a brief paragraph. Were your expectations confirmed?
  **a.** Support for same-sex marriage by political ideology:

| Supports Same-Sex Marriage? | Political Ideology | | | |
| --- | --- | --- | --- | --- |
| | Liberal | Moderate | Conservative | Totals |
| Favour | 309 | 234 | 154 | 697 |
| Oppose | 211 | 360 | 419 | 990 |
| Totals | 520 | 594 | 573 | 1,687 |

  **b.** Support for capital punishment by political ideology:

| Supports Capital Punishment? | Political Ideology | | | |
| --- | --- | --- | --- | --- |
| | Liberal | Moderate | Conservative | Totals |
| Favour | 440 | 693 | 693 | 1,826 |
| Oppose | 265 | 214 | 186 | 665 |
| Totals | 705 | 907 | 879 | 2,491 |

**c.** Support for the right of people with an incurable disease to commit suicide by political ideology:

| Supports the Right to Suicide? | Political Ideology | | | Totals |
|---|---|---|---|---|
| | Liberal | Moderate | Conservative | |
| Favour | 381 | 394 | 319 | 1,094 |
| Oppose | 120 | 229 | 261 | 610 |
| Totals | 501 | 623 | 580 | 1,704 |

**d.** Support for traditional gender roles by political ideology:

| Supports Traditional Gender Roles? | Political Ideology | | | Totals |
|---|---|---|---|---|
| | Liberal | Moderate | Conservative | |
| Favour | 59 | 90 | 108 | 257 |
| Oppose | 454 | 548 | 484 | 1,486 |
| Totals | 513 | 638 | 592 | 1,743 |

**e.** Support for legalizing marijuana by political ideology.

| Should Marijuana Be Legalized? | Political Ideology | | | Totals |
|---|---|---|---|---|
| | Liberal | Moderate | Conservative | |
| Favour | 132 | 78 | 52 | 262 |
| Oppose | 101 | 87 | 109 | 297 |
| Totals | 233 | 165 | 161 | 559 |

**8.8** Problem 8.7 analyzed the bivariate relationships between political ideology, the independent variable, and five different dependent variables using only percentages. Now, with the aid of measures of association, these characterizations should be easier to develop. Compute a phi and a lambda for each table in Problem 8.7. Compare the measures of association with your characterizations based on the percentages.

**You Are the Researcher**

## Using SPSS to Analyze Bivariate Association with the 2013 GSS

The demonstrations and exercises below use the shortened version of the 2013 GSS data set supplied with this textbook. Start SPSS and open the *GSS_2013_Shortened.sav* file.

### SPSS DEMONSTRATION 8.1 Does Health Vary by Income?

What's the relationship between income and health? To answer this question we'll run a **Crosstabs** on *incm* (respondent's total annual income) and *srh_110* (state of health). We must first recode *incm* because it has too many (12) categories (see Appendix G) to be used in a bivariate table. We will provide only a brief review here; a detailed guide on recoding *incm,* including adding labels to the values of the recoded variable, is given in Appendix F.5.

Click **Transform** from the main menu and choose **Recode into Different Variables**. Next, move the variable *incm* to the **Input Variable → Output Variable** box, then type a name—we suggest *income4*—in the **Output Variable** box. Click the **Change** button. Next, click on the **Old and New Values** button. We have decided to collapse the values of *incm* into four categories. The recoding instructions that should appear in the **Old → New** dialog box are:

$$1 \text{ thru } 6 \rightarrow 1$$
$$7 \text{ thru } 8 \rightarrow 2$$
$$9 \text{ thru } 10 \rightarrow 3$$
$$11 \text{ thru } 12 \rightarrow 4$$

Click **Continue**, and then **OK** after inputting these recode instructions.

We will also recode state of health, *srh_110*. As a general rule, it is best to collapse a variable into logical groups. We decided to collapse *srh_110* into a dichotomized variable: good health versus poor health. Click **Transform**, then **Recode into Different Variables**. Next, click the **Reset** button to reset all specifications in the dialog and sub-dialog boxes to their default state. Move the variable *srh_110* to the **Input → Variable Output Variable** box. Give the recoded variable a new name in the **Output Variable** box (we used *health*), then click the **Change** button. Click the **Old and New Values** button, and follow these recoding instructions:

$$1 \text{ thru } 3 \rightarrow 1$$
$$4 \text{ thru } 5 \rightarrow 2$$

Click **Continue,** and then **OK**. Scores 1 (excellent), 2 (very good), or 3 (good) on *srh_110* are grouped together into a score of 1 on *health,* and scores 4 (fair) or 5 (poor) on *srh_110* into a score of 2 on *health.*

We highly recommend that both new variables be added to the permanent data file because they will be used in future SPSS demonstrations and exercises. To do so, click **Save** from the **File** menu, and the updated data set with *income4* and *health* added will be saved to disk. If you are using the student version of SPSS, remember that your data set is limited to 50 variables.

To examine the effect of *income4* on *health,* click **Analyze, Descriptive Statistics**, and **Crosstabs**, then input *health* as the row variable and *income4* as the column variable. Click the **Cells** button and request column percentages by clicking the box next to **Column** in the **Percentages** box. With the dependent variable in the rows and the independent variable in the columns and with percentages calculated within columns, we will be able to read the table by following the rules developed in this chapter. Click the **Continue** button to return to the **Crosstabs** dialog box. Also, request chi square by clicking the **Statistics** button. Click **Continue**, then **OK**, and the following output will be produced. (The output has been modified slightly, including adding labels to the values of *income4* and *health* as illustrated in Appendix F.5, to improve readability.)

### Health * Income4 Cross-tabulation

| | | | | Income4 | | | |
|---|---|---|---|---|---|---|---|
| | | | <$30,000 | $30,000–$49,999 | $50,000–$79,999 | $80,000+ | Total |
| Health | Good | Count<br>% within Income4 | 410<br>87.0% | 253<br>87.5% | 198<br>91.7% | 194<br>95.6% | 1055<br>89.5% |
| | Poor | Count<br>% within Income4 | 61<br>13.0% | 36<br>12.5% | 18<br>8.3% | 9<br>4.4% | 124<br>10.5% |
| Total | | Count<br>% within Income4 | 471<br>100.0% | 289<br>100.0% | 216<br>100.0% | 203<br>100.0% | 1179<br>100.0% |

## Chi Square Tests

| | Value | df | Asymptotic Significance (2-sided) |
|---|---|---|---|
| Pearson chi square | 13.198[a] | 3 | .004 |
| Likelihood ratio | 15.024 | 3 | .002 |
| Linear-by-linear association | 11.991 | 1 | .001 |
| N of valid cases | 1179 | | |

[a] 0 cells (0.0%) have expected count less than 5. The minimum expected count is 21.35.

Inspecting the table column by column, you will see that there is a relationship and that it is weak in strength. The maximum difference is the same in both the top and bottom rows, and occurs in each row between the highest and lowest income columns. In the top row, the maximum difference is 95.6% − 87.0% = 8.6%. In the bottom row, the maximum difference is 13.0% − 4.4% = 8.6%.

Both variables are measured at the ordinal level, so we can also describe the direction. Is this relationship positive or negative? Remember that in a positive association, high scores on one variable will be associated with high scores on the other and low scores will be associated with low. In a negative relationship, high scores on one variable are associated with low scores on the other. Looking at the table again, we see that the relationship is negative: As the code value of income increases, the code value of health decreases.

This is a good opportunity to draw attention to the fact that SPSS calculates relationship direction on the basis of the relationship between the variables' response category code values. What does this mean, in our example?

Remember how we recoded *incm* and *srh_110*. For income4, the code value 1 represents the lowest income category (<$30,000), while the code value 4 represents the highest income category ($80,000+). An increasing income code value corresponds to an increasing income category amount. The opposite is true for health, where 1 represents good health and 2 represents poor health. In other words, an increasing health code value corresponds to declining health. So a negative relationship in our example means that as the income code value increases, the health code value decreases. Looking at the meaning of our codes, what this shows us is that as the amount of income increases, people's health gets better, while as income decreases, people's health becomes poorer.

We can provide a visual representation of the conditional distributions of *Y* in the above cross-tabulation by a creating a panelled pie chart and a clustered bar chart. To create the panelled pie chart, click on **Graphs**, then select **Legacy Dialogs**, and **Pie**. Keep **Data in Chart Are Summaries for groups of cases**, and click **Define**. At the top of the drop-down menu, click on **Slices Represent N of cases**. Next, click on *health* in the left variable name column, and move this dependent variable into the **Define slices by** box. Similarly, click on *income4* in the left variable column, but now move this independent variable into the **Panel by columns** box. When you click on **OK**, the panelled pie chart will appear in the output window.

Next, double-click on the panelled pie chart to open **Chart Editor**, and then click on the **Show Data Labels** icon. When you do this, the **Properties** window will open and the raw frequency counts will appear in each slice; however, we want the percentages to appear, so that we can see the direct connection between our chart and the conditional distributions of Y. So click once on one of the pies, and both pies will be selected. Now, scroll across the top of the **Properties** window until you arrive at **Data Value Labels**. **Count** will show up in the **Labels Displayed** box. Click on **Count**, and then click on the small red "x" (located to the right of the **Labels Displayed** box). This will remove the frequency count from the pie slices, and transfer it to the **Not Displayed** box. Next, click on **Percent**, and then on the small green arrow (located to the right of the **Not Displayed** box. This will move the percent to the **Labels Displayed** box. Click on **Apply**, and then on **Close**, to close the box. The raw frequency counts will now change to percentages in the panelled pie chart in the output window as follows (slightly edited for readability):

### Pie Chart Showing the Impact of Income on Health

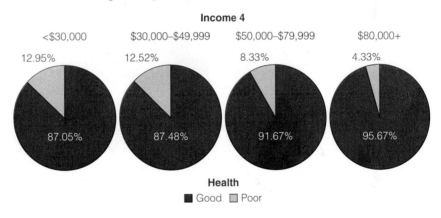

Income 4

| <$30,000 | $30,000–$49,999 | $50,000–$79,999 | $80,000+ |
|---|---|---|---|
| 12.95% | 12.52% | 8.33% | 4.33% |
| 87.05% | 87.48% | 91.67% | 95.67% |

Health
■ Good  ☐ Poor

Next, to create the clustered bar chart, click on **Graphs**, then select **Legacy Dialogs**, and **Bar**. Click on **Clustered**, keep **Data in Chart Are Summaries for groups of cases**, and then click **Define**. At the top of the drop-down menu, click on **Bars Represent % of cases**. Next, click on *health* in the left variable name column, and move this dependent variable into the **Category Axis** box. Similarly, click on *income4* in the left variable column, but now move this independent variable into the **Define Clusters By** box. When you click on **OK**, the clustered bar chart will appear in the output window.

Then, double-click on the clustered bar chart to open **Chart Editor**, and then click on the **Show Data Labels** icon. When you do this, the percentages will automatically appear in each bar, and the **Properties** window will open. Since we want the percentages, in order to see the direct connection between our chart and the conditional distributions of Y, we do not need to make any further changes. Simply close the Properties window, as well as the Chart Editor editing window. The percentages will now appear in the clustered bar chart in the output window as follows (slightly edited for readability):

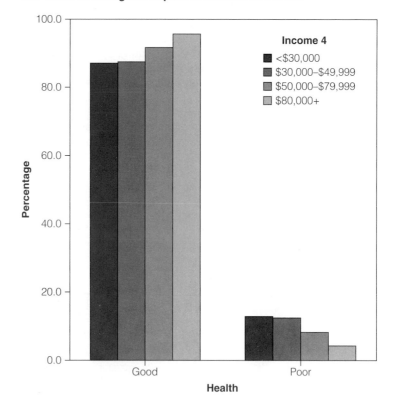

**Bar Chart Showing the Impact of Income on Health**

The panelled pie chart and the clustered bar chart represent the conditional distributions of Y directly, so they can help us to interpret our cross-tabulation. In the panelled pie chart, we see four pies. Each pie represents 100% of the cases in one of the income categories, while the slices in each pie show how the health categories are distributed within that pie. So for example, we can see how the "poor health" slice is largest for the "<$30,000" income category, but this slice becomes smaller as the income level increases; conversely, the size of the "good health" slice increases as income increases. Comparing the sizes of the independent variable slices, for each dependent variable pie, is equivalent to comparing column percentages across in a cross-tabulation, in order to identify variable relationships. At the same time, in every pie, we see that the largest pie slice is always comprised of people who have said that their health is good. In other words, most people, across all income categories, have good health; however, we are more likely to find people with poor health among people with low income than we are to find them among people with high income.

Turning to the clustered bar chart, the bars represent the income categories, such that each of the bars of a single colour represents 100% of the cases in that income category. Comparing the heights of the bars, for each dependent variable value on the *x*-axis, is equivalent to comparing column percentages across in a cross-tabulation, in order to identify variable relationships. So, for example, among people with good health, we can see that the bar representing people with incomes of $80,000 and over is the tallest, while the bar representing people with <$30,000 is the shortest; this pattern is reversed for people with poor health. At the same time, the greater height of all the bars in the "good health" category, compared with all the bars in the "poor health" category, shows us that across all income categories, most people said that their health is good.

Finally, the exact probability value of chi square is 0.004, below the standard alpha indicator of a significant result, 0.05, so we reject the null hypothesis that the variables are independent and conclude that there is a statistically significant relationship between income and health. However, this is a situation where we have a statistically significant finding but not necessarily an unimportant one (recall that the maximum percentage point difference was only 8.6%). As noted in Chapter 7, a statistically significant finding does not guarantee that it is important in any other sense, especially if sample size is large as in our case.

As a final point, let us direct your attention to the "Total" (or total number of cases) column in the "Cross-Tabulation" output. There is a total of 1,179 people in the analysis. The original sample included over 1,500 people, however. What happened to all those "missing cases"? These missing cases are respondents who did not provide information on health and/or income. All statistics produced by the crosstabs command apply to only those that provide information on both variables; all other cases are deleted from the analysis. This is called *pairwise* deletion of missing data, as only those cases that have non-missing values for *both* variables are included in the crosstab. The phenomenon of diminishing sample size is a common problem in survey research that at some point, may jeopardize the integrity of the inquiry.

## SPSS DEMONSTRATION 8.2 Does Volunteer Behaviour Vary by Sex? Another Look

In Demonstration 7.1, we used the **Crosstabs** procedure to examine the relationship between *vcg_300* (volunteered in the past 12 months) and *sex* (respondent's sex). We saw that the relationship was statistically significant, and that females were more likely than males to have volunteered in the past 12 months. In this demonstration, we will re-examine the relationship and have SPSS compute some measures of association.

Click **Analyze**, then **Descriptive Statistics**, and then **Crosstabs**. Move *vcg_300* into the **Row(s)** box and *sex* into the **Column(s)** box. Click the **Cells** button and request column percentages. Click the **Statistics** button and request chi square, phi, Cramer's *V*, and lambda. Click **Continue**, and then **OK**, and the following output, slightly edited to improve readability, will be produced.

The measures of association are reported below the output for the chi square tests. Three values for lambda are reported in the "Directional Measures" output block. Remember that lambda is asymmetric and will change value depending on which variable is taken as dependent. (Symmetric lambda is more or less an average of the two asymmetric lambda values, and should only be used when it is not possible to determine which variable is dependent and which is independent.) In this case, *vcg_300* (volunteered in the past 12 months) is the dependent variable, so lambda is 0.000, a value that indicates no relationship between the variables. Looking at the first block in the output "Cross-tabulation," we see, however, that the conditional distributions do change, indicating that there actually is a relationship. The problem here is that every independent variable category shares the same dependent variable modal category; in other words, the mode for both males and females is "no," did not volunteer in the past 12 months. This is a problem of a "false" zero; lambda is misleading and should be disregarded (see Section 8.8). (Goodman and Kruskal tau is similar to lambda, and is based on the logic of proportional reduction in error. It is also an asymmetric measure of association.)

Phi and Cramer's *V* are reported in the "Symmetric Measures" output block. The statistics are identical in value, 0.086, as they will be whenever the table has either two rows or two columns. (We can ignore the directional sign of phi.) The measures reveal an association between the variables, albeit a weak one.

### Volunteer work—12 months * Sex of respondent Cross-tabulation

| | | | Sex of Respondent | | Total |
|---|---|---|---|---|---|
| | | | Male | Female | |
| Volunteer work—12 months | Yes | Count | 249 | 310 | 559 |
| | | % within sex of respondent | 31.2% | 39.4% | 35.2% |
| | No | Count | 550 | 477 | 1027 |
| | | % within sex of respondent | 68.8% | 60.6% | 64.8% |
| Total | | Count | 799 | 787 | 1586 |
| | | % within sex of respondent | 100.0% | 100.0% | 100.0% |

### Chi Square Tests

| | Value | df | Asymptotic Significance (2-sided) | Exact Sig. (2-sided) | Exact Sig. (1-sided) |
|---|---|---|---|---|---|
| Pearson chi square | 11.755[a] | 1 | .001 | | |
| Continuity correction[b] | 11.398 | 1 | .001 | | |
| Likelihood ratio | 11.772 | 1 | .001 | | |
| Fisher's exact test | | | | .001 | .000 |
| Linear-by-linear association | 11.748 | 1 | .001 | | |
| N of valid cases | 1586 | | | | |

[a] 0 cells (0.0%) have expected count less than 5. The minimum expected count is 277.39.

[b] Computed only for a 2 × 2 table.

## Directional Measures

| | | | Value | Asymptotic Standard Error[a] | Approximate T[b] | Approximate Significance |
|---|---|---|---|---|---|---|
| Nominal by nominal | Lambda | Symmetric | .045 | .017 | 2.585 | .010 |
| | | Volunteer work—12 months dependent | .000 | .000 | .[c] | .[c] |
| | | Sex of respondent dependent | .078 | .029 | 2.585 | .010 |
| | Goodman and Kruskal tau | Volunteer work—12 months dependent | .007 | .004 | | .001[d] |
| | | Sex of respondent dependent | .007 | .004 | | .001[d] |

[a.] Not assuming the null hypothesis.

[b.] Using the asymptotic standard error assuming the null hypothesis.

[c.] Cannot be computed because the asymptotic standard error equals zero.

[d.] Based on chi square approximation.

## Symmetric Measures

| | | Value | Approximate Significance |
|---|---|---|---|
| Nominal by nominal | Phi | −.086 | .001 |
| | Cramer's V | .086 | .001 |
| N of valid cases | | 1586 | |

The significance value of chi square, 0.001, reported in the "Chi-Square Tests" output block, is lower than 0.05, so we reject the null hypothesis and conclude that the relationship between sex and volunteering behaviour is statistically significant. Even though phi and Cramer's V tell us that the relationship between sex and volunteering behaviour is rather weak, chi square indicates that it is statistically significant. This reminds us once again that association and statistical significance are two different things.

## Exercises (using *GSS_2013_Shortened.sav*)

**8.1** As long as *srh_110* has already been recoded, examine the relationship between recoded *srh_110* as dependent or row variable and *sex* (sex) as the independent or column variable using the **Crosstabs** procedure. Be sure to request column percentage in the cells and the chi square test. To assist your interpretation of the column percentages in the cross-tabulation, also produce a panelled pie chart and a clustered bar chart. Write a paragraph summarizing the results. Describe the relationships in terms of strength and pattern.

**8.2** Following up on Demonstration 8.2, select two more variables that you think might be related to *vcg_300*. Run the **Crosstabs** procedure with *vcg_300* as dependent or row variable and your other variables as the independent or column variables. Be sure to request column percentage in the cells, as well as phi and lambda. Write a few sentences describing each relationship.

# 9

# Measures of Association for Variables Measured at the Ordinal Level

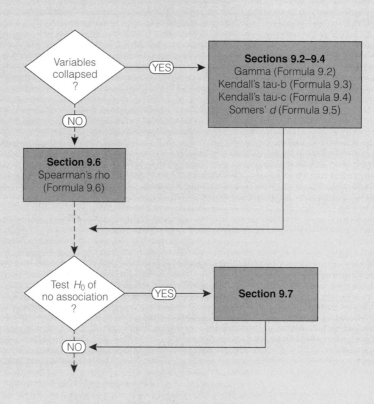

## LEARNING OBJECTIVES

By the end of this chapter, you will be able to

1. Calculate and interpret gamma, Kendall's tau-b and tau-c, Somers' $d$, and Spearman's rho.

2. Explain the logic of pairs as it relates to measuring association.

3. Use gamma, Kendall's tau-b and tau-c, Somers' $d$, and Spearman's rho to analyze and describe a bivariate relationship in terms of the three questions introduced in Chapter 8.

4. Test gamma and Spearman's rho for significance.

## 9.1 INTRODUCTION

There are two common types of ordinal-level variables. Some have many possible scores and look, at least at first glance, like interval-ratio-level variables. We will call these "continuous ordinal variables." An attitude scale that incorporated many different items and, therefore, had many possible values would produce this type of variable.

The second type, which we will call a "collapsed ordinal variable," has only a few (no more than five or six) values or scores and can be created either by collecting data in collapsed form or by collapsing a continuous ordinal scale. For example, we would produce collapsed ordinal variables by measuring social class as upper, middle, or lower or by reducing the scores on an attitude scale to just a few categories (such as high, moderate, and low).

A number of measures of association have been developed for use with collapsed ordinal-level variables. The most commonly used statistics in this group include **gamma (G)**, **Somers' $d$ ($d_{yx}$)**, **Kendall's tau-b ($\tau_b$)**, and a variant of Kendall's tau-b called **Kendall's tau-c ($\tau_c$)**. These statistics are covered in the first part of this chapter. For continuous ordinal variables, a statistic called **Spearman's rho ($r_s$)** is typically used. We will cover this measure of association toward the end of the chapter.

This chapter will expand your understanding of how bivariate associations can be described and analyzed, but it is important to remember that we are still trying to answer the three questions raised in Chapter 8: Are the variables associated? How strong is the association? What is the direction of the association?

## 9.2 THE LOGIC OF PAIRS

Gamma, Kendall's tau-b and tau-c, and Somers' $d$ are conceptually similar to one another. They each measure strength and direction of association by comparing each respondent to every other respondent, called a "pair of respondents" or more simply a "pair," in terms of their rankings on the independent and dependent variable. The total number of unique pairs of respondents in a data set can be found by the following formula:

**FORMULA 9.1**

$$\text{Total number of unique pairs of respondents} = \frac{n(n-1)}{2}$$

where $n$ = the total number of respondents

Pairs can be further divided into five subgroups. A pair of respondents is "similar" if the respondent with the larger value on the independent variable also has the larger value on the dependent variable. A pair is "dissimilar" if the respondent with the larger value on the independent variable has the smaller value on the dependent variable. A pair is "tied" if respondents have the same value on either the independent or dependent variable, or on both. Specifically, a pair is "tied on the independent variable" if both respondents have the same score on the independent but not dependent variable; a pair is "tied on the dependent variable" if both respondents have

**TABLE 9.1   Data on Length of Service and Burnout for Five Teachers**

| Teacher | Length ($X$) | Burnout ($Y$) |
|---|---|---|
| Omar | 1 | 1 |
| Camil | 2 | 2 |
| Joseph | 2 | 3 |
| Karina | 3 | 3 |
| Steven | 3 | 3 |

For length of service: 1 = low, 2 = moderate, 3 = high.
For burnout: 1 = low, 2 = moderate, 3 = high.

the same score on the dependent but not independent variable; and a pair is "tied on both variables" if both respondents have the same independent and dependent variable scores.

As an example, let's assume that a researcher is concerned about the causes of "burnout" (i.e., demoralization and loss of commitment) among elementary school teachers and wonders about the relationship between years of service (independent or $X$ variable) and level of burnout (dependent or $Y$ variable). To examine this relationship, five elementary school teachers were sampled and asked about number of years employed as a teacher (1 = low, 2 = moderate, or 3 = high) and level of teacher burnout (1 = low, 2 = moderate, or 3 = high). Their scores are reported in Table 9.1.

Using Formula 9.1, we find that there are 10 unique pairs among the five teachers:

$$\frac{5(5-1)}{2} = \frac{20}{2} = 10$$

Table 9.2 lists each of the 10 pairs by type of pair. So, for example, looking at Camil and Steven in Table 9.1, we see that Steven is ranked above

**TABLE 9.2   Pairs of Teachers by Type of Pair**

| Pair | Type of Pair |
|---|---|
| Omar–Camil | Similar |
| Omar–Joseph | Similar |
| Omar–Karina | Similar |
| Omar–Steven | Similar |
| Camil–Joseph | Tied on the independent variable |
| Camil–Karina | Similar |
| Camil–Steven | Similar |
| Joseph–Karina | Tied on the dependent variable |
| Joseph–Steven | Tied on the dependent variable |
| Karina–Steven | Tied on both variables |

Camil on length of service. Steven is also ranked above Camil on burnout. Camil–Steven is therefore a similar pair. On the other hand, Joseph–Steven is a tied pair on the dependent variable, since they each have the same score on burnout but not on length of service, while Camil–Joseph is a tied pair on the independent variable, since they each have the same score on length of service but not on burnout. We also see that Karina–Steven is a tied pair on both variables, as both respondents have the same independent and dependent variable scores.

An example of a dissimilar pair would be a teacher who is ranked above another teacher on length of service, but below that teacher on burnout. (As you can see, however, this table does not include any dissimilar pairs.) For example, if the teacher Margaret were included in Table 9.1, and she had a high length of service (score of 3) but a low level of burnout (score of 1), then Joseph–Margaret and Camil–Margaret would both be examples of dissimilar pairs.

## 9.3 ANALYZING RELATIONSHIPS WITH GAMMA, KENDALL'S TAU-B AND TAU-C, AND SOMERS' *D*

**Determining Strength of Relationships.** Gamma, Kendall's tau-b and tau-c, and Somers' *d* measure the strength of association between variables by considering the number of similar versus dissimilar pairs. When there is an equal number of similar and dissimilar pairs, the value of these statistics will be equal to 0.00, indicating no association between the independent and dependent variables. As the number of similar relative to dissimilar *or* dissimilar relative to similar pairs increases, the value moves closer to 1.00. Thus, the larger the difference between the number of similar and dissimilar pairs, the stronger the association. When all pairs are either similar *or* dissimilar, the value of these statistics will be equal to 1.00, indicating a perfect relationship.

Table 9.3 provides some additional assistance with interpreting the values of gamma, Kendall's tau-b and tau-c, and Somers' *d* in a format similar to Tables 8.5 and 8.14. As with the latter tables, the relationship between the values and the descriptive terms is arbitrary, so the outline presented in Table 9.3 is intended as a general guideline only.

**TABLE 9.3  The Relationship Between the Value of Ordinal-Level Measures of Association and the Strength of the Relationship**

| Value | Strength |
|---|---|
| *If the value is* | *The strength of the relationship is* |
| between 0.00 and 0.10 | weak |
| between 0.11 and 0.30 | moderate |
| greater than 0.30 | strong |

**Determining Direction of Relationships.** Nominal measures of association, like phi and lambda, measure only the strength of a bivariate association. Ordinal measures of association are more sophisticated and add information about the overall direction of the relationship (positive or negative). It is also relatively easy to determine direction: If the sign of the statistic is a plus, the direction is positive; a minus sign indicates a negative relationship. So, for example, a value of $+1.00$ indicates a perfect *positive* relationship between the variables, while a value of $-1.00$ indicates a perfect *negative* relationship. (Note that the strength of a relationship is independent of its direction. That is, a value of $-1.00$ would be exactly as strong as a value of $+1.00$, but opposite in direction.)

A positive relationship means that the scores of respondents tend to be ranked in the same order on both variables. In more general terms, a positive relationship means that the variables change in the same direction. That is, as scores on one variable increase (or decrease), scores on the other variable also increase (or decrease). Table 9.4 illustrates the general shape of a positive relationship. In a positive relationship, the scores of respondents tend to fall along a diagonal from upper left to lower right (assuming, of course, that the tables have been constructed with the column variable increasing from left to right and the row variable increasing from top to bottom).

Negative relationships are the opposite of positive relationships. Low scores on one variable are associated with high scores on the other, and high scores on one variable are associated with low scores on the other. This pattern means that the cases will tend to fall along a diagonal from lower left to upper right (when the tables have been constructed with the column variable increasing from left to right and the row variable increasing from top to bottom). Table 9.5 illustrates a generalized negative relationship.

The above comments about the pattern of increase of the variables in the columns and rows highlights an additional complication. The coding for ordinal-level variables is arbitrary, and a higher score may mean *more* or *less* of the variable being measured. For example, if we measured social

**TABLE 9.4 A Generalized Positive Relationship**

| Variable Y | Variable X | | |
|---|---|---|---|
| | Low | Moderate | High |
| Low | X | | |
| Moderate | | X | |
| High | | | X |

**TABLE 9.5 A Generalized Negative Relationship**

| Variable Y | Variable X | | |
|---|---|---|---|
| | Low | Moderate | High |
| Low | | | X |
| Moderate | | X | |
| High | X | | |

class as upper, middle, and lower, we could assign scores to the categories in either of two ways:

| A | B |
|---|---|
| (1) Upper | (3) Upper |
| (2) Middle | (2) Middle |
| (3) Lower | (1) Lower |

While coding according to scheme "B" might seem preferable (because higher scores go with a higher class position), both schemes are perfectly legitimate, and the direction of a relationship will change depending on which scheme is selected. Using scheme "B," we would find positive relationships between social class and education: As education increased, so would class.

Using scheme "A," however, the same relationship would appear to be negative because the numerical scores (1, 2, 3) are coded in reverse order, with the highest social class assigned the lowest score, and so forth. If you didn't check the coding scheme, you might conclude that a negative gamma, Kendall's tau-b or tau-c, or Somers' *d* means that class decreases as education increases when, actually, the opposite is true.

Unfortunately, this source of confusion cannot be avoided when working with ordinal-level variables. Coding schemes will always be arbitrary for these variables, and you need to exercise additional caution when interpreting the direction of ordinal-level variables.

**Gamma.** Gamma, Kendall's tau-b, and Somers' *d* are computed by subtracting the number of similar pairs from dissimilar pairs, then dividing this result by the total number of pairs. Where these statistics differ is in how they treat tied pairs—each deals with tied pairs in a different way. (In other words, the value of all these statistics will be identical when there are no tied pairs.)

Gamma is the number of similar over dissimilar pairs as a proportion of all pairs excluding ties. The formula for gamma is

**FORMULA 9.2**

$$G = \frac{n_s - n_d}{n_s + n_d}$$

where $n_s$ = number of pairs of respondents ranked the same on both variables (i.e., similar pairs)

$n_d$ = number of pairs of respondents ranked differently on the two variables (i.e., dissimilar pairs)

Gamma ranges from $-1.00$ for a negative relationship to $+1.00$ for a positive relationship. A value of zero indicates no relationship. Gamma is a symmetrical measure of association, so its value will be the same regardless of which variable is taken as the dependent.

To illustrate the computation of $G$, let's consider the relationship between levels of burnout and years of service for the five elementary school teachers in Table 9.1. To compute gamma, we must find the number of similar pairs, $n_s$, and dissimilar pairs, $n_d$. Turning to Table 9.2, we see that there are a total of six (6) similar pairs and zero (0) dissimilar pairs. Next, we substitute these numbers into the numerator and denominator of the formula:

$$G = \frac{n_s - n_d}{n_s + n_d}$$

$$G = \frac{6 - 0}{6 + 0}$$

$$G = \frac{6}{6}$$

$$G = +1.00$$

Thus, ignoring ties, there is perfect agreement between the teachers: A teacher with a *higher* length of service also has a *higher* level of burnout. That is, there is a perfect positive association between the variables.

**Gamma as a PRE Measure.** In addition to interpretation of strength and direction of association, gamma has a PRE (proportional reduction in error) interpretation. In Chapter 8, we saw that for nominal-level variables the logic of PRE was based on two different "predictions" of the scores of cases on the dependent variable ($Y$): one that ignored the independent variable ($X$) and a second that took the independent variable into account. We also saw that the value of lambda showed the extent to which taking the independent variable into account improved accuracy when predicting the score of the dependent variable.

The PRE logic for variables measured at the ordinal level is similar, and gamma, like lambda, measures the proportional reduction in error gained by predicting one variable while taking the other into account. The major difference lies in the way predictions are made. In the case of gamma, we predict the *order* of pairs of respondents rather than a score on the dependent variable. That is, we predict whether one respondent will have a higher or lower score than the other. First, we predict the order of a pair of respondents on one variable while ignoring their order on the other. Second, we predict the order on one variable while taking order on the other variable into account.

As an illustration, let's look at the question of burnout and years of service among elementary school teachers. One way to state this question is to ask whether teachers with more years of service have higher levels of burnout. Another way to ask the same question is: Do teachers who rank higher on years of service also rank higher on burnout? If we knew that teacher A had more years of service than teacher B, would we be able to predict that teacher A is also more burned out than teacher B? That is, would knowledge of the order of this pair of teachers on one variable help us predict their order on the other?

If the two variables are associated, we will reduce our errors when our predictions about one of the variables are based on knowledge of the other variable. Furthermore, the stronger the association, the fewer the errors we will make. When there is no association between the variables, gamma will be 0.00, and knowledge of the order of a pair of respondents on one variable will not improve our ability to predict their order on the other. A gamma of $\pm 1.00$ denotes a perfect relationship: the order of all pairs of respondents on one variable will be predictable without error from their order on the other variable, as is the case for the length of service and level of burnout example.

**Limitation of Gamma.**    Gamma ignores tied pairs of cases and is based only on pairs (similar and dissimilar) that inherently reflect a relationship between the variables. (As an example, just 6 of the 10 unique pairs shown in Table 9.2 are used in calculating gamma.) Thus, gamma can *exaggerate* the strength of association between two ordinal variables. Kendall's tau-b and tau-c (named after British statistician, Maurice Kendall) and Somers' $d$ (developed by the sociologist Robert H. Somers) were designed to correct this problem.

Kendall's tau-b and tau-c and Somers' $d$ are extensions or modifications of gamma. Like gamma, they contain the same quantity in the numerator, $n_s - n_d$. However, their denominator is more complex.

Kendall's tau-b includes both pairs tied on the independent variable and pairs tied on the dependent variable. Kendall's tau-c is used as an alternative to Kendall's tau-b in certain circumstances. Somers' $d$ includes only pairs tied on the dependent variable. Kendall's tau-b and tau-c are symmetrical measures of association (the same value is produced regardless of which variable is considered the dependent), while Somers' $d$ is designed specifically as an asymmetric measure and assumes that you can identify one of the variables as the dependent variable. Thus, Somers' $d$ corrects only for pairs tied on the dependent variable. These statistics will always be lower than gamma, except when there are no ties, because their denominators will be larger than the denominator of gamma.

**Kendall's tau-b.** The formula for computing Kendall's tau-b is

FORMULA 9.3

$$\tau_b = \frac{n_s - n_d}{\sqrt{(n_s + n_d + t_x)(n_s + n_d + t_y)}}$$

where $n_s$ = number of similar pairs
$n_d$ = number of dissimilar pairs
$t_x$ = number of pairs tied on the independent variable, $X$
$t_y$ = number of pairs tied on the dependent variable, $Y$

Kendall's tau-b ranges from $-1.00$ to $+1.00$. Kendall's tau-b does *not* have a PRE interpretation.

Let's again consider the relationship between burnout and years of service. In addition to the number of similar and dissimilar pairs, to compute tau-b we must find the number of pairs tied on the independent variable and the number of pairs tied on the dependent variable. Looking at Table 9.2, we see that there are a total of six (6) similar pairs, one (1) pair tied on the independent variable, and two (2) pairs tied on the dependent variable. Substituting these numbers into the numerator and denominator of Formula 9.3, the value of Kendall's tau-b is

$$\tau_b = \frac{n_s - n_d}{\sqrt{(n_s + n_d + t_x)(n_s + n_d + t_y)}}$$

$$\tau_b = \frac{6 - 0}{\sqrt{(6 + 0 + 1)(6 + 0 + 2)}}$$

$$\tau_b = \frac{6}{\sqrt{(7)(8)}}$$

$$\tau_b = \frac{6}{\sqrt{56}}$$

$$\tau_b = \frac{6}{7.48}$$

$$\tau_b = +0.80$$

The computed value of tau-b of $+0.80$ means that there is a strong positive relationship between the variables.

**Kendall's tau-c.** Kendall's tau-b is limited in that it can reach a maximum of 1.00 only when the independent and dependent variables have the same number of categories. In the example above, tau-b is an appropriate measure of association since each variable (teacher-burnout and years of service) contains three categories (i.e., low, moderate, and high). When the independent and dependent variables do not have the same number of categories, Kendall's tau-c, a variant of Kendall's tau-b, should be used instead. Kendall's tau-c adjusts for number of categories. It is designed to reach a maximum of 1.00 for variables with different numbers of categories. Therefore, tau-b is used when there are an equal number of categories in the independent and dependent variables, and tau-c is used when the numbers of categories are not the same.

The formula for Kendall's tau-c is

**FORMULA 9.4**
$$\tau_c = \frac{2m(n_s - n_d)}{n^2(m - 1)}$$

where $n_s$ = number of similar pairs
$n_d$ = number of dissimilar pairs
$n$ = number of respondents
$m$ = minimum value, whichever is less of the number of categories on the independent variable or the number of categories on the dependent variable

Like tau-b, tau-c ranges from −1.00 to +1.00, is a symmetrical measure, and does *not* have a PRE interpretation.

While tau-b is the appropriate measure for the burnout and years of service data in Table 9.1, we will compute tau-c for purposes of illustration. In all, there are six (6) similar pairs, five (5) respondents, and a minimum value of three (3) (because the variables have the same number of categories, we may use the number of categories on either the independent or dependent variable as the minimum value). Therefore,

$$\tau_c = \frac{2m(n_s - n_d)}{n^2(m - 1)}$$

$$\tau_c = \frac{(2 \times 3)(6 - 0)}{5^2(3 - 1)}$$

$$\tau_c = \frac{(6)(6)}{25(2)}$$

$$\tau_c = \frac{36}{50}$$

$$\tau_c = +0.72$$

The computed value of tau-c of +0.72 means that there is a strong positive relationship between the variables.

**Somers' $d$.** The formula for computing Somers' $d$ is

**FORMULA 9.5**

$$d_{yx} = \frac{n_s - n_d}{n_s + n_d + t_y}$$

where $n_s$ = number of similar pairs
$n_d$ = number of dissimilar pairs
$t_y$ = number of pairs tied on the dependent variable, $Y$

Somers' $d$ ranges from $-1.00$ (for negative relationships) to $+1.00$ (for positive relationships). It is an asymmetric measure. Thus, two values of Somers' $d$ can be computed: $d_{yx}$ where $Y$ is treated as the dependent variable and $d_{xy}$ where $X$ is treated as the dependent. In the example to follow, we assume $Y$ is the dependent. Somers' $d$ does *not* have a PRE interpretation.

For the data displayed in Table 9.1, there are a total of six (6) similar pairs and two (2) pairs tied on the dependent. Therefore, Somers' $d$ is

$$d_{yx} = \frac{n_s - n_d}{n_s + n_d + t_y}$$
$$d_{yx} = \frac{6 - 0}{6 + 0 + 2}$$
$$d_{yx} = \frac{6}{8}$$
$$d_{yx} = +0.75$$

Somers' $d$ equals $+0.75$, and, like Kendall's tau-b ($+0.80$), is lower than gamma ($+1.00$). As previously mentioned, this will always be the case because the denominators of these statistics will be larger than the denominator of gamma, except when there are no ties. Nonetheless, each measure indicates a very strong and positive association between length of service and burnout.

**Which Measure to Use?** There is no hard and fast rule regarding which ordinal measure of association to use. When there are relatively few ties, gamma should be used because it has a PRE interpretation and the others do not. When there are many ties (which becomes more likely as table size decreases), gamma tends to exaggerate the strength of relationship, so an adjusted measure (one that takes ties into account) should be used. Use Kendall's tau-b when the independent and dependent variables have the same number of categories; use Kendall's tau-c when the variables have an unequal number of categories; or alternatively, use Somers' $d$ when one of the variables is specifically identified as the dependent.

**9.4 GAMMA, KENDALL'S TAU-B AND TAU-C, AND SOMERS' *D* FOR BIVARIATE TABLES**

In the previous section, just a handful of cases were used to compute gamma, Kendall's tau-b and tau-c, and Somers' $d$. Keeping the number of respondents to a minimum helped simplify the logic of pairs underlying

**TABLE 9.6   Burnout by Length of Service for 100 Teachers**

| Burnout | Length of Service | | | |
|---------|-----|----------|------|--------|
|         | Low | Moderate | High | Totals |
| Low      | 20 | 6  | 4  | 30  |
| Moderate | 10 | 15 | 5  | 30  |
| High     | 8  | 11 | 21 | 40  |
| Totals   | 38 | 32 | 30 | 100 |

these statistics and their calculations. In most situations, however, we have a relatively large number of cases, which have been grouped into a bivariate table. While it is still possible to list all pairs of respondents, as we did in Table 9.2, in such situations it becomes cumbersome to do so and, in fact, unnecessary. This is because there is an easy and direct method for finding the number of similar, dissimilar, and tied pairs in a bivariate table.

**Gamma.**   Let's suppose that 100 elementary school teachers were sampled and asked about their number of years employed as a teacher and level of teacher burnout, and then their scores were organized into a bivariate table as shown in Table 9.6. Recall that to compute gamma, we must find the number of pairs of respondents that are ranked the same, $n_s$, and ranked differently, $n_d$, on the variables. We find these numbers by working with the cell frequencies in the bivariate table.

To find the number of pairs of respondents ranked the same ($n_s$), begin with the cell containing the respondents who were ranked the lowest on both variables. In Table 9.6, this would be the upper-left-hand cell. (Note that not all tables are constructed with values increasing from left to right across the columns and from top to bottom down the rows. When using other tables, always check that you have located the proper cell.) The 20 respondents in the upper-left-hand cell all rank low on both burnout and length of service. Now, form a pair of respondents by selecting one respondent from this cell and one from any other cell—for example, the middle cell in the table. All 15 respondents in this cell are moderate on both variables. Any pair of respondents formed between these two cells will be ranked the same on both variables. The total number of pairs of respondents is given by multiplying the cell frequencies. So, the contribution of these two cells to the total $n_s$ is (20)(15), or 300.

Following this logic, to find the total number of pairs of cases ranked the same on both variables, multiply the number of cases in each cell by the total of all frequencies below and to the right of that cell. Repeat this procedure for each cell and add the resultant products. The total of these products is $n_s$. Remember that gamma ignores all pairs of respondents that are tied on one or both variables, that is, pairs formed within the same row,

**FIGURE 9.1 Computing $n_s$ in a 3 × 3 Table**

|  | LOW | MODERATE | HIGH |
|---|---|---|---|
| LOW | 20 | 6 | 4 |
| MODERATE | 10 | 15 | 5 |
| HIGH | 8 | 11 | 21 |

20(15 + 5 + 11 + 21) = 1,040

|  | LOW | MODERATE | HIGH |
|---|---|---|---|
| LOW | 20 | 6 | 4 |
| MODERATE | 10 | 15 | 5 |
| HIGH | 8 | 11 | 21 |

6(5 + 21) = 156

|  | LOW | MODERATE | HIGH |
|---|---|---|---|
| LOW | 20 | 6 | 4 |
| MODERATE | 10 | 15 | 5 |
| HIGH | 8 | 11 | 21 |

10(11 + 21) = 320

|  | LOW | MODERATE | HIGH |
|---|---|---|---|
| LOW | 20 | 6 | 4 |
| MODERATE | 10 | 15 | 5 |
| HIGH | 8 | 11 | 21 |

15(21) = 315

column, or cell. This means that in computing $n_s$, we will work with only the pairs of respondents that can be formed between each cell and the cells below and to the right of it.

Figure 9.1, which reproduces the data from Table 9.6, shows the direction of multiplication for each of the four cells that, in a 3 × 3 table, can contribute to $n_s$. (Note that none of the cells in the bottom row or the right-hand column can contribute to $n_s$ because they have no cells below and to the right of them.) The frequency in the darker shaded cell is multiplied by the product of the frequencies in the lighter shaded cells. In this example, we find that a total of 1,831 (1,040 + 156 + 320 + 315) pairs of cases are ranked the same on both variables; that is, $n_s = 1,831$.

Our next step is to find the number of pairs of cases ranked differently ($n_d$) on both variables. To do so, we begin with the upper-right-hand cell and multiply the number of cases in the cell by the total frequency of cases below and to the left; that is, the four respondents in the upper-right-hand cell are low on $Y$ and high on $X$; if a pair is formed with any respondent from this cell and any cell below and to the left, the respondents will be ranked differently on the two variables. Repeat this procedure for each cell and add the resultant products. The total of these products is $n_d$. Note that the pattern for computing $n_d$ is the reverse of the pattern for $n_s$.

The computation of $n_d$ for a 3 × 3 table is shown in Figure 9.2. Again, the frequency in the darker shaded cell is multiplied by the product of the frequencies in the lighter shaded cells. We find that the total number of

**FIGURE 9.2   Computing $n_d$ in a 3 × 3 Table**

|  | LOW | MODERATE | HIGH |
|---|---|---|---|
| LOW | 20 | 6 | 4 |
| MODERATE | 10 | 15 | 5 |
| HIGH | 8 | 11 | 21 |

$4(10 + 15 + 8 + 11) = 176$

|  | LOW | MODERATE | HIGH |
|---|---|---|---|
| LOW | 20 | 6 | 4 |
| MODERATE | 10 | 15 | 5 |
| HIGH | 8 | 11 | 21 |

$6(10 + 8) = 108$

|  | LOW | MODERATE | HIGH |
|---|---|---|---|
| LOW | 20 | 6 | 4 |
| MODERATE | 10 | 15 | 5 |
| HIGH | 8 | 11 | 21 |

$5(8 + 11) = 95$

|  | LOW | MODERATE | HIGH |
|---|---|---|---|
| LOW | 20 | 6 | 4 |
| MODERATE | 10 | 15 | 5 |
| HIGH | 8 | 11 | 21 |

$15(8) = 120$

pairs of cases ranked in different order on the variables is 499 (176 + 108 + 95 + 120).

Since there are many more cases of similar relative to dissimilar pairs (1,831 versus 499) for Table 9.6, we know the value of gamma will be positive. Using Formula 9.2, the value of gamma is

$$G = \frac{n_s - n_d}{n_s + n_d}$$
$$G = \frac{1{,}831 - 499}{1{,}831 + 499}$$
$$G = \frac{1{,}332}{2{,}330}$$
$$G = +0.57$$

A gamma of +0.57 indicates that length of service has a strong and positive association with degree of burnout. Since gamma also has a PRE interpretation, a value of 0.57 indicates that we would make 57% fewer errors if we predicted the order of pairs of cases on one variable from the order of pairs of cases on the other (as opposed to predicting order while ignoring the other variable). In other words, knowing the respective ordering of two teachers on length of service in our example will help us predict their ordering on burnout.

---

**ONE STEP AT A TIME** Computing and Interpreting Gamma in a Bivariate Table

**To Compute Gamma**

**1:** Make sure the table is arranged with the column variable increasing from left to right and the row variable increasing from top to bottom.

**2:** To compute $n_s$, start with the upper-left-hand cell. Multiply the number of cases in this cell by the total number of cases in all cells below and to the right. Repeat this process for each cell in the table. Add up these subtotals to find $n_s$.

**3:** To compute $n_d$, start with the upper-right-hand cell. Multiply the number of cases in this cell by the total number of cases in all cells below and to the left. Repeat this process for each cell in the table. Add up these subtotals to find $n_d$.

**4:** Subtract the value of $n_d$ from $n_s$.

**5:** Add the value of $n_d$ to $n_s$.

**6:** Divide the value you found in step 4 by the value you found in step 5. This value is gamma.

**Interpreting the Strength of the Relationship**

**1:** Always begin with the column percentages: The bigger the change in column percentages, the stronger the relationship.

**2:** There are two ways to use gamma to interpret strength. You can use either or both:

a. Use Table 9.3 to describe strength in general terms.

b. Use the logic of proportional reduction in error. Multiply gamma by 100. This value represents the percentage improvement in our predictions of the dependent variable by taking the independent variable into account.

**Interpreting the Direction of the Relationship**

**1:** Always begin by looking at the pattern of the column percentages. If the cases tend to fall in a diagonal from upper left to lower right, the relationship is positive. If the cases tend to fall in a diagonal from lower left to upper right, the relationship is negative.

**2:** The sign of the gamma also tells the direction of the relationship. However, be very careful when interpreting direction with ordinal-level variables. Remember that coding schemes for these variables are arbitrary and that a positive gamma may mean that the actual relationship is negative, and vice versa.

**Kendall's tau-b and tau-c.** In computing gamma for the data in Table 9.6, only 2,330 ($n_s + n_d$) of the 4,950 possible pairs were used. Formula 9.1 shows there are $[n (n - 1)]/2$ or 4,950 unique pairs to work with when $n$ equals 100. The rest (tied pairs) were ignored.

Kendall's tau-b, by contrast, includes pairs tied on the dependent variable, $t_y$, and independent variable, $t_x$. To find $t_y$, begin with the cell containing the cases ranked the lowest on both variables (the upper-left-hand cell in Table 9.6). Next, multiply the frequency in that cell by the total of all frequencies immediately to the right of that cell. Repeat this procedure for each cell and add the products together.

Figure 9.3, again produced from the data in Table 9.6, shows the direction of multiplication for each of the six cells in a $3 \times 3$ table that can contribute to $t_y$. The frequency in the darker shaded cell is multiplied by the product of the frequencies in the lighter shaded cells. Hence, $t_y = 200 + 200 + 256 + 24 + 75 + 231 = 986$. There are 986 pairs tied on the dependent variable "burnout."

**FIGURE 9.3  Computing $t_y$ in a 3 × 3 Table**

|  | LOW | MODERATE | HIGH |
|---|---|---|---|
| LOW | 20 | 6 | 4 |
| MODERATE | 10 | 15 | 5 |
| HIGH | 8 | 11 | 21 |

**20(6 + 4) = 200**

|  | LOW | MODERATE | HIGH |
|---|---|---|---|
| LOW | 20 | 6 | 4 |
| MODERATE | 10 | 15 | 5 |
| HIGH | 8 | 11 | 21 |

**6(4) = 24**

|  | LOW | MODERATE | HIGH |
|---|---|---|---|
| LOW | 20 | 6 | 4 |
| MODERATE | 10 | 15 | 5 |
| HIGH | 8 | 11 | 21 |

**10(15 + 5) = 200**

|  | LOW | MODERATE | HIGH |
|---|---|---|---|
| LOW | 20 | 6 | 4 |
| MODERATE | 10 | 15 | 5 |
| HIGH | 8 | 11 | 21 |

**15(5) = 75**

|  | LOW | MODERATE | HIGH |
|---|---|---|---|
| LOW | 20 | 6 | 4 |
| MODERATE | 10 | 15 | 5 |
| HIGH | 8 | 11 | 21 |

**8(11 + 21) = 256**

|  | LOW | MODERATE | HIGH |
|---|---|---|---|
| LOW | 20 | 6 | 4 |
| MODERATE | 10 | 15 | 5 |
| HIGH | 8 | 11 | 21 |

**11(21) = 231**

To find $t_x$, we follow the same logic, but in the opposite direction. As shown in Figure 9.4, $t_x = 360 + 156 + 104 + 80 + 165 + 105 = 970$. There are 970 pairs tied on the independent variable "length of service."

So, for the burnout and years of service problem, the value of Kendall's tau-b (using Formula 9.3) is

$$\tau_b = \frac{n_s - n_d}{\sqrt{(n_s + n_d + t_x)(n_s + n_d + t_y)}}$$

$$\tau_b = \frac{1,831 - 499}{\sqrt{(1,831 + 499 + 970)(1,831 + 499 + 986)}}$$

$$\tau_b = \frac{1,332}{3,308}$$

$$\tau_b = +0.40$$

Since there are an equal number of categories on the independent and dependent variables, tau-b is more appropriate than tau-c for this problem.

**FIGURE 9.4 Computing $t_x$ in a 3 × 3 Table**

|  | LOW | MODERATE | HIGH |
|---|---|---|---|
| LOW | 20 | 6 | 4 |
| MODERATE | 10 | 15 | 5 |
| HIGH | 8 | 11 | 21 |

**20(10 + 8) = 360**

|  | LOW | MODERATE | HIGH |
|---|---|---|---|
| LOW | 20 | 6 | 4 |
| MODERATE | 10 | 15 | 5 |
| HIGH | 8 | 11 | 21 |

**10(8) = 80**

|  | LOW | MODERATE | HIGH |
|---|---|---|---|
| LOW | 20 | 6 | 4 |
| MODERATE | 10 | 15 | 5 |
| HIGH | 8 | 11 | 21 |

**6(15 + 11) = 156**

|  | LOW | MODERATE | HIGH |
|---|---|---|---|
| LOW | 20 | 6 | 4 |
| MODERATE | 10 | 15 | 5 |
| HIGH | 8 | 11 | 21 |

**15(11) = 165**

|  | LOW | MODERATE | HIGH |
|---|---|---|---|
| LOW | 20 | 6 | 4 |
| MODERATE | 10 | 15 | 5 |
| HIGH | 8 | 11 | 21 |

**4(5 + 21) = 104**

|  | LOW | MODERATE | HIGH |
|---|---|---|---|
| LOW | 20 | 6 | 4 |
| MODERATE | 10 | 15 | 5 |
| HIGH | 8 | 11 | 21 |

**5(21) = 105**

(Remember, tau-b is used when there are an equal number of categories on the variables and tau-c is used when the variables have an unequal number of categories.) However, we will compute tau-c for purposes of demonstration. Substituting the appropriate numbers into the numerator and denominator of Formula 9.4, the value of Kendall's tau-c is

$$\tau_c = \frac{2m(n_s - n_d)}{n^2(m - 1)}$$

$$\tau_c = \frac{(2 \times 3)(1{,}831 - 499)}{100^2(3 - 1)}$$

$$\tau_c = \frac{(6)(1{,}332)}{(10{,}000)(2)}$$

$$\tau_c = \frac{7{,}992}{20{,}000}$$

$$\tau_c = +0.40$$

The computed values for Kendall's tau-b and tau-c are virtually identical, and both indicate a strong and positive association between the variables.

**Somers' _d_.** While Kendall's tau-b includes pairs tied on both variables, Somers' _d_ uses ties only on the dependent variable, $t_y$. Using Formula 9.5 the value of Somers' _d_ is

$$d_{yx} = \frac{n_s - n_d}{n_s + n_d + t_y}$$

$$d_{yx} = \frac{1{,}831 - 499}{1{,}831 + 499 + 986}$$

$$d_{yx} = \frac{1{,}332}{3{,}316}$$

$$d_{yx} = +0.40$$

Somers' _d_, like gamma and Kendall's tau-b and tau-c, indicates a strong and positive association between length of service and burnout.

**Summary.** Gamma, Kendall's tau-b and tau-c, and Somers' _d_ measure association by comparing respondents to each other, called pairs of respondents, in terms of their rankings on the independent and dependent variables. As such, these statistics can be calculated for variables measured at the ordinal level or higher. Gamma ignores tied pairs of cases and tends to exaggerate the strength of association, especially for small tables where there are many ties. Alternatively, Kendall's tau-b (when bivariate tables have an equal number of rows and columns), Kendall's tau-c (when tables have an unequal number of rows and columns), or Somers' _d_ (when one of the variables can be identified as the dependent variable) should be used instead of gamma in such situations.

As a final note, it is important to stress that to use the computational routines for these statistics presented in Figures 9.1 to 9.4, you must arrange the table in the manner of Table 9.6, with the column variable increasing in value as you move from left to right and the row variable increasing in value from top to bottom. Be careful to construct your tables according to this format. If you are working with data already in table format, you may have to rearrange the table or rethink the direction of patterns. _(To practise computing and interpreting gamma, Kendall's tau-b or tau-c, and Somers' d, see Problems 9.1 to 9.10 and 9.15. Begin with some of the smaller, 2 × 2 tables until you are comfortable with these procedures.)_

## Applying Statistics 9.1: Gamma, Kendall's tau-b, and Somers' $d$

A group of 40 nations have been rated as high or low on religiosity (based on the percentage of a random sample of citizens who described themselves as "a religious person") and as high or low in their support for single mothers (based on the percentage of a random sample of citizens who said they would approve of a woman choosing to be a single parent). Are more religious nations less approving of single mothers?

| Approval | Religiosity | | Totals |
|---|---|---|---|
| | Low | High | |
| Low | 4 | 9 | 13 |
| High | 11 | 16 | 27 |
| Totals | 15 | 25 | 40 |

We will compute gamma, Kendall's tau-b (since there is an equal number of categories on the independent and dependent variables), and Somers' $d$ to summarize the strength and direction of the association. First, we must find the number of similar pairs, $n_s$, and dissimilar pairs, $n_d$, as well as the number of pairs tied on the dependent variable (approval), $t_y$, and independent variable (religiosity), $t_x$.

The number of pairs of cases ranked in the same order on both variables ($n_s$) is

$$n_s = 4(16) = 64$$

The number of pairs of cases ranked in a different order on both variables ($n_d$) is

$$n_d = 9(11) = 99$$

The number of pairs tied on the dependent variable ($t_y$) is

$$t_y = 4(9) + 11(16) = 36 + 176 = 212$$

The number of pairs tied on the independent variable ($t_x$) is

$$t_x = 4(11) + 9(16) = 44 + 144 = 188$$

Gamma is

$$G = \frac{n_s - n_d}{n_s + n_d} = \frac{64 - 99}{64 + 99} = \frac{-35}{163} = -0.21$$

Kendall's tau-b is

$$\tau_b = \frac{n_s - n_d}{\sqrt{(n_s + n_d + t_x)(n_s + n_d + t_y)}}$$

$$= \frac{64 - 99}{\sqrt{(64 + 99 + 188)(64 + 99 + 212)}}$$

$$= \frac{-35}{362.80} = -0.10$$

Somers' $d$ is

$$d_{yx} = \frac{n_s - n_d}{n_s + n_d + t_y}$$

$$= \frac{64 - 99}{64 + 99 + 212} = \frac{-35}{375} = -0.09$$

A gamma of $-0.21$ means that, when predicting the order of pairs of cases on the dependent variable (approval of single mothers), we would make 21% fewer errors by taking the independent variable (religiosity) into account. The values for gamma, Kendall's tau-b, and Somers' $d$ show that there is a moderate to weak negative association between these two variables. As religiosity increases, approval decreases (or, more religious nations are less approving of single mothers than are less religious nations).

## Applying Statistics 9.2: Another Look at Computing Gamma, Kendall's tau-c, and Somers' *d*

There is no age at which individuals are immune to stress. However, do levels of stress vary by age? Are younger Canadians more stressed out than older Canadians? We will examine the relationship between age and stress using an actual random sample of 958 respondents from the Canadian Mental Health and Well-being Survey. Age has been grouped as 15 to 44 years of age, 45 to 64 years of age, and 65 years of age and older.

Stress was measured in the survey with the following question, "Thinking about the amount of stress in your life, would you say that most days are: not at all, not very, a bit, quite a bit, [or] extremely [stressful]?" The "not at all" and "not very" categories have been grouped as "low" stress, and the "a bit," "quite a bit," and "extremely" categories have been grouped as "high" stress.

| Stress | Age | | | |
|--------|-------|-------|------|--------|
|        | 15–44 | 45–64 | 65+  | Totals |
| Low    | 109   | 117   | 168  | 394    |
| High   | 251   | 182   | 131  | 564    |
| Totals | 360   | 299   | 299  | 958    |

We will compute gamma, Kendall's tau-c (since there is an unequal number of categories on the independent and dependent variables), and Somers' *d* to summarize the strength and direction of the association. To calculate the statistics, we must find the number of similar and dissimilar pairs, and the number of pairs tied on the dependent (stress) variable.

The number of pairs of cases ranked in the same order on both variables ($n_s$) is

$$n_s = 109(182 + 131) + 117(131)$$
$$= 34,117 + 15,327 = 49,444$$

The number of pairs of cases ranked in different order on both variables ($n_d$) is

$$n_d = 168(182 + 251) + 117(251)$$
$$= 72,744 + 29,367 = 102,111$$

The number of pairs tied on the dependent variable ($t_y$) is

$$t_y = 109(117 + 168) + 117(168)$$
$$+ 251(182 + 131) + 182(131)$$
$$= 31,065 + 19,656 + 78,563 + 23,842$$
$$= 153,126$$

Gamma is

$$G = \frac{n_s - n_d}{n_s + n_d} = \frac{49,444 - 102,111}{49,444 + 102,111} = \frac{-52,667}{151,555}$$
$$= -0.35$$

Kendall's tau-c is

$$\tau_c = \frac{2m(n_s - n_d)}{n^2(m-1)} = \frac{(2 \times 2)(49,444 - 102,111)}{958^2(2-1)}$$
$$= \frac{-210,668}{917,764} = -0.23$$

Somers' *d* is

$$d_{yx} = \frac{n_s - n_d}{n_s + n_d + t_y}$$
$$= \frac{49,444 - 102,111}{49,444 + 102,111 + 153,126}$$
$$= \frac{-52,667}{304,681} = -0.17$$

A gamma of −0.35 means that, when predicting the order of pairs of cases on stress level, we would make 35% fewer errors by taking age into account, as opposed to ignoring it. The values for gamma, tau-c, and Somers' *d* indicate a strong to moderate negative association between these two variables. As age increases, stress level decreases: Older Canadians are less likely to report high levels of stress.

Source: Statistics Canada, *2014 Canadian Community Health Survey*.

**9.5 INTERPRETING STATISTICS: WHAT ARE THE SOURCES OF VOLUNTEERISM IN CANADA?**

In this section, we will examine an important feature of Canadian life: community participation and civic engagement. We will look specifically at what kind of person is most engaged in volunteerism. Put differently, what factors are related to volunteerism?

We will use data from the 2013 General Social Survey on Giving, Volunteering and Participating to answer this question. This survey, which began in 1997, is conducted every few years by Statistics Canada to collect information on how and why Canadians donate their money, time, and other resources to charitable and not-for-profit organizations. It was administered to a randomly selected sample, and includes approximately 14,700 adult Canadians.

To measure volunteerism (the dependent variable), we used a series of variables that asked people whether they had engaged, without pay on behalf of a group(s) or an organization(s), over the past 12 months in the following activities: canvassing, fundraising, committee or board membership, teaching or mentoring, event or activity organization, administrative duties, coaching or officiating, counselling or advising, health care support, collection or serving of food or other goods, facilities/grounds maintenance or repair, volunteer driving, first aid, environmental conservation, or other unpaid activities. We created a composite variable that counted the number of activities undertaken by each respondent. Their level of volunteerism was then rated as high, moderate, or low. People rated as low had been engaged in no activities in the previous year, and those rated as moderate had volunteered for one or two activities. Individuals volunteering for three or more activities in the past year were coded as high.

This simple variable will not be a perfectly accurate measurement of volunteerism. For example, people might help others directly on their own (e.g., visiting the elderly or unpaid babysitting) or be involved in the daily life of their community but not actually belong to any formal groups or organizations. This kind of "informal" volunteering will not be captured by the variable we created. Or, some people might be involved in many volunteer activities but actually spend very little time (e.g., just a few hours once or twice a year) on each activity. These people will be classified as highly involved on the variable we created, even though their involvement is actually minimal. Like almost all variables of interest to the social sciences, volunteerism is complex and subtle and cannot be adequately captured with a single measurement. Nonetheless, we should be able to develop some insight into the issue, even if the variable is not perfect. Researchers typically have to settle for partial or incomplete measurement of their concepts.

What should we use as independent variables? In other words, what factors might have causal relationships with volunteerism? In this section, we investigate three possibilities. First, we predict that health has a positive impact on volunteerism, for good health facilitates one's ability to do volunteer work. Second, because studies show that education is positively related to job performance, we predict that it has a similar relationship with

### TABLE 9.7   Volunteerism by Health Status*

| Volunteerism | Health Status | | Totals |
|---|---|---|---|
| | Poor | Good | |
| Low | 1,244 (64.19%) | 5,349 (45.10%) | 6,593 (47.79%) |
| Moderate | 353 (18.21%) | 2,927 (24.68%) | 3,280 (23.77%) |
| High | 341 (17.60%) | 3,583 (30.21%) | 3,924 (28.44%) |
| Totals | 1,938 (100.00%) | 11,859 (99.99%) | 13,797 (100.00%) |

Gamma = 0.33, $p < 0.05$
*Percentages may not total to 100% because of rounding error.
Source: Data from Statistics Canada, 2013 *Canada Survey on Giving, Volunteering and Participating*.

volunteer work. Finally, we argue that religiosity, measured by frequency of religious service attendance, is an important predictor of charitable activity because most religious faiths and organizations encourage—and provide the mechanisms for—volunteering, altruistic giving, and civic participation.

The level of measurement of each of these independent variables, as well as the dependent variable, is ordinal; the categories can be distinguished in terms of "more or less." We will use tables, column percentages, and gamma (although we could have just as appropriately used Kendall's tau-b, Kendall's tau-c, or Somers' *d*) to examine which of these arguments has support and to compare the strength and direction of each relationship.

Table 9.7 shows that the relationship between health status and volunteering is strong and positive in direction (gamma = 0.33) and is statistically significant ($p < 0.05$). The column percentages in the table show that volunteerism increases as health status increases: Only 17.60% of people with poor health are highly involved in volunteer activities compared to 30.21% of people with good health.

The relationship between volunteering and education in Table 9.8 is significant at the 0.05 level, moderate in strength, and in the predicted

### TABLE 9.8   Volunteerism by Education

| Volunteerism | Education | | | | Totals |
|---|---|---|---|---|---|
| | Less Than High School | High School | Other Post-Secondary | University | |
| Low | 1,199 (63.91%) | 2,062 (55.27%) | 2,049 (46.35%) | 1,259 (33.69%) | 6,569 (47.72%) |
| Moderate | 390 (20.79%) | 843 (22.59%) | 1,128 (25.51%) | 907 (24.27%) | 3,268 (23.74%) |
| High | 287 (15.30%) | 826 (22.14%) | 1,244 (28.14%) | 1,571 (42.04%) | 3,928 (28.54%) |
| Totals | 1,876 (100.00%) | 3,731 (100.00%) | 4,421 (100.00%) | 3,737 (100.00%) | 13,765 (100.00%) |

Gamma = 0.29, $p < 0.05$
Source: Data from Statistics Canada, 2013 *Canada Survey on Giving, Volunteering and Participating*.

**TABLE 9.9 Volunteerism by Religious Service Attendance***

| Volunteerism | Religious Service Attendance | | | Totals |
|---|---|---|---|---|
| | Never | Yearly or Monthly | Daily or Weekly | |
| Low | 3,488 (56.72%) | 2,169 (44.49%) | 869 (32.64%) | 6,526 (47.68%) |
| Moderate | 1,383 (22.49%) | 1,180 (24.21%) | 695 (26.11%) | 3,258 (23.80%) |
| High | 1,279 (20.80%) | 1,526 (31.30%) | 1,098 (41.25%) | 3,903 (28.52%) |
| Totals | 6,150 (100.01%) | 4,875 (100.00%) | 2,662 (100.00%) | 13,687 (100.00%) |

Gamma = 0.28, $p < 0.05$
*Percentages may not total to 100% because of rounding error.
Source: Data from Statistics Canada, 2013 *General Social Survey on Giving, Volunteering and Participating*.

direction. Looking at the bottom row of the table, we see that the percentage of each education group that is highly involved in volunteer activities increases as education increases. The column percentages show that just 15.30% of respondents with less than a high school education are high on volunteerism versus 42.04% of those with a university education.

Table 9.9 shows the relationship between volunteering and religiosity. The relationship is significant, and changes in the column percentages are rather large. Persons who attend religious service daily or weekly are more likely to be highly involved in volunteer activities (41.25%) than those that never attend (20.80%). As indicated by gamma, this is a positive relationship (as frequency of religious service attendance increases, volunteering increases) that is moderately strong.

In summary, we can see that people in good health, those with higher education, and frequent attendees of religious services are more actively involved in volunteer activities. Health, education, and religiosity seem to be relatively important causes of volunteerism. While these bivariate results cannot show which variable is cause and which is effect (remember that association is not the same thing as causation), they are worthy of additional investigation. Multivariate techniques designed to be used with nominal- and ordinal-level variables, covered on the website for this textbook, might be a logical next step in the process of analyzing each of the relationships.

**9.6 SPEARMAN'S RHO ($r_s$)**

To this point, we have considered ordinal variables that have a limited number of categories (possible values) and are presented in tables. However, many ordinal-level variables have a broad range of scores and many distinct values. Such data may be collapsed into a few broad categories (such as high, moderate, and low), organized into a bivariate table, and analyzed with gamma or any of the other measures of association discussed previously. Collapsing scores in this manner may be beneficial and desirable in many instances, but some important distinctions between cases may be obscured or lost as a consequence.

For example, suppose a researcher wished to test the claim that jogging is beneficial not only physically but also psychologically. Do joggers have

**TABLE 9.10**  **The Scores of 10 Subjects on Involvement in Jogging and a Measure of Self-Esteem**

| Joggers | Involvement in Jogging (X) | Self-esteem (Y) |
| --- | --- | --- |
| Wendy | 18 | 15 |
| Debbie | 17 | 18 |
| Alicia | 15 | 12 |
| Ava | 12 | 16 |
| Evelyn | 10 | 6 |
| Camille | 9 | 10 |
| Tori | 8 | 8 |
| Isabel | 8 | 7 |
| Maxine | 5 | 5 |
| Lynn | 1 | 2 |

an enhanced sense of self-esteem? To deal with this issue, 10 female joggers are measured on two scales, the first measuring involvement in jogging and the other measuring self-esteem. Scores are reported in Table 9.10.

These data could be collapsed and a bivariate table produced. We could, for example, dichotomize both variables to create only two values (high and low) for both variables. Although collapsing scores in this way is certainly legitimate and often necessary,* two difficulties with this practice must be noted. First, the scores seem continuous, and there are no obvious or natural division points in the distribution that would allow us to distinguish, in a non-arbitrary fashion, between high scores and low ones. Second, and more important, grouping these cases into broader categories will cause us to lose information. That is, if both Wendy and Debbie are placed in the category "high" on involvement, the fact that they had different scores on the variable will be obscured. If differences like this are important and meaningful, then we should opt for a measure of association that permits the retention of as much detail and precision in the scores as possible.

**The Computation of Rho.**  Spearman's rho ($r_s$) is a measure of association for ordinal-level variables that have a broad range of many different scores and few ties between cases on either variable. Scores on ordinal-level variables cannot, of course, be manipulated mathematically except for judgments of "greater than" or "less than." To compute Spearman's rho, cases are first ranked from high to low on each variable, and then the ranks (not the scores) are manipulated to produce the final measure. Table 9.11 displays the original scores and the rankings of the cases on both variables.

---

*For example, collapsing scores may be advisable when the researcher is not sure that fine distinctions between scores are meaningful.

**TABLE 9.11 Computing Spearman's Rho**

| | Involvement (X) | Rank | Self-esteem (Y) | Rank | D | D² |
|---|---|---|---|---|---|---|
| Wendy | 18 | 1 | 15 | 3 | −2 | 4 |
| Debbie | 17 | 2 | 18 | 1 | 1 | 1 |
| Alicia | 15 | 3 | 12 | 4 | −1 | 1 |
| Ava | 12 | 4 | 16 | 2 | 2 | 4 |
| Evelyn | 10 | 5 | 6 | 8 | −3 | 9 |
| Camille | 9 | 6 | 10 | 5 | 1 | 1 |
| Tori | 8 | 7.50 | 8 | 6 | 1.50 | 2.25 |
| Isabel | 8 | 7.50 | 7 | 7 | 0.50 | 0.25 |
| Maxine | 5 | 9 | 5 | 9 | 0 | 0 |
| Lynn | 1 | 10 | 2 | 10 | 0 | 0 |
| | | | | | $\Sigma D = 0$ | $\Sigma D^2 = 22.50$ |

To rank the cases, first find the highest score on each variable and assign it rank 1. Wendy has the high score on $X$ (18) and is thus ranked number 1. Debbie, on the other hand, is highest on $Y$ and is ranked first on that variable. All other cases are then ranked in descending order of scores. If any cases have the same score on a variable, assign them the average of the ranks they would have used up had they not been tied. Tori and Isabel have identical scores of 8 on involvement. Had they not been tied, they would have used up ranks 7 and 8. The average of these two ranks is 7.50, and this average of used ranks is assigned to all tied cases. (For example, if Maxine had also had a score of 8, three ranks—7, 8, and 9—would have been used, and all three tied cases would have been ranked eighth.)

The formula for Spearman's rho is

**FORMULA 9.6**
$$r_s = 1 - \frac{6\Sigma D^2}{n(n^2 - 1)}$$

where $\Sigma D^2$ = the sum of the squared differences in ranks

To compute $\Sigma D^2$, the rank of each case on $Y$ is subtracted from its rank on $X$ ($D$ is the difference between the rank on $Y$ and the rank on $X$). A column has been provided in Table 9.11 so that these differences may be recorded on a case-by-case basis. Note that the sum of this column ($\Sigma D$) is 0. That is, the negative differences in rank are equal to the positive differences, as will always be the case, and you should use the total of this column as a check on your computations to this point. If the $\Sigma D$ is not equal to 0, you have made a mistake either in ranking the cases or in subtracting the differences.

In the column headed $D^2$, each difference is squared to eliminate negative signs. The sum of this column is $\Sigma D^2$ and this quantity is entered directly into the formula. For our sample problem:

$$r_s = 1 - \frac{6\Sigma D^2}{n(n^2 - 1)}$$

$$r_s = 1 - \frac{6(22.50)}{10(100 - 1)}$$

$$r_s = 1 - \frac{135}{990}$$

$$r_s = 1 - 0.14$$

$$r_s = +0.86$$

---

## ONE STEP AT A TIME   Computing and Interpreting Spearman's Rho

**To Compute Spearman's Rho**

**1:** Set up a computing table like Table 9.11 to organize the computations. In the far left-hand column, list the cases in order, with the case with the highest score on the independent variable ($X$) stated first.

**2:** In the next column, list the scores on $X$.

**3:** In the third column, list the rank of each case on $X$, beginning with rank 1 for the highest score. If any cases have the same score, assign them the average of the ranks they would have used up had they not been tied.

**4:** In the fourth column, list the score of each case on $Y$; then, in the fifth column, rank the cases on $Y$ from high to low. Assign the rank of 1 to the case with the highest score on $Y$, and assign any tied cases the average of the ranks they would have used up had they not been tied.

**5:** For each case, subtract the rank on $Y$ from the rank on $X$ and write the difference ($D$) in the sixth column. Add up this column. If the sum is not zero, you have made a mistake and need to recompute.

**6:** Square the value of each $D$ and record the result in the seventh column. Add this column up to find $\Sigma D^2$, and substitute this value into the numerator of Formula 9.6.

**7:** Multiply $\Sigma D^2$ by 6.

**8:** Square $n$ and subtract 1 from the result.

**9:** Multiply the quantity you found in step 8 by $n$.

**10:** Divide the quantity you found in step 7 by the quantity you found in step 9.

**11:** Subtract the quantity you found in step 10 from 1. The result is $r_s$.

**Interpreting the Strength of the Relationship**

**1:** Use either or both of the following to interpret strength:

a. Use Table 9.3 to describe strength in general terms.

b. Square the value of rho and multiply by 100. This value represents the percentage improvement in our predictions of the dependent variable by taking the independent variable into account.

**Interpreting the Direction of the Relationship**

**1:** Use the sign of $r_s$. Be careful when interpreting direction with ordinal-level variables. Remember that coding schemes for these variables are arbitrary and that a positive $r_s$ may mean that the actual relationship is negative, and vice versa.

**Interpretation of Rho.** Spearman's rho is an index of the strength of association between the variables; it ranges from 0.00 (no association) to ±1.00 (perfect association). A perfect positive association ($r_s = +1.00$) would exist if there were no disagreements in ranks between the two variables (i.e., if cases were ranked in exactly the same order on both variables). A perfect negative relationship ($r_s = -1.00$) would exist if the ranks were in perfect disagreement (i.e., if the case ranked highest on one variable were lowest on the other, and so forth). A Spearman's rho of +0.86 indicates a strong positive relationship between these two variables. The respondents who were highly involved in jogging also ranked high on self-esteem. These results are supportive of claims regarding the psychological benefits of jogging.

Spearman's rho is an index of the relative strength of a relationship, and values between 0.00 and ±1.00 have no direct interpretation. However, if the value of rho is squared, a PRE interpretation is possible. Rho squared ($r_s^2$) represents the proportional reduction in errors of prediction when predicting rank on one variable from rank on the other variable, as compared to predicting rank while ignoring the other variable. In the example above, $r_s$ was 0.86 and $r_s$ squared would be 0.74. Thus, our errors of prediction would be reduced by 74% if, when predicting the rank of a subject on self-esteem, the rank of the subject on involvement in jogging were taken into account. (*For practice in computing and interpreting Spearman's rho, see Problems 9.11 to 9.14. Problem 9.11 has the fewest number of cases and is probably a good choice for a first attempt at these procedures.*)

## 9.7 TESTING THE NULL HYPOTHESIS OF "NO ASSOCIATION" WITH GAMMA AND SPEARMAN'S RHO

Whenever a researcher is working with random samples he or she will need to ascertain whether the sample findings can be generalized to the population. In Chapter 6, we considered various ways that information taken from a sample—for example, the sample mean or proportion—could be generalized to the population from which the sample was drawn. In Chapter 7, we began our examination of hypothesis testing and saw that a test of the null hypothesis, regardless of the form or specific test used, asks essentially whether the patterns (or differences, or relationships) that have been observed in the samples can be assumed to exist in the population. Measures of association can also be tested for significance. When data have been collected from a random sample, we will not only need to measure the strength and direction of the association, but we will also want to know if we can assume that the variables are related in the population.

For nominal- and ordinal-level variables, the statistical significance of a relationship is usually judged by the chi square test. However, chi square

## Applying Statistics 9.3: Spearman's Rho

The Human Development Index (HDI) is a measure of a country's "human development" achievements in health (life expectancy), literacy (educational attainment), and standard of living (income). UN member states are ranked annually according to their computed HDI score. The higher the HDI score, the higher the level of "human development" in a country. The table below lists the top five ranked (i.e., most developed) countries in 2014 according to the HDI (note that only ranks, not actual HDI scores, are provided in the table). Canada, for example, ranked ninth out of the 188 countries in 2014.

The table also shows how these five countries rank, among themselves, according to the United Nations' Gender Inequality Index (GII), which measures the level of gender equality in countries (i.e., reproductive health, political and

educational empowerment, and labour market participation). The higher the GII score, the higher the level of gender equality in the country. Again, we only show how these five nations ranked among themselves, not their actual GII scores or ranking among all nations.

Overall, the HDI and GII provide powerful measures of human well-being. However, are they related? Do countries with higher human development have more gender equality? We have the ranks of the HDI and GII scores for each country, so we will compute Spearman's rho to summarize the strength and direction of the association. (While the data in this application are real, the number of cases is far too small to draw any serious conclusions, and thus, this is intended only for purposes of illustration and to simplify computations.)

| Country | HDI Rank | GII Rank | $D$ | $D^2$ |
|---|---|---|---|---|
| Norway | 1 | 2 | $-1$ | 1 |
| Australia | 2 | 1 | 1 | 1 |
| Switzerland | 3 | 5 | $-2$ | 4 |
| Denmark | 4 | 4 | 0 | 0 |
| Netherlands | 5 | 3 | 2 | 4 |
| | | | $\Sigma D = 0$ | $\Sigma D^2 = 10$ |

Spearman's rho for these variables is

$$r_s = 1 - \frac{6\Sigma D^2}{n(n^2 - 1)}$$

$$r_s = 1 - \frac{(6)(10)}{5(25 - 1)}$$

$$r_s = 1 - \left(\frac{60}{120}\right)$$

$$r_s = 1 - 0.50$$

$$r_s = +0.50$$

For these five countries, the variables have a strong positive association. The higher the human development, the greater the gender equality within a country. The value of $r_s^2$ is 0.25 ($0.50^2 = 0.25$), which indicates that we will make 25% fewer errors when predicting rank on one variable from rank on the other, as opposed to ignoring rank on the other variable, for these five nations.

Source: United Nations Development Program (2015).

tests deal with the probability that the observed cell frequencies occurred by chance alone and are therefore not a direct test of the significance of the measure of association itself. In this section, we will look at tests of significance for two measures: gamma and Spearman's rho.

When testing gamma and Spearman's rho for statistical significance, the null hypothesis will state that there is no association between the variables in the population and that, therefore, the population value for the measure is 0.00. Population values will be denoted by the Greek letters gamma ($\gamma$) and rho ($\rho_s$). For both measures, the test procedures will be organized around the familiar five-step model (see Chapter 7).

**Test Gamma for Significance.** To illustrate the test of significance for gamma, we will use Table 9.6, where gamma was +0.57.

**Step 1. Make Assumptions and Meet Test Requirements.** When sample size is greater than 10, the sampling distribution of all possible sample gammas can be assumed to be normal in shape.

> Model: Random sampling
> Level of measurement is ordinal
> Sampling distribution is normal

**Step 2. State the Null Hypothesis.**

$$H_0: \gamma = 0.0$$
$$(H_1: \gamma \neq 0.0)$$

**Step 3. Select the Sampling Distribution and Establish the Critical Region.** For samples of 10 or more, the $Z$ distribution (Appendix A) can be used to find areas under the sampling distribution:

$$\text{Sampling distribution} = Z \text{ distribution}$$
$$\text{Alpha} = 0.05$$
$$Z \text{ (critical)} = \pm 1.96$$

**Step 4. Compute the Test Statistic.**

FORMULA 9.7
$$Z \text{ (obtained)} = G\sqrt{\frac{n_s + n_d}{n(1 - G^2)}}$$

$$Z \text{ (obtained)} = G\sqrt{\frac{n_s + n_d}{n(1 - G^2)}} = 0.57\sqrt{\frac{1{,}831 + 499}{100(1 - 0.33)}} = 0.57\sqrt{\frac{2{,}330}{100(0.67)}}$$

$$Z \text{ (obtained)} = 0.57\sqrt{34.78} = 3.36$$

**Step 5. Make a Decision and Interpret the Results of the Test.** Comparing the $Z$ (obtained) with the $Z$ (critical):

$$Z \text{ (obtained)} = 3.36$$

$$Z \text{ (critical)} = \pm 1.96$$

We see that the null hypothesis can be rejected. The sample gamma is unlikely to have occurred by chance alone, and we may conclude that these variables are related in the population from which the sample was drawn. *(For practice in conducting and interpreting the test of significance for gamma, see Problems 9.2, 9.7, and 9.10.)*

**Test Spearman's Rho for Significance.** When testing Spearman's rho, the null hypothesis states that the population value ($\rho_s$) is actually 0 and, therefore, that the value of the sample Spearman's rho ($r_s$) is the result of mere random chance. When the number of cases in the sample is 10 or more, the sampling distribution of Spearman's rho approximates the $t$ distribution, and we will use this distribution to conduct the test. To illustrate, the Spearman's rho computed in Section 9.6 will be used.

**Step 1. Make Assumptions and Meet Test Requirements.**

> Model: Random sampling
> Level of measurement is ordinal
> Sampling distribution is normal

**Step 2. State the Null Hypothesis.**

$$H_0: \rho_s = 0.0$$

$$(H_1: \rho_s \neq 0.0)$$

**Step 3. Select the Sampling Distribution and Establish the Critical Region.**

> Sampling distribution = $t$ distribution
> Alpha = 0.05
> Degrees of freedom = $n - 2 = 8$
> $t$ (critical) = $\pm 2.306$

**Step 4. Compute the Test Statistic.**

FORMULA 9.8

$$t \text{ (obtained)} = r_s \sqrt{\frac{n-2}{1-r_s^2}}$$

$$t \text{(obtained)} = r_s \sqrt{\frac{n-2}{1-r_s^2}} = 0.86 \sqrt{\frac{10-2}{1-0.74}} = 0.86 \sqrt{\frac{8}{0.26}}$$

$$t \text{(obtained)} = 0.86 \sqrt{30.77} = (0.86)(5.55) = 4.77$$

**Step 5. Make a Decision and Interpret the Results of the Test.** Comparing the test statistic with the critical region:

$$t \text{ (obtained)} = 4.77$$

$$t \text{ (critical)} = \pm 2.306$$

We see that the null hypothesis can be rejected. We may conclude, with a 0.05 chance of making an error, that the variables are related in the population from which the samples were drawn. *(For practice in conducting and interpreting the test of significance for Spearman's rho, see Problems 9.11 and 9.14.)*

### READING STATISTICS 8: Bivariate Tables and Associated Statistics

The statistics associated with any bivariate table will usually be reported directly below the table itself. This information would include the name of the measure of association, its value, and (if relevant) its sign. Also, if the research involves a random sample, the results of the chi square test or a test for the significance of the measure itself will be reported. So the information might look something like this:

$$\chi^2 = 13.23 \ (p < 0.05), \lambda = 0.47$$

Note that the alpha level is reported in the "$p$" format, which we have discussed previously.

Besides simply reporting the value of these statistics, the researcher will interpret them in the text of the article. These statistics might be characterized by the statement, "The association between the variables is statistically significant and strong." Again we see that researchers will avoid our rather wordy (but more careful) style of stating results. Where we might say, "A lambda of 0.47 indicates that we will reduce our errors of prediction by 47% when predicting the dependent variable from the independent variable, as opposed to predicting the dependent while ignoring the

independent," the researcher will simply report the value of lambda and characterize that value in a word or two (e.g., "The association is strong"). The researcher assumes that his or her audience is statistically literate and can make the more detailed interpretations.

#### STATISTICS IN THE PROFESSIONAL LITERATURE

While gender inequality seems to be a nearly universal characteristic of human society, the extent of men's advantage is highly variable. Why are some societies more unequal than others? Sociologists Stephen Sanderson, Alex Heckert, and Joshua Dubrow sought some answers to this question by examining the correlates of gender inequality in a sample of preindustrial societies. They tested a number of hypotheses but found the most support for what they called "materialist" theories, which argued that "the greater the extent to which women are involved in economic production, the higher their status tends to be" (p. 1,426). Table 1 reports their findings for the hypotheses derived from this theory. The entries in the table are gammas, and

*(continued)*

## TABLE 1

| Measures Related to Materialist Theories (Independent Variables) | Measures of Women's Status (Dependent Variables) | | |
|---|---|---|---|
| | Domestic Authority | Control of Sexuality | Female Solidarity |
| Female contribution to gathering | 0.23 | 0.38* | 0.45*** |
| Female contribution to subsistence | 0.05 | 0.13 | −0.01 |
| Female contribution to agriculture | 0.46*** | 0.12 | 0.57*** |
| Use of the plough | −0.51** | −0.63** | −0.58*** |

*n*'s range from 67 to 93.
*$p < 0.05$; **$p < 0.01$; ***$p < 0.001$.

the asterisks indicate the statistical significance of the relationship.

To read this table, note that the three variables in the columns measure the dependent variable, or the status of women. The four row variables measure the independent variable, or the importance of women for various economic activities. The first three row variables are self-explanatory, and the higher the score of the society on these variables, the greater the economic importance of women. The variable in the bottom row measures the extent to which the society depends on the plough as an instrument of production, and its meaning may not be so obvious. Since it requires a good deal of upper-body strength, plough agriculture is generally "men's work," and the greater the extent to which the society uses ploughs, the lower the economic importance of women.

Is the materialist theory supported? The relationships between the first three measures of women's economic importance and women's status (the three column variables) are positive in direction (with one exception) and, for the most part, are moderate to strong in strength. The

positive relationships indicate that women's status increases as their economic importance increases, and the strength and significance of the relationships provide reasonable (but not overwhelming) support for the theory being tested. Looking at the bottom row, we see somewhat stronger support for the materialist theory. All three relationships are statistically significant at less than the 0.05 level, strong, and negative—the direction predicted by the materialist theory ("The greater the reliance on the plough, the lower the status of women").

Although we have not reproduced them here, the tests of competing theories showed weaker and less significant relationships, and the authors conclude that the materialist perspective is most consistent with the empirical relationships they were able to examine. Although these results cannot be considered proof (remember that correlation is not the same thing as causation), they are very consistent with the predictions of materialist theory.

Source: S. Sanderson, A. Heckert, and J. Dubrow, 2005, "Militarist, Marxian, and Non-Marxian Theories of Gender Inequality: A Cross-Cultural Test." *Social Forces*.

## SUMMARY

1. Measures of association for variables with collapsed ordinal scales (gamma, Kendall's tau-b and tau-c, and Somers' *d*) were covered along with a measure (Spearman's rho) appropriate for "continuous" ordinal variables. These measures summarize the overall strength and direction of the association between the variables. Gamma and Spearman's rho-squared also have PRE interpretations.

2. Gamma, Kendall's tau-b and tau-c, and Somers' *d* are based on the concept of pairs. They measure association by comparing each respondent to every other respondent (i.e., a pair) on their rankings on the independent and dependent variable, then counting the number of various types of pairs (similar, dissimilar, or tied).

3. Spearman's rho is computed from the ranks of the scores of the cases on two "continuous" ordinal variables.

4. Both gamma and Spearman's rho can be directly tested for their statistical significance when computed for a random sample drawn from a defined population. The null hypothesis is that the variables are not related in the population, and the test can be organized by using the familiar five-step model.

## SUMMARY OF FORMULAS

| | | |
|---|---|---|
| Total number of unique pairs in a sample | 9.1 | $\dfrac{n(n-1)}{2}$ |
| Gamma | 9.2 | $G = \dfrac{n_s - n_d}{n_s + n_d}$ |
| Kendall's tau-b | 9.3 | $\tau_b = \dfrac{n_s - n_d}{\sqrt{(n_s + n_d + t_x)(n_s + n_d + t_y)}}$ |
| Kendall's tau-c | 9.4 | $\tau_c = \dfrac{2m(n_s - n_d)}{n^2(m-1)}$ |
| Somers' *d* | 9.5 | $d_{yx} = \dfrac{n_s - n_d}{n_s + n_d + t_y}$ |
| Spearman's rho | 9.6 | $r_s = 1 - \dfrac{6\sum D^2}{n(n^2-1)}$ |
| Z (obtained) for gamma | 9.7 | $Z\text{ (obtained)} = G\sqrt{\dfrac{n_s + n_d}{n(1 - G^2)}}$ |
| *t* (obtained) for Spearman's rho | 9.8 | $t\text{ (obtained)} = r_s\sqrt{\dfrac{n-2}{1 - r_s^2}}$ |

## GLOSSARY

**Gamma (*G*).** A measure of association appropriate for any two variables measured with "collapsed" ordinal scales.

**Kendall's tau-b ($\tau_b$).** A measure of association appropriate for two variables measured with "collapsed" ordinal scales with an equal number of categories.

**Kendall's tau-c ($\tau_c$).** A measure of association appropriate for two variables measured with "collapsed" ordinal scales with an unequal number of categories.

**Somers' $d$ ($d_{yx}$).** A measure of association appropriate for two variables measured with "collapsed" ordinal scales where one variable is identified as the dependent.

**Spearman's rho ($r_s$).** A measure of association appropriate for two ordinally measured variables that are "continuous" in form.

## MULTIMEDIA RESOURCES

   nelson.com/student

Visit the companion website for the fourth Canadian edition of *Statistics: A Tool for Social Research* to access a wide range of student resources. Begin by clicking on the Student Resources section of the textbook's website to access online chapters and study tools.

## PROBLEMS

For Problems 9.1 to 9.10 and 9.15, calculate percentages for the bivariate tables as described in Chapter 8. Use the percentages to help analyze the strength and direction of the association.

**9.1**  SOC  A small sample of immigrants to Canada, none of whom speak either of the nation's two official languages, has been interviewed about their level of adjustment. Is the pattern of adjustment affected by length of residence in Canada? For each table compute gamma and summarize the relationship in terms of strength and direction. *(HINT: In 2 × 2 tables, only two cells can contribute to $n_s$ or $n_d$. To compute $n_s$, multiply the number of cases in the upper-left-hand cell by the number of cases in the lower-right-hand cell. For $n_d$, multiply the number of cases in the upper-right-hand cell by the number of cases in the lower-left-hand cell.)*

**a.** Facility in English or French:

| | Length of Residence | | |
|---|---|---|---|
| English/ French Facility | Less Than Five Years (Low) | More Than Five Years (High) | Totals |
| Low | 20 | 10 | 30 |
| High | 5 | 15 | 20 |
| Totals | 25 | 25 | 50 |

**b.** Total family income:

| | Length of Residence | | |
|---|---|---|---|
| Income | Less Than Five Years (Low) | More Than Five Years (High) | Totals |
| Below average | 18 | 8 | 26 |
| Above average | 7 | 17 | 24 |
| Totals | 25 | 25 | 50 |

**c.** Extent of contact with country of origin:

| | Length of Residence | | |
|---|---|---|---|
| Contact | Less Than Five Years (Low) | More Than Five Years (High) | Totals |
| Rare | 5 | 20 | 25 |
| Frequent | 20 | 5 | 25 |
| Totals | 25 | 25 | 50 |

**9.2** Compute gamma for the tables presented in Problems 7.2, 7.6, 7.7, 7.9, 7.10, and 7.12. Because these tables are based on random samples, test the gammas you computed for significance.

**9.3** Compute gamma for the table presented in Problem 8.1. Summarize the relationship in terms of strength and direction.

**9.4** CJ A random sample of 150 cities has been classified as small, medium, or large by population and as high or low on crime rate. Compute gamma, Kendall's tau-c, and Somers' *d*. Compare the measures of association. Are they similar in value? Do they characterize the strength of the association in the same way? *(NOTE: Make sure to compute Kendall's tau-c, and not tau-b, since the table has an unequal number of rows and columns.)*

| Crime Rate | City Size | | | Totals |
|---|---|---|---|---|
| | Small | Medium | Large | |
| Low | 21 | 17 | 8 | 46 |
| High | 29 | 33 | 42 | 104 |
| Totals | 50 | 50 | 50 | 150 |

**9.5** SOC Some research has shown that families vary by how they socialize their children to sports, games, and other leisure activities. In middle-class families, such activities are carefully monitored by parents and are, in general, dominated by adults (e.g., minor league hockey). In working-class families, children more often organize and initiate such activities themselves, and parents are much less involved (e.g., sandlot or playground baseball games). Are the data below consistent with these findings? Compute gamma and summarize the relationship in a few sentences.

| As a Child, Did You Play Mostly Organized or Sandlot Sports? | Social-Class Background | | Totals |
|---|---|---|---|
| | White-Collar | Blue-Collar | |
| Organized | 155 | 123 | 278 |
| Sandlot | 101 | 138 | 239 |
| Totals | 256 | 261 | 517 |

**9.6** Is support for sexual freedom related to age? Is the relationship between the variables different for different nations? The World Values Survey has been administered to random samples drawn from Canada, the United States, and Mexico. Respondents were asked whether they agree or disagree that "individuals should have the chance to enjoy complete sexual freedom without being restricted." Compute gamma for each table. Is there a relationship? Describe the strength and direction of the relationship. Which age group is most supportive of sexual freedom? How does the relationship change from nation to nation?

**a.** Canada

| People Should Enjoy Sexual Freedom | Age | | | Totals |
|---|---|---|---|---|
| | 18–34 | 35–54 | 55+ | |
| Agree | 378 | 174 | 66 | 618 |
| Neither agree nor disagree | 626 | 710 | 586 | 1,922 |
| Disagree | 163 | 101 | 74 | 338 |
| Totals | 1,167 | 985 | 726 | 2,878 |

**b.** United States

| People Should Enjoy Sexual Freedom | Age | | | Totals |
|---|---|---|---|---|
| | 18–34 | 35–54 | 55+ | |
| Agree | 583 | 288 | 147 | 1,018 |
| Neither agree nor disagree | 877 | 982 | 1,061 | 2,920 |
| Disagree | 113 | 72 | 53 | 238 |
| Totals | 1,573 | 1,342 | 1,261 | 4,176 |

**c.** Mexico

| People Should Enjoy Sexual Freedom | Age | | | Totals |
|---|---|---|---|---|
| | 18–34 | 35–54 | 55+ | |
| Agree | 780 | 284 | 61 | 1,125 |
| Neither agree nor disagree | 1,300 | 847 | 275 | 2,422 |
| Disagree | 317 | 148 | 43 | 508 |
| Totals | 2,397 | 1,279 | 379 | 4,055 |

Source: World Values Survey Association, *Wave 5 World Values Survey.*

**9.7** PA All applicants for municipal jobs in Pearson, Ontario, are given an aptitude test, but the test has never been evaluated to see whether test scores are in any way related to job performance. The following table reports aptitude test scores and job performance ratings for a random sample of 75 city employees.

| Efficiency Ratings | Test Scores | | | Totals |
|---|---|---|---|---|
| | Low | Moderate | High | |
| Low | 11 | 6 | 7 | 24 |
| Moderate | 9 | 10 | 9 | 28 |
| High | 5 | 9 | 9 | 23 |
| Totals | 25 | 25 | 25 | 75 |

**a.** Are these two variables associated? Compute gamma, then describe the strength and direction of the relationship in a sentence or two.

**b.** Is gamma statistically significant?

**c.** Should the aptitude test continue to be administered? Why or why not?

**9.8** $\boxed{\text{SW}}$ A sample of children has been observed and rated for symptoms of depression. Their parents have been rated for authoritarianism. Compute gamma, Kendall's tau-b, and Somers' *d*. Compare the measures of association. Do they characterize the strength of the association in the same way? *(NOTE: Make sure to compute Kendall's tau-b, and not tau-c, since the table has an equal number of rows and columns.)*

| Symptoms of Depression | Authoritarianism | | | Totals |
|---|---|---|---|---|
| | Low | Moderate | High | |
| Few | 7 | 8 | 9 | 24 |
| Some | 15 | 10 | 18 | 43 |
| Many | 8 | 12 | 3 | 23 |
| Totals | 30 | 30 | 30 | 90 |

**9.9** $\boxed{\text{SOC}}$ Are levels of stress and education related? Compute gamma, and describe the strength and direction of the relationship.

| Stress Level | Level of Education | | | | Totals |
|---|---|---|---|---|---|
| | Less Than High School | High School | Some College/ University | College/ University Graduate | |
| Low | 48 | 50 | 61 | 42 | 201 |
| High | 45 | 43 | 33 | 27 | 148 |
| Totals | 93 | 93 | 94 | 69 | 349 |

**9.10** $\boxed{\text{SOC}}$ In a recent survey, a random sample of respondents was asked to indicate how happy they were with their situations in life. Are their responses related to income level?

| Happiness | Income | | | Totals |
|---|---|---|---|---|
| | Low | Moderate | High | |
| Not happy | 101 | 82 | 36 | 219 |
| Pretty happy | 40 | 227 | 100 | 367 |
| Very happy | 216 | 198 | 203 | 617 |
| Totals | 357 | 507 | 339 | 1,203 |

**a.** Compute gamma to describe the strength and direction of the relationship.

**b.** Is the relationship statistically significant?

**9.11** $\boxed{\text{SOC}}$ A random sample of 11 neighbourhoods in Pearson, Ontario, has been rated by an urban sociologist on a "quality-of-life" scale (which includes measures of affluence, availability of medical care, and recreational facilities) and a social cohesion scale. The results are presented below in scores. Higher scores indicate higher "quality of life" and greater social cohesion.

| Neighbourhood | Quality of Life | Social Cohesion |
|---|---|---|
| Queens Lake | 17 | 8.8 |
| North End | 40 | 3.9 |
| Mountaintop | 47 | 4.0 |
| Lakeside | 90 | 3.1 |
| Blossom Park | 35 | 7.5 |
| Kingswood | 52 | 3.5 |
| Cambridge Shores | 23 | 6.3 |
| Windsor Forest | 67 | 1.7 |
| College Park | 65 | 9.2 |
| Uplands | 63 | 3.0 |
| Riverview | 100 | 5.3 |

**a.** Are the two variables associated? Compute Spearman's rho, and describe the strength and direction of the association. Summarize the relationship in a sentence or two. *(HINT: Don't forget to square the value of Spearman's rho for a PRE interpretation.)*

**b.** Conduct a test of significance for this relationship. Summarize your findings.

**9.12** $\boxed{\text{SW}}$ Several years ago, a job-training program began, and a team of social workers screened the candidates for suitability for employment. Now the screening process is being evaluated, and the actual work performance of a sample of hired candidates has been rated. Did the screening process work? Is there a relationship between the original scores and the evaluation of on-the-job performance?

| Case | Original Score | Performance Evaluation |
|------|----------------|------------------------|
| A | 17 | 78 |
| B | 17 | 85 |
| C | 15 | 82 |
| D | 13 | 92 |
| E | 13 | 75 |
| F | 13 | 72 |
| G | 11 | 70 |
| H | 10 | 75 |
| I | 10 | 92 |
| J | 10 | 70 |
| K | 9 | 32 |
| L | 8 | 55 |
| M | 7 | 21 |
| N | 5 | 45 |
| O | 2 | 25 |

**9.13** SOC Below are the scores of a sample of 15 countries on a measure of ethnic diversity (the higher the number, the greater the diversity) and a measure of economic inequality (the higher the score, the greater the inequality). Are these variables related? Are ethnically diverse countries more economically unequal?

| Country | Diversity | Inequality |
|---------|-----------|------------|
| A | 91 | 29.7 |
| B | 87 | 58.4 |
| C | 83 | 57.5 |
| D | 75 | 31.5 |
| E | 72 | 48.4 |
| F | 69 | 32.7 |
| G | 65 | 32.0 |
| H | 63 | 41.0 |
| I | 57 | 30.1 |
| J | 50 | 50.3 |
| K | 44 | 32.5 |
| L | 31 | 33.7 |
| M | 16 | 25.6 |
| N | 4 | 35.9 |
| O | 3 | 27.2 |

**9.14** Random samples of foreign-born and non-foreign-born citizens from 20 countries were rated on a Social Distance Scale. Lower scores represent less social distance and less prejudice. How similar are these rankings? Is the relationship statistically significant?

| | Average Social Distance Scale Score | |
|---------|----------------------|----------------|
| Country | Non-foreign Born | Foreign Born |
| A | 1.2 | 2.6 |
| B | 1.4 | 2.9 |
| C | 1.5 | 3.6 |
| D | 1.6 | 3.6 |
| E | 1.8 | 3.9 |
| F | 1.9 | 3.3 |
| G | 2.0 | 3.8 |
| H | 2.1 | 2.7 |
| I | 2.2 | 3.0 |
| J | 2.3 | 3.3 |
| K | 2.4 | 4.2 |
| L | 2.4 | 1.3 |
| M | 2.8 | 3.5 |
| N | 2.9 | 3.4 |
| O | 3.4 | 3.7 |
| P | 3.7 | 5.1 |
| Q | 3.9 | 3.9 |
| R | 3.9 | 4.1 |
| S | 4.2 | 4.4 |
| T | 5.3 | 5.4 |

**9.15** In Problem 8.7, we looked at the relationships between five dependent variables and the independent variable political ideology. In this problem, we'll use income as an independent variable and assess its relationship with the same set of variables. For each table, calculate gamma. Describe the strength and direction of each relationship in a few sentences. *Be careful in interpreting direction.*

**a.** Support for same-sex marriage by income:

| | Income | | | |
|---|---|---|---|---|
| Same-Sex Marriage? | Less Than $24,900 | $24,900 to $50,000 | More Than $50,000 | Totals |
| Favour | 220 | 218 | 226 | 664 |
| Oppose | 366 | 299 | 250 | 915 |
| Totals | 586 | 517 | 476 | 1,579 |

**b.** Support for capital punishment by income:

| | Income | | | |
|---|---|---|---|---|
| Capital Punishment? | Less Than $24,900 | $24,900 to $50,000 | More Than $50,000 | Totals |
| Favour | 567 | 574 | 552 | 1,693 |
| Oppose | 270 | 183 | 160 | 613 |
| Totals | 837 | 757 | 712 | 2,306 |

**c.** Approval of suicide for people with an incurable disease by income:

| | Income | | | |
| Right to Suicide? | Less Than $24,900 | $24,900 to $50,000 | More Than $50,000 | Totals |
|---|---|---|---|---|
| Favour | 343 | 341 | 338 | 1,022 |
| Oppose | 227 | 194 | 147 | 568 |
| Totals | 570 | 535 | 485 | 1,590 |

**d.** Support for traditional gender roles by income:

| | Income | | | |
| Traditional Gender Roles? | Less Than $24,900 | $24,900 to $50,000 | More Than $50,000 | Totals |
|---|---|---|---|---|
| Favour | 130 | 71 | 39 | 240 |
| Oppose | 448 | 479 | 461 | 1,388 |
| Totals | 578 | 550 | 500 | 1,628 |

**e.** Support for legalizing marijuana by income:

| | Income | | | |
| Legalize Marijuana? | Less Than $24,900 | $24,900 to $50,000 | More Than $50,000 | Totals |
|---|---|---|---|---|
| Favour | 492 | 478 | 451 | 1,421 |
| Oppose | 85 | 68 | 53 | 206 |
| Totals | 577 | 546 | 504 | 1,627 |

**You Are the Researcher**

## Using SPSS to Produce Ordinal-Level Measures of Association with the 2013 GSS

The demonstrations and exercises below use the shortened version of the 2013 GSS data set supplied with this textbook. Start SPSS and open the *GSS_2013_Shortened.sav* file.

### SPSS DEMONSTRATION 9.1 Interpreting the Direction of Relationships—Another Look at Income and Health

In Demonstration 8.1, we used percentages to look at the relationship between recoded *srh_110* (state of health) and recoded *incm* (respondent's total annual income). Let's re-examine this relationship and find out whether gamma, Kendall's tau-c, and Somers' *d* can add any new information. We will use the **Crosstabs** program with *income4* (recoded *incm*) as the independent (column) variable and *health* (recoded *srh_110*) as the dependent (row) variable. If you no longer have access to the recoded version of these variables, follow the directions in Demonstration 8.1.

In the **Crosstabs** dialog box, click the **Statistics** button and request gamma, Somers' *d*, and Kendall's tau-c (we have selected Kendall's tau-c given the unequal number of categories on the independent and dependent variables). Don't forget to click the **Cells** button and request column percentages. Click **OK**, and the output (slightly edited for readability) should look like this:

## Health * Income4 Cross-tabulation

| | | | Income4 | | | | Total |
|---|---|---|---|---|---|---|---|
| | | | < $30,000 | $30,000–$49,999 | $50,000–$79,999 | $80,000+ | |
| Health | good | Count | 410 | 253 | 198 | 194 | 1055 |
| | | % within income4 | 87.0% | 87.5% | 91.7% | 95.6% | 89.5% |
| | poor | Count | 61 | 36 | 18 | 9 | 124 |
| | | % within income4 | 13.0% | 12.5% | 8.3% | 4.4% | 10.5% |
| Total | | Count | 471 | 289 | 216 | 203 | 1179 |
| | | % within income4 | 100.0% | 100.0% | 100.0% | 100.0% | 100.0% |

## Directional Measures

| | | | Value | Asymptotic Standard Error[a] | Approximate T[b] | Approximate Significance |
|---|---|---|---|---|---|---|
| Ordinal by Ordinal | Somers' *d* | Symmetric | −.072 | .020 | −3.544 | .000 |
| | | Health dependent | −.045 | .013 | −3.544 | .000 |
| | | Income4 dependent | −.172 | .047 | −3.544 | .000 |

a. Not assuming the null hypothesis.

b. Using the asymptotic standard error assuming the null hypothesis.

## Symmetric Measures

| | | Value | Asymptotic Standard Error[a] | Approximate T[b] | Approximate Significance |
|---|---|---|---|---|---|
| Ordinal by ordinal | Kendall's tau-b | −.088 | .024 | −3.544 | .000 |
| | Kendall's tau-c | −.065 | .018 | −3.544 | .000 |
| | Gamma | −.246 | .069 | −3.544 | .000 |
| N of valid cases | | 1179 | | | |

a. Not assuming the null hypothesis.

b. Using the asymptotic standard error assuming the null hypothesis.

Let's look first at gamma in the "Symmetric Measures" box. A value of −.246 indicates a moderate and negative relationship. So, the higher the income, the lower the health, right? Wrong. Look at the codes for health. A low score indicates a high level of health. The negative sign for gamma is telling us that higher scores on *income4* are associated with a low score (a score of 1 or good) on health. Despite the negative sign, this is really a "positive" relationship in the sense that health improves with income. Always inspect tables carefully to make sure that you are interpreting the direction of the relationship properly.

Looking next at Kendall's tau-c. A value of $-.065$ indicates a weak relationship. This value is much lower than gamma, as is Somers' $d$ reported in the "Directional Measures" output box. Also, notice that there are three values of Somers' $d$. The "Symmetric" version of Somers' $d$ ($-.072$) is a type of average of the two asymmetrical (i.e., directional) versions of Somers' $d$: $d_{yx}$ ($-.045$) ("Health dependent") and $d_{xy}$ ($-.172$) ("Income4 dependent").

So, which of these statistics should we use? Gamma tends to exaggerate the strength of relationship, so either Kendall's tau-c or Somers' $d$ will likely offer a more realistic picture of the strength of association between income and health. Furthermore, if one of the variables is specifically identified as the dependent variable (e.g., health), then asymmetrical Somers' $d$ ($-.045$) is likely the most appropriate measure of association. That having been said, gamma offers a PRE interpretation whereas Kendall's tau and Somers' $d$ do not, and PRE interpretations are intuitively meaningful and appealing. For this reason, we often include more than one statistic to describe a relationship between variables—just as, in the univariate situation, we often use more than one measure of central tendency or dispersion to describe a distribution of variable values. We simply need to keep in mind the particular advantages and limitations of the statistics that we choose to include, in order to be able to interpret them appropriately.

## SPSS DEMONSTRATION 9.2 Does Social Networking Use Vary by Age?

Let's take another look at a relationship between two ordinal-level variables: *icr_30* (how often do you access your social networking site(s)?—asked to respondents who had indicated that they do have a social networking account) as the dependent variable and *agegr10* (age) as the independent variable. The latter has more categories (7) than we need for our analysis (see Appendix G), so we will first recode the variable to simplify it. We have decided to collapse the values of *agegr10* into three categories that reflect general life stages: young adult and early career, middle age, and senior citizen.

Click **Transform** and **Recode into Different Variables**. Next, move the variable *agegr10* to the **Input Variable** $\rightarrow$ **Output Variable** box, then type a name— we suggest *age3*—in the **Output Variable** box. Click the **Change** button. Next, click on the **Old and New Values** button. The recoding instructions that should appear in the **Old** $\rightarrow$ **New** box of the **Recode into Different Variables: Old and New Values** window should be:

| | | |
|---|---|---|
| 1 thru 2 | $\rightarrow$ | 1 |
| 3 thru 5 | $\rightarrow$ | 2 |
| 6 thru 7 | $\rightarrow$ | 3 |

Click **Continue**, then **OK** after inputting these recode instructions. This scheme groups all respondents with scores 1 thru 2 on *agegr10* (15–34) together into a score of 1 on *age3*, scores 3 thru 5 on *agegr10* (35–64) together into a score of 2 on *age3*, and scores 6 thru 7 on *agegr10* (65+) together into a score of 3 on *age3*.

Again, we highly recommend that this variable be added to the permanent data file as it will be used in subsequent demonstrations and exercises. Click **Save** from the **File** menu, and the updated data set with *age3* added will be saved to disk. Remember that your data set is limited to 50 variables in the SPSS student version.

Let's now examine the relationship between *icr_30* and *age3* with gamma, Kendall's tau-c, and Somers' *d*. Use **Crosstabs** once again with *age3* as the independent (column) variable. The dependent variable *icr_30* will go in the rows. Request gamma, Kendall's tau-c (since the independent and dependent variables do not have an equal number of categories), Somers' *d*, and column percentages. The output, slightly edited for readability, should look like this:

### Social Networking Account—Frequency of Access * Age3 Cross-tabulation

| | | | Age3 | | | |
|---|---|---|---|---|---|---|
| | | | 15 to 34 years | 35 to 64 years | 65 to 75 years and over | Total |
| Social networking account— frequency of access | Several times a day | Count<br>% within Age3 | 229<br>50.9% | 142<br>32.5% | 12<br>22.2% | 383<br>40.7% |
| | About once a day | Count<br>% within Age3 | 112<br>24.9% | 119<br>27.2% | 15<br>27.8% | 246<br>26.1% |
| | 3–5 times a week | Count<br>% within Age3 | 49<br>10.9% | 37<br>8.5% | 4<br>7.4% | 90<br>9.6% |
| | 1–2 times a week | Count<br>% within Age3 | 19<br>4.2% | 55<br>12.6% | 11<br>20.4% | 85<br>9.0% |
| | A few times per month | Count<br>% within Age3 | 15<br>3.3% | 53<br>12.1% | 7<br>13.0% | 75<br>8.0% |
| | Less than once a month | Count<br>% within Age3 | 23<br>5.1% | 31<br>7.1% | 5<br>9.3% | 59<br>6.3% |
| | Never | Count<br>% within Age3 | 3<br>0.7% | 0<br>0.0% | 0<br>0.0% | 3<br>0.3% |
| Total | | Count% within Age3 | 450<br>100.0% | 437<br>100.0% | 54<br>100.0% | 941<br>100.0% |

### Directional Measures

| | | | Value | Asymptotic Standard Error[a] | Approximate T[b] | Approximate Significance |
|---|---|---|---|---|---|---|
| Ordinal by ordinal | Somers' *d* | Symmetric | .202 | .027 | 7.353 | .000 |
| | | Social networking account—frequency of access dependent | .236 | .032 | 7.353 | .000 |
| | | Age3 dependent | .177 | .024 | 7.353 | .000 |

a. Not assuming the null hypothesis.

b. Using the asymptotic standard error assuming the null hypothesis.

## Symmetric Measures

| | | Value | Asymptotic Standard Error[a] | Approximate T[b] | Approximate Significance |
|---|---|---|---|---|---|
| Ordinal by ordinal | Kendall's tau-b | .204 | .028 | 7.353 | .000 |
| | Kendall's tau-c | .196 | .027 | 7.353 | .000 |
| | Gamma | .313 | .041 | 7.353 | .000 |
| N of valid cases | | 941 | | | |

a. Not assuming the null hypothesis.

b. Using the asymptotic standard error assuming the null hypothesis.

A gamma of 0.313 indicates a strong, positive relationship—but as we saw when we examined the relationship between age and health, we need to check the order of the response category codes in order to interpret the meaning of the directional sign correctly. So in the case of *icr_30*, what we find again is that lower response category codes represent higher frequencies of social networking use, while higher response category codes represent lower frequencies of use. The positive directional sign in our analysis is thus reflecting the generally less frequent use of social networking by older respondents (a score of 3 on *age3*), who had the highest percentage who reported "Less than once a month" or "A few times per month," and the generally more frequent social networking use by younger respondents, who had the highest percentage who reported "Several times a day." As age increases, people's frequency of social networking use decreases. It will be very interesting to see whether this pattern will remain among currently younger respondents, who grew up with many new social networking tools, when they become older.

Not surprisingly, Kendall's tau-c, with a value of 0.196, is lower than gamma, and indicates a moderate relationship. Similarly, if we take *icr_30* as the dependent variable, then Somers' *d* (.236) also offers a more modest picture of the strength of relationship between age and social networking use.

## Exercises (using *GSS_2013_Shortened.sav*)

**9.1** Use gamma, Kendall's tau (tau-b when a bivariate table has an equal number of rows and columns, otherwise tau-c), and Somers' *d* to analyze and describe the relationship between any two ordinal-level variables.* Summarize the strength and direction of the relationship in a few sentences.

**9.2** Follow up on Demonstration 9.2 with two new ordinal-level independent variables. What other factors might affect *icr_30*? As a suggestion, try *ehg_all* and *incm* as independent variables.* Summarize the strength and direction of the relationships in a few sentences. Are these relationships stronger or weaker than those with recoded *agegr10*? Be careful in interpreting the direction of the relationships.

*If necessary, use the **Recode** command illustrated in Appendix F.5 to reduce the number of categories in your variables.

# 10

# Hypothesis Testing with Means and Proportions
## The One-Sample Case

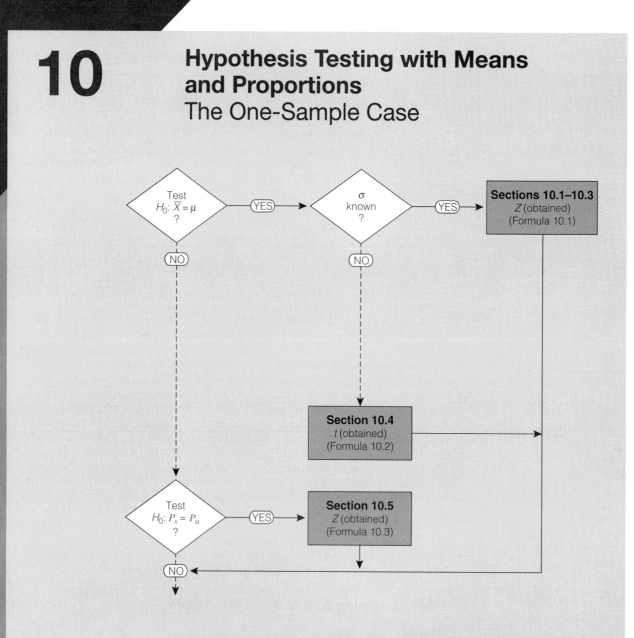

**LEARNING OBJECTIVES**

By the end of this chapter, you will be able to

1. Explain the logic of hypothesis testing as applied to the one-sample case.

2. Identify and cite examples of situations in which one-sample tests of hypotheses are appropriate.

3. Test the significance of single-sample means and proportions using the five-step model and correctly interpret the results.

4. Explain the difference between one- and two-tailed tests and specify when each is appropriate.

5. Conduct a single-sample hypothesis test using a confidence interval.

**10.1 INTRODUCTION**

Chapter 7 introduced the techniques of hypothesis testing (significance testing) for nominal and ordinal bivariate relationships. Chapters 8 and 9 then showed how to use measures of association to determine the strength, and for ordinal variables also the direction, of these relationships. This chapter will introduce the techniques for hypothesis testing of a single sample mean (when you have an interval-ratio variable) or sample proportion (nominal or ordinal variable). It also lays the groundwork for Chapters 11 and 12, which look at how to test a hypothesis about a relationship between a nominal or ordinal independent variable and interval-ratio dependent variable.

Single-sample hypothesis tests could be used in situations such as the following:

1. A researcher has selected a sample of 789 senior citizens who live in a particular province and also has information on the percentage of the entire population of the province that was victimized by crime during the past year. Are older citizens, as represented by this sample, more or less likely to be victimized than the population in general?
2. Are the GPAs of university varsity athletes different from the GPAs of the student body as a whole? To investigate, the academic records of a random sample of 105 student athletes from a large university are compared with the overall GPA of all students.
3. The Law School Admission Test (LSAT) is a standardized test required for admission to most Canadian and American law schools. The LSAT assesses reading and verbal reasoning skills and, along with GPA, is considered a critical factor in determining admission to law school. Companies offer an LSAT preparation (i.e., training) course, for a fee, with the claim that graduates of their course on average obtain higher scores on the LSAT than the general population of LSAT test takers. To test this claim, you randomly sample 100 graduates of LSAT training courses and find that, on average, those in the sample have higher LSAT scores than the population of LSAT writers as a whole. Do training-course graduates score higher than LSAT writers in general?

In each of these situations, we have randomly selected samples (of senior citizens, athletes, or graduates of an LSAT training course) that we want to compare to a population (the entire province, student body, or community of LSAT writers). As with all situations in which we use hypothesis testing, we are not interested in the sample per se but in the larger group from which it was selected (*all* senior citizens in the province, *all* athletes on this campus, or *all* graduates of an LSAT training course). Specifically, we want to know if the groups represented by the samples are different from the populations on a specific trait or variable (victimization rates, GPAs, or LSAT scores).

## 10.2 HYPOTHESIS TESTING WITH THE ONE-SAMPLE CASE

Let us use our third research situation above as an example of hypothesis testing in the one-sample case. The main question here is, "Do graduates of an LSAT preparation course in Canada have an average LSAT score that is higher than other Canadians who write the LSAT?" In other words, the researcher wants to compare the LSAT scores of *all* graduates (the Canadian graduates of an LSAT training course) with the LSAT scores of all test takers (the entire Canadian population of LSAT test takers). If she had complete information for both of these groups (all graduates of an LSAT preparation course and all LSAT writers), she could answer the question easily and completely.

The problem is that the researcher does not have the time and/or money to gather information on the thousands of people who have graduated from an LSAT preparation course in Canada. So instead, she has drawn a random sample, following the rule of EPSEM, of 100 graduates from records provided by the companies offering an LSAT training course in Canada. Information on LSAT scores for the sample of LSAT preparation-course graduates and the entire population of LSAT test takers is as follows:

| Entire Canadian Population of LSAT Test Takers* | Sample of Canadian Graduates from LSAT Preparation Course |
|---|---|
| $\mu = 153$ | $\overline{X} = 156$ |
| $\sigma = 9$ | $n = 100$ |

*Source: S. Dalessandro, L. Anthony, and L. Reese, 2012, *LSAT Performance with Regional, Gender, and Racial/Ethnic Breakdowns: 2005–2006 through 2011–2012 Testing Years.*

Information from the Law School Admission Council, the organization that administers the LSAT, shows that the population of test takers in Canada has a mean LSAT score of 153. At 156, the average LSAT score for the sample is higher than the average score for the entire population. (To put this information in context, there are 101 multiple choice questions on the LSAT. One point is given for each question answered correctly. Total test scores, ranging from 0 to 101, are converted into an LSAT score ranging from 120, the lowest possible score, to 180, the highest possible score.) Although it is tempting, we cannot draw any conclusions yet because we are working with a random sample of the population in which we are interested, not the population itself (all graduates of an LSAT preparation course).

Figure 10.1 should clarify these relationships. The entire Canadian population of LSAT test takers is symbolized by the largest circle because it is the largest group. The Canadian population of graduates of an LSAT training course is also symbolized by a large circle because it is a sizable group, although only a fraction of the population of LSAT writers as a whole. The random sample of 100 Canadian graduates of an LSAT training course, the smallest of the three groups, is symbolized by the smallest circle.

**FIGURE 10.1 A Test of Hypothesis for Single Sample Means**

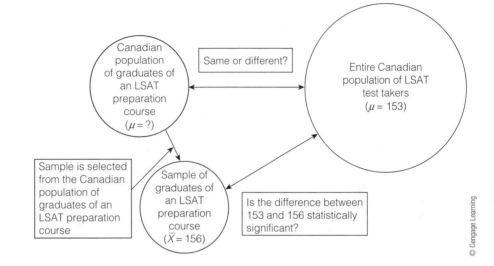

© Cengage Learning

The arrows between the circles show how they are connected in this research situation. The researcher wants to know if the average LSAT score of all graduates of a preparation course is the "same or different" from the average LSAT score of the entire population of LSAT writers. Instead of comparing all graduates (a group that is too large to gather information on) with the entire population of LSAT writers, the researcher compares the LSAT scores of a random sample of graduates with the entire population.

We observe that the mean of the sample is higher than the mean of the population (156 vs. 153). This suggests that graduates of a preparation course do better on the LSAT. However, the graduates are represented by a random sample, and we know that even the most carefully chosen sample may, on rare occasion, be unrepresentative. Does the difference between the *sample mean* and the *population mean* reflect a real difference between all graduates of the preparation course and the entire population of LSAT writers? Or was this difference caused by mere random chance? This is the question that a test of hypothesis is designed to answer. In other words, there are two possible explanations for the difference, and we will consider them one at a time.

The first explanation, which we will label explanation A, is that the difference between the population mean of 153 and the sample mean of 156 reflects a real difference in LSAT scores between all graduates and the entire population. The difference is "statistically significant" in the sense that it is very unlikely to have occurred by random chance alone. If explanation A is true, then the population of all graduates of the preparation course is different from the entire population of LSAT writers. The sample did *not* come from a population with a mean LSAT score of 153.

The second explanation, or explanation B, is that the observed difference between sample and population means was caused by mere random chance. There is no important difference between graduates and the population of LSAT writers as a whole, and the difference between the sample mean of 156 and the population mean of 153 is trivial and due to random chance. If explanation B is true, the population of LSAT preparation course graduates is just like everyone else and has a mean LSAT score of 153.

Which explanation is correct? As long as we are working with a sample rather than the entire group, we cannot know the answer to this question for sure. However, we can set up a decision-making procedure so conservative that one of the two explanations can be chosen, with the knowledge that the probability of choosing the incorrect explanation is very low.

This decision-making process, in broad outline, begins with the assumption that explanation B is correct. Symbolically, the assumption that the mean LSAT score for all graduates of a preparation course is the same as the mean LSAT score for the population of LSAT writers as a whole can be stated as

$$\mu = 153$$

Remember that this $\mu$ refers to the mean for all LSAT preparation course graduates, not just the 100 in the sample. This assumption, $\mu = 153$, can be tested statistically.

If explanation B (the population of graduates of the preparation course is not different from the population of LSAT writers as a whole and has a $\mu$ of 153) is true, then the probability of getting the observed sample outcome ($\overline{X} = 156$) can be found. Let us add an objective decision rule in advance. If the odds of getting the observed difference are less than 0.05 (5 out of 100, or 1 in 20), we will reject explanation B. If, on the other hand, this explanation were true, a difference of this size (153 vs. 156) would be a very rare event, and in hypothesis testing, as we saw in Chapter 7, we always bet against rare events.

How can we estimate the probability of the observed sample outcome ($\overline{X} = 156$) if explanation B is correct? This value can be determined by using our knowledge of the sampling distribution of all possible sample outcomes. Looking back at the information we have and applying the Central Limit Theorem (see Chapter 5), we can assume that the sampling distribution is normal in shape, has a mean of 153 (because $\mu_{\overline{X}} = \mu$), and has a standard deviation of $9/\sqrt{100}$ because $\sigma_{\overline{X}} = \sigma/\sqrt{n}$. We also know that the standard normal distribution can be interpreted as a distribution of probabilities (see Chapter 4) and that the particular sample outcome noted above ($\overline{X} = 156$) is one of thousands of possible sample outcomes. The sampling distribution, with the sample outcome noted, is depicted in Figure 10.2.

Using our knowledge of the standardized normal ($Z$) distribution, we can add further useful information to this sampling distribution of sample

**FIGURE 10.2   The Sampling Distribution of All Possible Sample Means**

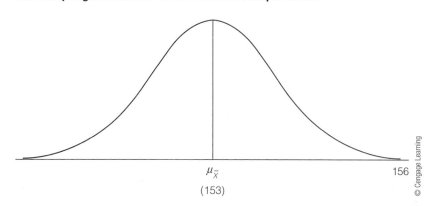

**FIGURE 10.3   The Sampling Distribution of All Possible Sample Means, with Rejection Areas in Shade**

means. Specifically, with $Z$ scores, we can depict the decision rule stated previously: Any sample outcome with probability less than 0.05 (assuming that explanation B is true) will cause us to reject explanation B. The probability of 0.05 can be translated into an area and divided equally into the upper and lower tails of the sampling distribution. Using Appendix A, we find that the $Z$ score equivalent of this area is ±1.96. The areas and $Z$ scores are depicted in Figure 10.3.

The decision rule can now be rephrased. Any sample outcome falling in the shaded areas depicted in Figure 10.3 by definition has a probability of occurrence of less than 0.05. Such an outcome would be a rare event and would cause us to reject explanation B.

All that remains is to translate our sample outcome into a $Z$ score so that we can see where it falls on the curve. To do this, we use the standard

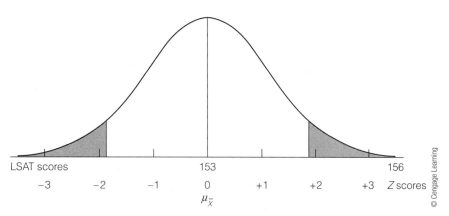

formula for locating any particular raw score under a normal distribution. When we use known or empirical distributions, this formula (as described in Chapter 4) is expressed as

$$Z = \frac{X_i - \overline{X}}{s}$$

Or, to find the equivalent $Z$ score for any raw score, subtract the mean of the distribution from the raw score and divide by the standard deviation of the distribution. Because we are now concerned with the sampling distribution of all sample means rather than an empirical distribution, the symbols in the formula will change, but the form remains the same:

**FORMULA 10.1**
$$Z(\text{obtained}) = \frac{\overline{X} - \mu}{\sigma/\sqrt{n}}$$

So, to find the equivalent $Z$ score for any sample mean subtract the mean of the sampling distribution, which is equal to the population mean or $\mu$, from the sample mean and divide by the standard deviation of the sampling distribution. (Recall from Chapter 5 that the standard deviation of the sampling distribution of sample means—called the standard error of the mean—is equal to the population standard deviation divided by the square root of $n$.)

Continuing with the LSAT example, we can now find the $Z$ score equivalent of the sample mean as:

$$Z = \frac{156 - 153}{9/\sqrt{100}}$$
$$Z = \frac{3}{0.90}$$
$$Z = +3.33$$

In Figure 10.4, this $Z$ score of $+3.33$ is noted on the distribution of all possible sample means and we see that the sample outcome does fall in

**FIGURE 10.4  The Sampling Distribution of Sample Means with the Sample Outcome ($\overline{X} = 156$) Noted in $Z$ Scores, with Rejection Areas in Shade**

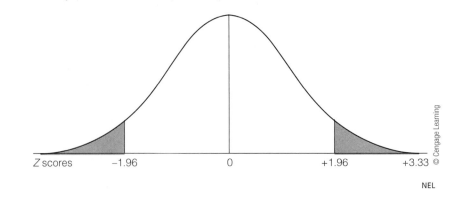

the shaded area. If explanation B is true, this particular sample outcome has a probability of occurrence of less than 0.05. The sample outcome ($\bar{X} = 156$ or $Z = +3.33$) would therefore be rare if explanation B was true, and the researcher may reject explanation B. If explanation B were true, this sample outcome would be extremely unlikely. The sample of 100 graduates of an LSAT preparation course comes from a population that is significantly different from the population of LSAT writers as a whole on LSAT scoring. Or, to put it another way, the sample does not come from a population that has a mean LSAT score of 153.

Remember that our decisions in significance testing are based on information gathered from random samples. On rare occasions, a sample may not be representative of the population from which it was selected. The decision-making process outlined above has a very high probability of resulting in correct decisions, but as long as we must work with samples rather than populations, we face an element of risk. That is, the decision to reject explanation B might be incorrect if this sample happens to be one of the few that is unrepresentative of the population of graduates of the LSAT training course. Fortunately, as we have already seen (in Chapter 7), one important strength of hypothesis testing is that the probability of making an incorrect decision can be estimated. In the example at hand, explanation B was rejected and the probability of this decision being incorrect is 0.05—the decision rule established at the beginning of the process. To say that the probability of rejecting explanation B incorrectly is 0.05 means that, if we repeated this same test an infinite number of times, we would incorrectly reject explanation B only 5 times out of every 100.

We are now ready to put our LSAT example into the five-step model of hypothesis testing, introduced in Chapter 7, as follows:

**Step 1. Make Assumptions and Meet Test Requirements.** Three criteria have to be satisfied when conducting a test of hypothesis with a single sample mean. First, all tests of hypothesis must be based on a random sample that has been selected according to the rules of EPSEM. Second, to justify computation of a mean, the variable being tested must be interval-ratio in level of measurement. Finally, we must assume that the sampling distribution of all possible sample means is normal in shape so that we may use the standardized normal ($Z$) distribution to find areas under the sampling distribution. We can be sure that this assumption is satisfied by either using a large sample—and applying the Central Limit Theorem—or assuming that the population is normally distributed.

> Model: Random sampling
> Level of measurement is interval-ratio
> Sampling distribution is normal

**Step 2. State the Null Hypothesis**. The null hypothesis is represented by explanation B in our LSAT example, and is always a statement of "no difference." Thus, in the single-sample case, the null hypothesis states that the sample comes from a population with a certain characteristic. In our example, the null hypothesis is that the population of LSAT preparation course graduates is "no different" from the population of LSAT writers as a whole, that their average LSAT score is also 153, and that the difference between 153 and the sample mean of 156 is caused by random chance. Symbolically, the null hypothesis would be stated as

$$H_0: \mu = 153$$

where $\mu$ refers to the mean of the population of graduates of an LSAT preparation course. As we saw in Chapter 7, the null hypothesis is always the central element in any test of hypothesis because the entire process is aimed at rejecting or failing to reject the $H_0$.

By contrast, in our example, the research hypothesis ($H_1$) simply asserts that the population from which the sample was selected did not have a certain characteristic or, in terms of our example, had a mean that was not equal to a specific value:

$$(H_1: \mu \neq 153)$$

where $\neq$ means "not equal to"

Symbolically, this statement asserts that the sample does not come from a population with a mean of 153, or that the population of graduates of an LSAT preparation course is different from the population of LSAT writers as a whole. Even though the research hypothesis has no formal standing or role in the hypothesis-testing process, it will help us to choose between "one-tailed" and "two-tailed" tests, as we shall see in Section 10.3.

**Step 3. Select the Sampling Distribution and Establish the Critical Region.** By assuming that the null hypothesis is true, we can attach values to the mean and standard deviation of the sampling distribution and thus measure the probability of any specific sample outcome. With the large sample size ($n = 100$) used in our LSAT example, we can use the sampling distribution described by the standard normal ($Z$) curve as summarized in Appendix A.

Recall that the critical region (or region of rejection) consists of the areas under the sampling distribution that include unlikely sample outcomes, and we must define, prior to the test of hypothesis, what we mean by "unlikely." The critical region allows us to specify in advance those sample outcomes that are so unlikely that they will lead us to reject the $H_0$. In our example, this area corresponded to a $Z$ score of $\pm 1.96$, called **Z (critical)**, which was graphically displayed in Figure 10.4. The shaded area is the critical region. Any sample outcome for which the $Z$ score equivalent fell in this area (i.e., below $-1.96$ or above $+1.96$) would have caused us to reject the null hypothesis. This gives us an alpha level (i.e., the size of the critical region) of 0.05.

In abbreviated form, all of the decisions made in this step are noted below. The critical region is noted by the $Z$ scores that mark its beginnings.

$$\text{Sampling distribution} = Z \text{ distribution}$$

$$\alpha = 0.05$$

$$Z \text{ (critical)} = \pm 1.96$$

*(For practice in finding Z (critical) scores, see Problem 10.1a.)*

**Step 4. Compute the Test Statistic.** To evaluate the probability of any given sample outcome, the sample value must be converted into a $Z$ score. Solving the equation for $Z$ score equivalents will give us the test statistic, referred to as **Z (obtained)** in order to differentiate the test statistic from the critical region. In our example, we found a $Z$ (obtained) of $+3.33$. *(For practice in computing obtained Z scores for means, see Problems 10.2, 10.4, and 10.6.)*

**Step 5. Make a Decision and Interpret the Results of the Test.** We are now ready to compare the test (obtained) statistic with the critical statistic, in order to determine whether or not the test statistic falls into the critical region. Recall that if the test statistic does fall into the critical region, our decision will be to reject the null hypothesis. If the test statistic does not fall into the critical region, we fail to reject the null hypothesis. In our example, the two values were

$$Z \text{ (critical)} = \pm 1.96$$

$$Z \text{ (obtained)} = +3.33$$

---

**ONE STEP AT A TIME** Completing Step 4 of the Five-Step Model: Compute **Z (obtained)**

Use these procedures if the population standard deviation ($\sigma$) is known and sample size is large ($n = 100$ or more) or the population is normally distributed; otherwise, see Section 10.4, "The Student's $t$ Distribution and the One-Sample Case."

**To Compute the Test Statistic Using Formula 10.1**

**1:** Find the square root of $n$.

**2:** Divide the square root of $n$ into the population standard deviation.

**3:** Subtract the population mean ($\mu$) from the sample mean ($\overline{X}$).

**4:** Divide the quantity you found in step 3 by the quantity you found in step 2. This value is $Z$ (obtained).

---

**ONE STEP AT A TIME** Completing Step 5 of the Five-Step Model:
Make a Decision and Interpret Results of the Test

**1:** Compare the $Z$ (obtained) to the $Z$ (critical). If $Z$ (obtained) is *in* the critical region, *reject* the null hypothesis. If $Z$ (obtained) is *not in* the critical region, *fail to reject* the null hypothesis.

**2:** Interpret your decision in the terms of the original question. For example, our conclusion for the example problem was "Graduates of an LSAT preparation course do significantly better on the LSAT test than LSAT writers as a whole."

---

and we saw that the $Z$ (obtained) fell in the critical region (see Figure 10.4). Our decision was therefore to reject the null hypothesis, which stated that graduates of an LSAT preparation course have a mean LSAT score of 153 or that there is no difference between LSAT preparation course graduates and LSAT writers as a whole. When we reject this null hypothesis, we are saying that graduates do *not* have a mean LSAT score of 153 and that there *is* a difference between them and the population of LSAT writers as a whole. In other words, the difference between the sample mean of 156 and the mean of 153 for the entire population of LSAT writers is statistically significant or unlikely to be caused by random chance alone. In terms of LSAT score, graduates of an LSAT preparation course are different from the population of LSAT writers as a whole.

## 10.3 ONE-TAILED AND TWO-TAILED TESTS OF HYPOTHESIS

The five-step model for hypothesis testing is fairly rigid, and the researcher has little room for making choices. Nonetheless, the researcher must still make another crucial decision when conducting a significance test in the one-sample case. Specifically, he or she must decide between a one-tailed and a two-tailed test. This decision concerns the placement of alpha in the left tail only, the right tail only, or divided equally between both the left and right tails. This decision did not arise when we examined the chi square test because the right-skewed nature of the chi square distribution necessarily placed all the alpha in the right tail only. When we are using the symmetrical normal distribution (or the Student's $t$ distribution), this is a new consideration that we must additionally address.

The choice between a one- and two-tailed test is based on the researcher's expectations about the population from which the sample was selected. These expectations are reflected in the research hypothesis ($H_1$), which is contradictory to the null hypothesis and usually states what the researcher believes to be "the truth." In most situations, the researcher will wish to support the research hypothesis by rejecting the null hypothesis.

The format for the research hypothesis can take either of two forms, depending on the relationship between what the null hypothesis states and what the researcher believes to be the truth. The null hypothesis states that the population has a specific characteristic. In the example that has served us throughout this chapter, the null hypothesis stated that the "population of graduates of an LSAT preparation course have the *same* mean LSAT score (153) as the entire population of LSAT writers." The researcher might believe that the population of graduates actually scores *lower* on the LSAT (their population mean is *lower than* the value stated in the null hypothesis), or *higher* on the LSAT (their population mean is *greater than* the value stated in the null hypothesis), or he or she might be unsure about the direction of the difference.

If the researcher is unsure about the direction, the research hypothesis states only that the population mean is "not equal" to the value stated in the null hypothesis. The research hypothesis stated in Section 10.2 ($\mu \neq 153$) was in this format. This is called a **two-tailed test** of significance because it means that the researcher will be equally concerned with the possibility that the true population value is greater than the value specified in the null hypothesis and the possibility that the true population value is less than the value specified in the null hypothesis.

In other situations, the researcher might be concerned only with differences in a specific direction. If the direction of the difference can be predicted, or if the researcher is concerned only with differences in one direction, a **one-tailed test** can be used. A one-tailed test may take one of two forms, depending on the researcher's expectations about the direction of the difference. If the researcher believes that the true population value is greater than the value specified in the null hypothesis, the research hypothesis will reflect that belief. In our example, if we had predicted that graduates of an LSAT preparation course had *higher* LSAT scores than the entire population of LSAT writers (or, an average LSAT score *greater than* 153) our research hypothesis would have been as follows:

$$(H_1 : \mu > 153)$$

where $>$ signifies "greater than"

In this situation, the critical region would be defined to include all values less than or equal to 153, thus giving us the following revised null hypothesis:

$$(H_0 : \mu \leq 153)$$

where $\leq$ signifies "less than or equal to"

Notice that the null hypothesis must always include an equal sign, even when a directional symbol is also included. This is one of the features which distinguishes it from the research hypothesis, whose possible directional signs include only "$<$," "$>$," or "$\neq$"—but never "$=$".

On the other hand, if we predicted that graduates had *lower* LSAT scores than the entire population of LSAT writers (or, an average LSAT score *less than* 153), our research hypothesis would have been as follows:

$$(H_1: \mu < 153)$$

where $<$ signifies "less than"

In this situation, the critical region would be defined to include all values greater than or equal to 153, thus giving us the following revised null hypothesis:

$$(H_0: \mu \geq 153)$$

where $\geq$ signifies "greater than or equal to"

One-tailed tests are often appropriate when programs designed to solve a problem or improve a situation are being evaluated. If an LSAT training course resulted in lower LSAT scoring, for example, the course would be considered a failure. In a situation like this, the researcher may well focus only on outcomes that would indicate that the program is a success (i.e., when graduates of an LSAT preparation course have higher LSAT scores) and conduct a one-tailed test with a research hypothesis in the form: $H_1: \mu > 153$.

As another example, consider the evaluation of a program designed to increase youth employment. The evaluators would be concerned only with outcomes that show an increase in the youth employment rate. If the rate shows no change or if youth employment decreases, the program is a failure. Thus, the evaluators could legitimately use a one-tailed test that stated that youth employment rates for graduates of the program would be greater than ($>$) rates of employment among all youth.

In terms of the five-step model, the choice of a one-tailed or two-tailed test determines what we do with the critical region under the sampling distribution in step 3. This decision shows how important it is to state the null and research hypotheses carefully and precisely! In a two-tailed test, we split the critical region equally into the upper and lower tails of the sampling distribution. In a one-tailed test, we place the entire critical region in one tail of the sampling distribution. If we believe that the population characteristic is greater than the value stated in the null hypothesis (if the $H_1$ includes the $>$ symbol), we place the entire critical region in the upper tail. If we believe that the characteristic is less than the value stated in the null hypothesis (if the $H_1$ includes the $<$ symbol), the entire critical region goes in the lower tail.

For example, in a two-tailed test with alpha equal to 0.05, the critical region begins at $Z$ (critical) $= \pm 1.96$. In a one-tailed test at the same alpha level, the $Z$ (critical) is $+1.65$ if the upper tail is specified and $-1.65$ if the lower tail is specified. Table 10.1 summarizes the procedures to follow in

**TABLE 10.1   One- vs. Two-Tailed Tests, $\alpha = 0.05$**

| If the Research Hypothesis Uses | The Test Is | And Concern Is with | $Z$ (critical) = |
|---|---|---|---|
| $\neq$ | Two-tailed | Both tails | $\pm 1.96$ |
| $>$ | One-tailed | Upper tail | $+1.65$ |
| $<$ | One-tailed | Lower tail | $-1.65$ |

terms of the nature of the research hypothesis. The difference in placing the critical region is graphically summarized in Figure 10.5, and the critical $Z$ scores for the most common alpha levels are given in Table 10.2 for both one- and two-tailed tests.

Note that the critical $Z$ values for one-tailed tests are always closer to the mean of the sampling distribution. Thus, a one-tailed test is more likely to reject the $H_0$ without changing the alpha level (assuming that we have specified the correct tail). One-tailed tests are a way of statistically both having and eating your cake and should be used whenever (1) the direction of the difference can be confidently predicted, or (2) the researcher is concerned only with differences in one tail of the sampling distribution.

An example will clarify how the one-tailed test is used. After many years of work, a sociologist has noted that sociology majors seem more sophisticated, charming, and cosmopolitan than the rest of the student body. A "Sophistication Scale" test has been administered to the entire student body and to a random sample of 100 sociology majors, and these results have been obtained:

| Student Body | Sociology Majors |
|---|---|
| $\mu = 17.3$ | $\overline{X} = 19.2$ |
| $\sigma = 7.4$ | $n = 100$ |

We will use the five-step model to test the $H_0$ of no difference between sociology majors and the general student body.

**Step 1. Make Assumptions and Meet Test Requirements.** Because we are using a mean to summarize the sample outcome, we must assume that the Sophistication Scale generates interval-ratio-level data. With a sample size of 100, the Central Limit Theorem applies, and we can assume that the sampling distribution is normal in shape.

> Model:  Random sampling
> Level of measurement is interval-ratio
> Sampling distribution is normal

**FIGURE 10.5** **Establishing the Critical Region, One-Tailed Tests Versus Two-Tailed Tests, with Rejection Region for Alpha = 0.05 in Shade**

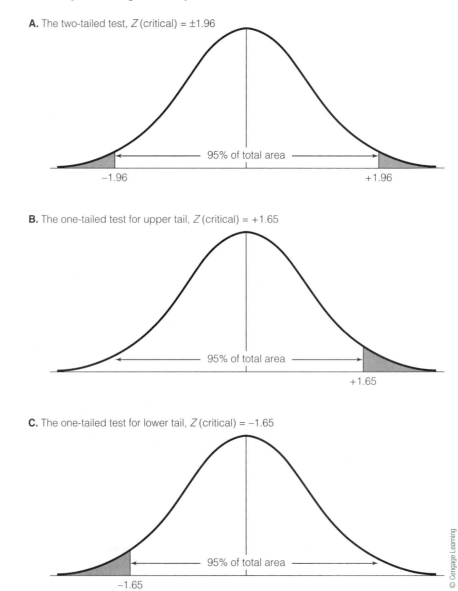

**A.** The two-tailed test, $Z$ (critical) = ±1.96

95% of total area

−1.96    +1.96

**B.** The one-tailed test for upper tail, $Z$ (critical) = +1.65

95% of total area

+1.65

**C.** The one-tailed test for lower tail, $Z$ (critical) = −1.65

95% of total area

−1.65

© Cengage Learning

**Step 2. State the Null Hypothesis.** The null hypothesis states that there is no difference between sociology majors and the general student body. The research hypothesis ($H_1$) will also be stated at this point. The researcher has predicted a direction for the difference ("Sociology majors are *more*

**TABLE 10.2  Finding Critical *Z* Scores for One- and Two-Tailed Tests (Single-Sample Means)**

| Alpha | Two-Tailed Value | One-Tailed Value Upper Tail | Lower Tail |
|---|---|---|---|
| 0.10 | ±1.65 | +1.29 | −1.29 |
| 0.05 | ±1.96 | +1.65 | −1.65 |
| 0.01 | ±2.58 | +2.33 | −2.33 |
| 0.001 | ±3.29 | +3.10 | −3.10 |

sophisticated"), so a one-tailed test is justified. The two hypotheses may be stated as

$$H_0: \mu \leq 17.3$$

$$(H_1: \mu > 17.3)$$

**Step 3. Select the Sampling Distribution and Establish the Critical Region.** We will use the standardized normal distribution (see Appendix A) to find areas under the sampling distribution. If alpha is set at 0.05, the critical region will begin at the *Z* score +1.65. That is, the researcher has predicted that sociology majors are *more* sophisticated and that this sample comes from a population that has a mean *greater than* 17.3, so he will be concerned only with sample outcomes in the upper tail of the sampling distribution. If sociology majors are *the same as* other students in terms of sophistication (if the $H_0$ is true), or if they are *less* sophisticated (and come from a population with a mean less than 17.3), the theory is disproved. These decisions may be summarized as

$$\text{Sampling distribution} = Z \text{ distribution}$$

$$\alpha = 0.05$$

$$Z \text{(critical)} = +1.65$$

**Step 4. Compute the Test Statistic.**

$$Z \text{(obtained)} = \frac{\bar{X} - \mu}{\sigma/\sqrt{n}}$$

$$Z \text{(obtained)} = \frac{19.2 - 17.3}{7.4/\sqrt{100}}$$

$$Z \text{(obtained)} = +2.57$$

**Step 5. Make a Decision and Interpret the Results of the Test.** Comparing the *Z* (obtained) with the *Z* (critical):

$$Z \text{(critical)} = +1.65$$

$$Z \text{(obtained)} = +2.57$$

**FIGURE 10.6**   *Z* **(Obtained) Versus** *Z* **(Critical) for the One-Tailed Test, with Rejection Region for Alpha = 0.05 in Shade**

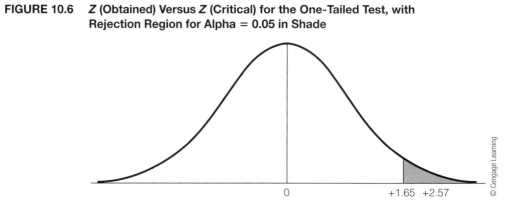

We see that the test statistic falls into the critical region. This outcome is depicted graphically in Figure 10.6. We will reject the null hypothesis because, if the $H_0$ were true, a difference of this size would be very unlikely. There is a significant difference between sociology majors and the general student body in terms of sophistication. Because the null hypothesis has been rejected, the research hypothesis (sociology majors are more sophisticated) is supported.

Now that we have completed a one-tailed example, let us consider the implications of one-tailed and two-tailed decisions for the risk of a Type I error (i.e., rejecting a true null hypothesis) and a Type II error (i.e., retaining a false null hypothesis). Which decision about the placement of alpha—one-tailed or two-tailed—do you think most reduces the risk of a Type I error, the type of error that scientists usually prefer to minimize?

If you said "two-tailed," you are correct! Two-tailed tests are sometimes regarded as more conservative because the division of alpha equally between the two tails increases the magnitude of the critical statistic. This means that you will need a test statistic with an even larger magnitude than you would have needed if you had placed all the alpha in one tail only.

Compare, for the sake of illustration, the following alpha levels and values for *Z* (critical) for two-tailed tests. As you may recall, this information was also presented in Table 6.1.

| If Alpha Equals | The Two-Tailed Critical Region Will Begin at *Z* (Critical) Equal to |
|---|---|
| 0.10 | ±1.65 |
| 0.05 | ±1.96 |
| 0.01 | ±2.58 |
| 0.001 | ±3.29 |

For instance, with an obtained $Z$ score of $+2.57$ for the previous "sophistication" example, we rejected the null hypothesis that there is no difference between sociology majors and the general student body (or that sociology majors are less sophisticated than the general student body) in a one-tailed test at the 0.05 alpha level, where the critical region begins at $+1.65$.

Clearly, the obtained $Z$ score of $+2.57$ is quite a bit larger than the critical $Z$ score of $+1.65$. If we had conducted a two-tailed test instead, also with alpha $= 0.05$, the critical $Z$ score would have been $\pm1.96$. We still would have been able to reject the null hypothesis, since $+2.57$ is larger than $+1.96$; however, the difference between the critical and obtained values $Z$ is smaller. Suppose we had had an obtained $Z$ score of $+1.75$ instead. In this case, we would only have been able to reject the null hypothesis in the one-tailed case, since $+1.75$ is larger than $+1.65$, but we would not have been able to reject it if the test had been two-tailed, since $+1.75$ is not larger than $+1.96$. The choice of one-tailed or two-tailed thus can make a difference in our decision to reject the null hypothesis, and it can likewise also affect our risk of making a Type I error. *(For practice in dealing with tests of significance for means that may call for one-tailed tests, see Problems 10.2b, 10.3, 10.6, 10.8, and 10.17.)*

## 10.4 THE STUDENT'S *t* DISTRIBUTION AND THE ONE-SAMPLE CASE

To this point, we have only considered hypothesis tests involving single-sample means where the value of the population standard deviation ($\sigma$) was known. Needless to say, the value of $\sigma$ will not be known in most research situations.

When $\sigma$ is unknown (and the sample size is large with 100 or more cases or the population from which the sample is taken is normally distributed), we can use the sample standard deviation ($s$) with the Student's $t$ distribution to find areas under the sampling distribution and establish the critical region. As we saw in Chapter 6, the shape of the $t$ distribution varies as a function of sample size, or more specifically as a function of degrees of freedom ($df$). Degrees of freedom are equal to $n - 1$ in the case of a single-sample mean, just as when we constructed a confidence interval.

The $t$ distribution is summarized in Appendix B. To find a ***t* (critical)** score, we follow three steps. First, compute the degrees of freedom. Second, choice between a one- and two-tailed test. If the test is one-tailed, use the top row labelled "Level of Significance for One-Tailed Test"; if the test is two-tailed, use the bottom row labelled "Level of Significance for Two-Tailed Test". Third, select the desired alpha level. The entries in the table are the $t$ scores, and mark the beginnings of the critical regions.

In terms of the five-step model, the changes required by using $t$ scores occur mostly in steps 3 and 4. In step 3, the sampling distribution will be the $t$ distribution, and degrees of freedom must be computed before locating the critical region. In step 4, a slightly different formula for computing the test statistic, **$t$ (obtained)**, will be used. Compared with the formula for $Z$ (obtained), $s$ will replace $\sigma$ and $n - 1$ will replace $n$. (Recall from Chapter 6 that $n - 1$, rather than $n$, is used to correct for the bias in estimating $\sigma$ with $s$) Specifically,

**FORMULA 10.2**

$$t\,(\text{obtained}) = \frac{\bar{X} - \mu}{s/\sqrt{n-1}}$$

To demonstrate the use of the $t$ test, let's work through the following problem. A researcher wonders if sociology students are different from the general student body in terms of academic achievement. She has gathered a random sample of 30 sociology students and has learned from the registrar that the distribution of grade point averages of all students is normally distributed with a mean of 2.50 ($\mu = 2.50$), but the standard deviation of the population ($\sigma$) has never been computed. Sample data are reported below. Is the sample from a population that has a mean of 2.50?

| Student Body | Sociology Students |
|---|---|
| $\mu = 2.50\,(=\mu_{\bar{X}})$ | $\bar{X} = 2.78$ |
| $\sigma = ?$ | $s = 1.23$ |
| | $n = 30$ |

**Step 1. Make Assumptions and Meet Test Requirements. With a sample size less than 100, we must assume that the population is normally distributed.**

Model: Random sampling
Level of measurement is interval-ratio
Sampling distribution is normal

**Step 2. State the Null Hypothesis.**

$$H_0\text{: } \mu = 2.50$$
$$(H_1\text{: } \mu \neq 2.50)$$

**ONE STEP AT A TIME Completing Step 4 of the Five-Step Model: Compute $t$ (Obtained)**

Follow these procedures when using the Student's $t$ distribution when the population standard deviation is unknown *and* sample size is large or the population normally distributed.

**To Compute the Test Statistic Using Formula 10.2**

**1:** Find the square root of $n - 1$.

**2:** Divide the quantity you found in step 1 into the sample standard deviation ($s$).
**3:** Subtract the population mean ($\mu$) from the sample mean ($\bar{X}$).
**4:** Divide the quantity you found in step 3 by the quantity you found in step 2. This value is $t$ (obtained).

You can see from the research hypothesis that the researcher has not predicted a direction for the difference. This will be a two-tailed test.

**Step 3. Select the Sampling Distribution and Establish the Critical Region.** Because $\sigma$ is unknown, the $t$ distribution (see Appendix A) will be used to find the critical region. Alpha will be set at 0.01.

$$\text{Sampling distribution} = t \text{ distribution}$$
$$\alpha = 0.01, \text{ two-tailed test}$$
$$df = (n - 1) = 29$$
$$t \text{ (critical)} = \pm 2.756$$

**Step 4. Compute the Test Statistic.**

$$t \text{ (obtained)} = \frac{\overline{X} - \mu}{s/\sqrt{n - 1}}$$

$$t \text{ (obtained)} = \frac{2.78 - 2.50}{1.23/\sqrt{29}}$$

$$t \text{ (obtained)} = \frac{0.28}{0.23}$$

$$t \text{ (obtained)} = +1.22$$

**Step 5. Make a Decision and Interpret the Results of the Test.** The test statistic does not fall into the critical region. Therefore, the researcher fails to reject the $H_0$. The difference between the sample mean (2.78) and the population mean (2.50) is no greater than what would be expected if only random chance were operating. The test statistic and critical regions are displayed in Figure 10.7.

FIGURE 10.7   **Sampling Distribution Showing $t$ (Obtained) Versus $t$ (Critical) for the Two-Tailed Test, with Rejection Region for Alpha = 0.01 ($df$ = 29) in Shade**

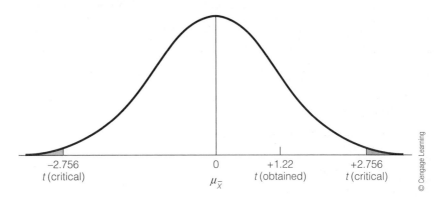

## Applying Statistics 10.1: Testing a Sample Mean for Significance

Despite many characteristics favourable to labour market success, such as better than average education and health, studies show that recent immigrants to Canada (those who have been in Canada for less than 10 years) face many obstacles and challenges in the labour market. We know that, based on the 2011 National Household Survey, the mean after-tax income of the Canadian population of full-time workers (30 hours or more per week) was \$45,447. A random sample of 443 recent immigrants employed full-time, from the Survey of Labour and Income Dynamics (a Statistics Canada–administered survey on labour market activity and income), reveals an average after-tax income of \$40,265 with a standard deviation of \$36,015 in 2011. Are these earnings of recent immigrants significantly different from the population of full-time workers as a whole? We will use the five-step model to organize the decision-making process.

**Step 1. Make Assumptions and Meet Test Requirements.**

Model:  Random sampling
Level of measurement is interval-ratio
Sampling distribution is normal

From the information given (this is a large sample with $n > 100$, and income is an interval-ratio variable), we can conclude that the model assumptions and test requirements are satisfied.

**Step 2. State the Null Hypothesis.** The null hypothesis says that the average income of *all* recent immigrants to Canada is equal to the national average. In symbols:

$$H_0: \mu = 45,447$$

The question does not specify a direction; it only asks whether the incomes of recent immigrants are "different from" (not higher or lower than) the national average. This suggests a two-tailed test:

$$H_1: \mu \neq 45,447$$

**Step 3. Select the Sampling Distribution and Establish the Critical Region.**

Sampling distribution = $t$ distribution
$$df = (n - 1) = 442$$
$$\alpha = 0.05, \text{ two-tailed test}$$
$$t(\text{critical}) = \pm 1.98$$

**Step 4. Compute the Test Statistic.** The necessary information for conducting a test of the null hypothesis is

| Recent Immigrants | Nation |
|---|---|
| $\overline{X} = 40,265$ | $\mu = 45,447$ |
| $s = 36,015$ | |
| $n = 443$ | |

The test statistic, $t$ (obtained), would be

$$t(\text{obtained}) = \frac{\overline{X} - \mu}{s/\sqrt{n - 1}}$$

$$t(\text{obtained}) = \frac{40,265 - 45,447}{36,015/\sqrt{443 - 1}}$$

$$t(\text{obtained}) = \frac{-5,182}{36,015/\sqrt{442}}$$

$$t(\text{obtained}) = \frac{-5,182}{1,713.37}$$

$$t(\text{obtained}) = -3.02$$

**Step 5. Make a Decision and Interpret the Results of the Test.** With alpha set at 0.05 (two-tailed test), the critical region would begin at $t$ (critical) $= \pm 1.98$. With an obtained $t$ score of $-3.02$, the null hypothesis would be rejected. This means that the difference between the after-tax incomes of recent immigrants to Canada and the after-tax incomes of Canadians as a whole is statistically significant. The difference is so large that we may conclude that it did not occur by random chance. The decision to reject the null hypothesis has a 0.05 probability of being wrong.

Source: Statistics Canada, *2011 National Household Survey* and *2011 Survey of Labour and Income Dynamics*.

---

**ONE STEP AT A TIME**  **Completing Step 5 of the Five-Step Model: Make a Decision and Interpret Results of the Test**

---

**1:** Compare the $t$ (obtained) to the $t$ (critical). If $t$ (obtained) is *in* the critical region, *reject* the null hypothesis. If $t$ (obtained) is *not in* the critical region, *fail to reject* the null hypothesis.

**2:** Interpret your decision in terms of the original question. For example, our conclusion for the example problem used in this section was "There is no significant difference between the grade point average of sociology students and the general student body."

---

**TABLE 10.3**  **Choosing a Sampling Distribution When Testing Single-Sample Means for Significance**

| If Population Standard Deviation ($\sigma$) Is | Sampling Distribution |
| --- | --- |
| known **and** $n \geq 100$ or population normally distributed | $Z$ distribution |
| unknown **and** $n \geq 100$ or population normally distributed | $t$ distribution |

To summarize, when testing single-sample means we must make a choice regarding the theoretical distribution we will use to establish the critical region. The choice is straightforward. If the population standard deviation ($\sigma$) is known *and* sample size is large ($n = 100$ or more cases) or the population from which the sample is taken is normally distributed, the $Z$ distribution (Appendix A) is used. If $\sigma$ is unknown, the $t$ distribution (Appendix B) is used. These decisions are summarized in Table 10.3. *(For practice in using the* t *distribution in a test of hypothesis, see Problems 10.3, 10.5, 10.7 to 10.10, 10.1 e to f, and 10.17.)*

**10.5 TESTS OF HYPOTHESES FOR SINGLE-SAMPLE PROPORTIONS (LARGE SAMPLES)**

In many cases, the sample variables we are interested in will not be measured in a way that justifies the assumption of interval-ratio level of measurement. One alternative in this situation would be to use a sample proportion ($P_s$) rather than a sample mean as the test statistic. As we shall see, the overall procedures for testing single-sample proportions are the same as those for testing means. The central question is still "Does the population from which the sample was drawn have a certain characteristic?" We still conduct the test based on the assumption that the null hypothesis is true, and we still evaluate the probability of the obtained sample outcome against a sampling distribution of all possible sample outcomes.

Our decision at the end of the test is also the same. If the obtained test statistic falls into the critical region (i.e., is unlikely, given the assumption that the $H_0$ is true), we reject the $H_0$.

Having stressed the continuity in procedures and logic, we must hastily point out the important differences as well. These differences are best related in terms of the five-step model for hypothesis testing. In step 1, when working with sample proportions, we assume that the variable is measured at the nominal or ordinal level of measurement. In step 2, the symbols used to state the null hypothesis are different even though the null hypothesis is still a statement of "no difference," "greater than or equal to," or "less than or equal to."

In step 3, we will use only the standardized normal curve (the $Z$ distribution) to find areas under the sampling distribution and locate the critical region. This will be appropriate as long as sample size is large ($n \geq 100$). We will not consider small-sample tests of hypothesis for proportions in this textbook.

In step 4, computing the test statistic, the form of the formula remains the same. That is, the test statistic, $Z$ (obtained), equals the sample statistic minus the mean of the sampling distribution, divided by the standard deviation of the sampling distribution. However, the symbols will change because we are basing the tests on sample proportions. The formula can be stated as

**FORMULA 10.3**

$$Z \text{ (obtained)} = \frac{P_s - P_u}{\sqrt{P_u(1 - P_u)/n}}$$

Step 5 is exactly the same as before. If the test statistic, $Z$ (obtained), falls into the critical region, as marked by $Z$ (critical), reject the $H_0$; if $Z$ (obtained) does not fall into the critical region, then fail to reject the $H_0$.

An example should clarify these procedures. A random sample of 122 households in a low-income neighbourhood revealed that 53 (or a proportion of 0.43) of the households were headed by females. In the city as a whole, the proportion of female-headed households is 0.39. Are households in the low-income neighbourhood significantly different from the city as a whole in terms of this characteristic? For this example, let us use the 90% level of confidence.

**Step 1. Make Assumptions and Meet Test Requirements.**

> Model: Random sampling
> Level of measurement is nominal or ordinal
> Sampling distribution is normal in shape

**Step 2. State the Null Hypothesis.** The research question, as stated above, asks only if the sample proportion is different from the population proportion. Because no direction is predicted for the difference, a two-tailed test will be used.

$$H_0: P_u = 0.39$$

$$(H_1: P_u \neq 0.39)$$

**Step 3.** Select the Sampling Distribution and Establish the Critical Region.

$$\text{Sampling distribution} = Z \text{ distribution}$$
$$\alpha = 0.10, \text{ two-tailed test}$$
$$Z \text{ (critical)} = \pm 1.65$$

---

## Applying Statistics 10.2: Testing a Sample Proportion for Significance

It was pointed out in Applying Statistics 10.1 that immigrants arriving in Canada in recent years tend to be well educated. In a random sample from Statistics Canada's Survey of Labour and Income Dynamics, 54% of 641 recent immigrants (those who have been in Canada for less than 10 years) aged 25+ had a university degree in 2011. National Household Survey figures from that same year show that 23% of the Canadian population age 25 or older had a university degree. Are recent immigrants significantly more likely to have a university education than the population as a whole?

**Step 1. Make Assumptions and Meet Test Requirements.**

Model:  Random sampling
Level of measurement is nominal or ordinal
Sampling distribution is normal

This is a large sample, so we may assume a normal sampling distribution. The variable, percent with a university degree, is nominal in level of measurement.

**Step 2. State the Null Hypothesis.** The null hypothesis says that recent immigrants are not different from the nation as a whole.

$$H_0 : P_u \le 0.23$$

The original question ("Are recent immigrants *more* likely to have a university education") suggests a one-tailed research hypothesis:

$$(H_1 : P_u > 0.23)$$

The research hypothesis says that we will be concerned only with outcomes in which recent immigrants are more likely to hold a degree or with sample outcomes in the upper tail of the sampling distribution.

**Step 3. Select the Sampling Distribution and Establish the Critical Region.**

$$\text{Sampling distribution} = Z \text{ distribution}$$
$$\alpha = 0.05$$
$$Z \text{ (critical)} = +1.65$$

**Step 4. Compute the Test Statistic.** The information necessary for a test of the null hypothesis, expressed in the form of proportions, is

| Recent Immigrants | Nation |
|---|---|
| $P_s = 0.54$ | $P_u = 0.23$ |
| $n = 641$ | |

The test statistic, $Z$ (obtained), would be

$$Z \text{ (obtained)} = \frac{P_s - P_u}{\sqrt{P_u(1 - P_u)/n}}$$

$$Z \text{ (obtained)} = \frac{0.54 - 0.23}{\sqrt{(0.23)(1 - 0.23)/641}}$$

$$Z \text{ (obtained)} = \frac{0.31}{\sqrt{(0.18)/641}}$$

$$Z \text{ (obtained)} = \frac{0.31}{0.017}$$

$$Z \text{ (obtained)} = +18.23$$

**Step 5. Make a Decision and Interpret the Results of the Test.** With alpha set at 0.05, one-tailed, the critical region would begin at $Z$ (critical) $= +1.65$. With an obtained $Z$ score of $+18.23$, the null hypothesis is rejected. The difference between recent immigrants and Canadians as a whole is statistically significant and in the predicted direction. Recent immigrants to Canada are significantly more likely to have a university degree.

Source: Statistics Canada, *2011 National Household Survey* and *2011 Survey of Labour and Income Dynamics*.

**FIGURE 10.8** Sampling Distribution Showing *Z* (Obtained) Versus *Z* (Critical) for the Two-Tailed Test, with Critical Region for Alpha = 0.10 in Shade

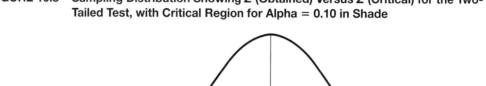

| −1.65 | 0 | +0.91 | +1.65 |
|:---:|:---:|:---:|:---:|
| *Z* (critical) | | *Z* (obtained) | *Z* (critical) |

© Cengage Learning

**Step 4. Compute the Test Statistic.**

$$Z \text{ (obtained)} = \frac{P_s - P_u}{\sqrt{P_u(1 - P_u)/n}}$$

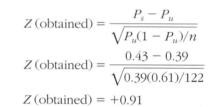

$$Z \text{ (obtained)} = \frac{0.43 - 0.39}{\sqrt{0.39(0.61)/122}}$$

$$Z \text{ (obtained)} = +0.91$$

**Step 5. Make a Decision and Interpret the Results of the Test.** The test statistic, *Z* (obtained), does not fall into the critical region. Therefore, we fail to reject the $H_0$. There is no statistically significant difference between the low-income community and the city as a whole in terms of the proportion of households headed by females. Figure 10.8 displays the sampling distribution, the critical region, and the *Z* (obtained). *(For practice in tests of significance using sample proportions, see Problems 10.11 to 10.14, 10.15 a to d, and 10.16.)*

---

**ONE STEP AT A TIME   Completing Step 4 of the Five-Step Model: Compute**
***Z* (Obtained)**

**To Compute the Test Statistic Using Formula 10.3**

**1:** Start with the denominator of Formula 10.3 and substitute in the value for $P_u$. This value will be given in the statement of the problem.
**2:** Subtract the value of $P_u$ from 1.
**3:** Multiply the value you found in step 2 by the value of $P_u$.

**4:** Divide the quantity you found in step 3 by *n*.
**5:** Take the square root of the value you found in step 4.
**6:** Subtract $P_u$ from $P_s$.
**7:** Divide the quantity you found in step 6 by the quantity you found in step 5. This value is *Z* (obtained).

---

---

**ONE STEP AT A TIME** Completing Step 5 of the Five-Step Model: Make a Decision and Interpret Results of the Test

---

**1:** Compare your Z (obtained) to your Z (critical). If Z (obtained) is *in* the critical region, *reject* the null hypothesis. If Z (obtained) is *not in* the critical region, *fail to reject* the null hypothesis.
**2:** Interpret the decision in terms of the original question. For example, our conclusion for the

example problem used in this section was "There is no significant difference between the low-income community and the city as a whole in the proportion of households that are headed by females."

---

**10.6 HYPOTHESIS TESTING USING CONFIDENCE INTERVALS**

Hypothesis testing and interval estimation (see Chapter 6) are the two main applications of inferential statistics. While the objective of each technique is different—*testing* a claim about a population parameter versus *estimating* a population parameter respectively—they are in reality just different ways of expressing the same information. This is especially easy to see when we compare the process of forming confidence intervals to estimate population means or proportions, with the process of hypothesis testing with means or proportions.

Specifically, if an interval estimate (i.e., confidence interval) does not contain the value of the parameter specified by the null hypothesis, then a hypothesis test will reject the null hypothesis, and vice versa. That is, if the value of $H_0$ *is* contained within the confidence interval at a given alpha level, then $H_0$ *is not* rejected at that level. On the other hand, if the value of $H_0$ *is not* contained within the confidence interval at a given alpha level, then $H_0$ *is* rejected at that level. So, if a 99% confidence interval does not contain the value of the parameter given by the null hypothesis, then the null hypothesis is rejected at the 0.01 level; if a 95% confidence interval does not contain it, then the null hypothesis is rejected at the 0.05 level; and so on. The ability to use confidence intervals to test hypotheses applies to all situations, including means and proportions, as well as to the one-sample case covered in this chapter and the two-sample case to be discussed in Chapter 11.

To see how the confidence interval for the sample mean corresponds to the hypothesis test for the sample mean, let us take another look at the LSAT example in Section 10.2. Recall that the null hypothesis stated that the population of graduates of an LSAT preparation course is just like everyone else and has a mean LSAT score of 153; that is, there is no difference in LSAT scoring between the graduates and LSAT writers as a whole, or

$$H_0: \mu = 153$$
$$(H_1: \mu \neq 153)$$

For a two-tailed test (the research hypothesis does not predict a direction for the difference) with alpha set at 0.05, the critical region begins at $Z$ (critical) $\pm1.96$, or

$$\text{Sampling distribution} = Z\text{distribution}$$
$$\alpha = 0.05, \text{two-tailed test}$$
$$Z(\text{critical}) = \pm1.96$$

We obtained a $Z$ score of $+3.33$, or

$$Z = \frac{\overline{X} - \mu}{\sigma/\sqrt{n}}$$

$$Z = \frac{156 - 153}{9/\sqrt{100}}$$

$$Z = +3.33$$

Then, we reject the null hypothesis, $H_0$, because the test statistic, $Z$ (obtained), falls into the critical region, as marked by $Z$ (critical).

Next, let us construct a 95% confidence interval for the sample mean using Formula 6.1 (see Chapter 6):

$$\text{c.i.} = \overline{X} \pm Z\left(\frac{\sigma}{\sqrt{n}}\right)$$

$$\text{c.i.} = 156 \pm 1.96\left(\frac{9}{\sqrt{100}}\right)$$

$$\text{c.i.} = 156 \pm (1.96)(0.90)$$

$$\text{c.i.} = 156 \pm 1.76$$

Based on this result, we estimate that the population mean is greater than or equal to 154.24 and less than or equal to 157.76 at the 95% level of confidence.

The relationship between the confidence interval and hypothesis test can now be seen. Because this interval does not include the value of the parameter specified by the null hypothesis, 153, we would reject the null hypothesis. The difference between graduates of an LSAT training course and the entire population of LSAT writers is statistically significant at the 0.05 level. This is precisely the decision we made above using the formal hypothesis-testing approach. In sum, it will always be true that if the confidence interval contains the value of the parameter specified by the null hypothesis, then the null hypothesis cannot be rejected at the stated alpha level. If it does not, then the null hypothesis can be rejected.

## SUMMARY

1. This chapter extended the examination of hypothesis testing that we began in Chapter 7. We saw how to test the null hypothesis of "no difference" for single sample means and proportions. In both cases, the central question is whether the population represented by the sample has a certain characteristic.

2. If we can predict a direction for the difference in stating the research hypothesis, a one-tailed test is called for. If no direction can be predicted, a two-tailed test is appropriate.

3. The choice of a one-tailed test or a two-tailed test can have an impact on the risk of making a Type I error. In general, a two-tailed test is more conservative, and can lessen the risk of making a Type I error.

4. When testing sample means, the $Z$ distribution is used to find the critical region when the population standard deviation is known and the $t$ distribution when it is unknown.

5. Sample proportions can also be tested for significance. Tests are conducted using the five-step model. Compared to the test for the sample mean, the major differences lie in the level-of-measurement assumption (step 1), the statement of the null hypothesis (step 2), and the computation of the test statistic (step 4).

6. Hypothesis testing and interval estimation (see Chapter 6) are just different ways of expressing the same information. If the confidence interval contains the value of the parameter specified by the null hypothesis in a one-sample test, then the null hypothesis is not rejected at the stated alpha level. Alternatively, the null hypothesis is rejected if the confidence interval does *not* contain the value.

## SUMMARY OF FORMULAS

Single-sample means, large samples (or normally distributed population) and population standard deviation is known:

10.1
$$Z(\text{obtained}) = \frac{\overline{X} - \mu}{\sigma/\sqrt{n}}$$

Single-sample means, large samples (or normally distributed population), and population standard deviation unknown:

10.2
$$t\,(\text{obtained}) = \frac{\overline{X} - \mu}{s/\sqrt{n - 1}}$$

Single-sample proportions, large samples:

10.3
$$Z(\text{obtained}) = \frac{P_s - P_u}{\sqrt{P_u(1 - P_u)/n}}$$

## GLOSSARY

**One-tailed test.** A type of hypothesis test used when (1) the direction of the difference can be predicted or (2) concern focuses on outcomes in only one tail of the sampling distribution.

**$t$ (critical).** The $t$ score that marks the beginning of the critical region of a $t$ distribution.

**$t$ (obtained).** The test statistic computed in step 4 of the five-step model. The sample outcome expressed as a $t$ score.

**Two-tailed test.** A type of hypothesis test used when (1) the direction of the difference cannot be predicted or (2) concern focuses on outcomes in both tails of the sampling distribution.

**$Z$ (critical).** The $Z$ score that marks the beginning of the critical region on a $Z$ distribution.

**$Z$ (obtained).** The test statistic computed in step 4 of the five-step model. The sample outcome expressed as a $Z$ score.

## MULTIMEDIA RESOURCES

 nelson.com/student

Visit the companion website for the fourth Canadian edition of *Statistics: A Tool for Social Research* to access a wide range of student resources. Begin by clicking on the Student Resources section of the textbook's website to access online chapters and study tools.

## PROBLEMS

**10.1 a.** For each situation, find $Z$ (critical).

| Alpha | Form | $Z$ (Critical) |
|-------|------|----------------|
| 0.05 | One-tailed | |
| 0.10 | Two-tailed | |
| 0.06 | Two-tailed | |
| 0.01 | One-tailed | |
| 0.02 | Two-tailed | |

**b.** For each situation, find the critical $t$ score.

| Alpha | Form | $n$ | $t$ (Critical) |
|-------|------|-----|----------------|
| 0.10 | Two-tailed | 31 | |
| 0.02 | Two-tailed | 24 | |
| 0.01 | Two-tailed | 121 | |
| 0.01 | One-tailed | 31 | |
| 0.05 | One-tailed | 61 | |

**c.** Compute the appropriate test statistic ($Z$ or $t$) for each situation:

**1.** $\mu = 2.40$    $\bar{X} = 2.20$
     $\sigma = 0.75$    $n = 200$
**2.** $\mu = 17.1$    $\bar{X} = 16.8$
           $s = 0.9$
           $n = 45$

**3.** $\mu = 10.2$    $\bar{X} = 9.4$
                $s = 1.7$
                $n = 150$
**4.** $P_\mu = 0.57$    $P_s = 0.60$
                $n = 117$
**5.** $P_\mu = 0.32$    $P_s = 0.30$
                $n = 322$

**10.2** SOC **a.** The student body at Algebra University attends an average of 3.3 parties per month, with a standard deviation of 0.53. A random sample of 117 sociology majors averages 3.8 parties per month. Are sociology majors significantly different from the student body as a whole? *(HINT: The wording of the research question suggests a two-tailed test. This means that the alternative or research hypothesis in step 2 will be stated as* $H_1$: $\mu \neq 3.3$ *and that the critical region will be split between the upper and lower tails of the sampling distribution. See Table 10.2 for value of* Z *(critical) for various alpha levels.)*

**b.** What if the research question were changed to "Do sociology majors attend a significantly *greater* number of parties"? How would the test conducted in 10.2a change? *(HINT: This wording implies a one-tailed test of significance. How would the research hypothesis change? For the alpha you used in Problem 10.2a, what would the value of Z (critical) be?)*

**10.3** SW **a.** Nationally, social workers average 10.2 years of experience. In a random sample, 203 social workers in the greater metropolitan area of Pearson, Ontario, average only 8.7 years with a standard deviation of 0.52. Are social workers in Pearson, Ontario, significantly less experienced? *(HINT: Note the wording of the research hypothesis. This situation may justify a one-tailed test of significance. If you chose a one-tailed test, what form would the research hypothesis take, and where would the critical region begin?)*

**b.** The same sample of social workers reports an average annual salary of $35,782 with a standard deviation of $622. Is this figure significantly higher than the national average of $34,509? *(HINT: The wording of the research hypothesis suggests a one-tailed test. What form would the research hypothesis take, and where would the critical region begin?)*

**10.4** SOC Nationally, the average score on the GRE (Graduate Record Examinations) verbal test is 453 with a standard deviation of 95. A random sample of 152 first-year graduate students entering Algebra University shows a mean score of 502. Is there a significant difference?

**10.5** SOC A random sample of 423 Albertans has finished an average of 12.7 years of formal education with a standard deviation of 1.7. Is this significantly different from the national average of 12.2 years?

**10.6** SOC A sample of 105 workers in the Roadster Division of the Toy Car Factory earns an average of $24,375 per year. The average salary for all workers is $24,230 with a standard deviation of $523. Are workers in the Roadster Division overpaid? Conduct both one- and two-tailed tests.

**10.7** SOC **a.** Nationally, the population as a whole watches an average of 6.2 hours of TV per day. A random sample of 1,017 senior citizens reports watching an average of 5.9 hours per day with a standard deviation of 0.7. Is the difference significant?

**b.** The same sample of senior citizens reports that they belong to an average of 2.1 voluntary organizations and clubs with a standard deviation of 0.5. Nationally, the average is 1.7. Is the difference significant?

**10.8** SOC A school system has assigned several hundred "chronic and severe underachievers" to an alternative educational experience. To assess the program, a random sample of 35 has been selected for comparison with all students in the system. *(Note: For each variable below, the distribution of all students is normally distributed.)*

**a.** In terms of GPA, did the program work?

| Systemwide GPA | Program GPA |
|---|---|
| $\mu = 2.47$ | $\overline{X} = 2.55$ |
| | $s = 0.70$ |
| | $n = 35$ |

**b.** In terms of absenteeism (number of days missed per year), what can be said about the success of the program?

| Systemwide | Program |
|---|---|
| $\mu = 6.13$ | $\overline{X} = 4.78$ |
| | $s = 1.11$ |
| | $n = 35$ |

**c.** In terms of standardized test scores in math and reading, was the program a success?

| Math Test Systemwide | Math Test Program |
|---|---|
| $\mu = 103$ | $\overline{X} = 106$ |
| | $s = 2.0$ |
| | $n = 35$ |

| Reading Test Systemwide | Reading Test Program |
|---|---|
| $\mu = 110$ | $\bar{X} = 113$ |
| | $s = 2.0$ |
| | $n = 35$ |

*(HINT: Note the wording of the research questions. Is a one-tailed test justified? Is the program a success if the students in the program are no different from students systemwide? What if the program students were performing at lower levels? If a one-tailed test is used, what form should the research hypothesis take? Where will the critical region begin?)*

**10.9** SOC A random sample of 26 sociology graduates in BC scored an average of 458 on the GRE Advanced Sociology test with a standard deviation of 20. Is this significantly different from the national average ($\mu = 440$)? (*Note: The distribution of all scores is normal.*)

**10.10** PA Nationally, the per capita property tax is $130 per month (and normally distributed). A random sample of 36 western cities averages $98 per month with a standard deviation of $5. Is the difference significant? Summarize your conclusions in a sentence or two.

**10.11** GER/CJ A survey shows that 10% of the population is victimized by property crime each year. A random sample of 527 older citizens (65 years or more of age) shows a victimization rate of 14%. Are older people more likely to be victimized? Conduct a one-tailed test of significance.

**10.12** CJ A random sample of 113 convicted sex offenders in a provincial prison system completed a program designed to change their attitudes toward women, sex, and violence before being released on parole. Fifty-eight eventually became repeat sex offenders. Is this recidivism rate significantly different from the rate for all offenders (57%) in that province? Summarize your conclusions in a sentence or two. (*HINT: You must use the*

*information given in the problem to compute a sample proportion. Remember to convert the population percentage to a proportion.*)

**10.13** PS In a recent provincial election, 55% of the voters rejected a proposal to institute a new provincial lottery. In a random sample of 150 voters from rural communities, 49% rejected the proposal. Is the difference significant? Summarize your conclusions in a sentence or two.

**10.14** CJ Provincially, the police clear by arrest 35% of the robberies and 42% of the aggravated assaults reported to them. A researcher takes a random sample of all the robberies ($n = 207$) and aggravated assaults ($n = 178$) reported to a metropolitan police department in one year and finds that 83 of the robberies and 80 of the assaults were cleared by arrest. Are the local arrest rates significantly different from the provincial rate? Write a sentence or two interpreting your decision.

**10.15** SOC/SW A researcher has compiled a file of information on a random sample of 317 families in a city that has chronic, long-term patterns of child abuse. Below are reported some of the characteristics of the sample along with values for the city as a whole. For each trait, test the null hypothesis of "no difference" and summarize your findings.

**a.** Mothers' educational level (proportion completing high school):

| City | Sample |
|---|---|
| $P_u = 0.63$ | $P_s = 0.61$ |

**b.** Family size (proportion of families with four or more children):

| City | Sample |
|---|---|
| $P_u = 0.21$ | $P_s = 0.26$ |

**c.** Mothers' work status (proportion of mothers with jobs outside the home):

| City | Sample |
|---|---|
| $P_u = 0.51$ | $P_s = 0.27$ |

**d.** Relations with relatives (proportion of families that have contact with relatives at least once a week):

| City | Sample |
|---|---|
| $P_u = 0.82$ | $P_s = 0.43$ |

**e.** Fathers' educational achievement (average years of formal schooling):

| City | Sample |
|---|---|
| $\mu = 12.3$ | $\overline{X} = 12.5$ |
| | $s = 1.7$ |

**f.** Fathers' occupational stability (average years in present job):

| City | Sample |
|---|---|
| $\mu = 5.2$ | $\overline{X} = 3.7$ |
| | $s = 0.5$ |

**10.16** SW You are the head of an agency seeking funding for a program to reduce unemployment among teenage males. Nationally, the unemployment rate for this group is 18%. A random sample of 323 teenage males in your area reveals an unemployment rate of 21.7%. Is the difference significant? Can you demonstrate a need for the program? Should you use a one-tailed test in this situation? Why or why not? Explain the result of your test of significance as you would to a funding agency.

**10.17** PA The city manager of Pearson, Ontario, has received a complaint from the local union of firefighters that they are underpaid. Not having much time, the city manager gathers the records of a random sample of 27 firefighters and finds that their average salary is $38,073 with a standard deviation of $575. If she knows that salaries (at the national level) are normally distributed with a mean of $38,202, how can she respond to the complaint? Should she use a one-tailed test in this situation? Why or why not? What would she say in a memo to the union to respond to the complaint?

**10.18** The following essay questions review the basic principles and concepts of inferential statistics. The order of the questions roughly follows the five-step model.

**a.** Hypothesis testing or significance testing can be conducted only with a random sample. Why?

**b.** Under what specific conditions can it be assumed that the sampling distribution is normal in shape?

**c.** Explain the role of the sampling distribution in a test of hypothesis.

**d.** The null hypothesis is an assumption about reality that makes it possible to test sample outcomes for their significance. Explain.

**e.** What is the critical region? How is the size of the critical region determined?

**f.** Describe a research situation in which a one-tailed test of hypothesis would be appropriate.

**g.** Thinking about the shape of the sampling distribution, why does use of the $t$ distribution (as opposed to the $Z$ distribution) make it more difficult to reject the null hypothesis?

**h.** What exactly can be concluded in the one-sample case when the test statistic falls into the critical region?

**You Are the Researcher**

## Using SPSS to Conduct a One-Sample Test with the 2012 CCHS

The demonstration and exercise below use the shortened version of the 2012 CCHS data. Start SPSS for Windows and open the *CCHS_2012_Shortened.sav* file.

### SPSS DEMONSTRATION 10.1 Using the Select Cases Command to Conduct a One-Sample Test

In this demonstration, we'll conduct a one-sample test to compare the number of hours worked per week of a sample of persons with poor health, which we will define as those with fair or poor self-perceived health, to the typical number of hours worked of all Canadians, which we will assume is 40 hours per week. We predict that individuals in poor health will work fewer hours than the general population. If we find that the average number of hours worked for the sample of persons in poor health is significantly less than that of the general population, we can conclude that individuals in poor health in Canada tend to work fewer hours per week than the population as a whole.

First, we need to use the **Select Cases** command to select those with fair or poor health for the analysis. Click **Data** from the menu bar of the **Data Editor** window, then click **Select Cases**. The **Select Cases** window appears and presents a number of different options. Click the button next to "If condition is satisfied," then click on the **If** button. The **Select Cases: If** dialog box will open, where you specify the cases to be included in the analysis. Find and highlight *gendhdi* (perceived health) from the variable list on the left side of the dialog box, then click the arrow to move *gendhdi* into the text box. In this text box, type $<= 1$ immediately to the right of the variable name *gendhdi*. This statement instructs SPSS to select any case with a value less than *or* equal to 1 (i.e., any case with a value of 0 *or* 1). A value 0 on *gendhdi* indicates a person with poor health and a value 1 a person with fair health. The expression **gendhdi** $<= 1$ should appear in the text box. Click **Continue**, then **OK**.

The **Select Cases** command confines all subsequent analysis to this subset of cases, individuals with fair or poor health. This is easily verified, as the status bar at the bottom of the SPSS window displays the message "Filter On." It is important to note that the unselected cases in the data file, while not included in the analysis, do remain in the data set.

Because the population standard deviation is unknown, we will use the One-Sample T Test procedure to test whether the mean number of hours worked per week for persons with poor health differs from that of all Canadians. From the main menu bar, click **Analyze**, **Compare Means**, then **One-Sample T Test**. The **One-Sample T Test** dialog box will open with the usual list of variables on the left. Find and move the cursor over *lbsghpw* (total hours worked) and click the top arrow in the middle of the window to move *lbsghpw* to the **Test Variable(s)** box. Next, click the **Test Value** box and type 40. Click **OK** and the following output will be produced. (Note, do not forget to turn filtering off after finishing the **One-Sample T Test** procedure. To do this, return to the **Select Cases** dialog box, select the "**All cases**" button, then click **OK**.)

**One-Sample Statistics**

|  | $N$ | Mean | Std. Deviation | Std. Error Mean |
|---|---|---|---|---|
| Total usual hrs. worked current | 100 | 34.82 | 20.573 | 2.059 |

**One-Sample Test**

| | Test Value = 40 | | | | | |
|---|---|---|---|---|---|---|
| | | | | | 95% Confidence Interval of the Difference | |
| | $t$ | $df$ | Sig. (2-tailed) | Mean Difference | Lower | Upper |
| Total usual hrs. worked current | −2.516 | 99 | 0.013 | −5.182 | −9.27 | −1.10 |

In the first block of output ("One-Sample Statistics") are some descriptive statistics. There are 100 persons with poor health with a mean number of hours worked per week of 34.82, which is different from the mean number of hours worked of 40 for the general population. Is the difference in means significant? The results of the test for significance are reported in the next block ("One-Sample Test") of output.

In the second output block, "One-Sample Test," we are given the values of $t$ (obtained) (−2.516) and degrees of freedom (99) needed to test whether the difference between the sample mean of 34.82 hours and the population mean of 40 hours is statistically significant. To test for significance, we look up the $t$ (critical) in the $t$ table in Appendix B, and then compare the $t$ (obtained) value to the $t$ (critical) value as practised throughout this chapter.

Because we predicted a direction for this difference (individuals in poor health work fewer hours than the general population), a one-tailed test in the upper tail of the sampling distribution is justified. With alpha equal to 0.05, our usual indicator of significance, and 99 degrees of freedom, we find the $t$ (critical) is −1.671. (The $t$ table does not include a value for 99 degrees of freedom, so we used the value for 60 degrees of freedom.)

The test statistic, $t$ (obtained), of −2.516 falls into the critical region (in other words, −2.516 is greater in magnitude—i.e., further away from the mean of the sampling distribution—than −1.671). We reject the null hypothesis. The difference is statistically significant, and the research hypothesis that individuals in poor health work fewer hours than the general population is supported.

However, we could have more conveniently used the "Sig. (2-tailed)" value (0.013) in the "One-Sample Test" output to test for significance. The value of 0.013 is the $p$ level, meaning that it is the *exact* probability of getting the observed difference between the sample mean of 34.82 hours and the population mean of 40 hours if only chance is operating. This value is a two-tailed test of significance. Because we want the value for a one-tailed test, which SPSS does not provide, we simply divide the value by two, or 0.013/2 = 0.0065. This value, 0.0065, is the significance for a one-tailed test. With the exact probability of a one-tailed test now in hand, there is no need to look up the test statistic in the *t* table. This value, 0.0065, is less than 0.05, so we reject the null hypothesis.

## Exercise (using *CCHS_2012_Shortened.sav*)

**10.1** Let's assume that the average Canadian worker works 40 hours per week. Are individuals who drink alcohol every day different from Canadians in general in terms of this characteristic (i.e., do those who drink every day work fewer or more hours per week than the national average)? Using Demonstration 10.1 as a guide, test for a significant difference between the mean number of hours worked per week (*lbsghpw*) of the sample of every-day drinkers (*alc_2* = 8) and the mean number of hours worked of 40 for the Canadian population. Write a sentence or two summarizing the results of this test. (Make sure to use the **Select Cases** procedure to include only those who drink alcohol ever day in the **One-Sample T Test** analysis, and use the two-tailed test.)

# 11

# Hypothesis Testing with Means and Proportions
## The Two-Sample Case

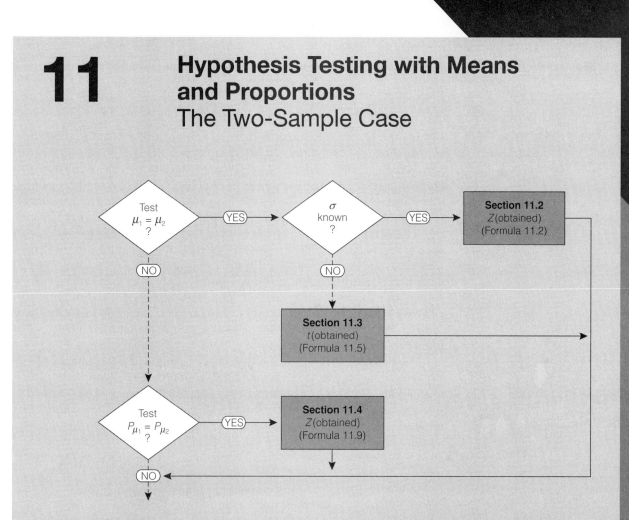

**LEARNING OBJECTIVES**

By the end of this chapter, you will be able to

1. Identify and cite examples of situations in which the two-sample test of hypothesis is appropriate.
2. Explain the logic of hypothesis testing as applied to the two-sample case.
3. Explain what an independent random sample is.
4. Perform a test of hypothesis for two-sample means or two-sample proportions following the five-step model and correctly interpret the results.
5. Conduct a two-sample hypothesis test using confidence intervals.

**11.1 INTRODUCTION**

In Chapter 10, we dealt with hypothesis testing in the one-sample case. In that situation, our concern was with the significance of the difference between a sample value and a population value. In this chapter, we will consider a research situation where we will be concerned with the significance of the difference between two separate populations. This situation is equivalent to looking at how to test a hypothesis about a relationship between two variables, where the independent variable has only two categories and is measured at the nominal or ordinal level and the dependent variable at the interval-ratio level (for means) or at the nominal or ordinal level (for proportions). For example, we may ask, "Do men and women vary in their support for gun control?" Obviously, we cannot ask every male and female for their opinion on gun control. Instead, we must draw random samples of both groups and use the information gathered from these samples to infer population patterns.

The central question asked in hypothesis testing in the two-sample case is, "Is the difference between the samples large enough to allow us to conclude (with a known probability of error) that the populations represented by the samples are different?" If we find a large enough difference in support for gun control between random samples of men and women, we can argue that the difference between the samples did not occur by simple random chance but, rather, represents a real difference between men and women in the population.

In keeping with previous chapters on hypothesis testing, the five-step model will serve as a framework for organizing our decision making. And while the general flow of the hypothesis-testing process is very similar to the one followed in the one-sample case, we will need to consider some important differences.

**11.2 HYPOTHESIS TESTING WITH SAMPLE MEANS ($\sigma$ KNOWN)**

One major difference between the one- and two-sample situations occurs in step 1 of the five-step model. The one-sample case requires a random sample. The two-sample situation requires that the samples be selected *independently* as well as randomly. This requirement is met when the selection of a case for one sample has no effect on the probability that any particular case will be included in the other sample. In our example concerning gender differences in support of gun control, this would mean that the selection of a specific male for the sample would have no effect on the probability of selecting any particular female. This new requirement will be stated as **independent random sampling** in step 1.

The requirement of independent random sampling can be satisfied by drawing random samples from separate lists (e.g., one for females and one for males). It is usually more convenient, however, to draw a single random sample from a single list of the population and then subdivide the cases into separate groups (males and females, for example). As long as the original sample is selected randomly, any subsamples created by the researcher will meet the assumption of independent random samples.

The second important difference in the five-step model for the two-sample case relates to the form of the null hypothesis. The null hypothesis is still a statement of "no difference," "greater than or equal to," or "less than or equal to." Now, however, instead of saying that the population from which the sample is drawn has a certain characteristic, it will say that the two populations are either no different, concerning their mean or proportion, or that the mean or proportion of one of the populations is greater than or equal to, or less than or equal to, the mean or proportion of the other population. (In our example, the null hypothesis states that "there is no significant difference between men and women in their support of gun control.") If the test statistic falls in the critical region, the null hypothesis of no difference (or more than or equal to, or less than or equal to) between the populations can be rejected, and the argument that the populations are different, in the way described by the research hypothesis, based on the trait of interest will be supported.

A third important new element concerns the sampling distribution: the distribution of all possible sample outcomes. In Chapter 10, the sample outcome was either a mean or a proportion. Now, we are dealing with two samples and the sample outcome is the *difference between* the sample statistics. In terms of our example, the sampling distribution would include all possible differences in sample means for support of gun control between men and women. If the null hypothesis is true and men and women do *not* have different views about gun control, the difference between the population means will be zero, the mean of the sampling distribution of the differences in sample means will be zero, and the huge majority of differences between sample means will be zero (or, at any rate, very small in value). The greater the differences between the sample means, the farther the sample outcome (the *difference* between the two sample means) will be from the mean of the sampling distribution (zero), and the more likely the difference will reflect a real difference between the two populations represented by the two samples.

In situations where the population standard deviations ($\sigma_1$ and $\sigma_2$) are known, as long as sample size is large (i.e., combined number of cases in the two samples is 100 or more) or the populations normally distributed, the sampling distribution of the differences in sample means will be normal, and the normal curve (see Appendix A) can be used to establish the critical regions. The test statistic, $Z$ (obtained), will be computed by the usual formula: sample outcome (the difference between the sample means) minus the mean of the sampling distribution of the differences in sample means, divided by the standard deviation of the sampling distribution of the differences in sample means. The formula is presented as Formula 11.1. Note that numerical subscripts are used to identify the samples and the two populations they represent. The subscript attached to $\sigma$ ($\sigma_{\bar{x}-\bar{x}}$) indicates that we are dealing with the sampling distribution of the *differences* in sample means.

**FORMULA 11.1**
$$Z \text{ (obtained)} = \frac{(\bar{X}_1 - \bar{X}_2) - (\mu_1 - \mu_2)}{\sigma_{\bar{x}-\bar{x}}}$$

where $(\bar{X}_1 - \bar{X}_2)$ = the difference in the sample means
$(\mu_1 - \mu_2)$ = the difference in the population means
$\sigma_{\bar{x}-\bar{x}}$ = the standard deviation of the sampling distribution of the differences in sample means

The second term in the numerator, $(\mu_1 - \mu_2)$, reduces to zero because we assume that the null hypothesis (which will be stated as $H_0$: $\mu_1 = \mu_2$ in our example) is true. Recall that tests of significance are always based on the assumption that the null hypothesis is true. If the means of the two populations are equal, then the term $(\mu_1 - \mu_2)$ will be zero and can be dropped from the equation. In effect, then, the formula we will actually use to compute the test statistic in step 4 will be

**FORMULA 11.2**
$$Z \text{ (obtained)} = \frac{(\bar{X}_1 - \bar{X}_2)}{\sigma_{\bar{x}-\bar{x}}}$$

The numerator of this formula, the standard deviation of the sampling distribution of the differences in sample means, is defined as

**FORMULA 11.3**
$$\sigma_{\bar{x}-\bar{x}} = \sqrt{\frac{\sigma_1^2}{n_1} + \frac{\sigma_2^2}{n_2}}$$

To illustrate the procedure for testing sample means, let's consider a hypothetical random sample of 300 Canadians to examine if men and women differ in their support for gun control (where support for gun control is measured on an interval-ratio level and higher scores indicate greater support). The outcomes for this sample are reported below, and illustrated in Figure 11.1. (It may be helpful to compare this diagram with Figure 10.1, which depicted the one-sample case.)

| Sample 1 (Men) | Sample 2 (Women) |
|:---:|:---:|
| $\bar{X}_1 = 14$ | $\bar{X}_2 = 21$ |
| $\sigma_1 = 3$ | $\sigma_2 = 6$ |
| $n_1 = 150$ | $n_2 = 150$ |

**FIGURE 11.1  A Test of Hypothesis for Two-Sample Means**

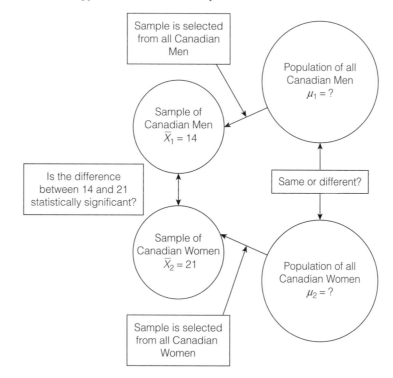

We see from the sample statistics that men have a lower average score on the support for gun control scale and are less supportive of gun control. The test of hypothesis will tell us if this difference is large enough to justify the conclusion that it did not occur by random chance alone but rather reflects an actual difference between the populations of men and women on this issue.

**Step 1. Make Assumptions and Meet Test Requirements.** Note that, although we now assume that the random samples are independent, the rest of the model is the same as in the one-sample case.

> Model: Independent random samples
>        Level of measurement is interval-ratio
>        Sampling distribution is normal

**Step 2. State the Null Hypothesis.** The null hypothesis states that the *populations* represented by the samples are not different on this variable. No direction for the difference has been predicted, so a two-tailed test is called for, as reflected in the research hypothesis.

$$H_0: \mu_1 = \mu_2$$
$$(H_1: \mu_1 \neq \mu_2)$$

**Step 3. Select the Sampling Distribution and Establish the Critical Region.** Because the population standard deviations are known (and the combined sample size large), the $Z$ distribution can be used to find areas under the sampling distribution and establish the critical region. Alpha will be set at 0.05.

$$\text{Sampling distribution} = Z \text{ distribution}$$
$$\text{Alpha} = 0.05$$
$$Z \text{ (critical)} = \pm 1.96$$

**Step 4. Compute the Test Statistic.** Before calculating the test statistic, find the standard deviation of the sampling distribution of the differences in sample means using Formula 11.3. This value will then be substituted into Formula 11.2 and $Z$ (obtained) will be computed.

$$\sigma_{\bar{x}-\bar{x}} = \sqrt{\frac{\sigma_1^2}{n_1} + \frac{\sigma_2^2}{n_2}}$$

$$\sigma_{\bar{x}-\bar{x}} = \sqrt{\frac{(3)^2}{150} + \frac{(6)^2}{150}}$$

$$\sigma_{\bar{x}-\bar{x}} = \sqrt{(0.06) + (0.24)}$$

$$\sigma_{\bar{x}-\bar{x}} = \sqrt{0.30}$$

$$\sigma_{\bar{x}-\bar{x}} = 0.548$$

$$Z \text{ (obtained)} = \frac{(\bar{X}_1 - \bar{X}_2)}{\sigma_{\bar{x}-\bar{x}}}$$

$$Z \text{ (obtained)} = \frac{14 - 21}{0.548}$$

$$Z \text{ (obtained)} = \frac{-7}{0.548}$$

$$Z \text{ (obtained)} = -12.77$$

**Step 5. Make a Decision and Interpret the Results of the Test.** Comparing the test statistic with the critical region:

$$Z \text{ (obtained)} = -12.77$$
$$Z \text{ (critical)} = \pm 1.96$$

---

**ONE STEP AT A TIME**   **Completing Step 4 of the Five-Step Model: Compute Z (Obtained)**

Use these procedures if the population standard deviations ($\sigma_1$ and $\sigma_2$) are known and sample size large (or populations normally distributed). Solve Formula 11.3 first and then solve Formula 11.2.

**To Solve Formula 11.3**

1: Square the value of the standard deviation for the first sample ($\sigma_1^2$).
2: Divide the quantity you found in step 1 by $n_1$.
3: Square the value of the standard deviation for the second sample ($\sigma_2^2$).
4: Divide the quantity you found in step 3 by $n_2$.

5: Add the quantity you found in step 4 to the quantity you found in step 2.
6: Take the square root of the quantity you found in step 5.

**To Solve Formula 11.2**

1: Subtract $\overline{X}_2$ from $\overline{X}_1$.
2: Divide the value you found in step 1 of "To Solve Formula 11.2" by the quantity you found in step 6 of "To Solve Formula 11.3." This is Z (obtained).

---

We see that the $Z$ score clearly falls into the critical region. This outcome indicates that a difference as large as $-7$ ($14 - 21$) between the sample means is unlikely if the null hypothesis is true. The null hypothesis of no difference can be rejected, and the notion that Canadian men and women are different in terms of their support of gun control is supported. The decision to reject the null hypothesis has only a 0.05 probability (the alpha level) of being incorrect.

Note that the value for $Z$ (obtained) is negative, indicating that men have significantly lower scores than women for support for gun control. The sign of the test statistics reflects our arbitrary decision to label men sample 1 and women sample 2. If we had reversed the labels and called women sample 1 and men sample 2, the sign of the $Z$ (obtained) would have been positive, but

---

**ONE STEP AT A TIME**   **Completing Step 5 of the Five-Step Model: Make a Decision and Interpret the Results of the Test**

1: Compare the $Z$ (obtained) to your $Z$ (critical). If $Z$ (obtained) is *in* the critical region, *reject* the null hypothesis. If $Z$ (obtained) is *not in* the critical region, *fail to reject* the null hypothesis.
2: Interpret the decision to reject or fail to reject the null hypothesis in terms of the original question.

For example, our conclusion for the example problem was "There is a significant difference between men and women in their support for gun control."

its value (12.77) would have been exactly the same, as would our decision in step 5. *(For practice in testing the significance of the difference between sample means with known σ, see Problems 11.1 to 11.7.)*

## 11.3 HYPOTHESIS TESTING WITH SAMPLE MEANS (σ UNKNOWN)

As with single-sample means, when the population standard deviation is unknown, the $Z$ distribution can no longer be used to find areas under the sampling distribution. Instead, we will use the $t$ distribution, provided that either the combined sample size is large with a total of 100 or more cases or the populations normally distributed, to find the critical region and identify unlikely sample outcomes. To utilize the $t$ distribution for testing two-sample means, we need to perform one additional calculation and make one additional assumption. The calculation is for degrees of freedom, a quantity required for proper use of the $t$ table (Appendix B). In the two-sample case, degrees of freedom are equal to $n_1 + n_2 - 2$.

The additional assumption is a more complex matter. We must assume that the variances of the populations of interest are equal in order to form a **pooled estimate** (pooled because it combines information from both samples) of the standard deviation of the sampling distribution of the differences in sample means. The assumption of equal variance in the population can be tested by an inferential statistical technique known as the analysis of variance or ANOVA (see Chapter 12). For our purposes here, however, we will simply assume equal population variances without formal testing. This assumption is safe as long as sample sizes are equal or nearly equal. (By nearly equal we mean that the *ratio* of the largest to the smallest sample size should be two or less. So, for example, if $n_1 = 150$ and $n_2 = 100$, the ratio would be 1.5, or 150/100, and we can safely proceed with the test.)

To illustrate, suppose we were interested in gender differences in the grade point average (GPA) of students enrolled in master's level graduate programs. For this problem, the following sample statistics were computed for random samples of male and female students.

| Sample 1 (Men) | Sample 2 (Women) |
|:---:|:---:|
| $\overline{X}_1 = 83.74$ | $\overline{X}_2 = 82.16$ |
| $s_1 = 6.59$ | $s_2 = 9.35$ |
| $n_1 = 39$ | $n_2 = 42$ |

With this information, and following the five-step model, a test for the significance of the difference in GPA can be conducted.

**Step 1. Make Assumptions and Meet Test Requirements.** With unknown population standard deviations and a combined sample size less than 100, we must assume that the populations have equal variances and normal distributions.

> Model: Independent random samples
> Level of measurement is interval-ratio
> Population variances are equal ($\sigma_1^2 = \sigma_2^2$)
> Sampling distribution is normal

**Step 2. State the Null Hypothesis.** Because no direction for the difference has been predicted, a two-tailed test will be used, as reflected in the research hypothesis.

$$H_0: \mu_1 = \mu_2$$
$$H_1: \mu_1 \neq \mu_2$$

**Step 3. Select the Sampling Distribution and Establish the Critical Region.** The $t$ distribution is used to establish the critical region. Alpha will be set at 0.05, and a two-tailed test will be used.

> Sampling distribution = $t$ distribution
> Alpha = 0.05, two-tailed
> Degrees of freedom = $n_1 + n_2 - 2 = 39 + 42 - 2 = 79$
> $t$ (critical) = $\pm 2.000$

**Step 4. Compute the Test Statistic.** First, Formula 11.4 is used for the pooled estimate of the standard deviation of the sampling distribution. This value is then substituted directly into the denominator of the formula for $t$ (obtained) given in Formula 11.5.

**FORMULA 11.4**
$$\sigma_{\bar{x}-\bar{x}} = \sqrt{\frac{n_1 s_1^2 + n_2 s_2^2}{n_1 + n_2 - 2}} \sqrt{\frac{n_1 + n_2}{n_1 n_2}}$$

$$\sigma_{\bar{x}-\bar{x}} = \sqrt{\frac{(39)(6.59)^2 + (42)(9.35)^2}{39 + 42 - 2}} \sqrt{\frac{39 + 42}{(39)(42)}}$$

$$\sigma_{\bar{x}-\bar{x}} = \sqrt{\frac{5{,}365.44}{79}} \sqrt{\frac{81}{1{,}638}}$$

$$\sigma_{\bar{x}-\bar{x}} = (8.24)(0.22)$$

$$\sigma_{\bar{x}-\bar{x}} = 1.81$$

---

**ONE STEP AT A TIME** Completing Step 4 of the Five-Step Model: Compute *t* (Obtained)

Solve Formula 11.4 first and then solve Formula 11.5 to compute the test statistic.

**To Solve Formula 11.4**

1: Add $n_1$ and $n_2$ and then subtract 2 from this total.
2: Square the standard deviation for the first sample ($s_1^2$) and multiply the result by $n_1$.
3: Square the standard deviation for the second sample ($s_2^2$) and multiply the result by $n_2$.
4: Add the quantities you found in steps 2 and 3.
5: Divide the quantity you found in step 4 by the quantity you found in step 1 and take the square root of the result.

6: Multiply $n_1$ by $n_2$.
7: Add $n_1$ and $n_2$.
8: Divide the quantity you found in step 7 by the quantity you found in step 6 and take the square root of the result.
9: Multiply the quantity you found in step 8 by the quantity you found in step 5.

**To Solve Formula 11.5**

1: Subtract $\bar{X}_2$ from $\bar{X}_1$.
2: Divide the difference between the sample means by the quantity you found in step 9 of "To Solve Formula 11.4." This is *t* (obtained).

---

**FORMULA 11.5**

$$t \text{ (obtained)} = \frac{(\bar{X}_1 - \bar{X}_2)}{\sigma_{\bar{x} - \bar{x}}}$$

$$t \text{ (obtained)} = \frac{83.74 - 82.16}{1.81}$$

$$t \text{ (obtained)} = \frac{1.58}{1.81}$$

$$t \text{ (obtained)} = 0.87$$

**Step 5. Make a Decision and Interpret the Results of the Test.** Comparing the test statistic with the critical region,

$$t \text{ (obtained)} = 0.87$$
$$t \text{ (critical)} = \pm 2.00$$

---

**ONE STEP AT A TIME** Completing Step 5 of the Five-Step Model: Make a Decision and Interpret the Results of the Test

1: Compare the *t* (obtained) to your *t* (critical). If *t* (obtained) is *in* the critical region, *reject* the null hypothesis. If *t* (obtained) is *not in* the critical region, *fail to reject* the null hypothesis.

2: Interpret the decision to reject or fail to reject the null hypothesis in terms of the original question. For example, our conclusion for the example problem was "There is not a significant difference in GPA between male and female master's students."

---

**FIGURE 11.2  The Sampling Distribution with Critical Region and Test Statistic Displayed**

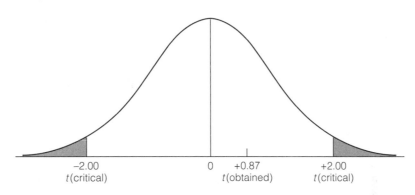

| | | |
|---|---|---|
| −2.00 | 0  +0.87 | +2.00 |
| *t*(critical) | *t*(obtained) | *t*(critical) |

we can see that the test statistic *t* (obtained) = 0.87 does not fall into the critical region as marked by the *t* (critical) of ±2.00. Thus, we fail to reject the null hypothesis. The difference between the sample means is trivial and is no greater than what would be expected if the null hypothesis were true and only random chance were operating. Male and female master's students are not significantly different in GPA. The test statistic and sampling distribution are depicted in Figure 11.2. *(For practice in testing the significance of the difference between sample means with unknown σ, see Problems 11.8, 11.9, and 11.15d to f)*

## 11.4 HYPOTHESIS TESTING WITH SAMPLE PROPORTIONS (LARGE SAMPLES)

Testing for the significance of the difference between two sample proportions is analogous to testing for two sample means. The null hypothesis states that no difference exists between the populations from which the samples are drawn on the trait being tested. The sample proportions form the basis of the test statistic computed in step 4, which is then compared with the critical region. When sample sizes are large (combined *n*'s of 100 or more), the *Z* distribution may be used to find the critical region. We will not consider tests of significance for proportions based on small samples in this textbook.

To find the value of the test statistics, several preliminary equations must be solved. Formula 11.6 uses the values of the two sample proportions ($P_s$) to give us a **pooled estimate of the population proportion** ($P_u$), that is, the proportion of cases in the population that have the trait under consideration, assuming the null hypothesis is true.

**FORMULA 11.6**

$$P_u = \frac{n_1 P_{s1} + n_2 P_{s2}}{n_1 + n_2}$$

The estimated value of $P_u$ is then used to determine a value for the standard deviation of the sampling distribution of the difference in sample proportions in Formula 11.7:

**FORMULA 11.7**
$$\sigma_{p-p} = \sqrt{P_u(1 - P_u)}\ \sqrt{\frac{(n_1 + n_2)}{n_1 n_2}}$$

This value is then substituted into the formula for computing the test statistic, presented as Formula 11.8:

**FORMULA 11.8**
$$Z\,(\text{obtained}) = \frac{(P_{s1} - P_{s2}) - (P_{u1} - P_{u2})}{\sigma_{p-p}}$$

where $(P_{s1} - P_{s2}) =$ the difference between the sample proportions
$(P_{u1} - P_{u2}) =$ the difference between the population proportions
$\sigma_{p-p} =$ the standard deviation of the sampling distribution of the difference between sample proportions

As was the case with sample means, the second term in the numerator is assumed to be zero by the null hypothesis. Therefore, the formula reduces to

**FORMULA 11.9**
$$Z\,(\text{obtained}) = \frac{(P_{s1} - P_{s2})}{\sigma_{p-p}}$$

Remember to solve these equations in order, starting with Formula 11.6 (and skipping Formula 11.8).

An example will make these procedures clearer. It is commonly thought that people become happier after they retire from work. However, does happiness really increase in retirement? The proportion of people who feel happy with their life in each age group is reported below, using random samples of people under age 65 (typically, working age) and people age 65 and over (typically, retirement age) from the 2013 Canadian Voice of the People survey.

| Sample 1 (Under Age 65) | Sample 2 (Age 65 and Over) |
|---|---|
| $P_{s1} = 0.81$ | $P_{s2} = 0.90$ |
| $n_1 = 338$ | $n_2 = 79$ |

Source: WIN/Gallup International Association. *Voice of the People End of Year Survey, 2013.*

The sample data reveal a difference in the predicted direction. Of the 338 respondents under the age of 65, 275 (or a proportion of 0.81) said that they were happy with life. For the 79 respondents aged 65 and over, the proportion is 0.90. The significance of this observed difference can be tested with the five-step model.

**Step 1. Make Assumptions and Meet Test Requirements.**

Model:   Independent random samples
Level of measurement is nominal or ordinal
Sampling distribution is normal

**Step 2. State the Null Hypothesis.** Because a direction has been predicted (people aged 65 and over are more likely to be happy with their life), a one-tailed test will be used, and the research hypothesis is stated in accordance with this decision.

$$H_0: P_{u1} \geq P_{u2}$$
$$(H_1: P_{u1} < P_{u2})$$

**Step 3. Select the Sampling Distribution and Establish the Critical Region.** Because the sample size is large, the $Z$ distribution will be used to establish the critical region. Alpha will be set at 0.05 for a one-tailed test.

$$\text{Sampling distribution} = Z \text{ distribution}$$
$$\text{Alpha} = 0.05, \text{one-tailed}$$
$$Z \text{ (critical)} = -1.65$$

**Step 4. Compute the Test Statistic.** Begin with the formula for estimating $P_u$ (see Formula 11.6), substitute the resultant value into Formula 11.7, then solve for $Z$ (obtained) with Formula 11.9.

$$P_u = \frac{n_1 P_{s1} + n_2 P_{s2}}{n_1 + n_2}$$

$$P_u = \frac{(338)(0.81) + (79)(0.90)}{338 + 79}$$

$$P_u = 0.83$$

$$\sigma_{p-p} = \sqrt{P_u(1 - P_u)}\ \sqrt{\frac{n_1 + n_2}{n_1 n_2}}$$

$$\sigma_{p-p} = \sqrt{(0.83)(0.17)}\ \sqrt{\frac{338 + 79}{(338)(79)}}$$

$$\sigma_{p-p} = (0.37)(0.12)$$

$$\sigma_{p-p} = 0.04$$

$$Z \text{ (obtained)} = \frac{(P_{s1} - P_{s2})}{\sigma_{p-p}}$$

$$Z \text{ (obtained)} = \frac{0.81 - 0.90}{0.04}$$

$$Z \text{ (obtained)} = -2.25$$

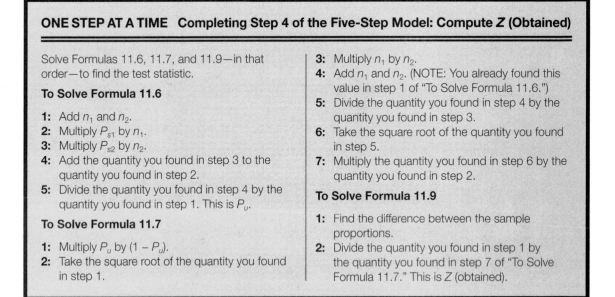

**ONE STEP AT A TIME** Completing Step 4 of the Five-Step Model: Compute *Z* (Obtained)

Solve Formulas 11.6, 11.7, and 11.9—in that order—to find the test statistic.

**To Solve Formula 11.6**

**1:** Add $n_1$ and $n_2$.
**2:** Multiply $P_{s1}$ by $n_1$.
**3:** Multiply $P_{s2}$ by $n_2$.
**4:** Add the quantity you found in step 3 to the quantity you found in step 2.
**5:** Divide the quantity you found in step 4 by the quantity you found in step 1. This is $P_u$.

**To Solve Formula 11.7**

**1:** Multiply $P_u$ by $(1 - P_u)$.
**2:** Take the square root of the quantity you found in step 1.

**3:** Multiply $n_1$ by $n_2$.
**4:** Add $n_1$ and $n_2$. (NOTE: You already found this value in step 1 of "To Solve Formula 11.6.")
**5:** Divide the quantity you found in step 4 by the quantity you found in step 3.
**6:** Take the square root of the quantity you found in step 5.
**7:** Multiply the quantity you found in step 6 by the quantity you found in step 2.

**To Solve Formula 11.9**

**1:** Find the difference between the sample proportions.
**2:** Divide the quantity you found in step 1 by the quantity you found in step 7 of "To Solve Formula 11.7." This is *Z* (obtained).

**Step 5. Make a Decision and Interpret the Results of the Test.** Comparing the test statistic with the critical region,

$$Z \text{ (obtained)} = -2.25$$
$$Z \text{ (critical)} = -1.65$$

we clearly see that the test statistic falls into the critical region. If the null hypothesis ($P_{u1} \geq P_{u2}$) were true, this would be a very unlikely outcome, so the null hypothesis can be rejected. There is a statistically significant difference between persons under age 65 and persons aged 65 and over (a difference so large that it is unlikely to be due to random chance) in the proportion of those who are happy with life. Specifically, elderly persons are significantly more likely than non-elderly persons to report happiness in life. *(For practice in testing the significance of the difference between sample proportions, see Problems 11.10 to 11.14 and 11.15a to c.)*

**ONE STEP AT A TIME** Completing Step 5 of the Five-Step Model: Make a Decision and Interpret the Results of the Test

**1:** Compare *Z* (obtained) to *Z* (critical). If *Z* (obtained) is *in* the critical region, *reject* the null hypothesis. If *Z* (obtained) is *not in* the critical region, *fail to reject* the null hypothesis.

**2:** Interpret the decision to reject or fail to reject the null hypothesis in terms of the original question. For example, our conclusion for the example problem was "Persons 65+ are significantly more likely to be happy than persons <65."

## Applying Statistics 11.1: Testing the Significance of the Difference Between Sample Proportions

Canadians feel strongly about helping people affected by emergencies and disasters abroad. In this application we ask whether rates of making a donation toward natural disaster relief differ between those with high school education or less and those with post-secondary education. We will use data from the 2010 Canada Survey of Giving, Volunteering and Participating to compute the proportion of persons who made a donation towards natural disaster relief in the past year for each education group.

| High School or Less | Post-Secondary Education |
|---|---|
| $P_{s1} = 0.30$ | $P_{s2} = 0.35$ |
| $n_1 = 3{,}359$ | $n_2 = 8{,}249$ |

This is all the information we will need to conduct a test of the null hypothesis following the familiar five-step model with alpha set at 0.05, two-tailed test.

### Step 1. Make Assumptions and Meet Test Requirements.

Model:   Independent random samples
Level of measurement is nominal or ordinal
Sampling distribution is normal

### Step 2. State the Null Hypothesis.

$$H_0: P_{u1} = P_{u2}$$
$$(H_1: P_{u1} \neq P_{u2})$$

### Step 3. Select the Sampling Distribution and Establish the Critical Region.

Sampling distribution = $Z$ distribution
Alpha = 0.05, two-tailed
$Z$ (critical) = $\pm 1.96$

### Step 4. Compute the Test Statistic.
Remember to start with Formula 11.6, substitute the value for $P_u$ into Formula 11.7, then substitute that value into Formula 11.9 to solve for $Z$ (obtained).

$$P_u = \frac{n_1 P_{s1} + n_2 P_{s2}}{n_1 + n_2}$$

$$P_u = \frac{(3{,}359)(0.30) + (8{,}249)(0.35)}{3{,}359 + 8{,}249}$$

$$P_u = \frac{3{,}895}{11{,}608}$$

$$P_u = 0.33$$

$$\sigma_{p-p} = \sqrt{P_u(1 - P_u)} \sqrt{\frac{n_1 + n_2}{n_1 n_2}}$$

$$\sigma_{p-p} = \sqrt{(0.33)(0.67)} \sqrt{\frac{3{,}359 + 8{,}249}{(3{,}359)(8{,}249)}}$$

$$\sigma_{p-p} = \sqrt{0.22} \sqrt{\frac{11{,}608}{27{,}708{,}391}}$$

$$\sigma_{p-p} = \sqrt{0.22} \sqrt{0.0004}$$

$$\sigma_{p-p} = (0.47)(0.02)$$

$$\sigma_{p-p} = 0.009$$

$$Z \text{ (obtained)} = \frac{(P_{s1} - P_{s2})}{\sigma_{p-p}}$$

$$Z \text{ (obtained)} = \frac{0.30 - 0.35}{0.009}$$

$$Z \text{ (obtained)} = \frac{-0.05}{0.009}$$

$$Z \text{ (obtained)} = -5.55$$

### Step 5. Make a Decision and Interpret the Results of the Test.
With an obtained $Z$ score of $-5.55$, we would reject the null hypothesis. There is a statistically significant difference between individuals with lower education and those with higher education in rates of giving for disaster relief.

Source: Statistics Canada, *2010 Canada Survey of Giving, Volunteering, and Participating.*

## 11.5 HYPOTHESIS TESTING USING INDIVIDUAL CONFIDENCE INTERVALS

In Chapter 10 we discussed the direct relationship between the confidence interval and hypothesis testing in the one-sample case. While the objective of each technique is different, they are just different ways of expressing the same information about a single sample. For this reason, a confidence interval can be used as a convenient substitute for hypothesis testing.

In the two-sample case, there is a close but not direct relationship between the techniques. We can assess whether the difference between two means (or proportions) is statistically significant by examining the overlap of the confidence interval for each mean (or proportion). However, confidence interval overlap is only an approximation of the formal hypothesis testing method discussed in Sections 11.2 through 11.4, and it is not equal to a formal hypothesis test.

When the individual confidence intervals for each mean (or proportion) do *not* overlap, the "confidence interval" and the formal hypothesis testing method lead to the same decision, so either approach can be used as a test for the significance of the difference between sample means or sample proportions. However, when confidence intervals overlap, the difference between the sample means or sample proportions is most likely (most of the time) not statistically significant. In the case of an overlap, we cannot rely on confidence intervals to determine statistical significance and instead must use formal hypothesis testing. To put it briefly, the overlap of confidence intervals should be used only to "eyeball," or roughly estimate, the significance of the difference between sample means or proportions.

## 11.6 INTERPRETING STATISTICS: ARE THERE SIGNIFICANT DIFFERENCES IN INCOME BETWEEN MEN AND WOMEN?

In Canada, as in many other nations around the globe, concerted efforts have been made to equalize working conditions for men and women. How successful have these efforts been? Do significant differences in the income of men and women persist? Is there a "gender gap" in income?

We will investigate the relationship between gender and personal after-tax income using random samples of men and women from the 2011 Survey of Labour and Income Dynamics (SLID), an annual survey conducted by Statistics Canada to collect information on the labour market activity and income of persons in the 10 Canadian provinces. If the difference between the samples of men and women is large enough, we can infer that there is a difference in average income between men and women in the population.

Before conducting the test, we need to deal with an important issue. We should not compare the personal incomes of all men and all women because some difference could be caused by the fact that women are less likely to be in the paid labour market (i.e., they may be occupied as wives and mothers) and, thus, less likely to have an income. We will deal with this by restricting the comparison to respondents who work full-time.

To test for the significance of the difference in personal after-tax income, the following sample information was calculated:

| Males | Females |
|---|---|
| $\overline{X}_1 = 49{,}519$ | $\overline{X}_2 = 39{,}273$ |
| $s_1 = 37{,}319$ | $s_2 = 22{,}991$ |
| $n_1 = 13{,}928$ | $n_2 = 11{,}212$ |

Source: Statistics Canada, *2011 Survey of Labour and Income Dynamics.*

It appears that there is a gender gap and that, on average, males earn more than females. Is this difference in sample means between males and females significant? Could it have occurred by random chance?

Because we are dealing with unknown population standard deviations, we will use the $t$ test as described in Section 11.3. The null hypothesis is that males and females have the same average income in the population ($\mu_1 = \mu_2$). We will skip the customary trip through the five-step model and simply report that the $t$ (obtained) calculated with Formula 11.5 (step 4) is 25.44, much greater than the $t$ (critical) score of $\pm 1.98$ associated with an alpha level of 0.05. The difference in sample means is so large that we must reject the null hypothesis and conclude (with a probability of error of 0.05) that the population means are different: Males and females do not earn the same amount.

The large obtained $t$ score reflects in part the large sample size of the SLID, since the probability of rejecting the null hypothesis increases with sample size. The obtained $t$ score and probability of rejecting the null hypothesis are further influenced by the size of the observed difference in means, and the SLID data show that men earn much more on average than women. We can conclude, then, that the results are significant and that they are likely to be important, given that males earn on average over $10,000 a year more than females.

Why does a significant gender gap in income exist? Is it the result of differences in levels of education? If females were significantly less educated than males, this would account for at least some of the difference in income. To test for a significance difference in education, we again turn to data from the 2011 SLID. The following information was calculated for years of education for the same random samples of males and females employed full-time:

| Males | Females |
|---|---|
| $\overline{X}_1 = 13.40$ | $\overline{X}_2 = 13.89$ |
| $s_1 = 2.81$ | $s_2 = 2.61$ |
| $n_1 = 13{,}924$ | $n_2 = 11{,}207$ |

Source: Statistics Canada, *2011 Survey of Labour and Income Dynamics.*

We can see that both males and females average more than 13 years of schooling and that the average for females is actually higher than the average for males. The test statistic computed in step 4 is a $t$ (obtained) of $-14.18$. The test statistic is in the critical region, as marked by a $t$ (critical) score of $\pm 1.98$ at the 0.05 level, so we reject the null hypothesis of no difference. Males and females differ in levels of schooling in the population in fact, females are significantly better educated than males. These results suggest that females are getting a lower return in income for their education and that education is unlikely to account for the difference in income.

If not education, what else might explain the significant income gap between males and females? To answer this question entirely is far beyond the bounds of this statistics textbook. We can suggest that one important part of the answer lies in the fact that men and women tend to pursue different kinds of careers and jobs. Men tend to be concentrated in more lucrative, higher prestige occupations while women tend to be concentrated in occupations that have lower levels of remuneration. According to the 2011 SLID, just over half of all women in the paid labour force work in either clerical or unskilled sales and service jobs, which tend to provide low wages. Just over 25% of all men work in these occupations.

## READING STATISTICS 8: Hypothesis Testing in the Professional Literature

Municipal services provided by cities and towns play a crucial role in the well-being of communities and their citizens. Health, safety, and quality of life depend on the effective delivery of services such as public transportation, works, and utilities, police, fire, and ambulance services, parks and recreation, and arts and culture. Not surprisingly, there has been considerable debate about whether to expand the role of the private sector in delivering such essential services.

A recent study by Robert Hebdon and Patrice Jalette examined delivery of municipal services and privatization in Canada and the United States. It was hypothesized by Hebdon and Jalette that, while Canadians and Americans have much in common, differences between the countries in attitude toward government, communitarian values, and union opposition would result in differences in the number of municipal services offered and in the privatization of those services. They hypothesized that municipalities would offer more services in Canada than in the United States and that municipal services are

more likely to be offered through the public sector in Canada than in the United States.

Using samples of 210 and 1,283 cities and towns in Canada and the United States, respectively, they found that, as expected, municipalities in Canada provide more services than their American counterparts: mean number of services offered per municipality was 37.1 in Canada and 33.7 in the United States. However, their data unexpectedly revealed that the private sector was more involved in service delivery in Canada than in the United States: On average, about 26% of the services offered in Canadian municipalities was delivered by the private for-profit sector compared to just 16% in the United States. Hebdon and Jalette suggest that the unexpected finding may reflect the devolution of services by provincial governments to municipal governments over the last decade or so, especially in Ontario and Alberta, without adequate funding to follow, thus putting greater pressure on municipalities in Canada to restructure and privatize compared to their American counterparts.

(continued)

Canada–US differences in both the number of services provided and in the percentage of services provided by the private sector were statistically significant at $p < 0.05$, as shown in the tables below (Recall that an alpha level reported as "$p < 0.05$" means that the probability of the observed difference occurring by chance alone, if the null hypothesis of no difference is true, is less than 0.05 or 5%.)

**Mean Number of Services per Municipality, Canada and the United States**

| Canada | United States |
|---|---|
| $\bar{X}_1 = 37.1$ | $\bar{X}_2 = 33.7$** |
| $s_1 = 12.1$ | $s_2 = 8.7$ |
| $n_1 = 210$ | $n_2 = 1{,}283$ |

**statistically significant difference in means between Canada and the United States at $p < 0.05$.

**Mean Rate of Services Offered by Private Sector per Municipality, Canada and the United States**

| Canada | United States |
|---|---|
| $\bar{X}_1 = 26.6$ | $\bar{X}_2 = 16.2$** |
| $s_1 = 16.6$ | $s_2 = 10.7$ |
| $n_1 = 210$ | $n_2 = 1{,}283$ |

**statistically significant difference in means between Canada and the United States at $p < 0.05$.

Source: R. Hebdon and P. Jalette, 2008, "The Restructuring of Municipal Services: A Canada-United States Comparison." *Environment and Planning C: Government and Policy.*

## SUMMARY

1. A common research situation is to test for the significance of the difference between two populations. Sample statistics are calculated for independent random samples of each population; then we test for the significance of the difference between the samples as a way of inferring differences between the specified populations.

2. When sample information is summarized in the form of sample means, and $\sigma$ is known, the $Z$ distribution is used to find the critical region. When $\sigma$ is unknown, the $t$ distribution is used to establish the critical region. In the latter circumstance, we must also assume equal population variances before forming a pooled estimate of the standard deviation of the sampling distribution.

3. Differences in sample proportions may also be tested for significance. For large samples (i.e., 100 or more), the $Z$ distribution is used to find the critical region.

4. A two-sample hypothesis test can be approximated using confidence intervals. When the confidence intervals for two samples do not overlap, the null hypothesis of no difference between the populations will be rejected at the stated alpha level. If the confidence intervals overlap, the difference will not be statistically significant most of the time. Hence, in the case of an overlap, we must further conduct the two-sample hypothesis test described in this chapter.

## SUMMARY OF FORMULAS

Test statistic for two-sample means, $\sigma$ known:

$$11.1 \qquad Z \text{ (obtained)} = \frac{(\bar{X}_1 - \bar{X}_2) - (\mu_1 - \mu_2)}{\sigma_{\bar{x}-\bar{x}}}$$

Test statistic for two-sample means, $\sigma$ is known (simplified formula):

$$11.2 \qquad Z \text{ (obtained)} = \frac{(\bar{X}_1 - \bar{X}_2)}{\sigma_{\bar{x}-\bar{x}}}$$

Standard deviation of the sampling distribution of the difference in sample means, $\sigma$ is known:

11.3 $\quad \sigma_{\bar{x}-\bar{x}} = \sqrt{\dfrac{\sigma_1^2}{n_1} + \dfrac{\sigma_2^2}{n_2}}$

Pooled estimate of the standard deviation of the sampling distribution of the difference in sample means, $\sigma$ is unknown:

11.4 $\quad \sigma_{\bar{x}-\bar{x}} = \sqrt{\dfrac{n_1 s_1^2 + n_2 s_2^2}{n_1 + n_2 - 2}} \sqrt{\dfrac{n_1 + n_2}{n_1 n_2}}$

Test statistic for two-sample means, $\sigma$ is unknown:

11.5 $\quad t\,(\text{obtained}) = \dfrac{(\bar{X}_1 - \bar{X}_2)}{\sigma_{\bar{x}-\bar{x}}}$

Pooled estimate of population proportion, large samples:

11.6 $\quad P_u = \dfrac{n_1 P_{s1} + n_2 P_{s2}}{n_1 + n_2}$

Standard deviation of the sampling distribution of the difference in sample proportions, large samples:

11.7 $\quad \sigma_{p-p} = \sqrt{P_u(1 - P_u)} \sqrt{\dfrac{n_1 + n_2}{n_1 n_2}}$

Test statistic for two-sample proportions, large samples:

11.8 $\quad Z\,(\text{obtained}) = \dfrac{(P_{s1} - P_{s2}) - (P_{u1} - P_{u2})}{\sigma_{p-p}}$

Test statistic for two-sample proportions, large samples (simplified formula):

11.9 $\quad Z\,(\text{obtained}) = \dfrac{(P_{s1} - P_{s2})}{\sigma_{p-p}}$

## GLOSSARY

**Independent random samples.** Random samples gathered in such a way that the selection of a particular case for one sample has no effect on the probability that any particular case will be selected for the other samples.

**Pooled estimate.** An estimate of the standard deviation of the sampling distribution of the difference in sample means based on the standard deviations of both samples.

**Pooled estimate of the population proportion.** An estimate of the population proportion based on the proportions of both samples.

## MULTIMEDIA RESOURCES

nelson.com/student

Visit the companion website for the fourth Canadian edition of *Statistics: A Tool for Social Research* to access a wide range of student resources. Begin by clicking on the Student Resources section of the textbook's website to access online chapters and study tools.

## PROBLEMS

**11.1** For each problem below, test for the significance of the difference in sample statistics using the five-step model.

**a.**

| Sample 1 | Sample 2 |
|---|---|
| $\bar{X}_1 = 72.5$ | $\bar{X}_2 = 76.0$ |
| $\sigma_1 = 14.3$ | $\sigma_2 = 10.2$ |
| $n_1 = 136$ | $n_2 = 257$ |

**b.**

| Sample 1 | Sample 2 |
|---|---|
| $\bar{X}_1 = 107$ | $\bar{X}_2 = 103$ |
| $\sigma_1 = 14$ | $\sigma_2 = 17$ |
| $n_1 = 175$ | $n_2 = 200$ |

**11.2** SOC Questionnaires were administered to samples of undergraduate students. Among other things, those questionnaires contained a scale that measured attitudes towards interpersonal violence (higher scores indicated greater approval of interpersonal violence). Test the results as reported below for differences in sex and social class background.

**a.**

| Sample 1 (Males) | Sample 2 (Females) |
|---|---|
| $\bar{X}_1 = 2.99$ | $\bar{X}_2 = 2.29$ |
| $\sigma_1 = 0.88$ | $\sigma_2 = 0.91$ |
| $n_1 = 122$ | $n_2 = 251$ |

**b.**

| Sample 1 (White Collar) | Sample 2 (Blue Collar) |
|---|---|
| $\bar{X}_1 = 2.46$ | $\bar{X}_2 = 2.67$ |
| $\sigma_1 = 0.91$ | $\sigma_2 = 0.87$ |
| $n_1 = 249$ | $n_2 = 97$ |

**c.** Summarize your results in terms of the significance and the direction of the differences. Which of these two factors seems to make the biggest difference in attitudes towards interpersonal violence?

**11.3** SOC Do athletes in different sports vary in terms of intelligence? Below are aptitude test scores of random samples of university varsity hockey and soccer players. Is there a significant difference? Write a sentence or two explaining the difference.

**a.**

| Sample 1 (Hockey Players) | Sample 2 (Soccer Players) |
|---|---|
| $\bar{X}_1 = 460$ | $\bar{X}_2 = 442$ |
| $\sigma_1 = 92$ | $\sigma_2 = 57$ |
| $n_1 = 102$ | $n_2 = 117$ |

What about male and female university athletes?

**b.**

| Sample 1 (Males) | Sample 2 (Females) |
|---|---|
| $\bar{X}_1 = 452$ | $\bar{X}_2 = 480$ |
| $\sigma_1 = 88$ | $\sigma_2 = 75$ |
| $n_1 = 107$ | $n_2 = 105$ |

**11.4** PA A number of years ago, the fire department in Pearson, Ontario, began recruiting females through an employment equity program. In terms of efficiency ratings as compiled by their superiors, how do the employment equity employees rate? The ratings of random samples of both groups were collected, and the results are reported below (higher ratings indicate greater efficiency).

| Sample 1 (Employment Equity) | Sample 2 (Regular) |
|---|---|
| $\bar{X}_1 = 15.2$ | $\bar{X}_2 = 15.5$ |
| $\sigma_1 = 3.9$ | $\sigma_2 = 2.0$ |
| $n_1 = 97$ | $n_2 = 100$ |

Write a sentence or two of interpretation.

**11.5** SOC Are middle-class families more likely than working-class families to maintain contact with relatives? Write a paragraph summarizing the results of these tests.

**a.** A sample of middle-class families reported an average of 7.3 visits per year with close relatives, while a sample of working-class families averaged 8.2 visits. Is the difference significant?

| Visits | |
|---|---|
| Sample 1 (Middle Class) | Sample 2 (Working Class) |
| $\bar{X}_1 = 7.3$ | $\bar{X}_2 = 8.2$ |
| $\sigma_1 = 0.3$ | $\sigma_2 = 0.5$ |
| $n_1 = 89$ | $n_2 = 55$ |

**b.** The middle-class families averaged 2.3 phone calls and 8.7 e-mail messages per month with close relatives. The working-class families averaged 2.7 calls and 5.7 e-mail messages per month. Are these differences significant?

**Phone Calls**

| Sample 1 (Middle Class) | Sample 2 (Working Class) |
|---|---|
| $\overline{X}_1 = 2.3$ | $\overline{X}_2 = 2.7$ |
| $\sigma_1 = 0.5$ | $\sigma_2 = 0.8$ |
| $n_1 = 89$ | $n_2 = 55$ |

**E-mail Messages**

| Sample 1 (Middle Class) | Sample 2 (Working Class) |
|---|---|
| $\overline{X}_1 = 8.7$ | $\overline{X}_2 = 5.7$ |
| $\sigma_1 = 0.3$ | $\sigma_2 = 1.1$ |
| $n_1 = 89$ | $n_2 = 55$ |

**11.6** SOC Are university students who live in residence significantly more involved in campus life than students who commute to campus? The data below report the average number of hours per week that students devote to extracurricular activities on campus. Is the difference between these randomly selected samples of commuter and residential students significant?

| Sample 1 (Residential) | Sample 2 (Commuter) |
|---|---|
| $\overline{X}_1 = 12.4$ | $\overline{X}_2 = 10.2$ |
| $\sigma_1 = 2.0$ | $\sigma_2 = 1.9$ |
| $n_1 = 158$ | $n_2 = 173$ |

**11.7** SOC Are senior citizens who live in retirement communities more socially active than those who live in age-integrated communities? Write a sentence or two explaining the results of these tests. (Note: The distribution for each variable is normally distributed in the population.)

**a.** A random sample of senior citizens living in a retirement village reported that they had an average of 1.42 face-to-face interactions per day with their neighbours. A random sample of those living in age-integrated communities reported 1.58 interactions. Is the difference significant?

| Sample 1 (Retirement Community) | Sample 2 (Age-Integrated Neighbourhood) |
|---|---|
| $\overline{X}_1 = 1.42$ | $\overline{X}_2 = 1.58$ |
| $\sigma_1 = 0.10$ | $\sigma_2 = 0.78$ |
| $n_1 = 43$ | $n_2 = 37$ |

**b.** Senior citizens living in the retirement village reported that they had 7.43 telephone calls with friends and relatives each week, while those in the age-integrated communities reported 5.50 calls. Is the difference significant?

| Sample 1 (Retirement Community) | Sample 2 (Age-Integrated Neighbourhood) |
|---|---|
| $\overline{X}_1 = 7.43$ | $\overline{X}_2 = 5.50$ |
| $\sigma_1 = 0.75$ | $\sigma_2 = 0.25$ |
| $n_1 = 43$ | $n_2 = 37$ |

**11.8** SW As the director of the local youth club, you have claimed for years that membership in your club reduces juvenile delinquency. Now, a cynical member of your funding agency has demanded proof of your claim. Fortunately, your local sociology department is on your side and springs to your aid with student assistants, computers, and hand calculators at the ready. Random samples of members and non-members are gathered and interviewed with respect to their involvement in delinquent activities. Each respondent is asked to enumerate the number of delinquent acts he or she has engaged in over the past year. The results are in and the average numbers of admitted acts of delinquency are reported below. What can you tell the funding agency? (Note: The distributions of scores are normal.)

| Sample 1 (Members) | Sample 2 (Non-Members) |
|---|---|
| $\overline{X}_1 = 10.3$ | $\overline{X}_2 = 12.3$ |
| $s_1 = 2.7$ | $s_2 = 4.2$ |
| $n_1 = 40$ | $n_2 = 55$ |

**11.9** SOC A survey has been administered to random samples of respondents in each of five nations. For each nation, are men and women significantly different in terms of their reported levels of satisfaction? Respondents were asked: "How satisfied are you with your life as a whole?" Responses varied from 1 (very dissatisfied) to 10 (very satisfied). Conduct a test for the significance of the difference in mean scores for each nation.

### Canada

| Males | Females |
|---|---|
| $\bar{X}_1 = 7.4$ | $\bar{X}_2 = 7.7$ |
| $s_1 = 0.20$ | $s_2 = 0.25$ |
| $n_1 = 1{,}005$ | $n_2 = 1{,}234$ |

### Nigeria

| Males | Females |
|---|---|
| $\bar{X}_1 = 6.7$ | $\bar{X}_2 = 7.8$ |
| $s_1 = 0.16$ | $s_2 = 0.23$ |
| $n_1 = 1{,}825$ | $n_2 = 1{,}256$ |

### China

| Males | Females |
|---|---|
| $\bar{X}_1 = 7.6$ | $\bar{X}_2 = 7.1$ |
| $s_1 = 0.21$ | $s_2 = 0.11$ |
| $n_1 = 1{,}400$ | $n_2 = 1{,}200$ |

### Mexico

| Males | Females |
|---|---|
| $\bar{X}_1 = 8.3$ | $\bar{X}_2 = 9.1$ |
| $s_1 = 0.29$ | $s_2 = 0.30$ |
| $n_1 = 1{,}645$ | $n_2 = 1{,}432$ |

### Japan

| Males | Females |
|---|---|
| $\bar{X}_1 = 8.8$ | $\bar{X}_2 = 9.3$ |
| $s_1 = 0.34$ | $s_2 = 0.32$ |
| $n_1 = 1{,}621$ | $n_2 = 1{,}683$ |

**11.10** For each of the following problems, test the sample statistics for the significance of the difference. *(HINT: In testing proportions, remember to begin with Formula 11.6, then solve Formulas 11.7 and 11.9.)*

**a.**

| Sample 1 | Sample 2 |
|---|---|
| $P_{s1} = 0.17$ | $P_{s2} = 0.20$ |
| $n_1 = 101$ | $n_2 = 114$ |

**b.**

| Sample 1 | Sample 2 |
|---|---|
| $P_{s1} = 0.62$ | $P_{s2} = 0.60$ |
| $n_1 = 532$ | $n_2 = 478$ |

**11.11** CJ About half of the police officers in Pearson, Ontario, have completed a special course in investigative procedures. Has the course increased their efficiency in clearing crimes by arrest? The proportions of cases cleared by arrest for samples of trained and untrained officers are reported below.

| Trained | Untrained |
|---|---|
| $P_{s1} = 0.47$ | $P_{s2} = 0.43$ |
| $n_1 = 157$ | $n_2 = 113$ |

**11.12** SW A large counselling centre needs to evaluate several experimental programs. Write a paragraph summarizing the results of these tests. Did the new programs work?

**a.** One program is designed for divorce counselling; the key feature of the program is its counsellors, who are married couples working in teams. About half of all clients have been randomly assigned to this special program and half to the regular program, and the proportion of cases that eventually ended in divorce has been recorded for both. The results for random samples of couples from both programs are reported below. In terms of preventing divorce, did the new program work?

| Special Program | Regular Program |
|---|---|
| $P_{s1} = 0.53$ | $P_{s2} = 0.59$ |
| $n_1 = 78$ | $n_2 = 82$ |

**b.** The agency is also experimenting with peer counselling for depressed children. About half of all clients were randomly assigned to peer counselling. After the program had run for a year, a random sample of children from the new program was compared with a random sample of children who did not receive peer counselling. In terms of the percentage who were judged to be "much improved," did the new program work?

| Peer Counselling | No Peer Counselling |
|---|---|
| $P_{s1} = 0.10$ | $P_{s2} = 0.15$ |
| $n_1 = 52$ | $n_2 = 56$ |

**11.13** $\boxed{\text{SOC}}$ At Algebra University, the sociology and psychology departments have been feuding for years about the respective quality of their programs. In an attempt to resolve the dispute, you have gathered data about the graduate school experience of random samples of both groups of majors. The following results are presented below: The proportion of majors who applied to graduate schools, the proportion of majors accepted into their preferred programs, and the proportion of these groups who completed their programs. As measured by these data, is there a significant difference in program quality?

**a.** Proportion of majors who applied to graduate school:

| Sociology | Psychology |
|---|---|
| $P_{s1} = 0.53$ | $P_{s2} = 0.40$ |
| $n_1 = 150$ | $n_2 = 175$ |

**b.** Proportion accepted by program of first choice:

| Sociology | Psychology |
|---|---|
| $P_{s1} = 0.75$ | $P_{s2} = 0.85$ |
| $n_1 = 80$ | $n_2 = 70$ |

**c.** Proportion completing the programs:

| Sociology | Psychology |
|---|---|
| $P_{s1} = 0.75$ | $P_{s2} = 0.69$ |
| $n_1 = 60$ | $n_2 = 60$ |

**11.14** $\boxed{\text{CJ}}$ The local police chief started a "crimeline" program some years ago and wonders if it's really working. The program publicizes unsolved violent crimes in the local media and offers cash rewards for information leading to arrests. Are "featured" crimes more likely to be cleared by arrest than other violent crimes? Results from random samples of both types of crimes are reported as follows:

| Crimeline Crimes Cleared by Arrest | Non-Crimeline Crimes Cleared by Arrest |
|---|---|
| $P_{s1} = 0.35$ | $P_{s2} = 0.25$ |
| $n_1 = 178$ | $n_2 = 212$ |

**11.15** $\boxed{\text{SOC}}$ Some results from a recent social survey administered to a random sample of adults are reported below in terms of differences by sex. Which of these differences, if any, are significant? Write a sentence or two of interpretation for each test.

**a.** Proportion favouring the legalization of marijuana:

| Sample 1 (Males) | Sample 2 (Females) |
|---|---|
| $P_{s1} = 0.37$ | $P_{s2} = 0.31$ |
| $n_1 = 202$ | $n_2 = 246$ |

**b.** Proportion strongly agreeing that "kids are life's greatest joy":

| Sample 1 (Males) | Sample 2 (Females) |
|---|---|
| $P_{s1} = 0.47$ | $P_{s2} = 0.58$ |
| $n_1 = 251$ | $n_2 = 351$ |

**c.** Proportion voting in the last federal election:

| Sample 1 (Males) | Sample 2 (Females) |
|---|---|
| $P_{s1} = 0.59$ | $P_{s2} = 0.47$ |
| $n_1 = 399$ | $n_2 = 509$ |

**d.** Average hours spent on e-mail each week:

| Sample 1 (Males) | Sample 2 (Females) |
|---|---|
| $\overline{X}_1 = 4.18$ | $\overline{X}_2 = 3.38$ |
| $s_1 = 7.21$ | $s_2 = 5.92$ |
| $n_1 = 431$ | $n_2 = 535$ |

**e.** Average number of times religious service attended each month:

| Sample 1 (Males) | Sample 2 (Females) |
|---|---|
| $\overline{X}_1 = 3.19$ | $\overline{X}_2 = 3.99$ |
| $s_1 = 2.60$ | $s_2 = 2.72$ |
| $n_1 = 641$ | $n_2 = 808$ |

**f.** Average number of children:

| Sample 1 (Males) | Sample 2 (Females) |
|---|---|
| $\overline{X}_1 = 1.49$ | $\overline{X}_2 = 1.93$ |
| $s_1 = 1.50$ | $s_2 = 1.50$ |
| $n_1 = 635$ | $n_2 = 803$ |

**You Are the Researcher**

## Using SPSS to Test the Significance of the Difference Between Two Means with the 2013 GSS

The demonstrations and exercises below use the shortened version of the 2013 GSS data set supplied with this textbook.

### SPSS DEMONSTRATION 11.1 Do Men and Women Differ in Social Activity?

SPSS includes several tests for the significance of the difference between means. In this demonstration, we'll use the **Independent-Samples T Test** to test for the significance of the difference between men and women in the number of close friends that they have, where "close friends" are defined as non-relatives with whom one feels at ease, in whom one can confide, or on whom one can call for help. If there is a statistically significant difference between the sample means for men and women, we can conclude that the populations (all Canadian adult men and women) are different on this variable.

Start SPSS and load the 2013 GSS database (*GSS_2013_Shortened.sav*). From the main menu bar, click **Analyze**, then **Compare Means**, then **Independent-Samples T Test**. The Independent-Samples T Test dialog box will open with the usual list of variables on the left. Find and move the cursor over *scf_100c* (number of close friends and click the top arrow in the middle of the window to move *scf_100c* to the **Test Variable(s)** box. Next, find and highlight *sex* and click the button arrow in the middle of the window to move *sex* to the **Grouping Variable** box. Two question marks will appear in the **Grouping Variable** box, and the **Define Groups** button will become active. SPSS needs to know which cases go in which groups. In the case at hand, the instructions we need to supply are straightforward. Males (indicated by a score of 1 on *sex*) go into Group 1 and females (a score of 2) go into Group 2.

Click the **Define Groups** button, and the **Define Groups** window will appear. Type a 1 in the box next to Group 1 (for males), then click the box next to Group 2 and type a 2 (for females). Click **Continue** to return to the **Independent-Samples T Test** window and click **OK**. The output below will be produced.

In the first block of output ("Group Statistics") there are some descriptive statistics. There were 786 males in the sample, and they had an average of 6.80 close friends, with a standard deviation of 7.482. The 783 females had an average of 5.60 close friends, with a standard deviation of 5.670.

We can see from this output that the sample means are different and that, on average, males have more close friends than females. Is the difference in sample means significant? The results of the test for significance are reported in the next block ("Independent Samples Test") of output.

For now, we will skip over the first two columns, which report the results of a test for equality of the population variances. The results in the remaining columns in the row labelled "Equal variances assumed" are based on the same model used in this chapter. To test the significance of the difference between two means we can either manually look up the $t$-critical value ($\pm 1.98$) in the $t$ table (see Appendix B), as practised throughout this chapter, or, more conveniently, use the "Sig. (2-tailed)" value (.000), where "Sig." means significance. The value of 0.000 is the *exact probability*

### Group Statistics

|  | Sex of respondent | N | Mean | Std. Deviation | Std. Error Mean |
|---|---|---|---|---|---|
| Number of close friends | Male | 786 | 6.80 | 7.482 | .267 |
|  | Female | 783 | 5.60 | 5.670 | .203 |

### Independent Samples Test

|  |  | Levene's Test for Equality of Variances | | t test for Equality of Means | | | | | | | |
|---|---|---|---|---|---|---|---|---|---|---|---|
|  |  |  |  |  |  |  |  |  | | 95% Confidence Interval of the Difference | |
|  |  | F | Sig. | t | df | Sig. (2-tailed) | Mean Difference | Std. Error Difference | Lower | Upper |
| Number of close friends | Equal variances assumed | 15.510 | .000 | 3.556 | 1568 | .000 | 1.192 | .335 | .534 | 1.849 |
|  | Equal variances not assumed |  |  | 3.558 | 1463.478 | .000 | 1.192 | .335 | .535 | 1.849 |

of getting the observed difference in sample means if only chance is operating. However, do not interpret 0.000 as a zero probability. It simply means that the exact probability value is less than 0.0005. The exact value is revealed by double-clicking on the "Sig. (2-tailed)" value in the output, but to save space, SPSS cuts it off at three decimal places, or 0.000.

Because SPSS provides the exact probability (cut off at three decimal places), there is no need to look up the critical statistic in a *t* table. This value (.000) is less than 0.05, our usual indicator of significance, so we reject the null hypothesis and conclude that the difference in means is statistically significant. On average, men and women do differ significantly in the number of their close friends.

These results are based on the assumption that the population variances are equal. In Section 11.3 we noted that this assumption is generally safe as long as sample sizes are approximately equal, as they are in this case. However, SPSS provides a *formal* test for equal variances in the populations: Levene's Test for Equality of Variances. If the Levene's Test for Equality of Variances is significant (i.e., if the value under the "Sig." column is less than 0.05, as per our usual indicator of significance), the variances will be significantly different. If this is the case, a modified *t* test should be used, which appears in the row labelled "Equal variances not assumed." A value *greater* than 0.05 indicates that the assumption of equal variances has been met and that the *t* test in that row can be used. The value of 0.000, in our example, is less than 0.05, so it was not appropriate for us to use the "Equal variances assumed" row; while the results of the *t* test are very similar, we should have used the results in the "Equal variances not assumed" row.

The last two columns report the 95% confidence interval for the difference in means. Recall from our discussion in Section 10.6 that a hypothesis test will reject a null hypothesis if a confidence interval does not contain the value of the parameter specified by the null hypothesis, and vice versa. Using the conventional hypothesis test approach, we rejected the null hypothesis that males and females on average have the same number of close friends in the population ($\mu_1 - \mu_2 = 0$) because the significance value of .000 was less than .05. We would make exactly the same decision using the 95% confidence interval for the difference in means. Because the interval, with a range of 0.535 to 1.849, does not contain the hypothesized null value, 0, the hypothesis is rejected at the 0.05 level.

## SPSS DEMONSTRATION 11.2 The Error Bar Graph

In Demonstration 6.2, we produced an error bar graph for the confidence interval for the mean. As we will demonstrate here, the error bar graph is especially useful when two (or more) groups are being compared because we can quickly assess if there is a statistically significant difference between two means by examining whether the two confidence intervals overlap.

It is very important to note, as discussed in Section 11.5, that using the overlap of confidence intervals for *each mean* provides only an approximation of the statistical significance of the difference between sample means. The confidence interval for the *difference in means* illustrated in Demonstration 11.1, on the other hand, provides a precise test for the significance of the difference. The latter procedure (confidence interval for the difference in means) is equal to formal hypothesis testing, the former procedure (overlap of confidence intervals for each mean) is not.

To produce an error bar graph of the 95% confidence interval of each mean, click **Graphs**, **Legacy Dialogs**, and then **Error Bar**. The **Error Bars** dialog box appears, with the **Simple** and **Summaries for Groups of Cases** buttons already highlighted. These are the ones we want, so just click **Define**. The **Define Simple Error Bar** dialog box will appear. Transfer the dependent variable, *scf_100c*, to the **Variable** box and the independent variable, *sex*, to the **Category Axis** box, then click **OK**, and the following error bars will be produced:

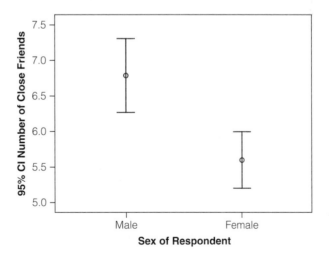

The error bars show that the sample means (marked by the small circles on each bar) are different, and that, on average, males have more close friends than females. Furthermore, the confidence intervals (indicated by the length of each bar) do not overlap, so the two means are significantly different from each other. This approximates the decision we made in Demonstration 11.1.

## SPSS DEMONSTRATION 11.3 Using the COMPUTE Command to Test for Income Differences in Overall Health

SPSS provides a variety of tools to transform and manipulate variables. One of these tools is the SPSS **Compute** command. Appendix F.5 provides a step-by-step demonstration of the **Compute** command to create a summary scale of overall health (*health*) by adding the scores on the two constituent items (*srh_110* and *srh_115*). You can quickly create the *health* variable by following that demonstration.

Here we will test health for the significance of the difference by income. Our question is: "Do people with no income compared to people with high income have a different level of overall health?" If the difference in the sample means is large enough, we can reject the null hypothesis and conclude that the populations are different.

To answer the question, follow the instructions in Demonstration 11.1 for using the **Independent-Samples T Test** command, and move *health* rather than *scf_100c* to the **Test Variable(s)** box. Instead of *sex*, make *incm* (annual personal income of the respondent in 2012) the grouping variable. Note that the *t* test requires the independent variable to have only two categories, but you can use a variable with more than two categories (e.g., *incm*) and just restrict the *t* test to any two groups (e.g., "no income" vs. "$100,000 or more"). To do this, put *incm* in the **Grouping Variable** box, and then click the **Define Groups** button to indicate the two groups you wish to compare. To compare respondents with no income and respondents with an annual personal income of $100,000 or more, type the value 1 ("no income") in the **Group 1** textbox and value 12 ("$100,000 or more") in the **Group 2** textbox, or vice versa, because the *t* test results will be exactly the same if you define "$100,000 or more" as group 1 and "no income" as group 2. Your output will be as shown:

Group Statistics

| | Annual personal income of the respondent - 2012 | N | Mean | Std. Deviation | Std. Error Mean |
|---|---|---|---|---|---|
| Health | No income | 107 | 4.5579 | 2.05985 | .19938 |
| | $ 100,000 or more | 122 | 3.3893 | 1.31744 | .11907 |

Independent Samples Test

| | | Levene's Test for Equality of Variances | | *t* Test for Equality of Means | | | | | | | |
|---|---|---|---|---|---|---|---|---|---|---|---|
| | | | | | | | | | | 95% Confidence Interval of the Difference | |
| | | F | Sig. | t | df | Sig. (2-tailed) | Mean Difference | Std. Error Difference | Lower | Upper | |
| Health | Equal variances assumed | 14.170 | .000 | 5.179 | 227 | .000 | 1.16851 | .22563 | .72391 | 1.61312 | |
| | Equal variances not assumed | | | 5.032 | 175.196 | .000 | 1.16851 | .23223 | .71018 | 1.62685 | |

We cannot assume equal variances because the Levene's Test for Equality of Variances is significant—the value under the "Sig." column is *less* than 0.05. Therefore, we must use the bottom row of the table, for equal variances not assumed. Next, the results show that the sample means are different in value (4.5579 vs. 3.3893); the test statistic ($t = +5.032$) shows us that the difference between the means is nevertheless still significant and unlikely to have occurred by random chance alone as indicated by the "Sig. (2-tailed)" value of .000. There is a significant income-based difference in overall health—a relationship that has been well-established in the overwhelming majority of population health studies. We should point out that *health* is only ordinal in level of measurement, however. Scales like this are often treated as interval-ratio variables, but we should still be cautious in interpreting the results.

## Exercises (using *GSS_2013_Shortened.sav*)

**11.1** Does the number of friends, who are not *close* friends or relatives, significantly differ between males and females? Using Demonstration 11.1 as a guide, test for a significant difference in the number of non-close friends (variable name *scf_110c*) between males and females. Write a sentence or two summarizing the results of this test.

**11.2** Using Demonstration 11.2 as a guide, create an error bar chart showing the difference in the number of non-close friends (*scf_110c*) that males and females have. Write a sentence or two summarizing how the result shown by the error bars compares with the result of the formal hypothesis test that you conducted in Exercise 11.1.

**11.3** What other types of social groups might differ either in the number of their close friends or the number of their non-close friends? Select three more independent variables besides *sex*, and conduct additional *t* tests to find out whether the number of close or non-close friends can be predicted on the basis of social group membership. Write a sentence or two summarizing the results of these tests.

# 12

# Hypothesis Testing with More Than Two Means
## One-Way Analysis of Variance

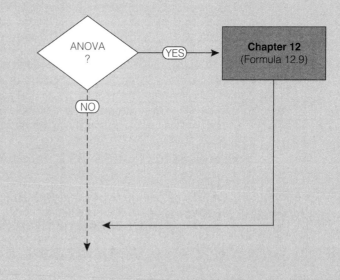

By the end of this chapter, you will be able to

1. Identify and cite examples of situations in which ANOVA is appropriate.

2. Explain the logic of hypothesis testing as applied to ANOVA.

3. Perform the one-way ANOVA test, using the five-step model as a guide, and correctly interpret the results.

4. Define and explain the concepts of population variance, total sum of squares, sum of squares between, sum of squares within, and mean square estimates.

5. Explain the difference between the statistical significance and the effect size of relationships between variables.

## 12.1 INTRODUCTION

In this chapter, we will examine a very flexible and widely used test of significance called the **analysis of variance** (often abbreviated as **ANOVA**). This test can be used in a number of situations where previously discussed tests are less than optimum or entirely inappropriate. ANOVA is designed to be used with interval-ratio-level dependent variables and is a powerful tool for analyzing the most sophisticated and precise measurements you are likely to encounter.

It is perhaps easiest to think of ANOVA as an extension of the $t$ test for the significance of the difference between two sample means, which was presented in Chapter 11. The $t$ test can be used only in situations in which our independent variable has exactly two categories under comparison (e.g., immigrants and non-immigrants). ANOVA, on the other hand, is appropriate whenever you want to test differences between the means of three or more categories. This application is called **one-way analysis of variance**, because it involves the effect of a single variable on another. (This is the simplest application of ANOVA, but the technique has numerous more advanced and complex forms that are beyond the scope of this textbook.) Further, like the two-sample test, one-way ANOVA is not only a test of significance of the difference between sample means, but can be interpreted as a test of significance of the relationship between a nominal or ordinal independent variable with three or more categories (e.g., married, common-law, single, widowed, separated, and divorced) and an interval-ratio dependent variable (e.g., income).

To illustrate, suppose we conducted an experiment in an introductory biology course at a large university to examine the effect of teaching method on student performance. One section was taught by the traditional "lecture-lab" method, a second was taught by an "all-lab" approach with no lectures, and a third was taught entirely by a series of "videotaped" lectures and demonstrations that the students were free to view at any time and as often as they wanted. Students were randomly assigned to one of three sections, and at the end of the semester, random samples of final exam scores were collected from each section. Is there a significant difference in student performance on the final exam by teaching method? Because the independent variable (teaching method) has three categories and the dependent variable (final exam score) is measured at the interval-ratio level, analysis of variance provides a very useful statistical context in which this question can be addressed.

## 12.2 THE LOGIC OF THE ANALYSIS OF VARIANCE

For ANOVA, the null hypothesis is that the populations from which the samples are drawn are equal on the characteristic of interest. As applied to our problem, the null hypothesis could be phrased as "Students in the three different sections of introductory biology at the university do not vary in their final exam scores," or symbolically as $\mu_1 = \mu_2 = \mu_3$. (Note that this is an extended version of the null hypothesis for the two-sample $t$ test for a difference in means, except that $\geq$ and $\leq$ may not be used in a one-way ANOVA null hypothesis.) As usual, the researcher will normally be interested in rejecting the null hypothesis and, in this case, showing that final exam grades are related to teaching method.

By contrast, if the null hypothesis of "no difference" in the populations is true, then any means calculated from randomly selected samples should be roughly equal in value. The average final exam score for the "lecture-lab" sample should be about the same as the average score for the "all-lab" sample and the "videotaped" sample. Note that the averages are unlikely to be exactly the same value even if the null hypothesis really is true, as we will always encounter some error or chance fluctuations in the measurement process. We are *not* asking: "Are there differences between the samples or categories of the independent variable (or, in our example, the sections of the introductory biology course)?" Rather, we are asking: "Are the differences between the samples large enough to reject the null hypothesis and justify the conclusion that the populations are different?"

Now, consider what kinds of outcomes we might encounter when conducting the teaching method experiment. Of the infinite variety of possibilities, let's focus on two extreme outcomes as exemplified by Tables 12.1 and 12.2. In the first set of hypothetical results (Table 12.1), we see that the means and standard deviations of the groups are quite similar. The average scores are about the same for every group of students, and all three groups exhibit about the same dispersion. These results would be quite consistent with the null hypothesis of no difference. Neither the average score nor the dispersion of the scores changes in any important way by section.

Now consider another set of fictitious results as displayed in Table 12.2. Here we see substantial differences in average scores from category to category, with the "Videotaped" group having the lowest average score and

**TABLE 12.1  Final Exam Scores by Teaching Method**

|  | Lecture-Lab | All-Lab | Videotaped |
|---|---|---|---|
| Mean = | 70.3 | 71.0 | 70.1 |
| Standard Deviation = | 12.4 | 11.9 | 12.2 |

**TABLE 12.2  Final Exam Scores by Teaching Method**

|  | Lecture-Lab | All-Lab | Videotaped |
|---|---|---|---|
| Mean = | 84.7 | 71.3 | 65.7 |
| Standard Deviation = | 12.4 | 11.9 | 12.2 |

the "Lecture-Lab" group having the highest. Also, the standard deviations are low and similar from group to group, indicating that there is not much variation within the groups of students. Table 12.2 shows marked differences *between* groups of students combined with homogeneity *within* groups of students, as indicated by the low values of the standard deviations. In other words, there are marked differences from group to group but there is little difference within each group. These results would contradict the null hypothesis and support the notion that final exam scores do vary by teaching method.

In principle, ANOVA makes the kinds of comparisons outlined above. The test compares the amount of variation between categories (e.g., from the "Lecture-Lab" group to the "All-Lab" group to the "Videotaped" group) with the amount of variation within categories (among the "Lecture-Lab" group, among the "All-Lab" group, and among the "Videotaped" group). The greater the differences between categories, relative to the differences within categories, the more likely the null hypothesis of "no difference" is false and can be rejected. If exam scores truly vary by teaching method, then the sample mean for each group of students should be quite different from the others and dispersion within the groups should be relatively low and similar.

## 12.3 THE COMPUTATION OF ANOVA

Even though we have been thinking of ANOVA as a test for the significance of the difference between sample means, the computational routine actually involves developing two separate estimates of the population variance, $\sigma^2$ (hence the name "analysis of variance"). Recall from Chapter 3 that the variance and standard deviation both measure dispersion and that the variance is simply the standard deviation squared. One estimate of the population variance is based on the amount of variation *within* each of the categories of the independent variable; the other is based on the amount of variation *between* categories.

Before constructing these estimates, we need to introduce some new concepts and statistics. The first new concept is the total variation of the scores, which is measured by a quantity called the **total sum of squares** or **SST**.

**FORMULA 12.1**

$$SST = \sum (X_i - \overline{X})^2$$

To find this quantity, we would take each score, subtract the mean, square the difference, and then add to get the total of the squared differences. If this formula seems vaguely familiar, it's because the same expression appears in the numerator of the formula for the sample variance and the standard deviation (see Chapter 3). This redundancy is not surprising, considering that the SST is also a way of measuring dispersion.

As the first step in constructing the two separate estimates of the population variance, the total variation (SST) is divided into two components. One of these reflects the pattern of variation within the categories and is called the **sum of squares within (SSW)**. The other component is based on the variation between categories and is called the **sum of squares between (SSB)**. SSW and SSB are components of SST, as reflected in Formula 12.2:

**FORMULA 12.2**

$$SST = SSB + SSW$$

The sum of squares within is defined as

**FORMULA 12.3**

$$SSW = \sum (X_i - \overline{X}_k)^2$$

where SSW = the sum of the squares within the categories
$\overline{X}_k$ = the mean of a category group

This formula directs us to take each score, subtract the mean of the category from the score, square the result, and then sum the squared differences. We will do this for each category separately and then sum the squared differences for all categories to find SSW.

The sum of squares between reflects the variation between the samples, with the category means serving as summary statistics for each category. Each category mean will be treated as a "case" for purposes of this estimate, and the formula for the sum of squares between is

**FORMULA 12.4**

$$SSB = \sum n_k(\overline{X}_k - \overline{X})^2$$

where SSB = the sum of squares between the categories
$n_k$ = the number of cases in a category
$\overline{X}_k$ = the mean of a category

To find SSB, subtract the overall mean of all scores from each category mean, square the difference, multiply by the number of cases in the category, and add the results across all the categories.

Let's pause for a second to remember what we are after here. If the null hypothesis is true, then there should not be much variation from category to category, relative to the variation within categories, and the two estimates of the population variance based on SSW and SSB should be roughly equal. The larger the difference between the two estimates, the more likely we will be to reject the null hypothesis. If the category means are about the same value, the differences will not be significant. The larger the differences between category means and the more homogeneous the categories, the more likely the differences are statistically significant.

The next step in the computational routine is to construct the estimates of the population variance. To do this, we must divide each sum of squares by its respective degrees of freedom. To find the degrees of freedom value associated with SSW ($dfw$), subtract the number of categories ($k$) from the number of cases ($n$). The degrees of freedom value associated with SSB ($dfb$) is the number of categories minus one. In summary,

**FORMULA 12.5**
$$dfw = n - k$$

where $dfw$ = degrees of freedom associated with SSW
$n$ = total number of cases
$k$ = number of categories

**FORMULA 12.6**
$$dfb = k - 1$$

where $dfb$ = degrees of freedom associated with SSB
$k$ = number of categories

The actual estimates of the population variance, called the **mean square within (MSW)** and **mean square between (MSB)**, are calculated by dividing each sum of squares by its respective degrees of freedom:

**FORMULA 12.7**
$$MSW = \frac{SSW}{dfw}$$

**FORMULA 12.8**
$$MSB = \frac{SSB}{dfb}$$

The test statistic calculated in step 4 of the five-step model is called the **$F$ ratio**, and its value is determined by the following formula:

**FORMULA 12.9**
$$F = \frac{MSB}{MSW}$$

As you can see, the value of the $F$ ratio will be a function of the amount of variation between categories to the amount of variation within the categories. The greater the variation between the categories relative to the variation within, the higher the value of the $F$ ratio and the more likely we will reject the null hypothesis.

## 12.4 A COMPUTA-TIONAL SHORTCUT

The computational routine for ANOVA, as summarized in the previous section, requires a number of separate steps and different formulas and will surely seem complicated the first time you see it. As is almost always the case, if you proceed systematically from formula to formula (in the correct order, of course), you will see that the computations aren't nearly as formidable as they appear at first glance. Unfortunately, they will still be lengthy and time-consuming. So, at the risk of stretching your patience, let us introduce a way to save some time and computational effort. This will require the introduction of even more formulas, but the eventual savings in time will be worth the effort. Formula 12.10 shows a quicker, more convenient way to calculate SST:

**FORMULA 12.10**
$$\text{SST} = \sum X^2 - n\overline{X}^2$$

To solve this formula, first find the sum of the squared scores (in other words, square each score and then add up the squared scores). Next, square the overall mean, multiply that value by the total number of cases in the sample ($n$), and subtract that quantity from the sum of the squared scores.

---

## ONE STEP AT A TIME  Computing ANOVA

To compute ANOVA, we will use Formulas 12.10, 12.4, and 12.11 to find SST, SSB, and SSW. Then we will calculate the degrees of freedom, the mean square estimates of the population variances, and the obtained $F$ ratio. It is strongly recommended that you use a computing table like Table 12.3 to organize the computations.

**To Find SST Using Formula 12.10**

**1:** Find $\sum X^2$ by squaring each score and adding all of the squared scores together.
**2:** Find $n\overline{X}^2$ by squaring the value of the mean and then multiplying by $n$.
**3:** Subtract the quantity you found in step 2 from the quantity you found in step 1.

**To Find SSB Using Formula 12.4**

**1:** Subtract the mean of all scores ($\overline{X}$) from the mean of each category ($\overline{X}_k$) and then square each difference.
**2:** Multiply each of the squared differences you found in step 1 by the number of cases in the category ($n_k$).
**3:** Add the quantities you found in step 2.

**To Find SSW Using Formula 12.11**

**1:** Subtract the value of SSB from the value of SST.

**To Calculate Degrees of Freedom**

**1:** For $dfw$, use Formula 12.5. Subtract the number of categories ($k$) from the number of cases ($n$).
**2:** For $dfb$, use Formula 12.6. Subtract 1 from the number of categories ($k$).

**To Construct the Two Mean Square Estimates of the Population Variance**

**1:** To find the MSW estimate, use Formula 12.7. Divide SSW by $dfw$.
**2:** To find the MSB estimate, use Formula 12.8. Divide SSB by $dfb$.

**To Find the Obtained $F$ Ratio**

**1:** Use Formula 12.9. Divide the MSB estimate by the MSW estimate.

Once we have the values of SST and SSB, we can find SSW by manipulating Formula 12.2 and doing some simple subtraction:

**FORMULA 12.11**

$$SSW = SST - SSB$$

The computational routine for ANOVA can be summarized as follows:

1. Find SST by Formula 12.10.
2. Find SSB by Formula 12.4.
3. Find SSW by subtraction (see Formula 12.11).
4. Calculate the degrees of freedom (*dfb* and *dfw*) (see Formulas 12.5 and 12.6).
5. Construct the two mean square estimates of the population variance (MSB and MSW) by dividing SSB and SSW by their respective degrees of freedom (see Formulas 12.7 and 12.8).
6. Find the obtained *F* ratio by dividing MSB by MSW (see Formula 12.9).

These computations and the actual test of significance will be illustrated in the next sections.

## 12.5 A COMPUTATIONAL EXAMPLE

Continuing with our teaching method problem, let us assume that we have final exam scores (where a score is the percent of a student's correct answers on the final exam) from a random sample of 27 students, equally divided into the three sections. All scores are reported in Table 12.3 along with the squared scores, the category means, and the overall mean. Our example is illustrated in Figure 12.1. (As a comparison, see Figures 10.1 and 11.1 depicting the one- and two-sample cases, respectively.)

**TABLE 12.3  Final Exam Scores by Teaching Method for 27 Students**

| | Lecture-Lab | | All-Lab | | Videotaped | |
|---|---|---|---|---|---|---|
| | $X$ | $X^2$ | $X$ | $X^2$ | $X$ | $X^2$ |
| | 55 | 3,025 | 56 | 3,136 | 50 | 2,500 |
| | 57 | 3,249 | 60 | 3,600 | 52 | 2,704 |
| | 60 | 3,600 | 62 | 3,844 | 60 | 3,600 |
| | 63 | 3,969 | 67 | 4,489 | 61 | 3,721 |
| | 72 | 5,184 | 70 | 4,900 | 63 | 3,969 |
| | 73 | 5,329 | 71 | 5,041 | 69 | 4,761 |
| | 79 | 6,241 | 82 | 6,724 | 71 | 5,041 |
| | 85 | 7,225 | 88 | 7,744 | 80 | 6,400 |
| | 92 | 8,464 | 95 | 9,025 | 82 | 6,724 |
| $\Sigma X =$ | 636 | | 651 | | 588 | |
| $\Sigma X^2 =$ | | 46,286 | | 48,503 | | 39,420 |
| $\bar{X}_k =$ | 70.67 | | 72.33 | | 65.33 | |
| | | | $\bar{X} = 1,875/27 = 69.44$ | | | |

**FIGURE 12.1   A Test of Hypothesis for Three-Sample Means**

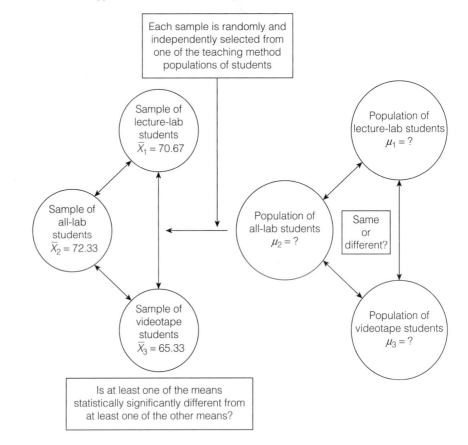

To organize our computations, we will follow the routine summarized at the end of Section 12.4 and in the One Step at a Time box. We begin by finding SST with Formula 12.10:

$$\text{SST} = \sum X^2 - n\bar{X}^2$$
$$= 134{,}209 - (27)(69.44)^2$$
$$= 4{,}017.33$$

SSB is found by Formula 12.4:

$$\text{SSB} = \sum n_k(\bar{X}_k - \bar{X})^2$$
$$= (9)(70.67 - 69.44)^2 + (9)(72.33 - 69.44)^2$$
$$\quad + (9)(65.33 - 69.44)^2$$
$$= 13.62 + 75.17 + 152.03$$
$$= 240.82$$

Now SSW can be found by subtraction (see Formula 12.11):

$$\text{SSW} = \text{SST} - \text{SSB}$$
$$= 4{,}017.33 - 240.82$$
$$= 3{,}776.51$$

To find the degrees of freedom for the two sums of squares, we use Formulas 12.5 and 12.6:

$$dfw = n - k = 27 - 3 = 24$$
$$dfb = k - 1 = 3 - 1 = 2$$

Finally, we are ready to construct the mean square estimates of the population variance. For the estimate based on SSW, we use Formula 12.7:

$$\text{MSW} = \frac{\text{SSW}}{dfw} = \frac{3{,}776.51}{24} = 157.35$$

For the between estimate, we use Formula 12.8:

$$\text{MSB} = \frac{\text{SSB}}{dfb} = \frac{240.82}{2} = 120.41$$

The test statistic, or obtained $F$ ratio, is found by Formula 12.9:

$$F = \frac{\text{MSB}}{\text{MSW}}$$
$$F = \frac{120.41}{157.35}$$
$$F = 0.77$$

This statistic must still be evaluated for its significance. *(For practice in computing these quantities and solving these formulas, solve any of the end-of-chapter problems.)*

## 12.6 A TEST OF SIGNIFICANCE FOR ANOVA

In this section, we will see how to test an $F$ ratio for significance and also take a look at some of the assumptions underlying the ANOVA test. As usual, we will follow the five-step model as a convenient way of organizing the decision-making process.

**Step 1. Make Assumptions and Meet Test Requirements.**

Model:    Independent random samples
Level of measurement is interval-ratio
Populations are normally distributed
Population variances are equal

The model assumptions are quite stringent and underscore the fact that ANOVA should be used only with dependent variables that have been carefully and precisely measured. However, as long as group sample sizes are fairly large and more or less equal, ANOVA can tolerate some violation of the model assumptions. In situations where you have small or very unequal samples, it is probably advisable to use an alternative test. (We will not consider any such alternative test in this textbook.)

**Step 2. State the Null Hypothesis.** For ANOVA, the null hypothesis always states that the means of the populations from which the samples were drawn are equal. For our example problem, we are concerned with three different populations or categories, so our null hypothesis will be

$$H_0: \mu_1 = \mu_2 = \mu_3$$

where $\mu_1$ represents the mean for students in the "Lecture-Lab" section, $\mu_2$ the mean for students in the "All-Lab" section, and $\mu_3$ the mean for students in the "Videotaped" section.

The research hypothesis states simply that at least one of the population means is different. The wording here is important. If we reject the null hypothesis, ANOVA does not identify which mean or means are significantly different. In the final section of the chapter, we will briefly discuss some advanced tests that can help us identify which pairs of means are significantly different.

($H_1$: At least one of the population means is different.)

**Step 3. Select the Sampling Distribution and Establish the Critical Region.** The sampling distribution for ANOVA is the $F$ distribution, which is summarized in Appendix D. Note that there are separate tables for alphas of 0.05 and 0.01, respectively. As with the $t$ table, the value of the critical $F$ score will vary by degrees of freedom. For ANOVA, there are two separate degrees of freedom, one for each estimate of the population variance. The numbers across the top of the table are the degrees of freedom associated with the between estimate ($dfb$), and the numbers down the side of the table are those associated with the within estimate ($dfw$). In our example, $dfb$ is ($k - 1$), or 2, and $dfw$ is ($n - k$), or 24 (see Formulas 12.5 and 12.6). So, if we set alpha at 0.05, our critical $F$ score will be 3.40.

Summarizing these considerations:

$$\text{Sampling distribution} = F \text{ distribution}$$

$$\text{Alpha} = 0.05$$

$$dfw = (n - k) = 24$$

$$dfb = (k - 1) = 2$$

$$F \text{ (critical)} = 3.40$$

Taking a moment to inspect the two $F$ tables, you will notice that all the values are greater than 1.00. This is because ANOVA is a one-tailed test, and we are concerned only with outcomes in which there is more variance between categories than within categories. *F* values of less than 1.00 would indicate that the between estimate was lower in value than the within estimate, and since we would always fail to reject the null hypothesis in such cases, we simply ignore this class of outcomes.

**Step 4. Compute the Test Statistic.** This was done in the previous section, where we found an obtained *F* ratio of 0.77.

**Step 5. Make a Decision and Interpret the Results of the Test.** Compare the test statistic with the critical value:

$$F \text{ (critical)} = 3.40$$

$$F \text{ (obtained)} = 0.77$$

Because the test statistic does not fall into the critical region, our decision will be to fail to reject the null hypothesis. Student performance does not differ significantly by teaching method, and the variation we observed in the sample means is highly likely to have occurred only by random chance. *(For practice in conducting the ANOVA test, see Problems 12.2 to 12.9. Begin with the lower-numbered problems as they have smaller data sets and fewer categories and, therefore, the simplest calculations.)*

---

### Applying Statistics 12.1: The Analysis of Variance

A researcher has been asked to evaluate the efficiency with which each of three social service agencies is administering a particular program. One area of concern is the speed of the agencies in processing paperwork and determining the eligibility of potential clients. The researcher has gathered information on the number of days required for processing a random sample of 10 cases in each agency. Is there a significant difference between the agencies? The data are reported in the table below, which also includes some additional information we will need to complete our calculations.

The ANOVA test will tell us if these differences are large enough to justify the conclusion that they did not occur by chance alone. Following the usual computational routine:

$$SST = \sum X^2 - n\overline{X}^2$$

$$SST = (524 + 1{,}816 + 2{,}462) - 30(11.67)^2$$

$$SST = 4{,}802 - 30(136.19)$$

$$SST = 4{,}802 - 4{,}085.70$$

$$SST = 716.30$$

$$SSB = \sum n_k(\overline{X}_k - \overline{X})^2$$

$$SSB = (10)(7.0 - 11.67)^2 + (10)(13.0 - 11.67)^2$$
$$+ (10)(15.0 - 11.67)^2$$

$$SSB = (10)(21.80) + (10)(1.77) + (10)(11.09)$$

$$SSB = 218.10 + 17.17 + 110.09$$

$$SSB = 346.70$$

$$SSW = SST - SSB$$

$$SSW = 716.30 - 346.70$$

$$SSW = 369.60$$

$$dfw = n - k = 30 - 3 = 27$$

$$dfb = k - 1 = 3 - 1 = 2$$

*(continued)*

**Number of Days Required to Process Cases for Three Agencies (fictitious data)**

| | Agency A | | Agency B | | Agency C | |
|---|---|---|---|---|---|---|
| Client | $X$ | $X^2$ | $X$ | $X^2$ | $X$ | $X^2$ |
| 1 | 5 | 25 | 12 | 144 | 9 | 81 |
| 2 | 7 | 49 | 10 | 100 | 8 | 64 |
| 3 | 8 | 64 | 19 | 361 | 12 | 144 |
| 4 | 10 | 100 | 20 | 400 | 15 | 225 |
| 5 | 4 | 16 | 12 | 144 | 20 | 400 |
| 6 | 9 | 81 | 11 | 121 | 21 | 441 |
| 7 | 6 | 36 | 13 | 169 | 20 | 400 |
| 8 | 9 | 81 | 14 | 196 | 19 | 361 |
| 9 | 6 | 36 | 10 | 100 | 15 | 225 |
| 10 | 6 | 36 | 9 | 81 | 11 | 121 |
| $\sum X =$ | 70 | | 130 | | 150 | |
| $\sum X^2 =$ | | 524 | | 1816 | | 2462 |
| $\overline{X}_k =$ | 7.0 | | 13.0 | | 15.0 | |
| | | | $\overline{X} = 350/30 = 11.67$ | | | |

© Cengage Learning

$$\text{MSW} = \frac{\text{SSW}}{dfw} = \frac{369.60}{27} = 13.69$$

$$\text{MSB} = \frac{\text{SSB}}{dfb} = \frac{346.70}{2} = 173.35$$

$$F \text{ (obtained)} = \frac{\text{MSB}}{\text{MSW}} = \frac{173.35}{13.69} = 12.66$$

We can now conduct the test of significance.

**Step 1. Make Assumptions and Meet Test Requirements.**

Model: Independent random samples
Level of measurement is interval-ratio
Populations are normally distributed
Population variances are equal

**Step 2. State the Null Hypothesis.**

$$H_0: \mu_1 = \mu_2 = \mu_3$$

($H_1$: At least one of the population means is different.)

**Step 3. Select the Sampling Distribution and Establish the Critical Region.**

Sampling distribution = $F$ distribution

Alpha = 0.05

$$dfw = (n - k) = (30 - 3) = 27$$

$$dfb = (k - 1) = (3 - 1) = 2$$

$$F \text{ (critical)} = 3.35$$

**Step 4. Compute the Test Statistic.** We found an obtained $F$ ratio of 12.66.

**Step 5. Make a Decision and Interpret the Results of the Test.** Compare the test statistic with the critical value

$$F \text{ (critical)} = 3.35$$

$$F \text{ (obtained)} = 12.66$$

The null hypothesis ("The population means are equal") can be rejected. The difference between the three agencies in the speed with which they process paperwork and determine eligibility is statistically significant.

## 12.7 AN ADDITIONAL EXAMPLE FOR COMPUTING AND TESTING THE ANALYSIS OF VARIANCE

In this section, we will work through an additional example of the computation and interpretation of the ANOVA test. We will first review matters of computation, then find the obtained $F$ ratio, and then test the statistic for its significance. In the computational section, we will follow the step-by-step guidelines presented at the end of Section 12.4 and in the One Step at a Time: Computing ANOVA box.

A random sample of 15 nations from three levels of development has been selected. "Low income" nations are largely agricultural and have the lowest quality of life. "High income" nations are industrial and the most affluent and modern. "Middle income" nations are between these extremes. Are these general characteristics reflected in differences in female life expectancy (the number of years the average female can expect to live at birth) among the three categories? The female life expectancy data for the 15 nations are reported in Table 12.4 along with the other quantities needed to complete the computations.

To find SST by the computational Formula 12.10:

$$\text{SST} = \sum X^2 - n\overline{X}^2$$
$$= (21{,}153 + 28{,}867 + 34{,}499) - 15(74.60)^2$$
$$= 84{,}519 - 83{,}477.40$$
$$= 1{,}041.60$$

To find SSB by Formula 12.4:

$$\text{SSB} = \sum n_k(\overline{X}_k - \overline{X})^2$$
$$= (5)(65.00 - 74.60)^2 + (5)(75.80 - 74.60)^2 + (5)(83.00 - 74.60)^2$$
$$= 460.80 + 7.20 + 352.80$$
$$= 820.80$$

### TABLE 12.4 Life Expectancy of Females at Birth by Income Level

| Low Income | | | Middle Income | | | High Income | | |
|---|---|---|---|---|---|---|---|---|
| Nation | $X$ | $X^2$ | Nation | $X$ | $X^2$ | Nation | $X$ | $X^2$ |
| Cambodia | 66 | 4,356 | China | 78 | 6,084 | Australia | 84 | 7,056 |
| Malawi | 64 | 4,096 | Indonesia | 73 | 5,329 | Canada | 84 | 7,056 |
| Nepal | 69 | 4,761 | Pakistan | 67 | 4,489 | Japan | 87 | 7,569 |
| Niger | 62 | 3,844 | Costa Rica | 82 | 6,724 | Russia | 77 | 5,929 |
| Sudan | 64 | 4,096 | Turkey | 79 | 6,241 | United Kingdom | 83 | 6,889 |
| $\sum X =$ | 325 | | | 379 | | | 415 | |
| $\sum X^2 =$ | | 21,153 | | | 28,867 | | | 34,499 |
| $\overline{X}_k =$ | 65.00 | | | 75.80 | | | 83.00 | |
| | | | $\overline{X} = 74.60$ | | | | | |

Source: Population Reference Bureau, *2016 World Population Data Sheet.*

Now we can find SSW by Formula 12.11:

$$SSW = SST - SSB$$
$$= 1,041.60 - 820.80$$
$$= 220.80$$

The degrees of freedom are found by Formulas 12.5 and 12.6:

$$dfw = n - k = 15 - 3 = 12$$
$$dfb = k - 1 = 3 - 1 = 2$$

The estimates of the population variances are found by Formulas 12.7 and 12.8:

$$MSW = \frac{SSW}{dfw} = \frac{220.80}{12} = 18.40$$

$$MSB = \frac{SSB}{dfb} = \frac{820.80}{2} = 410.40$$

The $F$ ratio (see Formula 12.9) is

$$F \text{ (obtained)} = \frac{\text{Mean square between}}{\text{Mean square within}}$$

$$F \text{ (obtained)} = \frac{410.40}{18.40}$$

$$F \text{ (obtained)} = 22.30$$

And we can now test this value for its significance.

### Step 1. Make Assumptions and Meet Test Requirements.

> Model: Independent random samples
> Level of measurement is interval-ratio
> Populations are normally distributed
> Population variances are equal

The researcher will always be in a position to judge the adequacy of the first two assumptions in the model. The second two assumptions are more problematical, but remember that ANOVA will tolerate some deviation from its assumptions as long as sample sizes are fairly large and roughly equal (note that for illustrative purposes, sample sizes in this example have been kept very small).

### Step 2. State the Null Hypothesis.

$H_0: \mu_1 = \mu_2 = \mu_3$

($H_1$: At least one of the population means is different.)

**Step 3. Select the Sampling Distribution and Establish the Critical Region.**

$$\text{Sampling distribution} = F \text{ distribution}$$
$$\text{Alpha} = 0.05$$
$$\text{Degrees of freedom (within)} = (n - k) = (15 - 3) = 12$$
$$\text{Degrees of freedom (between)} = (k - 1) = (3 - 1) = 2$$
$$F \text{ (critical)} = 3.89$$

**Step 4. Compute the Test Statistic.** We found an obtained $F$ ratio of 17.69.

**Step 5. Make a Decision and Interpret the Results of the Test.** Compare the test statistic with the critical value:

$$F \text{ (critical)} = 3.89$$
$$F \text{ (obtained)} = 22.30$$

The test statistic is in the critical region, and we would reject the null hypothesis of no difference. The differences between the three groupings are very unlikely to have occurred by chance alone. The difference in female life expectancy between nations at different income levels is statistically significant.

## 12.8 THE LIMITATIONS OF THE TEST

One important limitation of ANOVA is that it requires interval-ratio measurement of the dependent variable. This condition may be difficult to meet with complete confidence for many variables of interest to the social sciences. While social scientists occasionally overlook this requirement and treat ordinal-level variables as interval-ratio ones, and use more powerful statistics like ANOVA to analyze them, you should be aware of such limitations in planning your own research as well as in judging the adequacy of research conducted by others.

A second limitation of ANOVA actually applies to all forms of significance testing and was introduced in Section 7.12. These tests are designed to detect non-random differences—differences so large that they are very unlikely to be produced by random chance alone. The problem is that differences that are statistically significant are not necessarily important in any other sense (e.g., the relationship between variables may be relatively weak). In the next section, we look at a measure of association used to assess the strength of relationship when we have found a statistically significant result with ANOVA.

A final limitation of ANOVA relates to the research hypothesis. This hypothesis is not specific; it simply asserts that at least one of the population means is different from the others. Obviously, when we reject the null hypothesis, we would like to know *which* differences between the sample means are significant.

We can sometimes make this determination by simple inspection. In our problem involving the economic development of nations, for example, it is pretty clear from Table 12.4 that the "least developed" group is the source of most of the differences. This informal, "eyeball" method can be misleading, however, and you should exercise caution in drawing conclusions.

In Section 12.10, we provide an extended example of the interpretation of ANOVA and introduce a technique, called the **post hoc** or "after the fact" **test**, that permits us to identify significant differences between the sample means reliably. The post hoc test is similar to the $t$ test covered in Chapter 11, except that all possible pairs of sample means are tested. Post hoc analysis is like performing a series of $t$ tests; however, the computational routines for post hoc tests are beyond the scope of this text. Post hoc tests are commonly available in computerized statistical packages such as SPSS.

## 12.9 EFFECT SIZE MEASURE OF ASSOCIATION FOR ANOVA: ETA-SQUARED

In Chapters 8 and 9, we introduced various measures of association for nominal and ordinal variables to measure the strength and, where appropriate, direction of a statistically significant relationship. Similarly, we can use a statistic called **eta-squared ($\eta^2$)** to assess the strength of relationship when using one-way ANOVA. This statistic is simply the ratio of SSB to SST, as shown in Formula 12.12. Table 12.5 provides some assistance with interpreting the value of eta-squared in a format similar to Tables 8.5, 8.14, and 9.3.

**FORMULA 12.12**

$$\eta^2 = \frac{\text{SSB}}{\text{SST}}$$

To illustrate the computation of eta-squared, let's continue to examine the national income and female life expectancy example from Table 12.4, where SSB = 820.80 and SST = 1,041.60. Therefore, $\eta^2$ is

$$\eta^2 = \frac{\text{SSB}}{\text{SST}}$$

$$\eta^2 = \frac{820.80}{1,041.60}$$

$$\eta^2 = 0.7880$$

**TABLE 12.5** **The Relationship Between the Value of Eta-squared and the Strength of the Relationship**

| Value | Strength |
|---|---|
| If the value is | The strength of the relationship is |
| between 0.00 and 0.10 | weak |
| between 0.11 and 0.30 | moderate |
| greater than 0.30 | strong |

Since $\eta^2$ is greater than 0.30, national income level has a strong impact on female life expectancy. In addition to interpretation of strength of association, eta-squared also has a PRE (proportional reduction in error) interpretation. So, we improve our predictions of the dependent variable by 78.8% when taking the independent variable into account. *(For practice in computing $\eta^2$, solve any of the end-of-chapter problems.)*

## 12.10 INTERPRETING STATISTICS: DOES PERSONAL WELL-BEING VARY BY MARITAL STATUS?

Is there a relationship between marital status and personal well-being? Are unmarried individuals happier than married individuals? Are married persons more satisfied with life than divorced persons?

We will use data from the Canadian sample of the World Values Survey (WVS) to answer these questions scientifically. The WVS is administered by a network of social scientists about every five years to randomly selected samples of citizens from around the globe. It is designed to allow cross-national comparisons of values and norms on a wide variety of topics including opinions on life, family, work, traditional values, morality, religion, politics, the environment, and other contemporary social issues. The WVS sample data used in this analysis are based on a random sample of the population of Canada.

This analysis involves three variables. The independent variable is marital status, and there will be two separate dependent variables: happiness and life satisfaction. Marital status is a nominal-level variable with five categories. The two dependent variables are basically ordinal in level of measurement rather than the interval-ratio level required by ANOVA: happiness is measured on a 4-point scale, where 1 means "not at all happy" and 4 means "very happy," and life satisfaction on a 10-point scale, where 1 is "completely dissatisfied" and 10 is "completely satisfied." It is not unusual for social scientists to take liberties with this requirement, that is, to treat variables measured at the ordinal level as if they were interval-ratio and to analyze them with more powerful and interesting statistics like ANOVA. While this practice is common, we must be cautious in assessing the statistical results and in developing interpretations when the level of measurement criterion has been violated.

The summary statistics for the two personal well-being variables are presented in Table 12.6. Overall, Canadians have relatively high levels of

### TABLE 12.6  Descriptive Statistics for Personal Well-Being Variables

|  | Happiness | Life Satisfaction |
|---|---|---|
| Mean = | 3.41 | 7.75 |
| Standard Deviation = | 0.60 | 1.71 |
| $n$ = | 2,144 | 2,144 |

[1]Happiness scores range from 1 to 4 and life satisfaction scores range from 1 to 10, with higher scores indicating greater happiness and satisfaction.

Source: World Values Survey Association, *Wave 5 World Values Survey*.

both happiness and life satisfaction, with average scores of 3.41 and 7.75, respectively.

The next two tables report the means and standard deviations for happiness (Table 12.7) and life satisfaction (Table 12.8) for each marital status group. Looking at Table 12.7, the $F$ ratio for the differences in levels of happiness by marital status is 24.11, which is significant at less than the 0.001 level. We would conclude that marital status does make a significant difference in the happiness of Canadians. Comparing the category means, the results are what one might expect. Married individuals (which includes those in a common-law relationship) on average had the highest level of happiness (3.51) and separated persons the lowest level, with an average happiness score of 3.17. Widowed persons had the next highest average score (3.35). Divorced and never-married persons had average happiness scores of 3.27 and 3.23, respectively.

Table 12.8 reports the means and standard deviations for life satisfaction by marital status. Once again, married individuals on average had highest level of life satisfaction (8.03) and separated persons had the lowest level (6.95). Divorced respondents had the second-lowest average life satisfaction score (7.16), followed by never-married persons (7.28). As with happiness, widowed persons in general are relatively satisfied with life,

**TABLE 12.7  Happiness by Marital Status**

|  | Marital Status | | | | | ANOVA | |
| --- | --- | --- | --- | --- | --- | --- | --- |
|  | Married | Divorced | Separated | Widowed | Never Married | $F$ ratio | Alpha |
| Mean = | 3.51 | 3.27 | 3.17 | 3.35 | 3.23 | 24.11 | <0.001 |
| Standard Deviation = | 0.55 | 0.65 | 0.78 | 0.66 | 0.60 | | |
| $n$ = | 1,329 | 141 | 78 | 170 | 426 | | |

**TABLE 12.8  Life Satisfaction by Marital Status**

|  | Marital Status | | | | | ANOVA | |
| --- | --- | --- | --- | --- | --- | --- | --- |
|  | Married | Divorced | Separated | Widowed | Never Married | $F$ ratio | Alpha |
| Mean = | 8.03 | 7.16 | 6.95 | 7.65 | 7.28 | 26.82 | <0.001 |
| Standard Deviation = | 1.61 | 1.84 | 1.89 | 1.92 | 1.63 | | |
| $n$ = | 1,329 | 141 | 78 | 170 | 426 | | |

with an average score of 7.65. The $F$ ratio of 26.82 is significant at less than 0.001, so we can conclude that life satisfaction is significantly affected by marital status.

**Post Hoc Analysis**   Tables 12.7 and 12.8 indicate significant relationships, but which differences in the tables are most important and contribute the most to the significant $F$ ratios? We can see by inspection that the married group is very different from the others, but what other differences might be important? A post hoc analysis of the differences in sample means can provide objective answers to these questions.

We will not present the computational routines for post hoc tests, but the interpretation of the results of these tests is straightforward. The tests essentially compare the means of all possible pairs of categories (i.e., married with divorced, widowed with separated, and so forth). While post hoc tests are similar to the conventional two-sample tests that we learned about in Chapter 11, they are also different. Specifically, post hoc tests correct, by using more stringent criteria to identify significant differences between means, for the fact that we are making comparisons of *all* possible pairs of means and thereby increasing the probability of making an alpha or Type I error (i.e., falsely rejecting a true null hypothesis—see Chapter 7).

Table 12.9 presents the results of post hoc tests for both measures of personal well-being. The categories are listed at the left-hand side of

**TABLE 12.9**   **A Post Hoc Test for Differences in Personal Well-Being by Marital Status**

| Marital Status | Mean Differences in Happiness | | | | |
|---|---|---|---|---|---|
| | Married (3.51) | Divorced (3.27) | Separated (3.17) | Widowed (3.35) | Never Married (3.23) |
| Married (3.51) | | 0.24* | 0.34* | 0.16* | 0.28* |
| Divorced (3.27) | | | 0.10 | −0.08 | 0.04 |
| Separated (3.17) | | | | −0.18* | −0.06 |
| Widowed (3.35) | | | | | 0.12* |

| Marital Status | Mean Difference in Life Satisfaction | | | | |
|---|---|---|---|---|---|
| | Married (8.03) | Divorced (7.16) | Separated (6.95) | Widowed (7.65) | Never Married (7.28) |
| Married (8.03) | | 0.87* | 1.08* | 0.38* | 0.75* |
| Divorced (7.16) | | | 0.21 | −0.49* | −0.12 |
| Separated (6.95) | | | | −0.70* | −0.33 |
| Widowed (7.65) | | | | | 0.37* |

*Mean difference is significant at the 0.05 level, Modified Least Significant Differences Test.

the table and again across the top, along with the category means. The entries in the table are the differences in the means for the category listed at the left of the table and the category listed across the top. A positive difference indicates that the category listed to the left had a higher score, and a negative difference means that the category listed across the top had the higher score. For example, the average happiness score was 3.51 for married respondents (category listed on the left) and 3.27 for divorced respondents (category listed across the top). The difference between the two category means is $3.51 - 3.27$, or 0.24, the value reported at the intersection of the two categories. This value is positive, which indicates that married respondents (category to the left) had a higher score than divorced respondents (category across the top). An asterisk (*) next to the value means that the difference is significant at the 0.05 level.

Looking first at the top portion of the table (differences in levels of happiness), we can see that the married respondents were actually significantly happier on average than all other categories. We also see that separated respondents were significantly *less* happy than widowed respondents ($-0.18*$), and further, that the widowed were significantly happier in general than the "never married" ($0.12*$).

The differences in life satisfaction (reported in the bottom portion of the table) show similar patterns. The married group had significantly higher life satisfaction than every other group. The tests also reveal that widowed persons were significantly more satisfied with their lives compared to other non-married (divorced, separated, and never-married) persons. The fact that the married group was the "most different" was obvious from Tables 12.7 and 12.8, but these additional significant differences might well have escaped our attention had a post hoc test not been conducted.

In conclusion, the analysis of variance test shows that marital status makes a significant difference in levels of personal well-being of Canadians. Furthermore, the post hoc tests reveal that married individuals were significantly happier and more satisfied with their lives. Perhaps more interesting is the finding that the widowed reported higher levels of happiness and life satisfaction compared to the other non-married groups.

## SUMMARY

**1.** One-way analysis of variance is a powerful test of significance that is commonly used when comparisons across more than two categories or samples are of interest. It is perhaps easiest to conceptualize ANOVA as an extension of the *t* test for the difference in sample means.

**2.** ANOVA compares the amount of variation within categories to the amount of variation between categories. If the null hypothesis of no difference is false, there should be relatively great variation between categories and relatively little variation within categories. The greater the differences from category to category relative to the differences within the categories, the more likely we will be able to reject the null hypothesis. This should also be interpreted as indicating that the independent variable has a statistically significant effect on the dependent variable.

3. The computational routine for even simple applications of ANOVA can quickly become quite complex. The basic process is to construct separate estimates of the population variance based on the variation within the categories and the variation between the categories. The test statistic is the $F$ ratio, which is based on a comparison of these two estimates. The basic computational routine is summarized at the end of Section 12.4, and this is probably an appropriate time to mention the widespread availability of statistical packages such as SPSS, the purpose of which is to perform complex calculations such as these accurately and quickly. If you haven't yet learned how to use such programs, ANOVA may provide you with the necessary incentive.

4. The ANOVA test can be organized into the familiar five-step model for testing the significance of sample outcomes. The null hypothesis takes the familiar form of stating that there is no difference of any importance among the population values, while the research hypothesis asserts that at least one population mean is different from at least one other population mean. The sampling distribution is the $F$ distribution, and the test is always one-tailed. The decision to reject or to fail to reject the null hypothesis is based on a comparison of the obtained $F$ ratio with the critical $F$ ratio as determined for a given alpha level and degrees of freedom. The decision to reject the null hypothesis indicates only that one or more of the population means is different from at least one of the others. We can often determine which sample mean(s) account for the difference by inspecting the sample data, but this informal method should be used with caution. Post hoc tests are more reliable indicators of significant differences.

5. When a statistically significant result has been found, the PRE measure of association eta-squared ($\eta^2$) can be used to measure the strength of relationship between variables.

---

**SUMMARY OF FORMULAS**

Total sum of squares:

12.1 $\quad \text{SST} = \sum (X_i - \overline{X})^2$

The two components of the total sum of squares:

12.2 $\quad \text{SST} = \text{SSB} + \text{SSW}$

Sum of squares within:

12.3 $\quad \text{SSW} = \sum (X_i - \overline{X}_k)^2$

Sum of squares between:

12.4 $\quad \text{SSB} = \sum n_k (\overline{X}_k - \overline{X})^2$

Degrees of freedom for SSW:

12.5 $\quad dfw = n - k$

Degrees of freedom for SSB:

12.6 $\quad dfb = k - 1$

Mean square within:

12.7 $\quad MSW = \dfrac{SSW}{dfw}$

Mean square between:

12.8 $\quad MSB = \dfrac{SSB}{dfb}$

$F$ ratio:

12.9 $\quad F = \dfrac{MSB}{MSW}$

Computational formula for SST:

12.10 $\quad SST = \sum X^2 - n\overline{X}^2$

Finding SSW by subtraction:

12.11 $\quad SSW = SST - SSB$

Eta-squared:

12.12 $\quad \eta^2 = \dfrac{SSB}{SST}$

## GLOSSARY

**Analysis of variance (ANOVA).** A test of significance appropriate for situations in which we are concerned with the differences among more than two sample means.

**Eta-squared ($\eta^2$).** The PRE measure of association used with one-way ANOVA.

**$F$ ratio.** The test statistic computed in step 4 of the ANOVA test.

**Mean square between (MSB).** An estimate of the population variance calculated by dividing the sum of squares between (SSB) by the degrees of freedom between ($dfb$).

**Mean square within (MSW).** An estimate of the population variance calculated by dividing the sum of squares within (SSW) by the degrees of freedom within ($dfw$).

**One-way analysis of variance.** Application of ANOVA in which the effect of a single independent variable on a dependent variable is observed.

**Post hoc test.** A technique for determining which pair(s) of means is significantly different.

**Sum of squares between (SSB).** The sum of the squared deviations of the sample means from the overall mean, weighted by sample size.

**Sum of squares within (SSW).** The sum of the squared deviations of scores from the category means.

**Total sum of squares (SST).** The sum of the squared deviations of the scores from the overall mean.

## MULTIMEDIA RESOURCES

 nelson.com/student

Visit the companion website for the fourth Canadian edition of *Statistics: A Tool for Social Research* to access a wide range of student resources. Begin by clicking on the Student Resources section of the textbook's website to access online chapters and study tools.

## PROBLEMS

*(NOTE: The number of cases in these problems is very low—a fraction of the sample size necessary for any serious research—in order to simplify computations.)*

**12.1** Calculate the obtained $F$ ratio and, where appropriate, eta-squared, for each set of scores below. *(HINT: Follow the computational shortcut outlined in Section 12.4 and keep track of all sums and means by constructing computational tables like Table 12.3 or 12.4.)*

**a.** Category

| A | B | C |
|---|---|---|
| 5 | 10 | 12 |
| 7 | 12 | 16 |
| 8 | 14 | 18 |
| 9 | 15 | 20 |

**b.** Category

| A | B | C |
|---|---|---|
| 1 | 2 | 3 |
| 10 | 12 | 10 |
| 9 | 2 | 7 |
| 20 | 3 | 14 |
| 8 | 1 | 1 |

**c.** Category

| A | B | C | D |
|---|---|---|---|
| 13 | 45 | 23 | 10 |
| 15 | 40 | 78 | 20 |
| 10 | 47 | 80 | 25 |
| 11 | 50 | 34 | 27 |
| 10 | 45 | 30 | 20 |

**12.2** SOC What type of person is most involved in the neighbourhood and community? Who is more likely to volunteer for organizations such as Scouts, Big Sisters, or the United Way? A random sample of 15 people have been asked for their number of memberships in community voluntary organizations and some other information. Which differences are significant? Where appropriate, calculate eta-squared.

**a.** Membership by education:

| Less Than High School | High School | College/University |
|---|---|---|
| 0 | 1 | 0 |
| 1 | 3 | 3 |
| 2 | 3 | 4 |
| 3 | 4 | 4 |
| 4 | 5 | 4 |

**b.** Membership by length of residence in present community:

| Less Than 2 Years | 2–5 Years | More Than 5 Years |
|---|---|---|
| 0 | 0 | 1 |
| 1 | 2 | 3 |
| 3 | 3 | 3 |
| 4 | 4 | 4 |
| 4 | 5 | 4 |

**c.** Membership by extent of television watching:

| Little or None | Moderate | High |
|---|---|---|
| 0 | 3 | 4 |
| 0 | 3 | 4 |
| 1 | 3 | 4 |
| 1 | 3 | 4 |
| 2 | 4 | 5 |

**d.** Membership by number of children:

| None | One Child | More Than One Child |
|---|---|---|
| 0 | 2 | 0 |
| 1 | 3 | 3 |
| 1 | 4 | 4 |
| 3 | 4 | 4 |
| 3 | 4 | 5 |

**12.3** SOC In a local community, a random sample of 18 couples has been assessed on a scale that measures the extent to which power and decision making are shared (lower scores) or monopolized by one party (higher scores), and on a scale that measures marital happiness (lower scores indicate lower levels of happiness). The couples were also classified by type of relationship: traditional (only the husband works outside the home), dual-career (both parties work for pay), and cohabitational (parties living together but not legally married, regardless of work patterns). Does decision making or happiness vary significantly by type of relationship? Where appropriate, calculate eta-squared.

**a.** Decision Making

| Traditional | Dual-Career | Cohabitational |
|---|---|---|
| 7 | 8 | 2 |
| 8 | 5 | 1 |
| 2 | 4 | 3 |
| 5 | 4 | 4 |
| 7 | 5 | 1 |
| 6 | 5 | 2 |

**b.**

| Happiness | | |
|---|---|---|
| Traditional | Dual-Career | Cohabitational |
| 10 | 12 | 12 |
| 14 | 12 | 14 |
| 20 | 12 | 15 |
| 22 | 14 | 17 |
| 23 | 15 | 18 |
| 24 | 20 | 22 |

**12.4** CJ Two separate crime reduction programs have been implemented in the city of Pearson, Ontario. One involves a neighbourhood watch program with citizens actively involved in crime prevention. The second involves officers patrolling the neighbourhoods on foot rather than in patrol cars. In terms of the percentage reduction in crimes reported to the police over a one-year period, were the programs successful? Where appropriate, calculate eta-squared. The results are for random samples of 18 neighbourhoods drawn from the entire city.

| Neighbourhood Watch | Foot Patrol | No Program |
|---|---|---|
| −10 | −21 | +30 |
| −20 | −15 | −10 |
| +10 | −80 | +14 |
| +20 | −10 | +80 |
| +70 | −50 | +50 |
| +10 | −10 | −20 |

**12.5** SOC Are sexually active teenagers any better informed about AIDS and other potential health problems related to sex than teenagers who are sexually inactive? A 15-item test of general knowledge about sex and health was administered to random samples of teens who are sexually inactive, teens who are sexually active but with only a single partner ("going steady"), and teens who are sexually active with more than one partner. Is there any significant difference in the test scores? Where appropriate, calculate eta-squared.

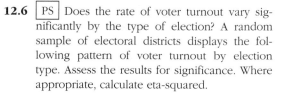

| Inactive | Active—One Partner | Active—More Than One Partner |
|---|---|---|
| 10 | 11 | 12 |
| 12 | 11 | 12 |
| 8 | 6 | 10 |
| 10 | 5 | 4 |
| 8 | 15 | 3 |
| 5 | 10 | 15 |

**12.6** PS Does the rate of voter turnout vary significantly by the type of election? A random sample of electoral districts displays the following pattern of voter turnout by election type. Assess the results for significance. Where appropriate, calculate eta-squared.

| Municipal | Provincial | Federal |
|---|---|---|
| 33 | 35 | 42 |
| 78 | 56 | 40 |
| 32 | 35 | 52 |
| 28 | 40 | 66 |
| 10 | 45 | 78 |
| 12 | 42 | 62 |
| 61 | 65 | 57 |
| 28 | 62 | 75 |
| 29 | 25 | 72 |
| 45 | 47 | 51 |
| 44 | 52 | 69 |
| 41 | 55 | 59 |

**12.7** GER Do older citizens lose interest in politics and current affairs? A brief quiz on recent headline stories was administered to random samples of respondents from each of four different age groups. Is there a significant difference? Where appropriate, calculate eta-squared. The data below represent numbers of correct responses.

| High School (15–18) | Young Adult (21–30) | Middle-Aged (40–55) | Retired (65+) |
|---|---|---|---|
| 0 | 0 | 2 | 5 |
| 1 | 0 | 3 | 6 |
| 1 | 2 | 3 | 6 |
| 2 | 2 | 4 | 6 |
| 2 | 4 | 4 | 7 |
| 2 | 4 | 5 | 7 |
| 3 | 4 | 6 | 8 |
| 5 | 6 | 7 | 10 |
| 5 | 7 | 7 | 10 |
| 7 | 7 | 8 | 10 |
| 7 | 7 | 8 | 10 |
| 9 | 10 | 10 | 10 |

**12.8** SOC A social survey was administered to a random sample of adults. A subsample of these adults, selected randomly, is shown below. Each respondent has been classified as either a city dweller, a suburbanite, or a rural dweller. Are there statistically significant differences by place of residence for any of the variables listed below? Where appropriate, calculate eta-squared.

**a.** Occupational Prestige (higher scores indicate greater prestige)

| Urban | Suburban | Rural |
|-------|----------|-------|
| 32 | 40 | 30 |
| 45 | 48 | 40 |
| 42 | 50 | 40 |
| 47 | 55 | 45 |
| 48 | 55 | 45 |
| 50 | 60 | 50 |
| 51 | 65 | 52 |
| 55 | 70 | 55 |
| 60 | 75 | 55 |
| 65 | 75 | 60 |

**b.** Number of Children

| Urban | Suburban | Rural |
|-------|----------|-------|
| 1 | 0 | 1 |
| 1 | 1 | 4 |
| 0 | 0 | 2 |
| 2 | 0 | 3 |
| 1 | 2 | 3 |
| 0 | 2 | 2 |
| 2 | 3 | 5 |
| 2 | 2 | 0 |
| 1 | 2 | 4 |
| 0 | 1 | 6 |

**c.** Monthly Family Income (in thousands of dollars)

| Urban | Suburban | Rural |
|-------|----------|-------|
| 5 | 6 | 5 |
| 7 | 8 | 5 |
| 8 | 11 | 11 |
| 11 | 12 | 10 |
| 8 | 12 | 9 |
| 9 | 11 | 6 |
| 8 | 11 | 10 |
| 3 | 9 | 7 |
| 9 | 10 | 9 |
| 10 | 12 | 8 |

**d.** Number of Times Religious Service Attended per Month

| Urban | Suburban | Rural |
|-------|----------|-------|
| 0 | 0 | 1 |
| 7 | 0 | 5 |
| 0 | 2 | 4 |
| 4 | 5 | 4 |
| 5 | 8 | 0 |
| 8 | 5 | 4 |
| 7 | 8 | 8 |
| 5 | 7 | 8 |
| 7 | 2 | 8 |
| 4 | 6 | 5 |

**e.** Hours of TV Watching per Day

| Urban | Suburban | Rural |
|-------|----------|-------|
| 5 | 5 | 3 |
| 3 | 7 | 7 |
| 12 | 10 | 5 |
| 2 | 2 | 0 |
| 0 | 3 | 1 |
| 2 | 0 | 8 |
| 3 | 1 | 5 |
| 4 | 3 | 10 |
| 5 | 4 | 3 |
| 9 | 1 | 1 |

**12.9** SOC Does support for doctor-assisted suicide ("death with dignity") vary by social class? Is this relationship different in different nations? If there is a statistically significant relationship, calculate the effect size using eta-squared. Small samples in three nations were asked if it is ever justified for a person with an incurable disease to obtain medical assistance to end his or her own life. Respondents answered in terms of a 10-point scale on which 10 was "always justified" (the strongest support for "death with dignity") and 1 was "never justified" (the lowest level of support).

| | Mexico | | |
|---|---|---|---|
| Lower Class | Working Class | Middle Class | Upper Class |
| 5 | 2 | 1 | 2 |
| 2 | 2 | 1 | 4 |
| 4 | 1 | 3 | 5 |
| 5 | 1 | 4 | 7 |
| 4 | 6 | 1 | 8 |
| 2 | 5 | 2 | 10 |
| 3 | 7 | 1 | 10 |
| 1 | 2 | 5 | 9 |
| 1 | 3 | 1 | 8 |
| 3 | 1 | 1 | 8 |

| Canada | | | | | United States | | | |
|---|---|---|---|---|---|---|---|---|
| Lower Class | Working Class | Middle Class | Upper Class | | Lower Class | Working Class | Middle Class | Upper Class |
| 7 | 5 | 1 | 5 | | 4 | 4 | 4 | 1 |
| 7 | 6 | 3 | 7 | | 5 | 5 | 6 | 5 |
| 6 | 7 | 4 | 8 | | 6 | 1 | 7 | 8 |
| 4 | 8 | 5 | 9 | | 1 | 4 | 5 | 9 |
| 7 | 8 | 7 | 10 | | 3 | 3 | 8 | 9 |
| 8 | 9 | 8 | 10 | | 3 | 3 | 9 | 9 |
| 9 | 5 | 8 | 8 | | 3 | 4 | 9 | 8 |
| 9 | 6 | 9 | 5 | | 5 | 2 | 8 | 6 |
| 6 | 7 | 9 | 8 | | 3 | 1 | 7 | 9 |
| 5 | 8 | 5 | 9 | | 6 | 1 | 2 | 9 |

**You Are the Researcher**

## Using SPSS to Conduct Analysis of Variance with the 2012 CCHS

The demonstrations and exercises below use the shortened version of the 2012 CCHS data. Start SPSS and open the *CCHS_2012_Shortened.sav* file.

### SPSS DEMONSTRATION 12.1 Using the RECODE Command to Test for Regional Differences in Consumption of Fruits and Vegetables

SPSS provides several different ways of conducting the analysis of variance test. We'll use the **One-Way ANOVA** procedure, which is the most accessible way to conduct the analysis of variance test, to answer the question, "Is there a significant difference in average daily consumption of fruits and vegetables by province?"

Before we do the analysis of variance, smaller provinces should be collapsed into groups or regions to create more equal sample sizes. We'll use the SPSS **Recode** command, a commonly used tool to transform and manipulate variables, to collapse *geogprv* (province) into six regions. (The original scores for *geogprv* are given in Appendix G, or they can be viewed by clicking **Utilities** and then **Variables** from the SPSS main menu bar.)

First, click **Transform** from the main menu and choose **Recode into Different Variables**. The **Recode into Different Variables** dialog box will open. Highlight *geogprv* and click on the arrow button to move the variable to the **Input Variable → Output Variable** box. In the **Output Variable** box on the right, click in the **Name** text box and type a name for the new (output) variable: We suggest *region*. Click the **Change** button.

Second, click on the **Old and New Values** button in the middle of the screen to open the **Recode into Different: Old and New Values** dialog box. Read down the left-hand column until you find the **Range** button. Click on the button, and the cursor will move to the small box immediately below. Type 10 into the first **Range** text box, then click on the second text box and type 13. Then, in the **New Value** box in the upper-right-hand corner of the screen, click the **Value** button and then type 1 in the adjacent text box. Finally, click the **Add** button. The expression "10 thru 13 → 1" will appear in the **Old → New** text box. This completes the first recode instruction to SPSS.

For the second recode instruction, click the **Value** button in the **Old Value** box. Move the cursor to the small text box immediately under the **Value** button. Type 24 in the text box. Next, in the **New Value** box, click the **Value** button and type 2 in the adjacent text box. Click the **Add** button. The expression "24 → 2" will appear in the **Old → New** box. Continue this sequence of operations until all old values of *geogprv* have been recoded into new values. The recoding instructions that need to be added in the **Old → New** box should contain all of the following expressions (the order is not important):

$$
\begin{array}{lcl}
10 \text{ thru } 13 & \rightarrow & 1 \\
24 & \rightarrow & 2 \\
35 & \rightarrow & 3 \\
46 \text{ thru } 47 & \rightarrow & 4 \\
48 & \rightarrow & 5 \\
59 & \rightarrow & 6
\end{array}
$$

This scheme groups all respondents with scores 10 (Nfld/Labrador), 11 (PEI), 12 (Nova Scotia), or 13 (New Brunswick) on *geogprv* together into a score of 1 on *region*; score 24 (Quebec) on *geogprv* into a score of 2 on *region*; score 35 (Ontario) on *geogprv* into a score of 3 on *region*; scores 46 (Manitoba) or 47 (Saskatchewan) on *geogprv* together into a score of 4 on *region*; score 48 (Alberta) on *geogprv* into a score of 5 on *region*; and score 59 (BC) on *geogprv* into a score of 6 on *region*. (Note that we do not need to recode the original response category code of 60 [Yukon/NWT/Nunavut] because the shortened version of the data set does not include any cases from this region.)

Third, click the **Continue** button at the bottom of the screen, and you will return to the **Recode into Different Variables** dialog box. Click **OK,** and SPSS will execute the transformation. It is always a good idea to check the frequency distribution of the recoded variable to make sure the computations were carried out correctly.

We have attached value labels to each score of *region* (1 = Atlantic Canada, 2 = Quebec, etc.) to make the SPSS output easier to read. For more practice using the recode command, including how to add value labels, see Appendix F.5.

To use the **One-Way ANOVA** procedure, click **Analyze, Compare Means**, and then **One-Way ANOVA**. The **One-Way ANOVA** window appears. Find *fvcdtot* (daily consumption of fruits and vegetables) in the variable list on the left and click the arrow to move the variable name into the **Dependent List** box. Next, find *region* (it may appear at the end of the variable list) and click the arrow to move the variable name into the **Factor** box. To request means and standard deviations along with the analysis of variance, click **Options** and then click the checkbox next to **Descriptive** in the **Statistics** section. Click **Continue**. Then click the **Post Hoc** button and check the box next to **"Tukey"** in the **Equal Variances Assumed** box. This will generate the Tukey HSD (honestly significant difference) post hoc test for the one-way ANOVA. (Tukey's post hoc test is often the preferred method for conducting post hoc tests.) Click **Continue** and then **OK**, and the output below will be produced (note that parts of the original output, such as confidence intervals, have been omitted here to conserve space).

## Descriptives

Daily cons. - total fruits and veg.

|  | N | Mean | Std. Deviation | Std. Error |
|---|---|---|---|---|
| Atlantic Canada | 143 | 4.170 | 2.2262 | .1861 |
| Quebec | 319 | 5.136 | 2.8469 | .1595 |
| Ontario | 672 | 4.994 | 2.3818 | .0919 |
| Manitoba/Saskatchewan | 99 | 5.351 | 2.9322 | .2949 |
| Alberta | 199 | 4.167 | 2.4390 | .1730 |
| British Columbia | 284 | 4.209 | 1.7598 | .1044 |
| Total | 1,716 | 4.746 | 2.4513 | .0592 |

## ANOVA

Daily cons. - total fruits and veg.

|  | Sum of Squares | df | Mean Square | F | Sig. |
|---|---|---|---|---|---|
| Between Groups | 322.089 | 5 | 64.418 | 11.034 | .000 |
| Within Groups | 9982.925 | 1710 | 5.838 |  |  |
| Total | 10305.014 | 1715 |  |  |  |

## Multiple Comparisons

Dependent Variable: Daily cons. - total fruits and veg.
Tukey HSD

| (I) region | (J) region | Mean Difference (I–J) | Std. Error | Sig. |
|---|---|---|---|---|
| Atlantic Canada | Quebec | −.9660* | .2431 | .001 |
|  | Ontario | −.8236* | .2224 | .003 |
|  | Manitoba/Saskatchewan | −1.1806* | .3160 | .003 |
|  | Alberta | .0038 | .2648 | 1.000 |
|  | British Columbia | −.0390 | .2476 | 1.000 |
| Quebec | Atlantic Canada | .9660* | .2431 | .001 |
|  | Ontario | .1425 | .1643 | .954 |
|  | Manitoba/Saskatchewan | −.2146 | .2782 | .972 |
|  | Alberta | .9698* | .2184 | .000 |
|  | British Columbia | .9270* | .1972 | .000 |
| Ontario | Atlantic Canada | .8236* | .2224 | .003 |
|  | Quebec | −.1425 | .1643 | .954 |
|  | Manitoba/Saskatchewan | −.3571 | .2603 | .744 |
|  | Alberta | .8273* | .1950 | .000 |
|  | British Columbia | .7846* | .1710 | .000 |
| Manitoba/Saskatchewan | Atlantic Canada | 1.1806* | .3160 | .003 |
|  | Quebec | .2146 | .2782 | .972 |
|  | Ontario | .3571 | .2603 | .744 |
|  | Alberta | 1.1844* | .2973 | .001 |
|  | British Columbia | 1.1416* | .2821 | .001 |
| Alberta | Atlantic Canada | −.0038 | .2648 | 1.000 |
|  | Quebec | −.9698* | .2184 | .000 |
|  | Ontario | −.8273* | .1950 | .000 |
|  | Manitoba/Saskatchewan | −1.1844* | .2973 | .001 |
|  | British Columbia | −.0428 | .2234 | 1.000 |

| (I) region | (J) region | Mean Difference (I–J) | Std. Error | Sig. |
|---|---|---|---|---|
| British Columbia | Atlantic Canada | .0390 | .2476 | 1.000 |
| | Quebec | −.9270* | .1972 | .000 |
| | Ontario | −.7846* | .1710 | .000 |
| | Manitoba/Saskatchewan | −1.1416* | .2821 | .001 |
| | Alberta | .0428 | .2234 | 1.000 |

* The mean difference is significant at the 0.05 level.

The "Descriptives" report displays various summary statistics. The results indicate that daily consumption of fruits and vegetables is distributed differently across the regions. On average, the sample as a whole (i.e., all provinces) consumes fruits and vegetables 4.7 times per day. Manitoba/Saskatchewan has the highest consumption rate in Canada and Alberta the lowest.

The output box labelled "ANOVA" includes sums of squares, degrees of freedom (*df*), mean square estimates, F ratio (11.034), and, at the far right, "Sig." value (.000), which is the exact probability of getting these results if the null hypothesis is true. (As discussed in Demonstration 11.1, when the exact probability value is less than 0.0005, SPSS cuts it off at three decimal places, or 0.000, to save space.) There is no need to look up the critical F ratio in the F table, Appendix D, when the exact probability is provided. Because the value 0.000 is less than 0.05, our usual indicator of significance, we reject the null hypothesis. The difference in mean daily consumption of fruits and vegetables between the regions is statistically significant.

From this result, we know that differences exist between the group (regional) means, and, therefore, that region has a statistically significant impact on the daily consumption of fruits and vegetables. Moreover, we can calculate the size of this impact with eta-squared, by dividing SSB by SST, both of which are provided in the "Sum of Squares" column of the ANOVA table. This is probably the simplest way to calculate eta-squared, since SPSS does not directly provide this statistic for us. What we find is that the relationship between region and province is weak $\left(\dfrac{SSB}{SST} = \dfrac{322.089}{10,305.014} = 0.0312\right)$.

Further investigation is now needed to determine exactly which group means are significantly different from each other. An exact method to determine which pairs of means are significantly different is the post hoc test, discussed in Section 12.8. The post hoc test is a multiple comparison test for the significance of the difference between two sample means. (Note that if we had failed to reject the null hypothesis as determined by the F ratio, we would of course have little reason to proceed to the calculations of eta-squared or the post hoc tests.)

The output box "Multiple Comparisons" shows the post hoc analysis for the one-way ANOVA. On the left side of the box, each region is paired with every other region. Since each pair appears twice, we can just ignore the pair when it appears again in the box. For each pair, the box reports the difference in means in the second column labelled "Mean Difference," the standard error for the difference in means ("Std. Error"), and the exact probability value for the difference between means ("Sig."). For example, the difference between the mean daily consumption of fruits and vegetables for Atlantic Canadians and Quebecers is −0.9660, or 4.170 − 5.136

(see the "Descriptives" box for the regional means). Atlantic Canadians consume almost one less serving of fruits and vegetables per day than Quebecers. The probability value for this difference is 0.001, meaning that these means are significantly different at the 0.05 level that we have been using. The mean differences between Atlantic Canada and Ontario ($p = 0.003$) and between Atlantic Canada and Manitoba/Saskatchewan ($p = 0.003$) are also statistically significant, but the differences between Atlantic Canada and Alberta ($p = 1.000$) and between Atlantic Canada and British Columbia ($p = 1.000$) are not. (Note that SPSS conveniently marks significant differences, at the 0.05 level, with an asterisk.)

### SPSS DEMONSTRATION 12.2 The Error Bar Graph

We can also use the error bar graph to get an indication of which pairs of means are significantly different, in a manner similar to Demonstration 11.2 where the overlap of error bars for individual confidence intervals was used to judge the significance of the difference between two samples.

To produce error bar graphs of the 95% confidence interval of each mean, click **Graphs, Legacy Dialogs,** and then **Error Bar**. The **Error Bar** dialog box will appear with the **Simple** and **Summaries for Groups of Cases** buttons already highlighted. These are the ones we want, so just click **Define**. The **Define Simple Error Bar** dialog box will appear. Transfer the dependent variable, *fvcdtot*, to the **Variable** box and the independent variable, *region*, to the **Category Axis** box, and click **OK**.

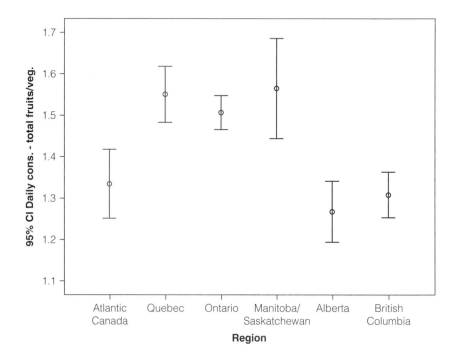

The error bar graph shows the mean daily consumption of fruits and vegetables for each region. The 95% confidence interval for each mean is also presented. By "eyeballing" the overlap of confidence intervals for each mean, we can get a sense of which means are significantly different. For example, there appears to be a significant difference in average daily consumption of fruits and vegetables between the Manitoba/Saskatchewan and Alberta populations, but not between the Alberta and British Columbia populations. These observations are indeed confirmed by post hoc analysis, as reported in the "Multiple Comparisons" output box in Demonstration 12.1.

## Exercises (using *CCHS_2012_Shortened.sav*)

**12.1** Use the **Recode** command illustrated in Demonstration 12.1 to collapse *geogprv* into the following three regions: (1) Atlantic Canada, (2) Ontario and Quebec, and (3) Manitoba, Saskatchewan, Alberta, and BC. (Again, note that we do not need to recode the original response category code 60 [Yukon/NWT/Nunavut] because the shortened version of the data set does not include any cases from this region.) The recoding instructions that should appear in the **Old → New** box are as follows:

$$10 \text{ thru } 13 \rightarrow 1$$
$$24 \text{ thru } 35 \rightarrow 2$$
$$46 \text{ thru } 59 \rightarrow 3$$

Next, use the **One-Way ANOVA** procedure, including the post hoc function, and test for a significant difference between recoded *geogprv* as the independent variable (factor) and *fvcdtot* as the dependent variable. In addition, use the SSB and SST values provided in the ANOVA table to calculate eta-squared. Write a few sentences summarizing the results of this analysis.

**12.2** Using Demonstration 12.2 as a guide, create an error bar graph for the variables in Exercise 12.1. Write a sentence or two of interpretation for the graph. Which regions appear to differ significantly from each other?

# 13

# Hypothesis Testing and Measures of Association for Variables Measured at the Interval-Ratio Level

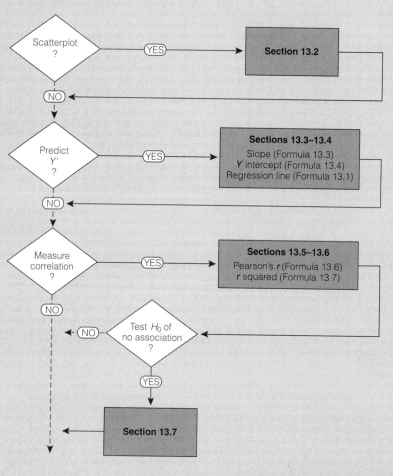

**LEARNING OBJECTIVES**

By the end of this chapter, you will be able to

1. Interpret a scatterplot.

2. Calculate and interpret slope ($b$), $Y$ intercept ($a$), and Pearson's $r$ and $r^2$.

3. Find and explain the least-squares regression line and use it to predict values of $Y$.

4. Explain the concepts of total, explained, and unexplained variance.

5. Use regression and correlation techniques to analyze and describe a bivariate relationship in terms of the three questions introduced in Chapter 8.

6. Test Pearson's $r$ for significance.

**13.1 INTRODUCTION**

In previous chapters, we looked at hypothesis testing and measures of association for two variables, where the independent variable is measured at the nominal or ordinal level and the dependent variable at either the nominal, ordinal, or interval-ratio level. This chapter looks at a set of statistical techniques (hypothesis tests and measures of association or correlation) used when both the independent and dependent variables are measured at the interval-ratio level.* As we shall see, these techniques, though rather different in their computation from those covered in previous chapters, still address the same three questions: Is there a relationship between the variables? How strong is the relationship? What is the direction of the relationship? You might become preoccupied with some of the technical details and computational routines in this chapter, so remind yourself occasionally that our ultimate goals are unchanged: We are trying to understand bivariate relationships, explore possible causal ties between variables, and improve our ability to predict scores.

**13.2 SCATTERPLOTS**

As seen over the past several chapters, we can look at sample means and proportions across groups or column percentages in bivariate tables to provide important information about bivariate associations. In addition to measures of association like phi, gamma, and eta-squared, the examination of means, proportions, and column percentages across categories of the independent variable almost always provide useful information and a better understanding of the relationship between variables.

By the same token, the usual first step in analyzing a relationship between interval-ratio variables is to construct and examine a **scatterplot**. Like bivariate tables, these graphs allow us to quickly identify several important features of a relationship. An example will illustrate the construction and use of scatterplots. Suppose a researcher is interested in analyzing how dual-wage-earner families (i.e., families where both husband and wife have jobs outside the home) cope with housework. Specifically, the researcher wonders if the number of children in the family is related to the amount of time the husband contributes to housekeeping chores. The relevant data for a sample of 12 dual-wage-earner families are displayed in Table 13.1.

A scatterplot, like a bivariate table, has two dimensions. The scores of the independent ($X$) variable are arrayed along the horizontal axis, and the scores of the dependent ($Y$) variable along the vertical axis. Each dot on the scatterplot represents a case in the sample and is located at a point determined by the scores of the case. Figure 13.1 shows a scatterplot displaying

---

*The term *correlation* is commonly used instead of *association* when discussing the relationship between interval-ratio variables. We will use the two terms interchangeably.

**TABLE 13.1   Number of Children and Husband's Contribution to Housework (fictitious data)**

| Family | Number of Children | Hours per Week Husband Spends on Housework |
|--------|--------------------|--------------------------------------------|
| A | 1 | 1 |
| B | 1 | 2 |
| C | 1 | 3 |
| D | 1 | 5 |
| E | 2 | 3 |
| F | 2 | 1 |
| G | 3 | 5 |
| H | 3 | 0 |
| I | 4 | 6 |
| J | 4 | 3 |
| K | 5 | 7 |
| L | 5 | 4 |

**FIGURE 13.1   Husband's Housework by Number of Children**

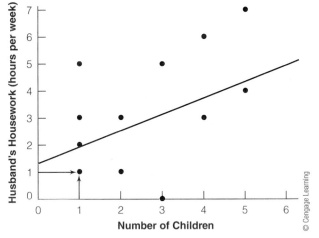

the relationship between "number of children" and "husband's housework" for the sample of 12 families presented in Table 13.1. Family A has a score of 1 on the $X$ variable (number of children) and 1 on the $Y$ variable (husband's housework) and is represented by the dot above the score of 1 on the $X$ axis and directly to the right of the score of 1 on the $Y$ axis. All 12 cases are similarly represented by dots on Figure 13.1. Also note that, as always, the scatterplot is clearly titled and both axes are labelled.

The overall pattern of the dots or cases summarizes the nature of the relationship between the two variables. The clarity of the pattern can be enhanced by drawing a straight line through the cluster of dots such that the line touches every dot or comes as close to doing so as possible. In Section 13.3, a precise technique for fitting this line to the pattern of the dots will be explained. For now, an "eyeball" approximation will suffice. This summarizing line is called the **regression line** and has already been added to the scatterplot.

Scatterplots, even when they are crudely drawn, can be used for a variety of purposes. They provide at least impressionistic information about the existence, strength, and direction of the relationship, and can also be used to check the relationship for linearity (i.e., how well the pattern of dots can be approximated with a straight line). Finally, the scatterplot can be used to predict the score of a case on one variable from the score of that case on the other variable. We will briefly examine each of these uses.

To determine the existence of a relationship, we can return to the basic definition of an association stated in Chapter 8. Two variables are associated if the distributions of $Y$ (the dependent variable) change for the various conditions of $X$ (the independent variable). In Figure 13.1, scores on $X$ (number of children) are arrayed along the horizontal axis. The dots above each score on $X$ are the scores (or conditional distributions) of $Y$. That is, the dots represent scores on $Y$ for each value of $X$. Figure 13.1 shows that there is a relationship between these variables because these conditional distributions of $Y$ (the dots above each score on $X$) change as $X$ changes. The existence of an association is further reinforced by the fact that the regression line lies at an angle to the $X$ axis. If these two variables had not been associated, the conditional distributions of $Y$ would not have changed, and the regression line would have been parallel to the horizontal axis.

The strength of the bivariate association can be judged by observing the spread of the dots around the regression line. In a perfect association, all dots would lie on the regression line. The more the dots are clustered around the regression line, the stronger the association.

The direction of the relationship can be detected by observing the angle of the regression line. Figure 13.1 shows a positive relationship: As $X$ (number of children) increases, husband's housework ($Y$) also increases. Husbands in families with more children tend to do more housework. If the relationship had been negative, the regression line would have sloped in the opposite direction to indicate that high scores on one variable were associated with low scores on the other.

To summarize these points about the existence, strength, and direction of the relationship, Figure 13.2 shows a perfect positive relationship, a perfect negative relationship, and a "zero relationship," or "non-relationship," between two variables.

**FIGURE 13.2  Positive, Negative, and Zero Relationships**

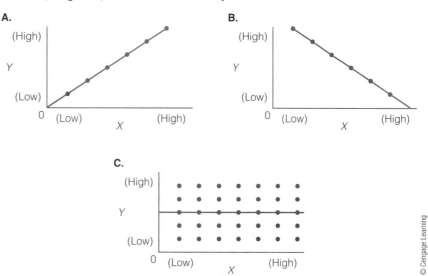

**FIGURE 13.3    Some Non-Linear Relationships**

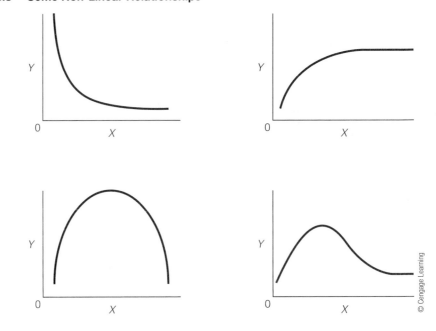

© Cengage Learning

One key assumption underlying the statistical techniques to be introduced later in this chapter is that the two variables have an essentially **linear relationship**. In other words, the observation points or dots in the scatterplot must form a pattern that can be approximated with a straight line. Significant departures from linearity would require the use of statistical techniques beyond the scope of this textbook. Examples of some common curvilinear relationships are presented in Figure 13.3. If the scatterplot shows that the variables have a non-linear relationship, the techniques described in this chapter should be used with great caution or not at all. Checking for the linearity of the relationship is perhaps the most important reason for constructing at least a crude, hand-drawn scatterplot before proceeding with the statistical analysis. If the relationship is non-linear, you might need to treat the variables as if they were ordinal rather than interval-ratio in level of measurement. *(For practice in constructing and interpreting scatterplots, see Problems 13.1 to 13.5.)*

**13.3 REGRESSION AND PREDICTION**

A final use of the scatterplot is to predict scores of cases on one variable from their score on the other. To illustrate, suppose that, based on the relationship between number of children and husband's housework displayed in Figure 13.1, we wish to predict the number of hours of housework a husband with a family of six children would do each week. The sample has no families with six children, but if we extend the axes and

**FIGURE 13.4    Predicting Husband's Housework**

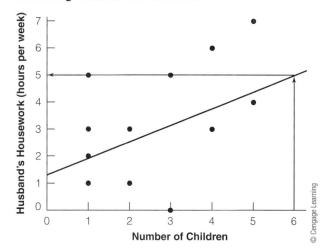

regression line in Figure 13.1 to incorporate this score, a prediction is possible. Figure 13.4 reproduces the scatterplot and illustrates how the prediction would be made.

The predicted score on $Y$—which is symbolized as $\boldsymbol{Y'}$ to distinguish predictions of $Y$ from actual $Y$ scores—is found by first locating the relevant score on $X$ ($X = 6$ in this case) and then drawing a straight line from that point to the regression line. From the regression line, another straight line parallel to the $X$ axis is drawn across to the $Y$ axis. The predicted $Y$ score ($Y'$) is found at the point where the line crosses the $Y$ axis. In our example, we would predict that, in a dual-wage-earner family with six children, the husband would devote about five hours per week to housework.

Of course, this prediction technique is crude, and the value of $Y'$ can change depending on how accurately the freehand regression line is drawn. One way to eliminate this source of error would be to find the straight line that most accurately summarizes the pattern of the observation points and therefore best describes the relationship between the two variables. Is there such a "best-fitting" straight line? If there is, how is it defined?

Recall that our criterion for the freehand regression line was that it touch all the dots or come as close to doing so as possible. Also recall that the dots above each value of $X$ can be thought of as conditional distributions of $Y$, the dependent variable. Within each conditional distribution of $Y$, the mean is the point around which the variation of the scores is at a minimum. In Chapter 3, we noted that the mean of any distribution of scores is the point around which the variation of the scores, as measured by squared deviations, is minimized:

$$\Sigma(X_i - \overline{X})^2 = \text{minimum}$$

Thus, if the regression line is drawn so that it touches each **conditional mean of $Y$**, it would be the straight line that comes as close as possible to all the scores.

Conditional means are found by summing all $Y$ values for each value of $X$ and then dividing by the number of cases. For example, four families had one child ($X = 1$), and the husbands of these four families devoted 1, 2, 3, and 5 hours per week to housework. Thus, for $X = 1$, $Y = 1, 2, 3$, and 5, and the conditional mean of $Y$ for $X = 1$ is 2.75 (11/4 = 2.75). Husbands in families with one child worked an average of 2.75 hours per week doing housekeeping chores. Conditional means of $Y$ are computed in the same way for each value of $X$ displayed in Table 13.2 and plotted in Figure 13.5.

Let us quickly remind ourselves of the reason for these calculations. We are seeking the single best-fitting regression line for summarizing the relationship between $X$ and $Y$, and we have seen that a line drawn through the conditional means of $Y$ will minimize the spread of the observation points. It will come as close to all the scores as possible and will therefore be the single best-fitting regression line.

Now, a line drawn through the points on Figure 13.5 (the conditional means of $Y$) will be the best-fitting line we are seeking, but you can see from the scatterplot that the line will not be straight. In fact, only rarely (when there is a perfect relationship between $X$ and $Y$) will conditional means fall in a perfectly straight line. Because we still must meet the condition of linearity, let us revise our criterion and define the regression line as the unique straight line that touches all conditional means of $Y$ or comes as close to doing so as possible. Formula 13.1 defines the

**FIGURE 13.5 Conditional Means of $Y$**

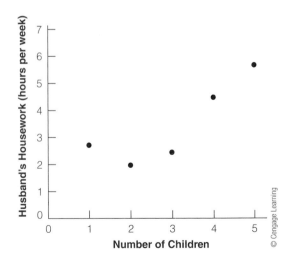

**TABLE 13.2  Conditional Means of $Y$ (husband's housework) for Various Values of $X$ (number of children)**

| Number of Children ($X$) | Husband's Housework ($Y$) | Conditional Means of $Y$ |
|:---:|:---:|:---:|
| 1 | 1,2,3,5 | 2.75 |
| 2 | 3,1 | 2.00 |
| 3 | 5,0 | 2.50 |
| 4 | 6,3 | 4.50 |
| 5 | 7,4 | 5.50 |

"least-squares" regression line, or the single straight regression line that best fits the pattern of the data points.

**FORMULA 13.1**
$$Y = a + bX$$

where $Y$ = score on the dependent variable

$a$ = the $Y$ intercept or the point where the regression line crosses the $Y$ axis

$b$ = the slope of the regression line or the amount of change produced in $Y$ by a unit change in $X$

$X$ = score on the independent variable

The formula introduces two new concepts. First, the **$Y$ intercept ($a$)** is the point at which the regression line crosses the vertical, or $Y$, axis. This means that the intercept is equal to the value of $Y$ when $X$ is zero. Second, the **slope ($b$)** of the least-squares regression line is the amount of change produced in the dependent variable ($Y$) by a unit change in the independent variable ($X$). Think of the slope of the regression line as a measure of the effect of the $X$ variable on the $Y$ variable. If the variables have a strong association, then changes in the value of $X$ will be accompanied by substantial changes in the value of $Y$, and the slope ($b$) will have a high value. The weaker the effect of $X$ on $Y$ (the weaker the association between the variables), the lower the value of the slope ($b$). If the two variables are unrelated, the least-squares regression line would be parallel to the $X$ axis, and $b$ would be 0.00 (the line would have no slope). As a final point, the intercept and the slope are both expressed in the *units* of the dependent variable (e.g., number of *hours* per week the husband spends on housework), and thus provide a direct and intuitive interpretation.

With the least-squares formula (Formula 13.1), we can predict values of $Y$ in a much less arbitrary and impressionistic way than through mere eyeballing. This will be so, remember, because the least-squares regression line as defined by Formula 13.1 is the single straight line that best fits the data because it comes as close as possible to all of the conditional means of $Y$. To see how predictions of $Y$ can be made, however, we must first calculate $a$ and $b$. *(For practice in using the regression line to predict scores on* Y *from scores on* X, *see Problems 13.1 to 13.3 and 13.5.)*

## 13.4 THE COMPUTATION OF $a$ AND $b$

Because the value of $b$ is needed to solve for $a$, we will begin with the computation of the slope of the least-squares regression line. The definitional formula for the slope is

**FORMULA 13.2**
$$b = \frac{\Sigma(X - \bar{X})(Y - \bar{Y})}{\Sigma(X - \bar{X})^2}$$

The numerator of this formula is called the *covariation* of $X$ and $Y$. It is a measure of how $X$ and $Y$ vary together, and its value will reflect both the direction and the strength of the relationship. These days, of course, computers and statistical packages like SPSS are used to compute complex statistics like $b$. However, for smaller samples (and for the end-of-chapter problems in this textbook), $b$ is sometimes still calculated using handheld calculators. In these situations, Formula 13.2 is awkward to use and the following computational formula, which can be derived from Formula 13.2, can be used instead:

**FORMULA 13.3**

$$b = \frac{n\Sigma XY - (\Sigma X)(\Sigma Y)}{n\Sigma X^2 - (\Sigma X)^2}$$

where $b$ = the slope

$n$ = the number of cases

$\Sigma XY$ = the summation of the crossproducts of the scores

$\Sigma X$ = the summation of the $X$ scores

$\Sigma Y$ = the summation of the $Y$ scores

$\Sigma X^2$ = the summation of the squared scores on $X$

Admittedly, this formula appears formidable at first glance, but it can be solved without too much difficulty if computations are organized into table format. The computing table displayed in Table 13.3 has a column for each

**TABLE 13.3  Computation of the Slope ($b$)**

| $X$ | $Y$ | $X^2$ | $Y^{2*}$ | $XY$ |
|---|---|---|---|---|
| 1 | 1 | 1 | 1 | 1 |
| 1 | 2 | 1 | 4 | 2 |
| 1 | 3 | 1 | 9 | 3 |
| 1 | 5 | 1 | 25 | 5 |
| 2 | 3 | 4 | 9 | 6 |
| 2 | 1 | 4 | 1 | 2 |
| 3 | 5 | 9 | 25 | 15 |
| 3 | 0 | 9 | 0 | 0 |
| 4 | 6 | 16 | 36 | 24 |
| 4 | 3 | 16 | 9 | 12 |
| 5 | 7 | 25 | 49 | 35 |
| 5 | 4 | 25 | 16 | 20 |
| $\Sigma X = 32$ | $\Sigma Y = 40$ | $\Sigma X^2 = 112$ | $\Sigma Y^2 = 184$ | $\Sigma XY = 125$ |

$$\bar{X} = \frac{32}{12} = 2.67$$

$$\bar{Y} = \frac{40}{12} = 3.33$$

*The quantity $\Sigma Y^2$ is not used in the computation of $b$. We will need it later, however, when we compute Pearson's $r$ (see Section 13.5).

of the four quantities needed to solve the formula. The data are from the dual-wage-earner family sample (see Table 13.1).

In Table 13.3, the first two columns list the original $X$ and $Y$ scores for each case. The third column contains the squared scores on $X$, and the fourth lists the squared scores on $Y$. The fifth column lists the crossproducts of the scores for each case. In other words, the entries in the last column are determined by multiplying both scores for each case. We can now replace the symbols in Formula 13.3 with the proper sums:

$$b = \frac{n\Sigma XY - (\Sigma X)(\Sigma Y)}{n\Sigma X^2 - (\Sigma X)^2}$$

$$b = \frac{(12)(125) - (32)(40)}{(12)(112) - (32)^2}$$

$$b = \frac{(1,500 - 1,280)}{(1,344 - 1,024)}$$

$$b = \frac{220}{320}$$

$$b = 0.69$$

A slope of 0.69 indicates that, for each unit change in $X$, there is an increase of 0.69 units in $Y$. For our example, the addition of each child (an increase of one unit in $X$) results in an increase of 0.69 hours of housework being done by the husband (an increase of 0.69 units—or hours—in $Y$).

Once the slope has been calculated, finding the intercept ($a$) is relatively easy. To compute the mean of $X$ and the mean of $Y$, divide the

## ONE STEP AT A TIME Computing the Slope (*b*)

**To Compute the Slope (*b*), Solve Formula 13.3**

1: Use a computing table like Table 13.3 to help organize the computations. List the scores of the cases on the independent variable ($X$) in column 1. Find the sum of this column.
2: List the score of each case on $Y$ in column 2. Find the sum of this column.
3: Square each value in column 1 and place the result in column 3. Find the sum of this column.
4: For each case, multiply the value in column 1 by the value in column 2. Place the result in column 5. Find the sum of this column.

5: Multiply the sum of column 5 by *n*.
6: Multiply the sum of column 1 by the sum of column 2.
7: Subtract the quantity you found in step 6 from the quantity you found in step 5.
8: Multiply the sum of column 3 by *n*.
9: Square the sum of column 1.
10: Subtract the quantity you found in step 9 from the quantity you found in step 8.
11: Divide the quantity you found in step 7 by the quantity you found in step 10. The result is the slope.

---

**ONE STEP AT A TIME   Computing the Y Intercept (a)**

---

**To Compute the Y Intercept (a), Solve Formula 13.4**

**1:** Multiply the slope (b) by the mean of X.

**2:** Subtract the value you found in step 1 from the mean of Y. This value is a, or the Y intercept.

---

sums of columns 1 and 2 of Table 13.3 by $n$ and enter these figures into Formula 13.4:

**FORMULA 13.4**
$$a = \overline{Y} - b\overline{X}$$

For our sample problem, the value of $a$ would be

$$a = \overline{Y} - b\overline{X}$$
$$a = 3.33 - (0.69)(2.67)$$
$$a = 3.33 - 1.84$$
$$a = 1.49$$

Thus, the least-squares regression line will cross the $Y$ axis at the point where $Y$ equals 1.49.

The full least-squares regression line for our sample data can now be specified:

$$Y = a + bX$$
$$Y = (1.49) + (0.69)X$$

This formula can be used to estimate or predict scores on $Y$ for any value of $X$. In Section 13.3, we used the freehand regression line to predict a score on $Y$ (husband's housework) for a family with six children ($X = 6$). Our prediction was that, in families of six children, husbands would contribute about five hours per week to housekeeping chores. By using the least-squares regression line, we can see how close our impressionistic, eyeball prediction was.

$$Y' = a + bX$$
$$Y' = (1.49) + (0.69)(6)$$
$$Y' = (1.49) + (4.14)$$
$$Y' = 5.63$$

Based on the least-squares regression line, we would predict that in a dual-wage-earner family with six children, husbands would devote 5.63 hours a week to housework. What would our prediction of husband's housework be for a family of seven children ($X = 7$)?

---

**ONE STEP AT A TIME   Using the Regression Line to Predict Scores on Y**

**1:** Choose a value for X. Multiply this value by the value of the slope (b).

**2:** Add the value you found in step 1 to the value of a, the Y intercept. The resulting value is the predicted score on Y.

---

Note that our predictions of Y scores are basically "educated guesses." We will be unlikely to predict values of Y exactly except in the (relatively rare) case where the bivariate relationship is perfect and perfectly linear. Note also, however, that the accuracy of our predictions will increase as relationships become stronger. This is because the dots are more clustered around the least-squares regression line in stronger relationships. *(The slope and Y intercept may be computed for any problem at the end of this chapter, but see Problems 13.1 to 13.5 in particular. These problems have smaller data sets and will provide good practice until you are comfortable with these calculations.)*

### 13.5 THE CORRELATION COEFFICIENT (PEARSON'S r)

We pointed out in Section 13.4 that the slope (b) of the least-squares regression line is a measure of the effect of X on Y. Because the slope is the amount of change produced in Y by a unit change in X, b will increase in value as the relationship increases in strength. However, b does not vary between zero and one and is therefore awkward to use as a measure of association. Instead, researchers rely heavily (almost exclusively) on a statistic called **Pearson's r**, or the correlation coefficient, to measure association between interval-ratio variables. Like the ordinal measures of association discussed in Chapter 9, Pearson's r varies from 0.00 to ±1.00, with 0.00 indicating no association and +1.00 and −1.00 indicating perfect positive and perfect negative relationships, respectively. The definitional formula for Pearson's r is

**FORMULA 13.5**

$$r = \frac{\Sigma(X - \overline{X})(Y - \overline{Y})}{\sqrt{\left[\Sigma(X - \overline{X})^2\right]\left[\Sigma(Y - \overline{Y})^2\right]}}$$

Note that the numerator of this formula is the covariation of X and Y, as was the case with Formula 13.2. When computing with a handheld calculator, computational Formula 13.6 is preferred over the definitional formula.

**FORMULA 13.6**

$$r = \frac{n\Sigma XY - (\Sigma X)(\Sigma Y)}{\sqrt{\left[n\Sigma X^2 - (\Sigma X)^2\right]\left[n\Sigma Y^2 - (\Sigma Y)^2\right]}}$$

A computing table such as Table 13.3 is strongly recommended as a way of organizing the quantities needed to solve this equation. For our sample problem involving dual-wage-earner families, the quantities displayed in Table 13.3 can be substituted directly into Formula 13.6:

$$r = \frac{(12)(125) - (32)(40)}{\sqrt{[(12)(112) - (32)^2][(12)(184) - (40)^2]}}$$

$$r = \frac{1{,}500 - 1{,}280}{\sqrt{(1{,}344 - 1{,}024)(2{,}208 - 1{,}600)}}$$

$$r = \frac{220}{\sqrt{194{,}560}}$$

$$r = +0.50$$

An $r$ value of $+0.50$ indicates a strong, positive linear relationship between the variables. As the number of children in the family increases, the hourly contribution of husbands to housekeeping duties also increases. *(Every problem at the end of this chapter requires the computation of Pearson's r. It is probably a good idea to practise with smaller data sets and easier computations first—see Problem 13.1 in particular.)*

---

## ONE STEP AT A TIME  Computing Pearson's *r*

### To Begin

**1:** Add a column to the computing table (Table 13.3) you used to compute the slope (*b*). Square each value in column 2 and record the result in this column (column 4).
**2:** Find the sum of column 4.

### To Find the Value of Pearson's *r* by Solving Formula 13.6

**1:** Multiply the sum of column 5 by *n*.
**2:** Multiply the sum of column 1 by the sum of column 2.
**3:** Subtract the quantity you found in step 2 from the quantity you found in step 1.
**4:** Multiply the sum of column 3 by *n*.
**5:** Square the sum of column 1.
**6:** Subtract the quantity you found in step 5 from the quantity you found in step 4.
**7:** Multiply the sum of column 4 by *n*.
**8:** Square the sum of column 2.
**9:** Subtract the quantity you found in step 8 from the quantity you found in step 7.

**10:** Multiply the quantity you found in step 6 by the quantity you found in step 9.
**11:** Take the square root of the value you found in step 10.
**12:** Divide the quantity you found in step 3 by the quantity you found in step 11. The result is Pearson's *r*.

### To Interpret the Strength of Pearson's *r*: Two Methods

Use Table 12.5 to describe strength in general terms.

or

Square the value of *r* and multiply by 100. This value represents the percentage of variation in *Y* that is explained by *X*.

### To Interpret the Direction of the Relationship

Look at the sign of *r*. If *r* has a plus sign (or if there is no sign), the relationship is positive and the variables change in the same direction. If *r* has a minus sign, the relationship is negative and the variables change in opposite directions.

## Applying Statistics 13.1: Computing the Regression Coefficients and Pearson's *r*

The table below shows data for five university students on their GPA (grade point average) and the average number of hours worked per week in the last semester. Are these variables associated? Columns have been added for all necessary sums.

| Student | Hours Worked (per week) $(X)$ | GPA $(Y)$ | $X^2$ | $Y^2$ | $XY$ |
|---|---|---|---|---|---|
| 1 | 25 | 61 | 625 | 3,721 | 1,525 |
| 2 | 20 | 72 | 400 | 5,184 | 1,440 |
| 3 | 15 | 82 | 225 | 6,724 | 1,230 |
| 4 | 8 | 87 | 64 | 7,569 | 696 |
| 5 | 0 | 67 | 0 | 4,489 | 0 |
| | 68 | 369 | 1,314 | 27,687 | 4,891 |

The slope (*b*) is

$$b = \frac{n\Sigma XY - (\Sigma X)(\Sigma Y)}{n\Sigma X^2 - (\Sigma X)^2}$$

$$b = \frac{(5)(4,891) - (68)(369)}{(5)(1,314) - (68)^2}$$

$$b = \frac{-637}{1,946}$$

$$b = -0.33$$

A slope of $-0.33$ means that for every unit change in $X$ (for every 1 hour increase in work per week), there was a change of $-0.33$ units in $Y$ (grade point average decreased by 0.33, or by one-third of a point). The $Y$ intercept (*a*) is

$$a = \bar{Y} - b\bar{X}$$

$$a = \frac{369}{5} - (-0.33)\left(\frac{68}{5}\right)$$

$$a = 73.8 - (-0.33)(13.6)$$

$$a = 73.8 + 4.49$$

$$a = 78.29$$

The least-squares regression equation is

$$Y = a + bX = 78.29 + (-0.33)X$$

The correlation coefficient is

$$r = \frac{n\Sigma XY - (\Sigma X)(\Sigma Y)}{\sqrt{[n\Sigma X^2 - (\Sigma X)^2][n\Sigma Y^2 - (\Sigma Y)^2]}}$$

$$r = \frac{(5)(4,891) - (68)(369)}{\sqrt{[(5)(1,314) - (68)^2][(5)(27,687) - (369)^2]}}$$

$$r = \frac{-637}{\sqrt{(1,946)(2,274)}}$$

$$r = \frac{-637}{\sqrt{442,5204}}$$

$$r = \frac{-637}{2,103.62}$$

$$r = -0.30$$

GPA and hours worked have a moderate to strong negative relationship. Grade point average decreases as the number of hours worked per week increases. The coefficient of determination, $r^2$, is $(-0.30)^2$, or 0.09. This indicates that 9% of the variance in GPA is explained by hours worked.

**13.6 INTERPRETING THE CORRELATION COEFFICIENT: $r^2$**

Pearson's $r$ is an index of the strength of the linear relationship between two variables. While a value of 0.00 indicates no linear relationship and a value of $\pm 1.00$ indicates a perfect linear relationship, values between these extremes have no direct interpretation. We can, of course, describe relationships in terms of how closely they approach the extremes (e.g., coefficients approaching 0.00 can be described as "weak" and those approaching $\pm 1.00$ as "strong"), but this description is somewhat subjective. Also, we can use the guidelines stated in Table 12.5 to attach descriptive words to the specific values of Pearson's $r$. In other words, values between 0.00 and 0.10 would be described as weak, values between 0.11 and 0.30 would be moderate, and values greater than 0.30 would be strong. Remember, of course, that these labels are arbitrary guidelines and will not be appropriate or useful in all possible research situations.

Fortunately, we can develop a less arbitrary, more direct interpretation of $r$ by calculating an additional statistic called the **coefficient of determination**. This statistic, which is simply the square of Pearson's $r$ ($r^2$), can be interpreted with a logic akin to proportional reduction in error (PRE). As you recall, the logic of PRE measures of association is to predict the value of the dependent variable under two different conditions. First, $Y$ is predicted while ignoring the information supplied by $X$, and second, the independent variable $X$ is taken into account. With $r^2$, both the method of prediction and the construction of the final statistic are somewhat different and require the introduction of some new concepts.

When working with variables measured at the interval-ratio level, the predictions of the $Y$ scores under the first condition (while ignoring $X$) will be the mean of $Y$. Given no information on $X$, this prediction strategy will be optimal because we know that the mean of any distribution is closer to all the scores than any other point in the distribution. We remind you of the principle of minimized variation introduced in Chapter 3 and expressed as

$$\Sigma(Y - \overline{Y})^2 = \text{minimum}$$

The scores of any variable vary less around the mean than around any other point. If we predict the mean of $Y$ for every case, we will make fewer errors of prediction than if we predict any other value for $Y$.

Of course, we will still make many errors in predicting $Y$ even if we faithfully follow this strategy. The amount of error is represented in Figure 13.6, which displays the relationship between number of children and husband's housework with the mean of $Y$ noted. The vertical lines from the actual scores to the predicted score represent the amount of error we would make when predicting $Y$ while ignoring $X$.

We can define the extent of our prediction error under the first condition (while ignoring $X$) by subtracting the mean of $Y$ from each actual $Y$ score and squaring and summing these deviations. The resulting figure, which can be denoted as $\Sigma(Y - \overline{Y})^2$, is called the **total variation** in $Y$. We now have a visual representation (Figure 13.6) and a method for calculating

**FIGURE 13.6**   **Predicting *Y* without *X* (dual-career families)**

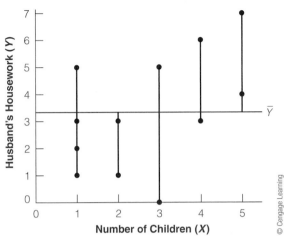

the error we incur by predicting *Y* without knowledge of *X*. As we shall see below, we do not need to actually calculate the total variation to find the value of the coefficient of determination, $r^2$.

Our next step will be to determine the extent to which knowledge of *X* improves our ability to predict *Y*. If the two variables have a linear relationship, then predicting scores on *Y* from the least-squares regression equation will incorporate knowledge of *X* and reduce our errors of prediction. So, under the second condition, our predicted *Y* score for each value of *X* will be

$$Y' = a + bX$$

Figure 13.7 displays the data from the dual-career families with the regression line, as determined by the above formula, drawn in. The vertical lines from each data point to the regression line represent the amount of error in predicting *Y* that remains even after *X* has been taken into account.

As was the case under the first condition, we can precisely define the reduction in error that results from taking *X* into account. Specifically, two different sums can be found and then compared with the total variation of *Y* to construct a statistic that will indicate the improvement in prediction. The first sum, called the **explained variation**, represents the improvement in our ability to predict *Y* when taking *X* into account. This sum is found by subtracting $\overline{Y}$ (our predicted *Y* score without *X*) from the score predicted by the regression equation ($Y'$, or the *Y* score predicted with knowledge of *X*) for each case and then squaring and summing these differences. These operations can be summarized as $\Sigma(Y' - \overline{Y})^2$ and the resulting figure can then be compared with the total variation in *Y* to determine the extent to

**FIGURE 13.7**    **Predicting *Y* with *X* (dual-career families)**

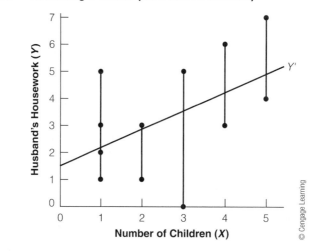

which our knowledge of *X* improves our ability to predict *Y*. Specifically, it can be shown mathematically that

**FORMULA 13.7**

$$r^2 = \frac{\Sigma(Y' - \overline{Y})^2}{\Sigma(Y - \overline{Y})^2} = \frac{\text{Explained variation}}{\text{Total variation}}$$

Thus, the coefficient of determination, or $r^2$, is the proportion of the total variation in *Y* attributable to or explained by *X*. Like other PRE measures, $r^2$ indicates precisely the extent to which *X* helps us predict, understand, or explain *Y*.

Above, we refer to the improvement in predicting *Y* with *X* as the explained variation. The use of this term suggests that some of the variation in *Y* will be "unexplained" or not attributable to the influence of *X*. In fact, the vertical lines in Figure 13.7 represent the **unexplained variation**, or the difference between our best prediction of *Y* with *X* and the actual scores. The unexplained variation is thus the scattering of the actual scores around the regression line and can be found by subtracting the predicted *Y* scores from the actual *Y* scores for each case and then squaring and summing the differences. These operations can be summarized as $\Sigma(Y - Y')^2$ and the resulting sum will measure the amount of error in predicting *Y* that remains even after *X* has been taken into account. The proportion of the total variation in *Y* unexplained by *X* can be found by subtracting the value of $r^2$ from 1.00. Unexplained variation is usually attributed to the influence of some combination of other variables, measurement error, and random chance.

As you may have recognized by this time, the explained and unexplained variations bear a reciprocal relationship with each other. As one of these sums increases in value, the other decreases. Furthermore, the stronger the linear relationship between $X$ and $Y$, the greater the value of the explained variation and the lower the unexplained variation. In the case of a perfect relationship ($r = \pm1.00$), the unexplained variation would be 0 and $r^2$ would be 1.00. This would indicate that $X$ explains or accounts for all of the variation in $Y$ and that we could predict $Y$ from $X$ without error. On the other hand, when $X$ and $Y$ are not linearly related ($r = 0.00$), the explained variation would be 0 and $r^2$ would be 0.00. In such a case, we would conclude that $X$ explains none of the variation in $Y$ and does not improve our ability to predict $Y$.

Relationships intermediate between these two extremes can be interpreted in terms of how much $X$ increases our ability to predict or explain $Y$. For the dual-career families, we calculated an $r$ of $+0.50$. Squaring this value yields a coefficient of determination of 0.25 ($r^2 = 0.25$), which indicates that number of children ($X$) explains 25% of the total variation in husband's housework ($Y$). When predicting the number of hours per week that husbands in such families devote to housework, we will make 25% fewer errors by basing the predictions on number of children and predicting from the regression line, as opposed to ignoring this variable and predicting the mean of $Y$ for every case. Also, 75% of the variation in $Y$ is unexplained by $X$ and presumably due to some combination of the influence of other variables, measurement error, and random chance. *(For practice in the interpretation of* $r^2$*, see any of the problems at the end of this chapter.)*

---

## Applying Statistics 13.2: Regression and Correlation

Are nations that have more educated populations more tolerant? Are more educated nations therefore less likely to see homosexuality as wrong? Random samples from 10 nations have been asked if they agree that homosexuality is "never acceptable." Information has also been gathered on the average years of school completed for people over 25 in each nation. How are these variables related? The data are presented in the table below. Columns have been added for all necessary sums.

The slope ($b$) is

$$b = \frac{n\Sigma XY - (\Sigma X)(\Sigma Y)}{n\,\Sigma X^2 - (\Sigma X)^2}$$

$$b = \frac{(10)(3{,}710) - (82)(502)}{(10)(736) - (82)^2}$$

$$b = \frac{37{,}100 - 41{,}164}{7{,}360 - 6{,}724}$$

$$b = \frac{-4{,}064}{636}$$

$$b = -6.39$$

A slope of $-6.39$ means that for every increase in years of education (a unit change in $X$), there is a decrease of 6.39 points in the percentage of people who feel that homosexuality is never justified.

*(continued)*

| Nation | Average Years of Schooling $(X)$ | Percentage Agreeing That Homosexuality Is "Always Wrong" $(Y)$ | $X^2$ | $Y^2$ | $XY$ |
|---|---|---|---|---|---|
| China | 6 | 88 | 36 | 7,744 | 528 |
| Brazil | 5 | 56 | 25 | 3,136 | 280 |
| United States | 12 | 45 | 144 | 2,025 | 540 |
| Japan | 10 | 42 | 100 | 1,764 | 420 |
| Mexico | 7 | 55 | 49 | 3,025 | 385 |
| India | 5 | 77 | 25 | 5,929 | 385 |
| South Africa | 6 | 61 | 36 | 3,721 | 366 |
| Finland | 10 | 37 | 100 | 1,369 | 370 |
| Canada | 11 | 26 | 121 | 676 | 286 |
| Germany | 10 | 15 | 100 | 225 | 150 |
| Totals | 82 | 502 | 736 | 29,614 | 3,710 |

Source: World Values Survey Association and United Nations.

The $Y$ intercept $(a)$ is

$$a = \overline{Y} - b\overline{X}$$

$$a = \frac{502}{10} - (-6.39)\left(\frac{82}{10}\right)$$

$$a = 50.2 - (-6.39)(8.2)$$

$$a = 50.2 + 52.4$$

$$a = 102.6$$

The least-squares regression equation is

$$Y = a + bX = 102.6 + (-6.39)X$$

The correlation coefficient is

$$r = \frac{n\sum XY - (\sum X)(\sum Y)}{\sqrt{\left[n\sum X^2 - (\sum X)^2\right]\left[n\sum Y^2 - (\sum Y)^2\right]}}$$

$$r = \frac{(10)(3,710) - (82)(502)}{\sqrt{[(10)(736) - (82)^2][(10)(29,614) - (502)^2]}}$$

$$r = \frac{37,100 - 41,164}{\sqrt{(7,360 - 6,724)(296,140 - 252,004)}}$$

$$r = \frac{-4,064}{\sqrt{(636)(44,136)}}$$

$$r = \frac{-4,064}{\sqrt{28,070,496}}$$

$$r = \frac{-4,064}{5,298.16}$$

$$r = -0.77$$

For these 10 nations, education and disapproval of homosexuality have a strong negative relationship. Disapproval of homosexuality decreases as education increases. The coefficient of determination, $r^2$, is $(0.77)^2$, or 0.59. This indicates that 59% of the variance in attitude toward homosexuality is explained by education for this sample of 10 nations.

## 13.7 TESTING PEARSON'S *r* FOR SIGNIFICANCE

If the data are based on a random sample, we will need to know if a relationship between the variables can be assumed to exist in the population from which the sample was drawn—we will want to test if Pearson's *r* or the slope ($b$) is statistically significant. Because the hypothesis tests for Pearson's $r$ and the slope ($b$) produce identical results in a bivariate regression, we will focus our attention on testing $r$ for statistical significance. To illustrate this test, the $r$ of 0.50 from the dual-wage-earner family sample will be used, where the null hypothesis states that there is no linear association between the two variables in the population. The population parameter is symbolized as $\rho$ (rho), and the appropriate sampling distribution is the $t$ distribution.

To conduct this test, we need to make a number of assumptions in step 1. Most should be quite familiar, but several are new. First, we must assume that both variables are normal in distribution **(bivariate normal distributions)**. Second, we must assume that the relationship between the two variables is roughly linear in form.

The third assumption involves a new concept: **homoscedasticity**. Basically, a homoscedastic relationship is one where the variance of the $Y$ scores is uniform for all values of $X$. That is, if the $Y$ scores are evenly spread above and below the regression line for the entire length of the line, the relationship is homoscedastic.

A visual inspection of the scatterplot will usually be sufficient to appraise the extent to which the relationship conforms to the assumptions of linearity and homoscedasticity. As a rule of thumb, if the data points fall in a roughly symmetrical, cigar-shaped pattern, whose shape can be approximated with a straight line, then it is appropriate to proceed with this test of significance. Any significant evidence of nonlinearity or marked departures from homoscedasticity may indicate the need for an alternative measure of association and thus a different test of significance.

**Step 1. Make Assumptions and Meet Test Requirements.**

> Model: Random sampling
>  Level of measurement is interval-ratio
>  Bivariate normal distributions
>  Linear relationship
>  Homoscedasticity
>  Sampling distribution is normal

**Step 2. State the Null Hypothesis.**

$$H_0: \rho = 0.0$$

$$(H_1: \rho \neq 0.0)$$

**Step 3. Select the Sampling Distribution and Establish the Critical Region.** With the null hypothesis of "no relationship" in the population, the sampling distribution of all possible sample $r$'s is approximated by the $t$ distribution. Degrees of freedom are equal to $(n - 2)$.

$$\text{Sampling distribution} = t \text{ distribution}$$
$$\text{Alpha} = 0.05$$
$$\text{Degrees of freedom} = n - 2 = 10$$
$$t \text{ (critical)} = \pm 2.228$$

**Step 4. Compute the Test Statistic.** The formula for computing the test statistic is given in Formula 13.8.

FORMULA 13.8
$$t \text{ (obtained)} = r\sqrt{\frac{n - 2}{1 - r^2}}$$

Substituting the values into the formula, we would have:

$$t \text{ (obtained)} = (0.50)\sqrt{\frac{12 - 2}{1 - (0.50)^2}}$$

$$t \text{ (obtained)} = (0.50)\sqrt{\frac{10}{0.75}}$$

$$t \text{ (obtained)} = (0.50)(3.65)$$

$$t \text{ (obtained)} = 1.83$$

**Step 5. Make a Decision and Interpret the Results of the Test.** Because the test statistic does not fall into the critical region as marked by $t$ (critical), we fail to reject the null hypothesis. We do not have sufficient evidence to conclude that the variables are related in the population. The test indicates that the sample value of $r = 0.50$ could have occurred by chance alone if the null hypothesis is true and the variables are unrelated in the population. *(For practice in conducting and interpreting tests of significance with Pearson's r, see Problems 13.1, 13.2, 13.4, 13.5, 13.8, and 13.9.)*

## 13.8 REGRESSION WITH NOMINAL- AND ORDINAL-LEVEL VARIABLES

A key assumption underlying the regression techniques discussed in this chapter is that both the independent and dependent variables are measured at the interval-ratio level. Still, there is a way to include nominal- or ordinal-level independent variables in the regression analysis. The solution is to treat these variables as dummy variables—that is, variables with only two values (0 and 1). We do not use this approach, however, when the dependent variable is nominal or ordinal. Instead, we can use a technique related to least-squares regression called *logistic regression*.

The logic and computational routines for the dummy variable solution and logistic regression are covered in detail on the website for this textbook.

## 13.9 INTERPRETING STATISTICS: THE CORRELATES OF CRIME

What causes crime? Sociologists have been researching this question since the discipline was founded. While we cannot contribute to this voluminous body of work in a textbook devoted to statistical analysis, we can investigate some of the relationships and correlations that are of continuing interest to criminologists.

One school of criminological thought argues that crime is related to poverty. A central proposition of this approach might be phrased this way: "Crime rates will be highest among the most disadvantaged and impoverished groups, those with the highest rates of unemployment and the lowest levels of 'economic viability' (job skills, levels of education) in the legitimate economy." In this section, we will take a look at the empirical relationship between a measure of criminality and a measure of poverty in Canada.

The units of analysis will be Canada's largest cities, called CMAs or Census Metropolitan Areas. A CMA is defined as an area consisting of one or more adjacent municipalities surrounding a major urban core with a population of at least 100,000. To make the data comparable, only those CMAs with populations of 500,000 and over will be examined.

We will use the police-reported crime rate (i.e., criminal offences reported to police per 100,000 population) in the year 2005 as an indicator of criminal activity as the dependent variable. Police-reported crime data are gathered by the Uniform Crime Reporting survey of the Canadian Centre for Justice Statistics at Statistics Canada. The reader should note that police-reported crime is not a perfect measure of crime. Victimization surveys usually produce higher rates of criminal activity than police-reported statistics. This is because victimization surveys collect crime information directly from the population, whether or not it has been reported to police. (There are various reasons why victims of criminal incidents do not report incidents to the police, including the seriousness of the incident, the victim's reluctance to get police involved, the belief that police cannot or will not do much, and fear of reprisals.) As the independent variable of our exercise, we will use the percentage of the population living below the poverty line in the year 2005.

The scores and basic descriptive statistics for the variables are reported in Table 13.4. On crime, cities range from a high of 11,226 offences per 100,000 population in Vancouver to a low of 4,528 per 100,000 population in Quebec City. Poverty rates range from a high of 21.4% in Montreal to a low of 13.4% in Calgary.

**TABLE 13.4** **Scores on Poverty and Crime for Nine Canadian Cities, with Descriptive Statistics**

| City | Crime Rate[1] ($Y$) | Poverty Rate[2] ($X$) |
| --- | --- | --- |
| Calgary | 6,954 | 13.4 |
| Edmonton | 10,529 | 14.0 |
| Hamilton | 5,625 | 15.8 |
| Montreal | 7,328 | 21.4 |
| Ottawa–Gatineau | 5,842 | 14.9 |
| Quebec City | 4,528 | 16.3 |
| Toronto | 5,355 | 18.4 |
| Vancouver | 11,226 | 21.1 |
| Winnipeg | 11,153 | 19.1 |
| Mean | 7,615 | 17.1 |
| Standard Deviation | 2,501 | 2.8 |
| Range | 6,698 | 8.0 |

[1]Number of criminal offences per 100,000 population, 2005.
[2]Percentage of population living below the poverty line, 2005.

Data from Statistics Canada, 2005 *Crime Statistics in Canada*, Catalogue no. 85-002-XIE (Crime rate) and 2006 Canadian Census (Poverty rate).

The first step in assessing an association between interval-ratio-level variables is to produce a scatterplot. Figure 13.8 plots the crime rate on the vertical or $Y$ axis and the poverty rate along the horizontal or $X$ axis. What can we say about this relationship? The regression line is not horizontal, so there is a relationship between these variables. The dots (cities) are fairly

**FIGURE 13.8** **Crime Rate by Poverty Rate for Nine Canadian Cities**

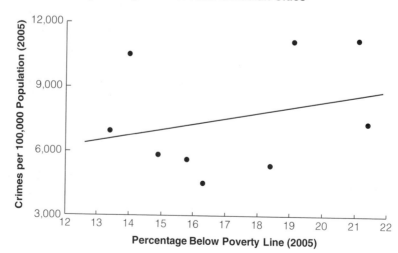

well scattered around the regression line, and we can see immediately that this will be, at best, a moderately strong relationship. The regression line slopes up from left to right, so this is a positive relationship: Cities that have higher poverty rates tend to have higher crime rates (or, crime rates tend to increase as poverty rates increase).

The second step in assessing this relationship is to specify the regression line. We will skip the mechanics of computation here and simply report the values for the regression coefficients ($a$ and $b$).

$$Y = a + bX$$

$$Y = 2,826 + (279)X$$

The regression line will cross the $Y$ axis at the point where $Y = 2,826$. In other words, when the poverty rate is 0%, the number of criminal offences per 100,000 population is 2,826. The slope of the regression, $b$, is 279. That is, every unit (i.e., percentage) increase in $X$ (poverty rate) increases the number of criminal offences by 279 per 100,000 population.

Next, we will calculate and interpret Pearson's $r$. Again, we will skip the details of the computation and report that $r = 0.31$, which reinforces the impression that there is a moderately strong relationship between crime and poverty rates. The coefficient of determination ($r^2$) is about 0.10, which means that poverty rate, by itself, explains about 10% of the variation in the crime rate.

In sum, the linear regression equation, the correlation coefficient, and the coefficient of determination suggest that there is a moderately strong relationship between poverty and crime. The amount of unexplained variation (90%) suggests that many other variables besides poverty have an influence on the crime rate.

We should also note two other limitations of this simple test. First, correlation is not the same thing as causation. Just because two variables are correlated does not mean that they have a causal relationship. Second, a related point, a criminal offence is by definition an individual act of behaviour, but the data we used in this test were collected from cities. Just because there is an association between the variables at the macro (city) level does not necessarily mean that the variables are related in the same way at the micro (individual) level. (This problem is called the *ecological fallacy*.) All we know from our analysis is that cities with higher rates of poverty tend to have higher rates of crime. Our theory would lead us to assume that it is the victims of poverty (poor people) who are the offenders, but this conclusion is not proven by this analysis. It may also be the wealthier residents of the poorer cities who are committing the crimes. We would need much more information—on both the micro and macro levels—before we develop final conclusions on the relation between poverty and crime.

## SUMMARY

This summary is based on the example used throughout the chapter.

1. We began with a question: Is the number of children in dual-wage-earner families related to the number of hours per week husbands devote to housework? We presented the observations in a scatterplot (see Figure 13.1), and our visual impression was that the variables were associated in a positive direction. The pattern formed by the observation points in the scatterplot could be approximated with a straight line; thus, the relationship was roughly linear.

2. Values of $Y$ can be predicted with the free-hand regression line, but predictions are more accurate if the least-squares regression line is used. The least-squares regression line is the line that best fits the data by minimizing the variation in $Y$. Using the formula that defines the least-squares regression line ($Y = a + bX$), we found a slope ($b$) of 0.69, which indicates that each additional child (a unit change in $X$) is accompanied by an increase of 0.69 hours of housework per week for the husbands. We also predicted, based on this formula, that in a dual-wage-earner family with six children ($X = 6$), husbands would contribute 5.63 hours of housework a week ($Y' = 5.63$ for $X = 6$).

3. Pearson's $r$ is a statistic that measures the overall linear association between $X$ and $Y$. Our impression from the scatterplot of a substantial positive relationship was confirmed by the computed $r$ of 0.50. We also saw that this relationship yields an $r^2$ of 0.25, which indicates that 25% of the total variation in $Y$ (husband's housework) is accounted for or explained by $X$ (number of children).

4. Assuming that the 12 families represented a random sample, we tested the Pearson's $r$ for its statistical significance and found that, at the 0.05 level, we could not assume that these two variables were also related in the population.

5. We acquired a great deal of information about this bivariate relationship. We know the strength and direction of the relationship and have also identified the regression line that best summarizes the effect of $X$ on $Y$. We know the amount of change we can expect in $Y$ for a unit change in $X$. In short, we have a greater volume of more precise information about this association between interval-ratio variables than we ever did about associations between ordinal or nominal variables. This is possible, of course, because the data generated by interval-ratio measurement are more precise and flexible than those produced by ordinal or nominal measurement techniques.

## SUMMARY OF FORMULAS

| | | |
|---|---|---|
| Least-squares regression line | 13.1 | $Y = a + bX$ |
| Definitional formula for the slope | 13.2 | $b = \dfrac{\Sigma(X - \overline{X})(Y - \overline{Y})}{\Sigma(X - \overline{X})^2}$ |
| Computational formula for the slope | 13.3 | $b = \dfrac{n\Sigma XY - (\Sigma X)(\Sigma Y)}{n\Sigma X^2 - (\Sigma X)^2}$ |
| $Y$ intercept | 13.4 | $a = \overline{Y} - b\overline{X}$ |

| Definitional formula for Pearson's $r$ | 13.5 | $r = \dfrac{\Sigma(X - \bar{X})(Y - \bar{Y})}{\sqrt{\left[\Sigma(X - \bar{X})^2\right]\left[\Sigma(Y - \bar{Y})^2\right]}}$ |
|---|---|---|
| Computational formula for Pearson's $r$ | 13.6 | $r = \dfrac{n\Sigma XY - (\Sigma X)(\Sigma Y)}{\sqrt{\left[n\Sigma X^2 - (\Sigma X)^2\right]\left[n\Sigma Y^2 - (\Sigma Y)^2\right]}}$ |
| Coefficient of determination | 13.7 | $r^2 = \dfrac{\Sigma(Y' - \bar{Y})^2}{\Sigma(Y - \bar{Y})^2}$ |
| $t$ (obtained) for Pearson's $r$ | 13.8 | $t \text{ (obtained)} = r\sqrt{\dfrac{n - 2}{1 - r^2}}$ |

## GLOSSARY

**Bivariate normal distributions.** The model assumption in the test of significance for Pearson's $r$ that both variables are normally distributed.

**Coefficient of determination ($r^2$).** The proportion of all variation in $Y$ that is explained by $X$. Found by squaring the value of Pearson's $r$.

**Conditional mean of $Y$.** The mean of all scores on $Y$ for each value of $X$.

**Explained variation.** The proportion of all variation in $Y$ that is attributed to the effect of $X$. Equal to $\Sigma(Y' - \bar{Y})^2$.

**Homoscedasticity.** The model assumption in the test of significance for Pearson's $r$ that the variance of the $Y$ scores is uniform across all values of $X$.

**Linear relationship.** A relationship between two variables in which the observation points (dots) in the scatterplot can be approximated with a straight line.

**Pearson's $r$ ($r$).** A measure of association for variables that have been measured at the interval-ratio

level; $\rho$ (Greek letter rho) is the symbol for the population value of Pearson's $r$.

**Regression line.** The single best-fitting straight line that summarizes the relationship between two variables. Regression lines are fitted to the data points by the least-squares criterion, whereby the line touches all conditional means of $Y$ or comes as close to doing so as possible.

**Scatterplot.** Graphic display device that depicts the relationship between two variables.

**Slope ($b$).** The amount of change in one variable per unit change in the other; $b$ is the symbol for the slope of a regression line.

**Total variation.** The spread of the $Y$ scores around the mean of $Y$. Equal to $\Sigma(Y - \bar{Y})^2$.

**Unexplained variation.** The proportion of the total variation in $Y$ that is not accounted for by $X$. Equal to $\Sigma(Y - Y')^2$.

**$Y$ intercept ($a$).** The point where the regression line crosses the $Y$ axis.

**$Y'$.** Symbol for predicted score on $Y$.

## MULTIMEDIA RESOURCES

nelson.com/student

Visit the companion website for the fourth Canadian edition of *Statistics: A Tool for Social Research* to access a wide range of student resources. Begin by clicking on the Student Resources section of the textbook's website to access online chapters and study tools.

## PROBLEMS

**13.1** [PS] Why does voter turnout vary from election to election? For municipal elections in five different cities, information has been gathered on the percentage of eligible voters who actually voted, unemployment rate, average years of education for the city, and the percentage of all political ads that used "negative campaigning" (personal attacks, negative portrayals of the opponent's record, etc.). For each relationship:

**a.** Draw a scatterplot and a freehand regression line.

**b.** Compute the slope ($b$) and find the $Y$ intercept ($a$). (HINT: Remember to compute b before computing a. A computing table such as Table 13.3 is highly recommended.)

**c.** State the least-squares regression line and predict the voter turnout for a city in which the unemployment rate was 12, a city in which the average years of schooling was 11, and an election in which 90% of the ads were negative.

**d.** Compute $r$ and $r^2$. (HINT: A computing table such as Table 13.3 is highly recommended. If you constructed one for computing b, you already have most of the quantities you will need to solve for r.)

**e.** Assume these cities are a random sample and conduct a test of significance for each relationship.

**f.** Describe the strength and direction of the relationships in a sentence or two. Which (if any) relationships were significant? Which factor had the strongest effect on turnout?

### Voter Turnout and Unemployment

| City | Voter Turnout | Unemployment Rate |
|------|---------------|-------------------|
| A | 55 | 5 |
| B | 60 | 8 |
| C | 65 | 9 |
| D | 68 | 9 |
| E | 70 | 10 |

### Voter Turnout and Level of Education

| City | Voter Turnout | Average Years of School |
|------|---------------|-------------------------|
| A | 55 | 11.9 |
| B | 60 | 12.1 |
| C | 65 | 12.7 |
| D | 68 | 12.8 |
| E | 70 | 13.0 |

### Voter Turnout and Negative Campaigning

| City | Voter Turnout | Percentage of Negative Advertisements |
|------|---------------|---------------------------------------|
| A | 55 | 60 |
| B | 60 | 63 |
| C | 65 | 55 |
| D | 68 | 53 |
| E | 70 | 48 |

**13.2** [SOC] Occupational prestige scores (higher scores indicate greater prestige) for a sample of fathers and their oldest son and oldest daughter are shown in the table.

| Family | Father's Prestige | Son's Prestige | Daughter's Prestige |
|--------|-------------------|----------------|---------------------|
| A | 80 | 85 | 82 |
| B | 78 | 80 | 77 |
| C | 75 | 70 | 68 |
| D | 70 | 75 | 77 |
| E | 69 | 72 | 60 |
| F | 66 | 60 | 52 |
| G | 64 | 48 | 48 |
| H | 52 | 55 | 57 |

Analyze the relationship between father's and son's prestige and the relationship between father's and daughter's prestige. For each relationship:

**a.** Draw a scatterplot and a freehand regression line.

**b.** Compute the slope ($b$) and find the $Y$ intercept ($a$).

**c.** State the least-squares regression line. What prestige score would you predict for a son whose father had a prestige score of 72? What prestige score would you predict for a daughter whose father had a prestige score of 72?

**d.** Compute $r$ and $r^2$.

**e.** Assume these families are a random sample and conduct a test of significance for both relationships.

**f.** Describe the strength and direction of the relationships in a sentence or two. Does the occupational prestige of the father have an impact on his children? Does it have the same impact for daughters as it does for sons?

**13.3** GER The residents of a housing development for senior citizens have completed a survey on which they indicated how physically active they are and how many visitors they receive each week. Are these two variables related for the 10 cases reported on the following table? Draw a scatterplot and compute $r$ and $r^2$. Find the least-squares regression line. What would be the predicted number of visitors for a person whose level of activity was a 5? How about a person who scored 18 on level of activity?

| Case | Level of Activity | Number of Visitors |
|---|---|---|
| A | 10 | 14 |
| B | 11 | 12 |
| C | 12 | 10 |
| D | 10 | 9 |
| E | 15 | 8 |
| F | 9 | 7 |
| G | 7 | 10 |
| H | 3 | 15 |
| I | 10 | 12 |
| J | 9 | 2 |

**13.4** PS The following variables were collected for a random sample of 10 electoral districts during the last federal election. Draw scatterplots and

compute $r$ and $r^2$ for each combination of variables and test the correlations for their significance. Write a paragraph interpreting the relationship between these variables.

| District | Percentage Working-Class | Unemployment Rate | Voter Turnout |
|---|---|---|---|
| A | 50 | 10 | 56 |
| B | 45 | 12 | 55 |
| C | 56 | 8 | 52 |
| D | 78 | 15 | 60 |
| E | 13 | 5 | 89 |
| F | 85 | 20 | 25 |
| G | 62 | 18 | 64 |
| H | 33 | 9 | 88 |
| I | 25 | 0 | 42 |
| J | 49 | 9 | 36 |

**13.5** SOC/CJ The table below presents the scores of 10 randomly selected cities on each of six variables: three measures of criminal activity and three measures of population structure. Crime rates are the number of incidents per 100,000 population. For each combination of crime rate and population characteristic:

**a.** Draw a scatterplot and a freehand regression line.

**b.** Compute the slope ($b$) and find the $Y$ intercept ($a$).

**c.** State the least-squares regression line. What homicide rate would you predict for a city with a growth rate of $-1$? What robbery rate would you predict for a city with a population density of 250? What auto theft rate would you predict for a city in which 50% of the population lived in the urban core?

| City | Crime Rates | | | Population | | |
|---|---|---|---|---|---|---|
| | Homicide | Robbery | Auto Theft | Growth[1] | Density[2] | Urbanization[3] |
| A | 1 | 19 | 104 | 3.8 | 41.7 | 52.6 |
| B | 5 | 214 | 286 | 5.5 | 402.7 | 92.1 |
| C | 4 | 138 | 344 | 4.7 | 277.8 | 81.2 |
| D | 2 | 37 | 184 | 5.4 | 52.3 | 45.3 |
| E | 6 | 89 | 252 | 14.4 | 181.5 | 78.1 |
| F | 5 | 81 | 230 | 9.6 | 102.3 | 48.8 |
| G | 6 | 145 | 447 | 22.8 | 81.5 | 84.8 |
| H | 7 | 146 | 842 | 40.0 | 46.7 | 88.2 |
| I | 3 | 99 | 594 | 21.1 | 90.0 | 83.1 |
| J | 6 | 178 | 537 | 13.6 | 221.2 | 96.7 |

[1]Percentage change in population over the last 10 years.
[2]Population per square kilometre of land area.
[3]Percentage of population living in urban core.
Source: U.S. Bureau of the Census, *Statistical Abstracts of the United States: 2001* (Washington, DC, 2002).

**d.** Compute $r$ and $r^2$.

**e.** Since these cities come from a random sample, conduct a test of significance for both relationships.

**f.** Describe the strength and direction of each of these relationships in a sentence or two.

**13.6** ⬛SOC Data on three variables have been collected for 15 nations. The variables are fertility rate (average number of children born to each woman), average education for females (expressed as a percentage of average education for men), and maternal mortality (death rate for mothers per 100,000 live births). On female education, a value of 100 means that men and women have equal levels of education, values over 100 mean that women have more education, and values less than 100 mean that women have less education than men.

| Nation | Fertility | Education of Females | Maternal Mortality |
|---|---|---|---|
| Niger | 7.2 | 50 | 590 |
| Cambodia | 4.8 | 74 | 470 |
| Guatemala | 4.7 | 86 | 190 |
| Ghana | 4.0 | 46 | 210 |
| Bolivia | 3.7 | 60 | 390 |
| Egypt | 3.2 | 41 | 170 |
| Dominican Republic | 3.0 | 87 | 230 |
| Mexico | 2.7 | 96 | 55 |
| Vietnam | 2.5 | 59 | 130 |
| Turkey | 2.2 | 49 | 130 |
| United States | 2.1 | 102 | 8 |
| China | 1.8 | 60 | 55 |
| Canada | 1.7 | 102 | 7 |
| Japan | 1.4 | 98 | 8 |
| Italy | 1.2 | 99 | 7 |

**a.** Compute $r$ and $r^2$ for each combination of variables.

**b.** Summarize these relationships in terms of strength and direction.

**13.7** ⬛SOC The basketball coach at a university believes that his team plays better and scores more points in front of larger crowds. The number of points scored and attendance for all home games last season are reported below. Do these data support the coach's argument?

| Game | Points Scored | Attendance |
|---|---|---|
| 1 | 54 | 378 |
| 2 | 57 | 350 |
| 3 | 59 | 320 |
| 4 | 80 | 478 |
| 5 | 82 | 451 |
| 6 | 75 | 250 |
| 7 | 73 | 489 |
| 8 | 53 | 451 |
| 9 | 67 | 410 |
| 10 | 78 | 215 |
| 11 | 67 | 113 |
| 12 | 56 | 250 |
| 13 | 85 | 450 |
| 14 | 101 | 489 |
| 15 | 99 | 472 |

**13.8** ⬛SOC The table below presents the scores of 15 large Canadian cities on three variables. Compute $r$ and $r^2$ for each combination of variables. Assume that these 15 cities are a random sample of Canada's 50 largest cities and test the correlations for their significance. Write a paragraph interpreting the relationships among these three variables.

| City | Per Capita Expenditures on Education | Percentage High School Graduates[1] | Rank in Per Capita Income |
|---|---|---|---|
| A | 1,102 | 82 | 48 |
| B | 1,339 | 90 | 7 |
| C | 1,907 | 88 | 1 |
| D | 1,171 | 84 | 25 |
| E | 1,621 | 86 | 9 |
| F | 1,276 | 88 | 24 |
| G | 1,159 | 81 | 45 |
| H | 1,412 | 86 | 5 |
| I | 1,487 | 86 | 18 |
| J | 1,041 | 80 | 50 |
| K | 1,194 | 90 | 22 |
| L | 1,262 | 88 | 6 |
| M | 1,163 | 79 | 32 |
| N | 1,223 | 86 | 15 |
| O | 1,549 | 90 | 20 |

[1]Based on percentage of population age 25 and older.

**13.9** [SOC] A social survey was administered to a random sample of adults. Fifteen individuals were then randomly selected from the sample. Their scores on five of the variables in the survey are reproduced below. Is there a relationship between occupational prestige (higher scores indicate greater prestige) and age? Between number of times religious service attended (per month) and number of children? Between number of children and hours of TV watching (per day)? Between age and hours of TV watching? Between age and number of children? Between hours of TV watching and occupational prestige? Which of these relationships are significant?

| Occupational Prestige | Number of Children | Age | Religious Service Attendance per Month | Hours of TV per Day |
|---|---|---|---|---|
| 32 | 3 | 34 | 3 | 1 |
| 50 | 0 | 41 | 0 | 3 |
| 17 | 0 | 52 | 7 | 2 |
| 69 | 3 | 67 | 0 | 5 |
| 17 | 0 | 40 | 0 | 5 |
| 52 | 0 | 22 | 2 | 3 |
| 32 | 3 | 31 | 0 | 4 |
| 50 | 0 | 23 | 8 | 4 |
| 19 | 9 | 64 | 1 | 6 |
| 37 | 4 | 55 | 0 | 2 |
| 14 | 3 | 66 | 5 | 5 |
| 51 | 0 | 22 | 6 | 0 |
| 45 | 0 | 19 | 3 | 7 |
| 44 | 0 | 21 | 4 | 1 |
| 46 | 4 | 58 | 2 | 0 |

## You Are the Researcher

### Using SPSS to Produce Pearson's *r* and the Regression Line with the 2012 CCHS

The demonstrations and exercises below use the shortened version of the 2012 CCHS data. Start SPSS and open the *2012_CCHS_Shortened.sav* file.

### SPSS DEMONSTRATION 13.1 The Scatterplot

The scatterplot provides a convenient look at the relationship between two variables. Here we will examine the effect of *pacdfm* (total number of times per month participated in leisure physical activities lasting more than 15 minutes) on *pmhdscr* (a mental health index with scores ranging from 0 to 70, where higher scores indicate higher levels of positive mental health) with the scatterplot. Click **Graphs, Legacy Dialogs,** then **Scatter/Dot**. The **Scatter/Dot** dialog box will appear with five choices. We want the **Simple Scatter,** so highlight this option and click **Define**. The **Simple Scatterplot** dialog box will appear. Transfer the dependent variable, *pmhdscr,* to the **Y Axis** box, and the independent variable, *pacdfm,* to the **X Axis** box. Click **OK**, and the following scatterplot will be produced.

We added the least-squares regression line to the scatterplot to provide a better sense of the relationship between the variables. To do this, double-click on any part of the scatterplot to open the **Chart Editor** window. Then click the **Elements** menu and choose **Fit Line at Total**. Close the **Chart Editor** window to return to the **Output** window.

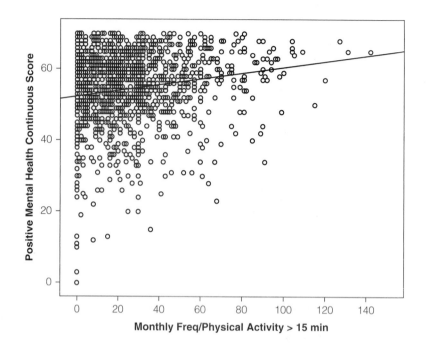

The regression line tells us that a relationship exists and that it is positive in direction. As frequency of physical activity increases, mental health increases. However, the strength and linearity (whether the data points approximate a straight line) of this relationship are more difficult to detect because the overall pattern of the dots around the regression line is obscured by overlapping data points (respondents with identical values on both the independent and dependent variable).

It is difficult to eliminate completely the problem of overplotting. One way to reduce the problem is to "jitter" the data, that is, to subtract or add a small random quantity to each value of the independent and dependent variable. Data points will be separated by this quantity, reducing the overlap and making it easier to assess the strength and linearity of the relationship in the scatterplot. Jittering disentangles overlapping data points and, in many cases, makes it possible to assess the nature of a relationship.

A second and more practical way to reduce overlap and assess the strength and linearity of a relationship is to take a random sample from the larger sample, then get a scatterplot from that sample. This will greatly reduce the number of cases and make the scatterplot easier to read. To do this, click **Data** from the menu bar of the **Data Editor** window and click **Select Cases**. Next, click the **Random Sample of Cases** button and then the **Sample** button. Request a 2% random sample by typing 2 into the box on the first line. (You can request a smaller or larger sample, but 2% should work well in most cases.) Click **Continue**, then **OK** to draw the random sample. Then use the **Simple Scatter** procedure once again. The output will look similar to this:

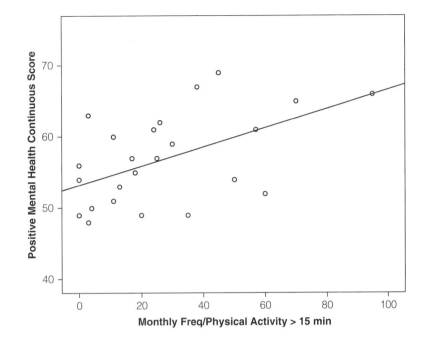

The nature of the relationship between the two variables is now exposed. The pattern of dots on the scatterplot indicates a strong, positive linear relationship between mental health and physical activity. The scores of $Y$ are also evenly spread at each value of $X$, indicating that the relationship is homoscedastic.

If you carry out this demonstration, your output will be based on a different set of randomly selected cases, so your scatterplot will look slightly different. You may wish to repeat the steps above several times to get a better sense of the nature of the relationship; each time you want to produce a new random sample and scatterplot, go back to the **Select Cases** dialog box and click the **OK** button.

### SPSS DEMONSTRATION 13.2 Assessing the Effect of Physical Activity on Mental Health with Linear Regression

After assessing the nature and verifying the linearity of the relationship with the scatterplot, we can proceed to find the slope ($b$) and the $Y$ intercept ($a$) of the least-squares regression line. In this demonstration, we will continue to examine the relationship between frequency of physical activity and mental health. (Make sure that the random sample filter is turned off by clicking the **Reset** button and then **OK** in the **Select Cases** dialog box.) Click **Analyze**, **Regression**, and **Linear**. In the **Linear Regression** window, move *pmhdscr* into the **Dependent** box and *pacdfm* into the **Independent(s)** box. Click **OK**, and the following output will appear.

## Model Summary

| Model | r | r Square | Adjusted r Square | Std. Error of the Estimate |
|---|---|---|---|---|
| 1 | .583[a] | .340 | .305 | 6.825 |

[a]Predictors: (Constant), Monthly freq/physical activity > 15 min

## ANOVA[a]

| Model | | Sum of Squares | df | Mean Square | F | Sig. |
|---|---|---|---|---|---|---|
| 1 | Regression | 456.576 | 1 | 456.576 | 9.803 | .005[b] |
| | Residual | 886.584 | 19 | 46.575 | | |
| | Total | 1343.160 | 20 | | | |

[a]Dependent Variable: Positive Mental Health Continuous Score

[b]Predictors: (Constant), Monthly freq/physical activity > 15 min

## Coefficients[a]

| Model | | Unstandardized Coefficients | | Standardized Coefficients | t | Sig. |
|---|---|---|---|---|---|---|
| | | B | Std. Error | Beta | | |
| 1 | (Constant) | 51.565 | 2.060 | .583 | 25.037 | .000 |
| | Monthly freq/physical activity > 15 min | .157 | .050 | | 3.131 | .005 |

[a]Dependent Variable: Positive Mental Health Continuous Score

The "Model Summary" block reports Pearson's r (.583) and r square (.340). The "ANOVA" output block shows the significance of the relationship (Sig. = .005). Because we have the exact probability, there is no need to look up the test statistic in a table. The exact probability value, 0.005, is well below the standard indicator of a significant result (alpha = 0.05), so we reject the null hypothesis and conclude that there is a statistically significant relationship between frequency of physical activity and mental health.

So far, we know that the independent variable explains 34.0% of the variance in *pmhdscr* and that this result is statistically significant. In the last output block, we see that the slope (*B*) is 0.157 and that the *Y* intercept (labelled as Constant) is 51.565. A slope of 0.157 means that for each additional physical activity performed per month, the average score on the mental health index increases by 0.157 of a point. Recall that scores on mental health range from 0 to 70. The *Y* intercept tells us that the average mental health score is 51.565 when zero physical activity is performed. Finally, we can use the least-squares regression line $Y = a + bX$, or $Y = (51.565) + (0.157)X$, to predict scores on *pmhdscr* for any value of *pacdfm*.

## Exercises (using *2012_CCHS_Shortened.sav*)

**13.1** Use the **Select Cases** command illustrated in Demonstration 13.1 to take a 10% random sample from the larger sample.

Next, use the **Scatter/Dot** procedure to examine the relationship between *alwddly*, the independent variable or "X Axis," and *smk_204*, the dependent variable or "Y Axis." What does the scatterplot reveal about the nature (linearity, strength, and direction) of the relationship between number of drinks consumed and number of cigarettes smoked per day? Write up your results.

**13.2** Using Demonstration 13.2 as a guide, conduct a linear regression analysis for the variables in Exercise 13.1. Write a paragraph summarizing the results of this analysis.

## Cumulative Exercises

Cumulative exercises provide practice in choosing, computing, and analyzing statistics. These online exercises present only data sets and research questions. Students choose appropriate statistics as part of the exercise. Cumulative exercises can be found at nelson.com/students.

# Part 4    Multivariate Techniques

Few research questions can be answered by a statistical analysis of only two variables, and, therefore, the typical research project will include many variables. In previous chapters, we saw how various statistical techniques can be applied to bivariate relationships. In Chapter 14, we will see how the regression techniques presented in Chapter 13 can be extended to probe the relationships among three or more variables measured at the interval-ratio level of measurement. (Techniques presented in previous chapters can also be extended to probe the relationships among three or more variables. Some of these multivariate techniques are covered on the website for this textbook.)

The multivariate techniques presented in Chapter 14 produce some of the most powerful and useful statistics available to social science researchers. The mathematics underlying these statistics can become very complicated, and the chapter focuses on the simplest possible applications. Furthermore, clearly labelled subsections divide the presentation of basic concepts and interpretation from the computations.

Before considering the techniques themselves, we should consider why they are important and what they might be able to tell us. There are two general reasons for utilizing multivariate techniques. First, and most fundamental, is the goal of simply gathering additional information about a specific bivariate relationship by observing how that relationship is affected (if at all) by the presence of a third variable (or a fourth or a fifth variable). Multivariate techniques will increase the amount of information we have on the basic bivariate relationship and (we hope) enhance our understanding of that relationship. A second and strongly related rationale for multivariate statistics involves the issue of causation. While multivariate statistical techniques cannot prove the existence of causal connections between variables, they can provide valuable evidence in support of causal arguments and are very important tools for testing and revising theory.

# 14 Partial Correlation and Multiple Regression and Correlation

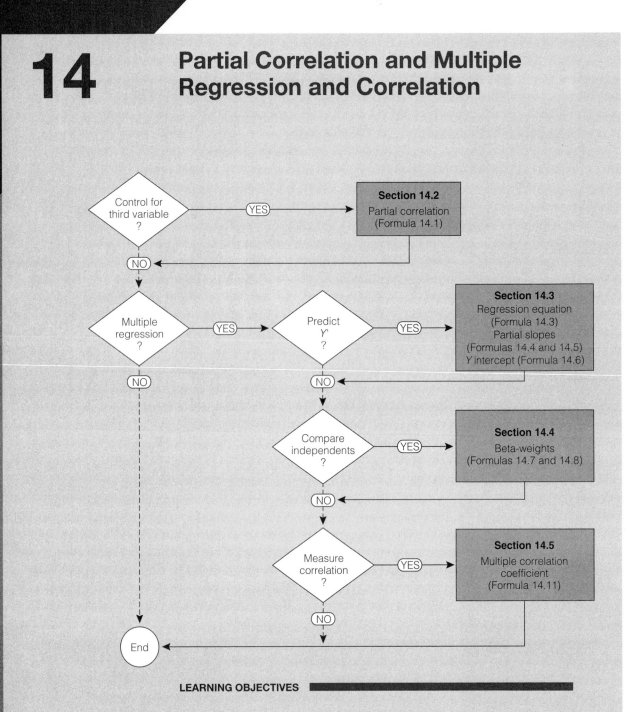

**LEARNING OBJECTIVES**

By the end of this chapter, you will be able to

1. Compute and interpret partial correlation coefficients.
2. Recognize and interpret direct or spurious and intervening relationships.
3. Find and interpret the least-squares multiple regression equation with partial slopes.
4. Calculate and interpret the multiple correlation coefficient ($R^2$).
5. Explain the limitations of partial and multiple regression analysis.

## 14.1 INTRODUCTION

Very few (if any) worthwhile research questions can be answered through a statistical analysis of only two variables. Social science research is, by nature, multivariate and often involves the simultaneous analysis of scores of variables. Some of the most powerful and widely used statistical tools for multivariate analysis of interval-ratio variables are introduced in this chapter. (Other techniques, namely those designed to be used with nominal- and ordinal-level variables, are covered on the website for this textbook.) We will cover techniques that are used to analyze causal relationships and to make predictions, both crucial endeavours in any science.

These techniques are based on the regression and correlation techniques presented in Chapter 13. We will first consider partial correlation analysis, a technique that allows us to examine a bivariate relationship while controlling for a third variable. The second technique involves multiple regression and correlation and allows the researcher to assess the effects, separately and in combination, of more than one independent variable on the dependent variable.

Throughout this chapter, we will focus on research situations involving three variables. This is the least complex application of these techniques, but extensions to situations involving four or more variables are relatively straightforward. Similarly, we will not look at hypothesis tests in this chapter, though the tests are conceptually similar to their bivariate counterparts. To deal efficiently with the computations required by the more complex applications (more than three variables and hypothesis tests), we refer you to any of the computerized statistical packages (such as SPSS) probably available on your campus.

## 14.2 PARTIAL CORRELATION

In Chapter 13, we used Pearson's $r$ to measure the strength and direction of bivariate relationships. To provide an example, we looked at the relationship between number of children ($X$) and husband's contribution to housework ($Y$) for a sample of 12 families. We found a positive relationship of moderate strength ($r = +0.50$), and concluded that husbands tend to make a larger contribution to housework as the number of children increases.

You might wonder, as researchers commonly do, whether this relationship always holds true for *all* types of families. For example, might husbands in strongly religious families respond differently from those in less religious families? Would husbands from families that were politically conservative behave differently from husbands in more liberal families? How about educated husbands? Would they respond differently than less educated husbands? We can address these kinds of issues by a technique called **partial correlation** in which we observe how the bivariate relationship changes when a third variable like religion, political ideology, or education is introduced. Third variables are often referred to as $Z$ variables or **control variables**.

Partial correlation is done by first computing Pearson's $r$ for the bivariate (or zero-order) relationship and then computing the partial (or first-order) correlation coefficient. If the partial correlation coefficient differs from the zero-order correlation coefficient, we can conclude that the third variable does affect the bivariate relationship. If, for example, well-educated husbands respond differently to an additional child compared to less well-educated husbands, the partial correlation coefficient will differ in strength (and perhaps in direction) from the bivariate correlation coefficient.

Before considering matters of computation, we'll consider the relationships between the partial and bivariate correlation coefficients and what they might mean. We will examine each of three possible patterns in turn.

**Types of Relationships.** One possible outcome is that the partial correlation coefficient is essentially the same as the bivariate correlation coefficient. Imagine, for example, that after we controlled for husband's education, we found a partial correlation coefficient of $+0.49$ compared to the zero-order Pearson's $r$ of $+0.50$. This would mean that the third variable (husband's education) has no effect on the relationship between number of children and husband's hours of housework. In other words, regardless of their education, husbands respond in a similar way to additional children. This outcome is consistent with the conclusion that there is a causal, or **direct, relationship** between $X$ and $Y$ and that the third variable ($Z$) is irrelevant to the investigation, as illustrated in Figure 14.1. In this case, the researcher would discard that particular $Z$ variable from further consideration but might run additional tests with the other likely control variables (e.g., the religion of the family).

**FIGURE 14.1 A Direct Relationship Between Two Variables**

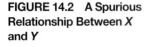

A second possible outcome occurs when the partial correlation coefficient is much weaker than the bivariate coefficient, perhaps dropping to zero. This outcome is consistent with two different relationships between the variables. The first is called a **spurious relationship**: The control variable ($Z$) is a cause of both the independent ($X$) and the dependent ($Y$) variable, as illustrated in Figure 14.2. This outcome would mean that there is no actual relationship between $X$ and $Y$ and that they appear to be related only because both depend on a common cause ($Z$). Once $Z$ is taken into account, the apparent relationship between $X$ and $Y$ disappears.

**FIGURE 14.2 A Spurious Relationship Between $X$ and $Y$**

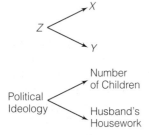

What would a spurious relationship look like? Imagine that we controlled for the political ideology of the parents in our 12-family sample and found that the partial correlation coefficient was much weaker than bivariate Pearson's $r$. This would indicate that the number of children does not actually change the husband's contribution to housework (i.e., the relationship between $X$ and $Y$ is not direct). Rather, political ideology is the mutual cause of both of the other variables: More conservative

**FIGURE 14.3 An Intervening Relationship Between *X* and *Y***

families would be more likely to follow traditional gender role patterns (in which husbands contribute less to housework) *and* have more children.

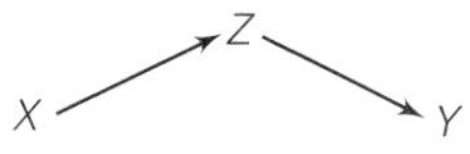

This pattern, in which the partial correlation is much weaker than the bivariate correlation, is also consistent with an **intervening relationship** between the variables, as illustrated in Figure 14.3. In this situation, *X* and *Y* are not linked directly but are causally connected through the *Z* variable. Again, once *Z* is controlled, the apparent relationship between *X* and *Y* disappears.

How can we tell the difference between spurious and intervening relationships? This distinction cannot be made on statistical grounds: Spurious and intervening relationships look exactly the same in terms of statistics. The researcher may be able to distinguish between these two relationships in terms of the order of the variables (i.e., which came first) or on theoretical grounds, but not on statistical grounds.

**Terminology and Formula.** The formula for partial correlation requires some new terminology. We will be dealing with more than one bivariate relationship and need to differentiate them with subscripts. Thus, the symbol $r_{yx}$ will refer to the correlation coefficient between variable *Y* and variable *X*, $r_{yz}$ will refer to the correlation coefficient between *Y* and *Z*, and $r_{xz}$ will refer to the correlation coefficient between *X* and *Z*. As previously mentioned, correlation coefficients calculated for bivariate relationships are referred to as **zero-order correlations.**

**Partial correlation coefficients**, when controlling for a single variable, are called first-order partials and are symbolized as $r_{yx.z}$. The variable to the right of the dot is the control variable. Thus, $r_{yx.z}$ refers to the partial correlation coefficient that measures the relationship between variables *X* and *Y* while controlling for variable *Z*. The formula for the first-order partial is

**FORMULA 14.1**

$$r_{yx.z} = \frac{r_{yx} - (r_{yz})(r_{xz})}{\sqrt{1 - r_{yz}^2}\sqrt{1 - r_{xz}^2}}$$

Note that you must first calculate the zero-order coefficients between all possible pairs of variables (variables *X* and *Y*, *X* and *Z*, and *Y* and *Z*) before solving this formula.

**Computation.** To illustrate the computation of a first-order partial, we will return to the relationship between number of children (*X*) and husband's contribution to housework (*Y*) for 12 dual-career families. The zero-order *r* between these two variables ($r_{yx} = 0.50$) indicated a strong positive relationship. Suppose the researcher wished to investigate the possible effects of husband's education on the bivariate relationship.

**TABLE 14.1** **Scores on Three Variables for 12 Dual-Wage-Earner Families**

| Family | Husband's Housework ($Y$) | Number of Children ($X$) | Husband's Years of Education ($Z$) |
|---|---|---|---|
| A | 1 | 1 | 12 |
| B | 2 | 1 | 14 |
| C | 3 | 1 | 16 |
| D | 5 | 1 | 16 |
| E | 3 | 2 | 18 |
| F | 1 | 2 | 16 |
| G | 5 | 3 | 12 |
| H | 0 | 3 | 12 |
| I | 6 | 4 | 10 |
| J | 3 | 4 | 12 |
| K | 7 | 5 | 10 |
| L | 4 | 5 | 16 |

The original data (from Table 13.1) and the scores of the 12 families on the new variable (years of education completed by the husband) are presented in Table 14.1.

The zero-order correlations, as presented in Table 14.2, indicate that the husband's contribution to housework is positively related to number of children ($r_{yx} = 0.50$), that better-educated husbands tend to do less housework ($r_{yz} = -0.30$), and that families with better-educated husbands have fewer children ($r_{xz} = -0.47$). (*NOTE: Zero-order correlations are calculated using Formula 13.6 for Pearson's* r.)*

**TABLE 14.2** **Zero-Order Correlations**

| | Husband's Housework ($Y$) | Number of Children ($X$) | Husband's Years of Education ($Z$) |
|---|---|---|---|
| Husband's Housework ($Y$) | 1.00 | 0.50 | −0.30 |
| Number of Children ($X$) | | 1.00 | −0.47 |
| Husband's Years of Education ($Z$) | | | 1.00 |

*A table like Table 14.2 is also known as a "correlation matrix." Social science research most often includes numerous variables, and the data analysis phase of the research typically begins with an examination of the relationships between all possible pairs of variables. The correlation matrix gives a quick, easy-to-read overview of the interrelationships in the data, and may suggest strategies or "leads" for further analysis. Furthermore, correlation matrix tables are quite often included in the professional research literature, and, in addition to the bivariate correlations, show other pieces of information such as number of cases on which the correlations are based and the statistical significance of the relationships.

Is the relationship between husband's housework and number of children affected by husband's education? Substituting the zero-order correlations into Formula 14.1, we would have

$$r_{yx.z} = \frac{r_{yx} - (r_{yz})(r_{xz})}{\sqrt{1 - r_{yz}^2}\sqrt{1 - r_{xz}^2}}$$

$$r_{yx.z} = \frac{(0.50) - (-0.30)(-0.47)}{\sqrt{1 - (-0.30)^2}\sqrt{1 - (0.47)^2}}$$

$$r_{yx.z} = \frac{(0.50) - (0.14)}{\sqrt{1 - 0.09}\sqrt{1 - 0.22}}$$

$$r_{yx.z} = \frac{0.36}{\sqrt{0.91}\sqrt{0.78}}$$

$$r_{yx.z} = \frac{0.36}{(0.95)(0.88)}$$

$$r_{yx.z} = \frac{0.36}{0.84}$$

$$r_{yx.z} = 0.43$$

**Interpretation.**   The first-order partial ($r_{yx.z} = 0.43$) measures the strength of relationship between husband's housework ($Y$) and number of children ($X$) while controlling for husband's education ($Z$). It is lower in value than the zero-order coefficient ($r_{yx} = 0.50$), but the difference in the two values is not great. This result suggests a direct relationship between variables $X$ and $Y$ (see Figure 14.1). That is, when controlling for husband's education, the statistical relationship between husband's housework and number of children is essentially unchanged. Regardless of education, husband's hours of housework increase with the number of children.

Our next step in statistical analysis would probably be to discard this control variable (husband's education) and select another. The more the bivariate relationship retains its strength across a series of controls for third variables ($Z$s), the stronger the evidence for a direct relationship between $X$ and $Y$.

**Summary.**   The possible outcomes of controlling for a third variable were introduced in this section. By observing the partial correlation coefficients, we can identify direct or spurious and intervening relationships. In a direct relationship, the partial correlation coefficient is more or less equal to the zero-order correlation coefficient (as demonstrated above with the problem involving number of children, husband's contribution to housework, and husband's education). If, however, the partial correlation coefficient is much lower in value than the zero-order coefficient, the bivariate relationship

---

**ONE STEP AT A TIME** **Computing and Interpreting the Partial Correlation Coefficient**

To begin, compute Pearson's $r$ for all pairs of variables. Be clear about which variable is independent ($X$), which is dependent ($Y$), and which is the control ($Z$).

**To Find the Partial Correlation Coefficient, Solve Formula 14.1**

**1:** Multiply $r_{yz}$ by $r_{xz}$.

**2:** Subtract the value you found in step 1 from $r_{yx}$. *This value is the numerator of Formula 14.1.*

**3:** Square the value of $r_{yz}$.

**4:** Subtract the quantity you found in step 3 from 1.

**5:** Take the square root of the quantity you found in step 4.

**6:** Square the value of $r_{xz}$.

**7:** Subtract the quantity you found in step 6 from 1.

**8:** Take the square root of the quantity you found in step 7.

**9:** Multiply the quantity you found in step 8 by the value you found in step 5. *This value is the denominator of Formula 14.1.*

**10:** Divide the quantity you found in step 2 by the quantity you found in step 9. *This is the partial correlation coefficient.*

**To Interpret the Partial Correlation Coefficient, Compare Its Value to the Zero-Order Correlation**

Choose the description below that comes closest to matching the relationship between the two values:

**1:** The partial correlation coefficient is roughly the same value as the zero-order or bivariate correlation. A good rule of thumb for "roughly the same" is a difference of less than 0.10. This outcome is evidence that the control variable ($Z$) has no effect and that the relationship between $X$ and $Y$ is direct.

**2:** The partial correlation coefficient is much less (say, more than 0.10 less) than the bivariate correlation. This is evidence that the control variable ($Z$) changes the relationship between $X$ and $Y$. The relationship between $X$ and $Y$ is either spurious ($Z$ causes both $X$ and $Y$) or intervening ($X$ and $Y$ are linked by $Z$).

Be aware that that $X$, $Y$, and $Z$ may have an interactive relationship in which the relationship between $X$ and $Y$ changes for each category of $Z$. Partial correlation analysis cannot detect interactive relationships.

---

between $X$ and $Y$ is either spurious or intervening.* That is, there is no direct association between $X$ and $Y$, and the zero-order relationship is due mainly to the effects of $Z$. In a spurious relationship, $X$ and $Y$ are both caused by $Z$, whereas an intervening relationship means that $X$ and $Y$ are linked by $Z$ (see Figures 14.2 and 14.3, respectively). In either case, the

---

*Since this outcome, where the partial correlation coefficient is much weaker than the zero-order coefficient, is consistent with *both* a spurious relationship *and* an intervening relationship, partial correlation techniques do not allow a researcher to distinguish between the relationships. Instead of statistical grounds, the differentiation between these two types of causal patterns must be made on the grounds of temporal ordering among the variables and/or theory.

**TABLE 14.3   A Summary of the Possible Results of Controlling for Third Variables**

| Partial Coefficient (compared with bivariate coefficient) Shows | Pattern | Implications for Further Analysis | Likely Next Step in Statistical Analysis | Theoretical Implications |
|---|---|---|---|---|
| Same relationship between $X$ and $Y$ | Direct relationship | Disregard $Z$ | Analyze another control variable | Theory that $X$ causes $Y$ is supported |
| Weaker relationship between $X$ and $Y$ | Spurious relationship | Incorporate $Z$ | Focus on relationship between $Z$ and $Y$ | Theory that $X$ causes $Y$ is not supported |
| | Intervening relationship | Incorporate $Z$ | Focus on relationships between $X$, $Y$, and $Z$ | Theory that $X$ causes $Y$ is partially supported but must be revised to take $Z$ into account |

relationship between $X$ and $Y$ disappears once the effect of $Z$ is controlled, and the next step in the statistical analysis would be to incorporate the control variable into the analysis as an independent variable. A guideline for decision making for each of the outcomes is provided in Table 14.3. *(For practice in computing and interpreting partial correlation coefficients, see Problems 14.1 to 14.3.)*

## 14.3 MULTIPLE REGRESSION: PREDICTING THE DEPENDENT VARIABLE

Partial correlation techniques are used when a researcher wants to observe how a specific relationship between an independent variable, $X$, and a dependent variable, $Y$, behaves in the presence of a control variable, $Z$. By observing the partial correlation coefficients, we can identify direct, spurious, or intervening relationships. However, it is often the case that a researcher wants to assess a causal model in which the variable taken as the independent variable ($X$) and the control variable ($Z$) each have a separate effect on the dependent variable ($Y$) and are uncorrelated with each other. This relationship is depicted in Figure 14.4. The absence of an arrow between $X$ and $Z$ indicates that they have no mutual relationship. This pattern means that both $X$ and $Z$ should be treated as independent variables, and the statistical analysis would probably involve multiple regression and correlation. As we shall see in this section and in the next one, these techniques enable the researcher to isolate the separate effects of several independent variables on the dependent variable, and thus to make judgments about which independent variable has the stronger effect on the dependent one.

**FIGURE 14.4   A Casual Relationship Among Three Variables $X$, $Z$, and $Y$**

In Chapter 13, the least-squares regression line was introduced as a way of describing the overall linear relationship between two interval-ratio variables and of predicting scores on $Y$ from scores on $X$. This line was the best-fitting line to summarize the bivariate relationship and was defined by the formula:

**FORMULA 14.2**

$$Y = a + bX$$

where $a$ = the $Y$ intercept
$b$ = the slope

The least-squares regression line can be modified to include (theoretically) any number of independent variables. This technique is called **multiple regression**. For ease of explication, we will confine our attention to the case involving two independent variables. The least-squares multiple regression equation is

**FORMULA 14.3**

$$Y = a + b_1X_1 + b_2X_2$$

where $b_1$ = the partial slope of the linear relationship between the first independent variable and $Y$

$b_2$ = the partial slope of the linear relationship between the second independent variable and $Y$

Some new notation and some new concepts are introduced in this formula. First, while the dependent variable is still symbolized as $Y$, the independent variables are differentiated by subscripts. Thus, $X_1$ identifies the first independent variable and $X_2$ the second. The symbol for the slope ($b$) is also subscripted to identify the independent variable with which it is associated.

**Partial Slopes.** A major difference between the multiple and bivariate regression equations concerns the slopes ($b$'s). In the case of multiple regression, the $b$'s are called **partial slopes**, and they show the amount of change in $Y$ for a unit change in the independent while controlling for the effects of the other independent(s) in the equation. The partial slopes are thus analogous to partial correlation coefficients (see Section 14.2) and represent the direct effect of the associated independent variable on $Y$.

**Computing and Interpreting Partial Slopes.** We use Formulas 14.4 and 14.5 to determine the partial slopes for the independent variables. The subscripts attached to the symbols ($b$, $s$, $r$) in the formulas identify the variables: "$Y$" is the dependent variable, "1" refers to the first independent variable, and "2" refers to the second independent variable.*

---

*Partial slopes can be computed from zero-order slopes but Formulas 14.4 and 14.5 are somewhat easier to use.

**FORMULA 14.4**
$$b_1 = \left(\frac{s_y}{s_1}\right)\left(\frac{r_{y1} - r_{y2}r_{12}}{1 - r_{12}^2}\right)$$

**FORMULA 14.5**
$$b_2 = \left(\frac{s_y}{s_2}\right)\left(\frac{r_{y2} - r_{y1}r_{12}}{1 - r_{12}^2}\right)$$

where $b_1$ = the partial slope of $X_1$ on $Y$
$b_2$ = the partial slope of $X_2$ on $Y$
$s_y$ = the standard deviation of $Y$
$s_1$ = the standard deviation of the first independent variable ($X_1$)
$s_2$ = the standard deviation of the second independent variable ($X_2$)
$r_{y1}$ = the bivariate correlation between $Y$ and $X_1$
$r_{y2}$ = the bivariate correlation between $Y$ and $X_2$
$r_{12}$ = the bivariate correlation between $X_1$ and $X_2$

To illustrate the computation of the partial slopes, we will assess the combined effects of number of children ($X_1$) and husband's education ($X_2$) on husband's contribution to housework. All the relevant information can be calculated from Table 14.1 and is reproduced below:

| Husband's Housework | Number of Children | Husband's Education |
|---|---|---|
| $\overline{Y} = 3.3$ | $\overline{X}_1 = 2.7$ | $\overline{X}_2 = 13.7$ |
| $s_y = 2.1$ | $s_1 = 1.5$ | $s_2 = 2.6$ |

Zero-order correlations
$r_{y1} = 0.50$
$r_{y2} = -0.30$
$r_{12} = -0.47$

The partial slope for the first independent variable, number of children or $X_1$, is

$$b_1 = \left(\frac{s_y}{s_1}\right)\left(\frac{r_{y1} - r_{y2}r_{12}}{1 - r_{12}^2}\right)$$

$$b_1 = \left(\frac{2.1}{1.5}\right)\left(\frac{0.50 - (-0.30)(-0.47)}{1 - (-0.47)^2}\right)$$

$$b_1 = (1.4)\left(\frac{0.50 - 0.14}{1 - 0.22}\right)$$

$$b_1 = (1.4)\left(\frac{0.36}{0.78}\right)$$

$$b_1 = (1.4)(0.46)$$

$$b_1 = 0.65$$

A slope of 0.65 indicates that there is an increase of 0.65 units in $Y$ for each unit change in $X_1$, while controlling for the effects of $X_2$. That is, there is an increase of 0.65 hours of housework per week being done by husbands with each additional child, regardless of their years of education.

For the second independent variable, husband's education or $X_2$, the partial slope is

$$b_2 = \left(\frac{s_y}{s_2}\right)\left(\frac{r_{y2} - r_{y1}r_{12}}{1 - r_{12}^2}\right)$$

$$b_2 = \left(\frac{2.1}{2.6}\right)\left(\frac{-0.30 - (-0.24)}{1 - 0.22}\right)$$

$$b_2 = (0.81)\left(\frac{-0.30 + 0.24}{0.78}\right)$$

$$b_2 = (0.81)\left(\frac{-0.06}{0.78}\right)$$

$$b_2 = (0.81)(-0.08)$$

$$b_2 = -0.07$$

This value of $-0.07$ means that contribution to housekeeping duties by husbands decreases by 0.07 hour per week with each additional year of education, regardless of number of children in the family.

**Finding and Interpreting the $Y$ Intercept.** Now that partial slopes have been determined for both independent variables, the $Y$ intercept ($a$) can be found. Note that $a$ is calculated from the mean of the dependent variable (symbolized as $\overline{Y}$) and the means of the two independent variables ($\overline{X}_1$ and $\overline{X}_2$).

**FORMULA 14.6**

$$a = \overline{Y} - b_1\overline{X}_1 - b_2\overline{X}_2$$

Substituting the proper values for the example problem at hand, we would have

$$a = \overline{Y} - b_1\overline{X}_1 - b_2\overline{X}_2$$

$$a = 3.3 - (0.65)(2.7) - (-0.07)(13.7)$$

$$a = 3.3 - (1.75) - (-0.96)$$

$$a = 3.3 - 1.75 + 0.96$$

$$a = 2.51$$

**ONE STEP AT A TIME**  Computing and Interpreting Partial Slopes

These procedures apply when there are two independent variables and one dependent variable. For more complex situations, use a computerized statistical package such as SPSS to do the calculations.

**To Compute the Partial Slope Associated with the First Independent Variable by Using Formula 14.4**

**1:** Divide $s_y$ by $s_1$.
**2:** Multiply $r_{y2}$ by $r_{12}$.
**3:** Subtract the value you computed in step 2 from $r_{y1}$.
**4:** Square the value of $r_{12}$.
**5:** Subtract the value you computed in step 4 ($r_{12}^2$) from 1.
**6:** Divide the value you computed in step 3 by the value you computed in step 5.
**7:** Multiply the value you computed in step 6 by the value you computed in step 1. *This value is the partial slope associated with the first independent variable.*

**To Compute the Partial Slope Associated with the Second Independent Variable by Using Formula 14.5**

**1:** Divide $s_y$ by $s_2$.
**2:** Multiply $r_{y1}$ by $r_{12}$.
**3:** Subtract the value you computed in step 2 from $r_{y2}$.
**4:** Square the value of $r_{12}$.
**5:** Subtract the value you computed in step 4 ($r_{12}^2$) from 1.
**6:** Divide the value you computed in step 3 by the value you computed in step 5.
**7:** Multiply the value you computed in step 6 by the value you computed in step 1. *This value is the partial slope associated with the second independent variable.*

**To Interpret Partial Slopes**

The value of a partial slope is the increase in the value of $Y$ for a unit increase in the value of the associated independent variable while controlling for the effects of the other independent variable.

**ONE STEP AT A TIME**  Computing the $Y$ Intercept

**To Find the $Y$ Intercept by Using Formula 14.6**

**1:** Multiply the mean of $X_2$ by $b_2$.
**2:** Multiply the mean of $X_1$ by $b_1$.

**3:** Subtract the quantity you found in step 1 from the quantity you found in step 2.
**4:** Subtract the quantity you found in step 3 from the mean of $Y$. *The result is the value of a, the $Y$ intercept.*

The $Y$ intercept is the point where the regression line crosses the $Y$ axis and is equal to the mean of $Y$ when all independents equal 0. Thus, husbands with no children and no years of education contribute an average of 2.51 hours per week to housekeeping chores.

```
ONE STEP AT A TIME    Using the Multiple Regression Line to Predict Scores on Y
```

**1:** Choose a value for $X_1$. Multiply this value by the value of $b_1$.

**2:** Choose a value for $X_2$. Multiply this value by the value of $b_2$.

**3:** Add the values you found in steps 1 and 2 to the value of $a$, the $Y$ intercept. *The resulting value is the predicted score on Y.*

**The Least-Squares Multiple Regression Line and Predicting $Y'$.**   For our example problem, the full least-squares multiple regression equation is

$$Y = a + b_1X_1 + b_2X_2$$
$$Y = 2.51 + (0.65)\, X_1 + (-0.07)\, X_2$$

As was the case with the bivariate regression line, this formula can be used to predict scores on the dependent variable from scores on the independent variables. For example, what would be our best prediction of husband's housework ($Y'$) for a family of four children ($X_1 = 4$) where the husband had completed 11 years of schooling ($X_2 = 11$)? Substituting these values into the least-squares formula, we would have

$$Y' = 2.51 + (0.65)(4) + (-0.07)(11)$$
$$Y' = 2.51 + 2.60 - 0.77$$
$$Y' = 4.34$$

Our prediction would be that this husband would contribute 4.34 hours per week to housework. This prediction is, of course, a kind of "educated guess," which is unlikely to be perfectly accurate. However, we will make fewer errors of prediction using the least-squares line (and, thus, incorporating information from the independent variables) than we would using any other method of prediction (assuming, of course, that there is a linear association between the independent and the dependent variables). *(For practice in predicting Y scores and in computing slopes and the Y intercept, see Problems 14.1 to 14.6.)*

**14.4 MULTIPLE REGRESSION: ASSESSING THE EFFECTS OF THE INDEPENDENT VARIABLES**

The least-squares multiple regression equation (see Formula 14.3) is used to isolate the separate effects of the independent variables and to predict scores on the dependent variable. However, in many situations, using this formula to determine the relative importance of the various independent variables will be awkward—especially when the independent variables differ in terms of units of measurement (e.g., number of children vs. years of education). When the units of measurement differ, a comparison of the partial slopes will not necessarily tell us which independent variable has the strongest effect and is thus the most important variable. Comparing the partial slopes of variables that differ in units of measurement is a little like comparing apples and oranges.

The comparability of the independent variables can be increased by converting all variables in the equation to a common scale and thereby eliminating variations in the values of the partial slopes that are solely a function of differences in units of measurement. We can, for example, standardize all distributions by changing the scores of all variables to $Z$ scores. Each distribution of scores would then have a mean of 0 and a standard deviation of 1 (see Chapter 4), and comparisons between the independent variables would be much more meaningful.

**Beta-Weights.** To standardize the variables to the normal curve, we could actually convert all scores into the equivalent $Z$ scores and then recompute the slopes and the $Y$ intercept. This would require a good deal of work, and, fortunately, a shortcut is available for directly computing the slopes of the standardized scores. These **standardized partial slopes** are called **beta-weights** and are symbolized $b^*$. The beta-weights show the amount of change in the standardized scores of $Y$ for a one-unit change in the standardized scores of each independent variable while controlling for the effects of all other independent variables.

**Formulas and Computation for Beta-Weights.** When we have two independent variables, the beta-weight for each is found by using Formula 14.7 and Formula 14.8:

**FORMULA 14.7**
$$b_1^* = b_1\left(\frac{s_1}{s_y}\right)$$

**FORMULA 14.8**
$$b_2^* = b_2\left(\frac{s_2}{s_y}\right)$$

We can now compute the beta-weights for our sample problem to see which of the two independents has the stronger effect on the dependent. For the first independent variable, number of children ($X_1$):

$$b_1^* = b_1\left(\frac{s_1}{s_y}\right)$$

$$b_1^* = (0.65)\left(\frac{1.5}{2.1}\right)$$

$$b_1^* = (0.65)(0.71)$$

$$b_1^* = 0.46$$

For the second independent variable, husband's years of education ($X_2$):

$$b_2^* = b_2\left(\frac{s_2}{s_y}\right)$$

$$b_2^* = (-0.07)\left(\frac{2.6}{2.1}\right)$$

$$b_2^* = (-0.07)(1.24)$$

$$b_2^* = -0.09$$

**Interpreting Beta-Weights.** Comparing the value of the beta-weights for our example problem, we see that number of children ($b_1^* = 0.46$) has a stronger effect than husband's education ($b_2^* = -0.09$) on husband's housework. Furthermore, the net effect (after controlling for the effect of education) of the first independent variable is positive, while the net effect of the second independent variable (after controlling for the effect of number of children) is negative. We can conclude that number of children is the more important of the two variables and that husband's contribution to housework increases as the number of children increases, regardless of husband's years of education.

---

**ONE STEP AT A TIME** Computing and Interpreting Beta-Weights (*b**)

These procedures apply when there are two independent variables and one dependent variable. For more complex situations, use a computerized statistical package such as SPSS to do the calculations.

**To Compute the Beta-Weight Associated with the First Independent Variable Using Formula 14.7**

**1:** Divide $s_1$ by $s_y$.
**2:** Multiply the value you found in step 1 by the partial slope of the first independent variable ($b_1$). *This value is the beta-weight associated with the first independent variable.*

**To Compute the Beta-Weight Associated with the Second Independent Variable Using Formula 14.8**

**1:** Divide $s_2$ by $s_y$.
**2:** Multiply the value you found in step a by the partial slope of the second independent variable ($b_2$). *This value is the beta-weight associated with the second independent variable.*

**To Interpret Beta-Weights**

**3:** A beta-weight (or standardized partial slope) shows the increase in the value of $Y$ for a unit increase in the value of the associated independent variable while controlling for the effects of the other independent variable after all variables have been standardized (or transformed to $Z$ scores).

**The Standardized Least-Squares Regression Line.**   Using standardized scores, the least-squares regression equation can be written as

FORMULA 14.9

$$Z_y = a_z + b_1^* Z_1 + b_2^* Z_2$$

where $Z$ indicates that all scores have been standardized to the normal curve.

The standardized regression equation can be further simplified by dropping the term for the $Y$ intercept; this term will always be zero when scores have been standardized.

Because the mean of any standardized distribution of scores is zero, the mean of the standardized $Y$ scores will be zero and the $Y$ intercept will also be zero ($a = \overline{Y} = 0$). Thus, Formula 14.9 simplifies to

FORMULA 14.10

$$Z_y = b_1^* Z_1 + b_2^* Z_2$$

The standardized regression equation, with beta-weights noted, would be

$$Z_y = (0.46)Z_1 + (-0.09)Z_2$$

and it is immediately obvious that the first independent variable has a much stronger direct effect on $Y$ than the second independent variable.

**Summary.**   Multiple regression analysis permits the researcher to summarize the linear relationship among two or more independent variables and a dependent variable. The unstandardized regression equation (see Formula 14.3) permits values of $Y$ to be predicted from the independent variables in the original units of the variables. The standardized regression equation (see Formula 14.10) allows the researcher to easily assess the relative importance of the various independent variables by comparing the beta-weights. *(For practice in computing and interpreting beta-weights, see any of the problems at the end of this chapter. It is probably a good idea to start with Problem 14.1 as it has the smallest data set and the least complex computations.)*

## 14.5 MULTIPLE CORRELATION

We use the multiple regression equations to disentangle the *separate* direct effects of each independent variable on the dependent one. Using **multiple correlation** techniques, we can also determine the *combined* effects of all independent variables on the dependent variable. We do so by computing the **multiple correlation coefficient ($R$)** and the **coefficient of multiple determination ($R^2$)**. The value of the latter statistic represents the proportion of the variance in $Y$ that is explained by all the independent variables combined.

In terms of zero-order correlation, we have seen that "number of children" ($X_1$) explains a proportion of 0.25 of the variance in $Y$ ($r_{y1}^2 = (0.50)^2 = 0.25$) by itself and that husband's education explains a proportion of 0.09 of the variance in $Y(r_{y2}^2 = (-0.30)^2 = 0.09)$. The two zero-order correlations cannot be simply added together to determine their combined effect on $Y$, because the two independent variables are also correlated with each other and, therefore, they will "overlap" in their effects on $Y$ and explain some of the same variance. This overlap is eliminated in Formula 14.11:

**FORMULA 14.11**

$$R^2 = r_{y1}^2 + r_{y2.1}^2(1 - r_{y1}^2)$$

where $R^2$ = the multiple correlation coefficient

$r_{y1}^2$ = the zero-order correlation between $Y$ and $X_1$, the quantity squared

$r_{y2.1}^2$ = the partial correlation of $Y$ and $X_2$, while controlling for $X_1$, the quantity squared

---

### Applying Statistics 14.1: Multiple Regression and Correlation

Five recently divorced men were asked about their dating behaviour (i.e., the number of dates they went on) in the last month. Is number of dates related to the length of time married? Is number of dates related to socioeconomic status as measured by yearly income?

| Case | Number of Dates ($Y$) | Years Married ($X_1$) | Income (dollars) ($X_2$) |
|------|------|------|------|
| A | 5 | 5 | 30,000 |
| B | 4 | 7 | 45,000 |
| C | 4 | 10 | 25,000 |
| D | 3 | 2 | 27,000 |
| E | 1 | 15 | 17,000 |

$\bar{Y} = 3.4$  $\bar{X}_1 = 7.8$  $\bar{X}_2 = 28,800.00$

$s_y = 1.4$  $s_1 = 4.5$  $s_2 = 9,173.88$

The zero-order correlations among these three variables are

| | Years Married ($X_1$) | Income ($X_2$) |
|------|------|------|
| Number of Dates ($Y$) | −0.62 | 0.62 |
| Years married ($X_1$) | | −0.49 |

These results suggest strong but opposite relationships between each independent and number of dates. Number of dates decreases as years married increases, and increases as income increases.

To find the multiple regression equation, we must find the partial slopes.

For years married ($X_1$):

$$b_1 = \left(\frac{s_y}{s_1}\right)\left(\frac{r_{y1} - r_{y2}r_{12}}{1 - r_{12}^2}\right)$$

$$b_1 = \frac{1.4}{4.5}\left(\frac{(-0.62) - (0.62)(-0.49)}{1 - (-0.49)^2}\right)$$

$$b_1 = (0.31)\left(\frac{(-0.62) - (-0.30)}{1 - 0.24}\right)$$

$$b_1 = (0.31)\left(\frac{-0.32}{0.76}\right)$$

$$b_1 = (0.31)(-0.42)$$

$$b_1 = -0.13$$

For income ($X_2$):

$$b_2 = \left(\frac{s_y}{s_2}\right)\left(\frac{r_{y2} - r_{y1}r_{12}}{1 - r_{12}^2}\right)$$

$$b_2 = \left(\frac{1.4}{9173.88}\right)\left(\frac{(0.62) - (-0.62)(-0.49)}{1 - (-0.49)^2}\right)$$

$$b_2 = (0.00015)\left(\frac{(0.62) - (0.30)}{1 - 0.24}\right)$$

$$b_2 = (0.00015)\left(\frac{0.32}{0.76}\right)$$

$$b_2 = (0.00015)(0.42)$$

$$b_2 = 0.000063$$

The $Y$ intercept would be

$$a = \bar{Y} - b_1\bar{X}_1 - b_2\bar{X}_2$$

$$a = 3.4 - (-0.13)(7.8) - (0.000063)(28{,}800)$$

$$a = 3.4 - (-1.01) - (1.81)$$

$$a = 3.4 + 1.01 - 1.81$$

$$a = 2.60$$

The multiple regression equation is

$$Y = a + b_1X_1 + b_2X_2$$
$$Y = 2.60 + (-0.13)X_1 + (0.000063)X_2$$

What is the number of dates we could predict for a male who had been married 30 years ($X_1 = 30$) and had an income of \$50,000 ($X_2 = 50{,}000$)?

$$Y' = 2.60 + (-0.13)(30) + (0.000063)(50{,}000)$$
$$Y' = 2.60 + (-3.9) + (3.15)$$
$$Y' = 1.85$$

To assess which of the two independent variables has the stronger effect on number of dates, the standardized partial slopes must be computed.

For years married ($X_1$):

$$b_1^* = b_1\left(\frac{s_1}{s_y}\right)$$

$$b_1^* = (-0.13)\left(\frac{4.5}{1.4}\right)$$

$$b_1^* = -0.42$$

For income ($X_2$):

$$b_2^* = b_2\left(\frac{s_2}{s_y}\right)$$

$$b_2^* = (0.000063)\left(\frac{9173.88}{1.4}\right)$$

$$b_2^* = 0.41$$

The standardized regression equation is

$$Z_y = b_1^*Z_1 + b_2^*Z_2$$
$$Z_y = (-0.42)Z_1 + (0.41)Z_2$$

and the independent variables have nearly equal but opposite effects on number of dates. To assess the combined effects of the two independent variables on number of dates, the coefficient of multiple determination must be computed.

$$R^2 = r_{y1}^2 + r_{y2.1}^2(1 - r_{y1}^2)$$
$$R^2 = (-0.62)^2 + (0.46)^2(1 - (-0.62)^2)$$
$$R^2 = 0.38 + (0.21)(1 - 0.38)$$
$$R^2 = 0.38 + (0.21)(0.62)$$
$$R^2 = 0.38 + 0.13$$
$$R^2 = 0.51$$

The first independent variable, years married, explains 38% of the variation in number of dates by itself. To this quantity, income explains an additional 13% of the variation in number of dates. Taken together, the two independent variables explain a total of 51% of the variation in number of dates.

The first term in this formula ($r_{y1}^2$) is the coefficient of determination for the relationship between $Y$ and $X_1$. It represents the amount of variation in $Y$ explained by $X_1$ by itself. To this quantity we add the amount of the variation remaining in $Y$ (given by $1 - r_{y1}^2$) that can be explained by $X_2$

after the effect of $X_1$ is controlled ($r^2_{y2.1}$). Basically, Formula 14.11 allows $X_1$ to explain as much of $Y$ as it can and then adds in the effect of $X_2$ after $X_1$ is controlled (thus eliminating the "overlap" in the variance of $Y$ that $X_1$ and $X_2$ have in common).

**Computing and Interpreting $R$ and $R^2$.** To observe the combined effects of number of children ($X_1$) and husband's years of education ($X_2$) on husband's housework ($Y$), we need two quantities. The correlation between $X_1$ and $Y$ ($r_{y1} = 0.50$) has already been found. Before we can solve Formula 14.11, we must first calculate the partial correlation of $Y$ and $X_2$ while controlling for $X_1$ ($r_{y2.1}$):

$$r_{y2.1} = \frac{r_{y2} - (r_{y1})(r_{12})}{\sqrt{1 - r^2_{y1}}\ \sqrt{1 - r^2_{12}}}$$

$$r_{y2.1} = \frac{(-0.30) - (0.50)(-0.47)}{\sqrt{1 - (0.50)^2}\ \sqrt{1 - (-0.47)^2}}$$

$$r_{y2.1} = \frac{(-0.30) - (-0.24)}{\sqrt{0.75}\sqrt{0.78}}$$

$$r_{y2.1} = \frac{-0.06}{0.77}$$

$$r_{y2.1} = -0.08$$

Formula 14.11 can now be solved for our sample problem:

$$R^2 = r^2_{y1} + r^2_{y2.1}(1 - r^2_{y1})$$

$$R^2 = (0.50)^2 + (-0.08)^2(1 - 0.50^2)$$

$$R^2 = 0.25 + (0.006)(1 - 0.25)$$

$$R^2 = 0.25 + 0.005$$

$$R^2 = 0.255$$

---

## Applying Statistics 14.2: $R^2$ and Beta-Weights

The following table presents information on three variables for a small sample of 10 nations. The dependent variable is the percentage of respondents who said they are "very happy" on a survey administered to random samples from each nation. The independent variables measure health and physical well-being (life expectancy,

or the number of years the average citizen can expect to live at birth) and income inequality (the amount of total income that goes to the richest 20% of the population). Our expectation is that happiness will have a positive correlation with life expectancy (the greater the health, the happier the population) and a negative relationship with inequality (the greater the inequality, the greater the discontent and the lower the level of happiness). In this analysis, we focus on $R^2$ and the beta-weights only.

| Nation | Percent "Very Happy" ($Y$) | Life Expectancy ($X_1$) | Income Inequality ($X_2$) |
|---|---|---|---|
| Brazil | 34.1 | 73 | 56.99 |
| Canada | 46.4 | 81 | 32.56 |
| Germany | 19.9 | 80 | 29.31 |
| Ghana | 50.1 | 59 | 40.79 |
| India | 29.0 | 64 | 36.80 |
| Japan | 29.2 | 83 | 24.85 |
| Mexico | 58.5 | 75 | 46.05 |
| Russia | 21.2 | 68 | 39.93 |
| Rwanda | 11.9 | 48 | 46.79 |
| United States | 34.4 | 78 | 40.81 |
| Mean = | 33.47 | 70.90 | 39.48 |
| Standard deviation = | 13.82 | 10.61 | 8.83 |

A correlation matrix presents the zero-order correlations:

| | Happiness | Life Expectancy | Inequality |
|---|---|---|---|
| Happiness | 1.00 | 0.29 | 0.13 |
| Life expectancy | | 1.00 | −0.46 |
| GDP per capita | | | 1.00 |

Consistent with our expectations, there is a positive, weak-to-moderate relationship between life expectancy and happiness. Unexpectedly, however, the relationship between inequality and happiness is positive, although weak in strength. The relationship between the two independent variables is moderate and negative, indicating that nations with more income inequality have lower life expectancy.

The combined effect of life expectancy and inequality on happiness is found by computing $R^2$:

$$R^2 = r_{y1}^2 + r_{y2.1}^2(1 - r_{y1}^2)$$
$$R^2 = (0.29)^2 + (0.31)^2(1 - 0.29^2)$$
$$R^2 = 0.08 + (0.10)(0.92)$$
$$R^2 = 0.08 + 0.09$$
$$R^2 = 0.17$$

By itself, life expectancy explains 8% of the variance in happiness. To this, income inequality adds another 9%, for a total of 17%. This leaves about 83% of the variance unexplained, a sizeable proportion but not unusually large in social science research.

We must calculate the beta-weights to assess the separate effects of the two independent variables. The unstandardized partial slopes needed for this computation are 0.58 for $X_1$ (life expectancy) and 0.53 for $X_2$ (income inequality).

For the first independent variable (life expectancy):

$$b_1^* = b_1\left(\frac{s_1}{s_y}\right)$$
$$b_1^* = (0.58)\left(\frac{10.61}{13.82}\right)$$
$$b_1^* = (0.58)(0.77)$$
$$b_1^* = 0.45$$

For the second independent variable (income inequality):

$$b_2^* = b_2\left(\frac{s_2}{s_y}\right)$$
$$b_2^* = (0.53)\left(\frac{8.83}{13.82}\right)$$
$$b_2^* = (0.53)(0.64)$$
$$b_2^* = 0.34$$

Recall that the beta-weights show the effect of each independent variable on the dependent variable while controlling for the other independent variables in the equation. In this case, life expectancy has the stronger effect, and the relationship is positive. The effect of income inequality is also positive.

In summary, for these nations, level of happiness has a moderate positive relationship with life expectancy and a weaker positive relationship with income inequality. Taken together, the independent variables explain 17% of the variation in happiness.

---

### ONE STEP AT A TIME  Computing and Interpreting the Coefficient of Multiple Determination

These procedures apply when there are two independent variables and one dependent variable. For more complex situations, use a computerized statistical package such as SPSS to do the calculations.

**To Compute the Coefficient of Multiple Determination by Using Formula 14.11**

1: Find the value of the partial correlation coefficient for $r_{y2.1}$.
2: Square the value you found in step 1.
3: Square the value of $r_{y1}$.
4: Subtract the value you found in step 3 from 1.00.

5: Multiply the value you found in step 4 by the value you found in step 2.
6: Add the value you found in step 5 to $r_{y1}^2$. The result is the coefficient of multiple determination ($R^2$).

**To Interpret the Coefficient of Multiple Determination ($R^2$)**

The coefficient of multiple determination is the total amount of the variation in $Y$ explained by all independent variables combined.

---

The first independent variable ($X_1$), number of children, explains 25% of the variance in $Y$ by itself. To this total, the second independent ($X_2$), husband's education, adds only half a percent, for a total explained variance of 25.5%. In combination, the two independent variables explain a total of 25.5% of the variation in the dependent variable. *(For practice in computing and interpreting R and R², see any of the problems at the end of this chapter. It is probably a good idea to start with Problem 14.1 as it has the smallest data set and the least complex computations.)*

**14.6 INTERPRETING STATISTICS: ANOTHER LOOK AT THE CORRELATES OF CRIME**

In Chapter 13, we assessed the association between poverty and crime. We found a strong and positive relationship ($r = 0.31$) between a measure of poverty and the crime rate for Canada's largest cities, an indication that there is an important relationship between these two variables. In this instalment of Interpreting Statistics, we will return to this relationship and add several independent variables to the analysis.*

Our first new independent variable is a measure of age: the percentage of the population less than 25. The rates for some crimes are strongly related to age: They are highest for people in their teens and twenties but decline dramatically as age rises. Thus, we can expect that there will be a substantial positive relationship between this measure of age and the crime rate (the higher the proportion of younger people in a population, the higher the crime rate).

---

*This analysis considers the effects of three independent variables, one more than was included in previous examples in this chapter. As you will see, the addition of an independent variable will not complicate interpretation and analysis unduly. However, the mathematics underlying multiple regression with three independent variables is complex and should be performed with the aid of a computerized statistics packages such as SPSS. We will not show the underlying computations in this analysis.

Our second new independent variable comes from research showing that crime rates follow a regional pattern in Canada, rising from east to west.* Thus, we should expect to find higher rates of crime in western cities (Calgary, Edmonton, Winnipeg, and Vancouver) compared to eastern cities (Hamilton, Montreal, Ottawa–Gatineau, Quebec, and Toronto).

Although it is reasonable to include region in this analysis, we must first confront an important problem. Region is a nominal-level variable but regression analysis requires that all variables be interval-ratio in level of measurement. We can resolve this problem by treating region as a "dummy variable," that is, a variable that can be treated as interval-ratio regardless of its actual level of measurement.

Dummy variables have exactly two categories, one coded as a score of zero and the other as a score of one. Treated this way, nominal-level variables such as gender (e.g., with males coded as 0 and females coded as 1) or immigration status (e.g., Canadian-born coded as 0 and foreign-born coded as 1) are commonly included as independent variables in regression equations. In this case, we will create a variable that is coded so that western cities are scored as "1" and non-western cities as "0." Coded this way, region should have a positive relationship with crime—as region "increases" (as we increase from a score of 0, non-western cities, to a score of 1, western cities), the crime rate also increases.

It is important to note that we could have as easily coded eastern cities as "1" and non-eastern cities as "0," with identical results. Correlation coefficients, slopes, and $R^2$ values would be the same regardless of which region we coded as 1 and 0. The only difference would be the direction of the relationship. If we instead decided to score eastern cities as "1" and non-eastern cities as "0," we would expect region to have a negative relationship (i.e., correlation coefficients and slopes would be negative) with crime. Coding of dummy variables is therefore a subjective decision made by the researcher. (Dummy variables are covered in more detail on the website for this textbook.)

Before beginning the multivariate analysis, we should examine the correlation coefficients between all possible pairs of variables. Zero-order correlations, and the scores used in computing them, for the variables are reported in Table 14.4. As we saw in Chapter 13, there is a strong positive relationship between poverty and crime: Cities with higher rates of poverty have higher rates of crime. Crime rate has a moderate positive relationship with age: Cities with younger populations tend to have slightly higher crime rates. Finally, crime rate has a very strong positive relationship with region: Western Canadian cities have higher rates of crime than non-western cities.

The results of the multivariate analysis are provided in Table 14.5. Looking at the unstandardized partial slopes ($b$), we see that the number of

*Source: Statistics Canada, 2001, *Crime Comparisons Between Canada and the United States*, Catalogue no. 85-002-XPE.

**TABLE 14.4**  **Scores on Poverty, Age, Region, and Crime for Nine Canadian Cities and Zero-Order Correlations**

| City | Crime[1] | Poverty[2] | Age[3] | Region[4] |
|------|------|---------|-----|--------|
| | | **Scores** | | |
| Calgary | 6,954 | 13.4 | 33.1 | 1 |
| Edmonton | 10,529 | 14.0 | 33.5 | 1 |
| Hamilton | 5,625 | 15.8 | 31.2 | 0 |
| Montreal | 7,328 | 21.4 | 30.2 | 0 |
| Ottawa–Gatineau | 5,842 | 14.9 | 32.1 | 0 |
| Quebec | 4,528 | 16.3 | 28.1 | 0 |
| Toronto | 5,355 | 18.4 | 32.3 | 0 |
| Vancouver | 11,226 | 21.1 | 29.9 | 1 |
| Winnipeg | 11,153 | 19.1 | 32.0 | 1 |

| | Crime | Poverty | Age | Region |
|------|-------|---------|-----|--------|
| | | **Zero-Order Correlations** | | |
| Crime | 1.00 | 0.31 | 0.26 | 0.84 |
| Poverty | | 1.00 | −0.50 | −0.08 |
| Age | | | 1.00 | 0.41 |
| Region | | | | 1.00 |

[1]Number of criminal offences per 100,000 population, 2005.
[2]Percentage of population living below the poverty line, 2005.
[3]Percentage of population under age 25, 2005.
[4]Western cities coded as 1; non-western cities coded as 0.

Data from Statistics Canada. 2001. Crime Statistics in Canada, 2000. Catalogue no. 85-002-XIE (Crime rate) and Statistics Canada, 2001 Canadian Census, individual PUMF (Age and Poverty rate).

**TABLE 14.5**  **Multiple Regression Analysis of the Crime Rate**

| Variable | $b$ | $b^*$ |
|----------|-----|-------|
| Poverty | 401 | 0.45 |
| Age | 219 | 0.14 |
| Region | 4,120 | 0.82 |
| Intercept (a) | −7,970 | |
| | $R^2 = 0.86$ | |

$b$ = partial slope
$b^*$ = standardized partial slopes

criminal offences per 100,000 people increases on average by 401 for each percentage increase in the poverty rate, while controlling for the effects of age and region. The slope for age is also positive—cities with younger populations tend to have higher crime rates. Crime also increases with region. On average, western Canadian cities experience 4,120 more criminal offences per 100,000 people compared to eastern Canadian cities, controlling for poverty and age. The standardized partial slopes ($b^*$) in Table 14.5

tell us that crime is more affected by region than by poverty or age. In fact, the effect of region on crime is 1.8 times that of poverty ($0.82/0.45 = 1.8$).

By itself, poverty explains almost 10% ($r = 0.31$, so $(0.31)^2 = 0.10$) of the variance in crime rates among the cities (see Table 14.4). To this, age and region add another 76% for a total of 86% ($R^2 = 0.86$). These three variables, together, account for over 85% of the variation in crime rates from city to city. This is a very substantial percentage, with only 14% of the variation remaining unaccounted for or unexplained. We might be able to raise the value of $R^2$ by adding more independent variables to the equation. However, it is common to find that additional independent variables will explain smaller and smaller proportions of the variance and have a diminishing effect on $R^2$. This phenomenon can be caused by many factors including the fact that the independent variables will usually be correlated with each other (e.g., see the relationship between region and age in Table 14.4) and will overlap in their effect on the dependent variable.

## READING STATISTICS 9: Multiple Regression and Partial Correlation

Research projects that analyze the interrelationships among many variables are particularly likely to employ multiple regression and correlation as central statistical techniques. The results of these projects will typically be presented in summary tables that report the multiple correlations, the slopes, and, if applicable, the significance of the results. The zero-order correlations are often presented in the form of a matrix that displays the value of Pearson's $r$ for every possible bivariate relationship in the data set. An example of such a matrix can be found in Section 14.6.

Usually, tables that summarize the multivariate analysis will report $R^2$ and the slope for each independent variable in the regression equation. An example of this kind of summary table would look like this:

| Independent Variables | Multiple $R^2$ | Beta-Weights |
|---|---|---|
| $X_1$ | 0.17 | 0.47 |
| $X_2$ | 0.23 | 0.32 |
| $X_3$ | 0.27 | 0.16 |
| ⋮ | ⋮ | ⋮ |

This table reports that the first independent variable, $X_1$, has the strongest direct relationship with the dependent variable and explains 17% of the variance in the dependent by itself ($R^2 = 0.17$). The second independent variable, $X_2$, adds 6% to the explained variance ($R^2 = 0.23$ after $X_2$ is entered into the equation). The third independent variable, $X_3$, adds 4% to the explained variance of the dependent variable ($R^2 = 0.27$ after $X_3$ is entered into the equation). Table 14.5 provides an alternative example of how the results of a multiple regression analysis may be reported.

In addition to multiple regression, partial correlation is also frequently used in research. As we will now see, partial correlation allows researchers to observe how a bivariate relationship behaves in the presence of a third variable.

### STATISTICS IN THE PROFESSIONAL LITERATURE

There are a great number of cross-national comparative studies on the topic of income inequality and population health. Reviews of the literature reveal that the majority of international studies support

*(continued)*

**TABLE 1** Correlation Coefficient for Income Inequality (Gini) and Life Expectancy for 18 Countries, by Sex, Before and After Controlling for Average Population Income.*

|  | Zero-Order Correlation r | Partial Correlation r |
|---|---|---|
| Male | −0.603[†] | −0.207 |
| Female | −0.605[†] | 0.024 |

*These countries are Australia, Austria, Belgium, Canada, Denmark, Finland, France, Germany, Greece, Ireland, Israel, the Netherlands, Norway, Spain, Sweden, Switzerland, the United Kingdom, and the United States.

[†]$p < 0.01$

Prus, S. and Brown, R., *Age-specific Income Inequality and Life Expectancy: New Evidence, Living to 100 Symposium Monograph*. Copyright © 2008 by The Society of Actuaries, Schaumburg Illinois. Reprinted with permission.

the hypothesis that income inequality has a negative effect on population health. In other words, the greater the dispersion of income in a country, the lower its life expectancy. According to this hypothesis, the United States would have a lower life expectancy than Canada, for example, because the former has more income inequality than the latter.

Income inequality as a determinant of population health, however, has become an increasingly contentious issue. It is argued that evidence of a population-level association between income inequality and health is slowly dissipating. To shed light on this issue, Canadian social scientists Rob Brown and Steven Prus tested the income inequality–population health hypothesis with the most currently available data at the time of their publication—data from the year 2000.

The correlation coefficient was used to examine the relationship between income inequality (Gini coefficient) and life expectancy, separately for males and females. The Gini coefficient, introduced in Chapter 3, is a measure of inequality that ranges from 0 to 1. If everyone in a given country had the same income, there would be no income inequality, and the Gini coefficient would be 0. If one individual held all income in a given country, the Gini coefficient would be equal to 1. So, the Gini coefficient increases as inequality increases. Life expectancy is

the expected number of years to be lived at birth in a given country.

The correlation coefficient was calculated before (zero-order) and after (partial) controlling for average income of the entire population to gauge the extent to which average population income changes the original relationship between income inequality and life expectancy. The results of their multivariate analysis are reported in Table 1.

Brown and Prus found that life expectancy is negatively and significantly related to income inequality regardless of sex. The zero-order correlation coefficients for males and females are approximately −0.60. That is, as income inequality increases, life expectancy decreases.

After controlling for average population income, the partial correlations are noticeably weaker and statistically insignificant compared to the zero-order correlations. The coefficients are reduced to −0.207 for males and 0.024 for females after removing the effect of average population income. This outcome weakens the hypothesis that there is a direct causal relationship between income inequality and life expectancy. Brown and Prus conclude that the zero-order relationship is spurious and due to the effects of average population income rather than income inequality itself.

In summary, the multivariate analysis indicates that poverty, age, and region have important, positive effects on crime rate. The standardized partial slopes show that region is clearly the most important of the three independent variables in understanding crime rates. Taken together, the three variables account for 86% of the variance in crime rate from city to city. However, with only nine cases (cities) in this analysis, we must be particularly cautious in interpreting and drawing conclusions from these findings.

## 14.7 THE LIMITATIONS OF PARTIAL CORRELATION AND MULTIPLE REGRESSION AND CORRELATION

Partial correlation and multiple regression and correlation are very powerful tools for analyzing the interrelationships among three or more variables. The techniques presented in this chapter permit the researcher to observe how a bivariate relationship behaves in the presence of a control variable(s), to predict scores on one variable from two or more other variables, to distinguish between independent variables in terms of the importance of their direct effects on a dependent variable, and to determine the total effect of a set of independent variables on a dependent variable. In terms of the flexibility of these techniques and the volume of information they can supply, partial correlation and multiple regression and correlation represent some of the most powerful statistical techniques available to social science researchers.

Powerful tools are not cheap. They demand high-quality data, and measurement at the interval-ratio level is difficult to accomplish at this stage in the development of the social sciences (although as illustrated in Section 14.6, we can resolve this problem for a nominal- or ordinal-level independent variable by treating it as a dummy variable). Furthermore, these techniques assume that the interrelationships among the variables follow a particular form. First, they assume that each independent variable has a linear relationship with the dependent variable.

Second, the techniques of multiple regression and correlation further assume that the effects of the independent variables are "additive." This means that we must assume that the best prediction of the dependent variable ($Y$) can be obtained by simply adding up the scores of the independent variables, as reflected by the plus signs in Formula 14.3. Not all combinations of variables will conform to this assumption. For example, some variables have "interactive" relationships with each other. These are relationships in which some of the scores of the variables combine in unusual, nonadditive ways. For example, consider a health survey that found positive and linear bivariate relationships between years of age ($X_1$), body weight ($X_2$), and number of health problems ($Y$). When combined in a regression analysis, however, certain combinations of scores on the independent variables (e.g., old age combined with high body weight) produced an especially high number of health problems. In other words, age and weight interact with each other, and persons who were old *and* high in body weight had more health problems than those persons who were old but did not have high body weight or those persons who had high body weight but were not old.

If there is interaction among the variables, we cannot accurately estimate or predict the dependent variable by simply adding the effects of the independent variables. There are techniques for handling interaction among the variables in the set, but these techniques are beyond the scope of this textbook.

Third, multiple regression and correlation techniques also assume that the independent variables are uncorrelated with each other. Strictly speaking, this condition means that the zero-order correlation among all pairs of independents should be zero, but practically, we act as if this assumption has been met if the intercorrelations among the independents are low.

To the extent that these assumptions are violated, the statistics introduced in this chapter become less and less trustworthy and the techniques less and less useful. A careful inspection of the bivariate scattergrams will help to assess the reasonableness of the assumptions of partial and multiple correlation and regression.

Finally, we should note that we have covered only the simplest applications of partial correlation and multiple regression and correlation. In terms of logic and interpretation, the extensions to situations involving more variables are relatively straightforward. However, the computations for these situations are extremely complex. If you are faced with a situation involving more than three variables, turn to one of the computerized statistical packages that are commonly available on university campuses (e.g., SPSS). These programs require minimal computer literacy and can handle complex calculations in, literally, the blink of an eye. Efficient use of these packages will enable you to avoid drudgery and will free you to do what social scientists everywhere enjoy doing most: pondering the meaning of your results and, by extension, the nature of social life.

## SUMMARY

1. Partial correlation involves controlling for the effect of a third variable ($Z$) on a bivariate relationship. Partial correlations permit the detection of direct and spurious or intervening relationships among $X$, $Y$, and $Z$.

2. Multiple regression includes statistical techniques by which predictions of the dependent variable from more than one independent variable can be made (by using partial slopes and the multiple regression equation) and by which we can disentangle the relative importance of the independent variables (by using standardized partial slopes).

3. The multiple correlation coefficient ($R^2$) summarizes the combined effects of all independent variables on the dependent variable in terms of the proportion of the total variation in $Y$ that is explained by all of the independent variables.

4. Partial correlation and multiple regression and correlation are some of the most powerful tools available to the researcher and demand high-quality measurement and relationships among the variables that are linear and non-interactive. Furthermore, correlations among the independent variables must be low (preferably zero). Although the price is high, these techniques pay considerable dividends in the volume of precise and detailed information they generate about the interrelationships among the variables.

## SUMMARY OF FORMULAS

Partial correlation coefficient:

$$14.1 \qquad r_{yx.z} = \frac{r_{yx} - (r_{yz})(r_{xz})}{\sqrt{1 - r_{yz}^2}\sqrt{1 - r_{xz}^2}}$$

Least-squares regression line (bivariate):

$$14.2 \qquad Y = a + bX$$

Least-squares multiple regression line:

$$14.3 \qquad Y = a + b_1 X_1 + b_2 X_2$$

Partial slope for $X_1$:

$$14.4 \qquad b_1 = \left(\frac{s_y}{s_1}\right)\left(\frac{r_{y1} - r_{y2}r_{12}}{1 - r_{12}^2}\right)$$

Partial slope for $X_2$:

$$14.5 \qquad b_2 = \left(\frac{s_y}{s_2}\right)\left(\frac{r_{y2} - r_{y1}r_{12}}{1 - r_{12}^2}\right)$$

$Y$ intercept:

$$14.6 \qquad a = \overline{Y} - b_1\overline{X}_1 - b_2\overline{X}_2$$

Standardized partial slope (beta-weight) for $X_1$:

$$14.7 \qquad b_1^* = b_1\left(\frac{s_1}{s_y}\right)$$

Standardized partial slope (beta-weight) for $X_2$:

$$14.8 \qquad b_2^* = b_2\left(\frac{s_2}{s_y}\right)$$

Standardized least-squares regression line:

$$14.9 \qquad Z_y = a_z + b_1^* Z_1 + b_2^* Z_2$$

Standardized least-squares regression line (simplified):

$$14.10 \qquad Z_y = b_1^* Z_1 + b_2^* Z_2$$

Coefficient of multiple determination:

$$14.11 \qquad R^2 = r_{y1}^2 + r_{y2.1}^2(1 - r_{y1}^2)$$

## GLOSSARY

**Beta-weights ($b^*$).** Standardized partial slopes.

**Coefficient of multiple determination ($R^2$).** A statistic that equals the total variation explained in the dependent variable by all independent variables combined.

**Control variable.** A "third variable" ($Z$) that might affect a bivariate relationship.

**Direct relationship.** A multivariate relationship in which the control variable has no effect on the bivariate relationship.

**Intervening relationship.** A multivariate relationship in which the bivariate relationship becomes substantially weaker after controlling for a third variable. The independent ($X$) and the dependent ($Y$) variables are linked primarily through the control variable ($Z$).

**Multiple correlation.** A multivariate technique for examining the combined effects of more than one independent variable on a dependent variable.

**Multiple correlation coefficient ($R$).** A statistic that indicates the strength of the correlation between a dependent variable and two or more independent variables.

**Multiple regression.** A multivariate technique that breaks down the separate effects of the independent variables on the dependent variable; used to make predictions of the dependent variable.

**Partial correlation.** A multivariate technique for examining a bivariate relationship while controlling for other variables.

**Partial correlation coefficient.** A statistic that shows the relationship between two variables while controlling for other variables; $r_{yx.z}$ is the symbol for the partial correlation coefficient when controlling for one variable.

**Partial slope.** In a multiple regression equation, the slope of the relationship between a particular independent variable and the dependent variable while controlling for all other independents in the equation.

**Spurious relationship.** A multivariate relationship in which the bivariate relationship becomes

substantially weaker after controlling for a third variable. The independent ($X$) and dependent ($Y$) variables are not causally linked. Rather, both are caused by the control variable ($Z$).

**Standardized partial slope.** The slope of the relationship between a particular independent variable and the dependent when all scores have been normalized.

**Zero-order correlations.** Correlation coefficients for bivariate relationships.

## MULTIMEDIA RESOURCES

 nelson.com/student

Visit the companion website for the fourth Canadian edition of *Statistics: A Tool for Social Research* to access a wide range of student resources. Begin by clicking on the Student Resources section of the textbook's website to access online chapters and study tools.

## PROBLEMS

**14.1** PS In Problem 13.1, data regarding voter turnout in five cities were presented. For the sake of convenience, the data for three of the variables are presented again here along with descriptive statistics and zero-order correlations.

| City | Turnout | Unemployment Rate | % Negative Ads |
|---|---|---|---|
| A | 55 | 5 | 60 |
| B | 60 | 8 | 63 |
| C | 65 | 9 | 55 |
| D | 68 | 9 | 53 |
| E | 70 | 10 | 48 |
| Mean = | 63.6 | 8.2 | 55.8 |
| s = | 5.5 | 1.7 | 5.3 |

| | Unemployment | Negative Ads |
|---|---|---|
| Turnout | 0.95 | −0.87 |
| Unemployment | | −0.70 |

**a.** Compute the partial correlation coefficient for the relationship between turnout ($Y$) and unemployment ($X$) while controlling for the effect of negative advertising ($Z$). What effect does this control variable have on the bivariate relationship? Is the

relationship between turnout and unemployment direct? *(HINT: Use Formula 14.1 and see Section 14.2.)*

**b.** Compute the partial correlation coefficient for the relationship between turnout ($Y$) and negative advertising ($X$) while controlling for the effect of unemployment ($Z$). What effect does this have on the bivariate relationship? Is the relationship between turnout and negative advertising direct? *(HINT: Use Formula 14.1 and see Section 14.2. You will need this partial correlation to compute the multiple correlation coefficient.)*

**c.** Find the unstandardized multiple regression equation with unemployment ($X_1$) and negative ads ($X_2$) as the independent variables. What turnout would be expected in a city in which the unemployment rate was 10% and 75% of the campaign ads were negative? *(HINT: Use Formulas 14.4 and 14.5 to compute the partial slopes and then use Formula 14.6 to find a, the Y intercept. The regression line is stated in Formula 14.3. Substitute 10 for $X_1$ and 75 for $X_2$ to compute predicted Y.)*

**d.** Compute beta-weights for each independent variable. Which has the stronger impact on turnout? *(HINT: Use Formulas 14.7 and 14.8 to calculate the beta-weights.)*

**e.** Compute the multiple correlation coefficient ($R$) and the coefficient of multiple determination ($R^2$). How much of the variance in voter turnout is explained by the two independent variables? *(HINT: Use Formula 14.11. You calculated the partial correlation coefficient in part b of this problem.)*

**f.** Write a paragraph summarizing your conclusions about the relationships among these three variables.

**14.2** | SOC | A scale measuring support for increases in the national defence budget has been administered to a sample. The respondents have also been asked to indicate how many years of school they have completed and how many years, if any, they served in the Canadian military. Take "support" as the dependent variable.

| Case | Support | Years of School | Years of Service |
|------|---------|-----------------|------------------|
| A | 20 | 12 | 2 |
| B | 15 | 12 | 4 |
| C | 20 | 16 | 20 |
| D | 10 | 10 | 10 |
| E | 10 | 16 | 20 |
| F | 5 | 8 | 0 |
| G | 8 | 14 | 2 |
| H | 20 | 12 | 20 |
| I | 10 | 10 | 4 |
| J | 20 | 16 | 0 |

**a.** Compute $r$ for all three relationships (Support and Years of School, Support and Years of Service, and Years of School and Years of Service). Compute the partial correlation coefficient for the relationship between support ($Y$) and years of school ($X$) while controlling for the effect of years of service ($Z$). What effect does the third variable (years of service or $Z$) have on the bivariate relationship? Is the relationship between support and years of school direct?

**b.** Compute the partial correlation coefficient for the relationship between support ($Y$)

and years of service ($X$) while controlling for the effect of years of school ($Z$). What effect does $Z$ have on the bivariate relationship? Is the relationship between support and years of service direct? *(HINT: You will need this partial correlation to compute the multiple correlation coefficient.)*

**c.** Find the unstandardized multiple regression equation with school ($X_1$) and service ($X_2$) as the independent variables. What level of support would be expected in a person with 13 years of school and 15 years of service?

**d.** Compute beta-weights for each independent variable. Which has the stronger impact on support?

**e.** Compute the multiple correlation coefficient ($R$) and the coefficient of multiple determination ($R^2$). How much of the variance in support is explained by the two independent variables? *(HINT: You calculated the partial correlation coefficient in part b of this problem.)*

**f.** Write a paragraph summarizing your conclusions about the relationships among these three variables.

**14.3** | SOC | Data on civil strife (number of incidents), unemployment, and urbanization have been gathered for 10 nations. Take civil strife as the dependent variable. Compute the zero-order correlations among all three variables.

| Number of Incidents of Civil Strife | Unemployment Rate | Percentage of Population Living in Urban Areas |
|----|----|----|
| 0 | 5.3 | 60 |
| 1 | 1.0 | 65 |
| 5 | 2.7 | 55 |
| 7 | 2.8 | 68 |
| 10 | 3.0 | 69 |
| 23 | 2.5 | 70 |
| 25 | 6.0 | 45 |
| 26 | 5.2 | 40 |
| 30 | 7.8 | 75 |
| 53 | 9.2 | 80 |

**a.** Compute the partial correlation coefficient for the relationship between strife ($Y$) and unemployment ($X$) while controlling for the effect of urbanization ($Z$). What effect does this have on the bivariate relationship? Is the relationship between strife and unemployment direct?

**b.** Compute the partial correlation coefficient for the relationship between strife ($Y$) and urbanization ($X$) while controlling for the effect of unemployment ($Z$). What effect does this have on the bivariate relationship? Is the relationship between strife and urbanization direct? *(HINT: You will need this partial correlation to compute the multiple correlation coefficient.)*

**c.** Find the unstandardized multiple regression equation with unemployment ($X_1$) and urbanization ($X_2$) as the independent variables. What level of strife would be expected in a nation in which the unemployment rate was 10% and 90% of the population lived in urban areas?

**d.** Compute beta-weights for each independent variable. Which has the stronger impact on strife?

**e.** Compute the multiple correlation coefficient ($R$) and the coefficient of multiple determination ($R^2$). How much of the variance in strife is explained by the two independent variables?

**f.** Write a paragraph summarizing your conclusions about the relationships among these three variables.

**14.4** | SOC | In problem 13.5, crime and population data were presented for each of 10 cities. The data are reproduced here.

Take the three crime variables as the dependent variables (one at a time) and

**a.** Find the multiple regression equations (unstandardized) with growth and urbanization as independent variables.

**b.** Make a prediction for each crime variable for a city with a 5% growth rate and a population that is 90% urbanized.

**c.** Compute beta-weights for each independent variable in each equation and compare their relative effect on each dependent.

**d.** Compute $R$ and $R^2$ for each crime variable, using the population variables as independent variables.

**e.** Write a paragraph summarizing your findings.

**14.5** | PS | Problem 13.4 presented data on 10 electoral districts. The information is reproduced here.

| District | Percentage Working-Class | Unemployment Rate | Voter Turnout |
|---|---|---|---|
| A | 50 | 10 | 56 |
| B | 45 | 12 | 55 |
| C | 56 | 8 | 52 |
| D | 78 | 15 | 60 |
| E | 13 | 5 | 89 |
| F | 85 | 20 | 25 |
| G | 62 | 18 | 64 |
| H | 33 | 9 | 88 |
| I | 25 | 0 | 42 |
| J | 49 | 9 | 36 |

| City | Crime Rate | | | Population | | |
|---|---|---|---|---|---|---|
| | Homicide | Robbery | Auto Theft | Growth | Density | Urbanization |
| A | 1 | 19 | 104 | 3.8 | 41.7 | 52.6 |
| B | 5 | 214 | 286 | 5.5 | 402.7 | 92.1 |
| C | 4 | 138 | 344 | 4.7 | 277.8 | 81.2 |
| D | 2 | 37 | 184 | 5.4 | 52.3 | 45.3 |
| E | 6 | 89 | 252 | 14.4 | 181.5 | 78.1 |
| F | 5 | 81 | 230 | 9.6 | 102.3 | 48.8 |
| G | 6 | 145 | 447 | 22.8 | 81.5 | 84.8 |
| H | 7 | 146 | 842 | 40.0 | 46.7 | 88.2 |
| I | 3 | 99 | 594 | 21.1 | 90.0 | 83.1 |
| J | 6 | 178 | 537 | 13.6 | 221.2 | 96.7 |

Take voter turnout as the dependent variable and

a. Find the multiple regression equations (unstandardized).

b. What turnout would you expect for a district in which 0% of the voters were working-class and 5% were unemployed?

c. Compute beta-weights for each independent variable and compare their relative effect on turnout. Which is the more important factor?

d. Compute $R$ and $R^2$.

e. Write a paragraph summarizing your findings.

**14.6** SW Twelve families have been referred to a counsellor, and she has rated each of them on a cohesiveness scale. Also, she has information on family income and number of children currently living at home. Take family cohesion as the dependent variable.

| Family | Cohesion Score | Family Income | Number of Children |
|--------|---------------|---------------|--------------------|
| A | 10 | 30,000 | 5 |
| B | 10 | 70,000 | 4 |
| C | 9 | 35,000 | 4 |
| D | 5 | 25,000 | 0 |
| E | 1 | 55,000 | 3 |
| F | 7 | 40,000 | 0 |
| G | 2 | 60,000 | 2 |
| H | 5 | 30,000 | 3 |
| I | 8 | 50,000 | 5 |
| J | 3 | 25,000 | 4 |
| K | 2 | 45,000 | 3 |
| L | 4 | 50,000 | 0 |

a. Find the multiple regression equations (unstandardized).

b. What level of cohesion would be expected in a family with an income of $20,000 and 6 children?

c. Compute beta-weights for each independent variable and compare their relative effect on cohesion. Which is the more important factor?

d. Compute $R$ and $R^2$.

e. Write a paragraph summarizing your findings.

**14.7** Problem 13.8 presented per capita expenditures on education for 15 large Canadian cities, along with rank on income per capita and the percentage of the population that has graduated from high school. The data are reproduced below. Take educational expenditures as the dependent variable.

| City | Per Capita Expenditures on Education | Percentage High School Graduates | Rank in Per Capita Income |
|------|--------------------------------------|----------------------------------|---------------------------|
| A | 1,102 | 82 | 48 |
| B | 1,339 | 90 | 7 |
| C | 1,907 | 88 | 1 |
| D | 1,171 | 84 | 25 |
| E | 1,621 | 86 | 9 |
| F | 1,276 | 88 | 24 |
| G | 1,159 | 81 | 45 |
| H | 1,412 | 86 | 5 |
| I | 1,487 | 86 | 18 |
| J | 1,041 | 80 | 50 |
| K | 1,194 | 90 | 22 |
| L | 1,262 | 88 | 6 |
| M | 1,163 | 79 | 32 |
| N | 1,223 | 86 | 15 |
| O | 1,549 | 90 | 20 |

a. Compute beta-weights for each independent variable and compare their relative effect on expenditures. Which is the more important factor?

b. Compute $R$ and $R^2$.

c. Write a paragraph summarizing your findings.

**14.8** SOC The scores on four variables for 20 individuals are reported below: hours of TV (number of hours of TV viewing each day), occupational prestige (higher scores indicate greater prestige), number of children, and age. Take TV viewing as the dependent variable and select two of the remaining variables as independents.

| Hours of TV | Occupational Prestige | Number of Children | Age |
|---|---|---|---|
| 4 | 50 | 2 | 43 |
| 3 | 36 | 3 | 58 |
| 3 | 36 | 1 | 34 |
| 4 | 50 | 2 | 42 |
| 2 | 45 | 2 | 27 |
| 3 | 50 | 5 | 60 |
| 4 | 50 | 0 | 28 |
| 7 | 40 | 3 | 55 |
| 1 | 57 | 2 | 46 |
| 3 | 33 | 2 | 65 |
| 1 | 46 | 3 | 56 |
| 3 | 31 | 1 | 29 |
| 1 | 19 | 2 | 41 |
| 0 | 52 | 0 | 50 |

| Hours of TV | Occupational Prestige | Number of Children | Age |
|---|---|---|---|
| 2 | 48 | 1 | 62 |
| 4 | 36 | 1 | 24 |
| 3 | 48 | 0 | 25 |
| 1 | 62 | 1 | 87 |
| 5 | 50 | 0 | 45 |
| 1 | 27 | 3 | 62 |

a. Compute beta-weights for each of the independent variables you selected and compare their relative effect on the hours of television watching. Which is the more important factor?
b. Compute $R$ and $R^2$.
c. Write a paragraph summarizing your findings.

## You Are the Researcher

## Using SPSS for Regression Analysis with the 2012 CCHS

The demonstration and exercise below use the shortened version of the 2012 CCHS data. Start SPSS and open the *2012_CCHS_Shortened.sav* file.

### SPSS DEMONSTRATION 14.1 What Are the Effects of Fruit and Vegetable Consumption and Sex on Body Mass Index?

We will use the **Linear Regression** procedure to examine the effects of daily consumption of fruits and vegetables (*fvcdtot*) and sex (*dhh_sex*) on body mass index or BMI (*hwtgbmi*). This demonstration represents a very sparing use of the power of the regression command and an extremely economical use of all the options available. We urge you to explore some of the variations and capabilities of this powerful data-analysis procedure.

Ideally, the independent variables in a linear regression analysis should be interval-ratio in level of measurement, but sex is a nominal-level variable, and its inclusion in a regression procedure may be surprising. However, nominal variables with only two categories—sometimes called "dummy variables"—are commonly used in regression (see Section 14.6).

With the 2012 CCHS loaded, click **Analyze**, **Regression**, and **Linear**. The **Linear Regression** window will appear. Move *hwtgbmi* into the **Dependent** box and *fvcdtot* and *dhh_sex* into the **Independent(s)** box. If you wish, you can click the **Statistics** button and then click **Descriptives** to get zero-order correlations, means, and standard deviations for the variables. Click **Continue**, and then **OK**, and the following output will appear (descriptive information about the variables and the zero-order correlations are omitted here to conserve space).

#### Model Summary

| Model | $R$ | $R$ Square | Adjusted $R$ Square | Std. Error of the Estimate |
|---|---|---|---|---|
| 1 | .158[a] | .025 | .024 | 5.05067 |

[a]Predictors: (Constant), Sex, Daily cons.—total fruits and veg.

## ANOVA[a]

| Model | | Sum of Squares | df | Mean Square | F | Sig. |
|---|---|---|---|---|---|---|
| 1 | Regression | 1119.102 | 2 | 559.551 | 21.935 | .000[b] |
| | Residual | 43697.990 | 1713 | 25.509 | | |
| | Total | 44817.092 | 1715 | | | |

[a]Dependent variable: BMI
[b]Predictors: (Constant), Sex, Daily cons.—total fruits and veg.

## Coefficients[a]

| Model | | Unstandardized Coefficients | | Standardized Coefficients | t | Sig. |
|---|---|---|---|---|---|---|
| | | B | Std. Error | Beta | | |
| 1 | (Constant) | 28.705 | .432 | | 66.502 | .000 |
| | Daily cons.—total fruits and veg. | −.196 | .050 | −.094 | −3.909 | .000 |
| | Sex | −1.189 | .246 | −.116 | −4.843 | .000 |

[a]Dependent variable: BMI

The "Model Summary" output block reports the multiple $R$ (0.158) and $R$ square (0.025), which indicates that the independent variables combined account for 2.5% of the variation in BMI. The "ANOVA" block shows that the relationship between the variables is statistically significance (Sig. = 0.000).

In the last output block, we see the slopes ($B$) of the independent variables on *hwtgbmi,* the standardized partial slopes (Beta), and the $Y$ intercept (reported as a constant of 28.705). The slope for daily consumption of fruits and vegetables indicates that BMI decreases by −0.196 of a point on average with each increase in the number of times per day a respondent eats fruits and vegetables while controlling for the effects of sex. The slope for sex is also negative (−1.189). In other words, BMI decreases as sex "increases," that is, BMI is lower for people with the "higher" score on sex. Because a male is coded as 1 and a female as 2, the average BMI score for females is 1.189 points lower than the average BMI score for males, even after controlling for daily consumption of fruits and vegetables. From this information, we can build a regression equation to predict scores on *hwtgbmi.*

The beta for *dhh_sex* (−0.116) is slightly larger than the beta for *fvcdtot* (−0.094). What does this mean? At least for this sample, a person's BMI is more affected by sex than by consumption of fruits and vegetables.

## Exercise (using *2012_CCHS_Shortened.sav*)

**14.1** Conduct the analysis in Demonstration 14.1 again but replace *fvcdtot* (daily consumption of fruits and vegetables) with *pacdee* (daily energy expenditure). Write a paragraph summarizing the results of this analysis.

# Appendix A    Area Under the Normal Curve

Column (a) lists $Z$ scores from 0.00 to 4.00 for the standard normal curve. Only positive scores are displayed, but because the normal curve is symmetrical, the areas for negative scores will be exactly the same as areas for positive scores. Column (b) lists the proportion of the total area between the $Z$ score and the mean. Figure A.1 displays areas of this type. Column (c) lists the proportion of the area beyond the $Z$ score, and Figure A.2 displays this type of area.

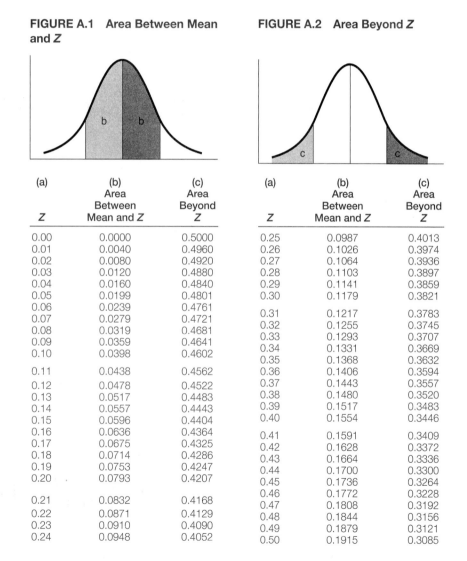

**FIGURE A.1   Area Between Mean and $Z$**

**FIGURE A.2   Area Beyond $Z$**

| (a) $Z$ | (b) Area Between Mean and $Z$ | (c) Area Beyond $Z$ | (a) $Z$ | (b) Area Between Mean and $Z$ | (c) Area Beyond $Z$ |
|---|---|---|---|---|---|
| 0.00 | 0.0000 | 0.5000 | 0.25 | 0.0987 | 0.4013 |
| 0.01 | 0.0040 | 0.4960 | 0.26 | 0.1026 | 0.3974 |
| 0.02 | 0.0080 | 0.4920 | 0.27 | 0.1064 | 0.3936 |
| 0.03 | 0.0120 | 0.4880 | 0.28 | 0.1103 | 0.3897 |
| 0.04 | 0.0160 | 0.4840 | 0.29 | 0.1141 | 0.3859 |
| 0.05 | 0.0199 | 0.4801 | 0.30 | 0.1179 | 0.3821 |
| 0.06 | 0.0239 | 0.4761 | | | |
| 0.07 | 0.0279 | 0.4721 | 0.31 | 0.1217 | 0.3783 |
| 0.08 | 0.0319 | 0.4681 | 0.32 | 0.1255 | 0.3745 |
| 0.09 | 0.0359 | 0.4641 | 0.33 | 0.1293 | 0.3707 |
| 0.10 | 0.0398 | 0.4602 | 0.34 | 0.1331 | 0.3669 |
| | | | 0.35 | 0.1368 | 0.3632 |
| 0.11 | 0.0438 | 0.4562 | 0.36 | 0.1406 | 0.3594 |
| 0.12 | 0.0478 | 0.4522 | 0.37 | 0.1443 | 0.3557 |
| 0.13 | 0.0517 | 0.4483 | 0.38 | 0.1480 | 0.3520 |
| 0.14 | 0.0557 | 0.4443 | 0.39 | 0.1517 | 0.3483 |
| 0.15 | 0.0596 | 0.4404 | 0.40 | 0.1554 | 0.3446 |
| 0.16 | 0.0636 | 0.4364 | | | |
| 0.17 | 0.0675 | 0.4325 | 0.41 | 0.1591 | 0.3409 |
| 0.18 | 0.0714 | 0.4286 | 0.42 | 0.1628 | 0.3372 |
| 0.19 | 0.0753 | 0.4247 | 0.43 | 0.1664 | 0.3336 |
| 0.20 | 0.0793 | 0.4207 | 0.44 | 0.1700 | 0.3300 |
| | | | 0.45 | 0.1736 | 0.3264 |
| | | | 0.46 | 0.1772 | 0.3228 |
| 0.21 | 0.0832 | 0.4168 | 0.47 | 0.1808 | 0.3192 |
| 0.22 | 0.0871 | 0.4129 | 0.48 | 0.1844 | 0.3156 |
| 0.23 | 0.0910 | 0.4090 | 0.49 | 0.1879 | 0.3121 |
| 0.24 | 0.0948 | 0.4052 | 0.50 | 0.1915 | 0.3085 |

| (a) Z | (b) Area Between Mean and Z | (c) Area Beyond Z | (a) Z | (b) Area Between Mean and Z | (c) Area Beyond Z |
|---|---|---|---|---|---|
| 0.51 | 0.1950 | 0.3050 | 1.03 | 0.3485 | 0.1515 |
| 0.52 | 0.1985 | 0.3015 | 1.04 | 0.3508 | 0.1492 |
| 0.53 | 0.2019 | 0.2981 | 1.05 | 0.3531 | 0.1469 |
| 0.54 | 0.2054 | 0.2946 | 1.06 | 0.3554 | 0.1446 |
| 0.55 | 0.2088 | 0.2912 | 1.07 | 0.3577 | 0.1423 |
| 0.56 | 0.2123 | 0.2877 | 1.08 | 0.3599 | 0.1401 |
| 0.57 | 0.2157 | 0.2843 | 1.09 | 0.3621 | 0.1379 |
| 0.58 | 0.2190 | 0.2810 | 1.10 | 0.3643 | 0.1357 |
| 0.59 | 0.2224 | 0.2776 | 1.11 | 0.3665 | 0.1335 |
| 0.60 | 0.2257 | 0.2743 | 1.12 | 0.3686 | 0.1314 |
| 0.61 | 0.2291 | 0.2709 | 1.13 | 0.3708 | 0.1292 |
| 0.62 | 0.2324 | 0.2676 | 1.14 | 0.3729 | 0.1271 |
| 0.63 | 0.2357 | 0.2643 | 1.15 | 0.3749 | 0.1251 |
| 0.64 | 0.2389 | 0.2611 | 1.16 | 0.3770 | 0.1230 |
| 0.65 | 0.2422 | 0.2578 | 1.17 | 0.3790 | 0.1210 |
| 0.66 | 0.2454 | 0.2546 | 1.18 | 0.3810 | 0.1190 |
| 0.67 | 0.2486 | 0.2514 | 1.19 | 0.3830 | 0.1170 |
| 0.68 | 0.2517 | 0.2483 | 1.20 | 0.3849 | 0.1151 |
| 0.69 | 0.2549 | 0.2451 | 1.21 | 0.3869 | 0.1131 |
| 0.70 | 0.2580 | 0.2420 | 1.22 | 0.3888 | 0.1112 |
| 0.71 | 0.2611 | 0.2389 | 1.23 | 0.3907 | 0.1093 |
| 0.72 | 0.2642 | 0.2358 | 1.24 | 0.3925 | 0.1075 |
| 0.73 | 0.2673 | 0.2327 | 1.25 | 0.3944 | 0.1056 |
| 0.74 | 0.2704 | 0.2296 | 1.26 | 0.3962 | 0.1038 |
| 0.75 | 0.2734 | 0.2266 | 1.27 | 0.3980 | 0.1020 |
| 0.76 | 0.2764 | 0.2236 | 1.28 | 0.3997 | 0.1003 |
| 0.77 | 0.2794 | 0.2206 | 1.29 | 0.4015 | 0.0985 |
| 0.78 | 0.2823 | 0.2177 | 1.30 | 0.4032 | 0.0968 |
| 0.79 | 0.2852 | 0.2148 | 1.31 | 0.4049 | 0.0951 |
| 0.80 | 0.2881 | 0.2119 | 1.32 | 0.4066 | 0.0934 |
| 0.81 | 0.2910 | 0.2090 | 1.33 | 0.4082 | 0.0918 |
| 0.82 | 0.2939 | 0.2061 | 1.34 | 0.4099 | 0.0901 |
| 0.83 | 0.2967 | 0.2033 | 1.35 | 0.4115 | 0.0885 |
| 0.84 | 0.2995 | 0.2005 | 1.36 | 0.4131 | 0.0869 |
| 0.85 | 0.3023 | 0.1977 | 1.37 | 0.4147 | 0.0853 |
| 0.86 | 0.3051 | 0.1949 | 1.38 | 0.4162 | 0.0838 |
| 0.87 | 0.3078 | 0.1922 | 1.39 | 0.4177 | 0.0823 |
| 0.88 | 0.3106 | 0.1894 | 1.40 | 0.4192 | 0.0808 |
| 0.89 | 0.3133 | 0.1867 | 1.41 | 0.4207 | 0.0793 |
| 0.90 | 0.3159 | 0.1841 | 1.42 | 0.4222 | 0.0778 |
| 0.91 | 0.3186 | 0.1814 | 1.43 | 0.4236 | 0.0764 |
| 0.92 | 0.3212 | 0.1788 | 1.44 | 0.4251 | 0.0749 |
| 0.93 | 0.3238 | 0.1762 | 1.45 | 0.4265 | 0.0735 |
| 0.94 | 0.3264 | 0.1736 | 1.46 | 0.4279 | 0.0721 |
| 0.95 | 0.3289 | 0.1711 | 1.47 | 0.4292 | 0.0708 |
| 0.96 | 0.3315 | 0.1685 | 1.48 | 0.4306 | 0.0694 |
| 0.97 | 0.3340 | 0.1660 | 1.49 | 0.4319 | 0.0681 |
| 0.98 | 0.3365 | 0.1635 | 1.50 | 0.4332 | 0.0668 |
| 0.99 | 0.3389 | 0.1611 | 1.51 | 0.4345 | 0.0655 |
| 1.00 | 0.3413 | 0.1587 | 1.52 | 0.4357 | 0.0643 |
| 1.01 | 0.3438 | 0.1562 | 1.53 | 0.4370 | 0.0630 |
| 1.02 | 0.3461 | 0.1539 | 1.54 | 0.4382 | 0.0618 |

| (a) | (b) Area Between Mean and Z | (c) Area Beyond Z | (a) | (b) Area Between Mean and Z | (c) Area Beyond Z |
|---|---|---|---|---|---|
| Z |  |  | Z |  |  |
| 1.55 | 0.4394 | 0.0606 | 2.08 | 0.4812 | 0.0188 |
| 1.56 | 0.4406 | 0.0594 | 2.09 | 0.4817 | 0.0183 |
| 1.57 | 0.4418 | 0.0582 | 2.10 | 0.4821 | 0.0179 |
| 1.58 | 0.4429 | 0.0571 | 2.11 | 0.4826 | 0.0174 |
| 1.59 | 0.4441 | 0.0559 | 2.12 | 0.4830 | 0.0170 |
| 1.60 | 0.4452 | 0.0548 | 2.13 | 0.4834 | 0.0166 |
| 1.61 | 0.4463 | 0.0537 | 2.14 | 0.4838 | 0.0162 |
| 1.62 | 0.4474 | 0.0526 | 2.15 | 0.4842 | 0.0158 |
| 1.63 | 0.4484 | 0.0516 | 2.16 | 0.4846 | 0.0154 |
| 1.64 | 0.4495 | 0.0505 | 2.17 | 0.4850 | 0.0150 |
| 1.65 | 0.4505 | 0.0495 | 2.18 | 0.4854 | 0.0146 |
| 1.66 | 0.4515 | 0.0485 | 2.19 | 0.4857 | 0.0143 |
| 1.67 | 0.4525 | 0.0475 | 2.20 | 0.4861 | 0.0139 |
| 1.68 | 0.4535 | 0.0465 | 2.21 | 0.4864 | 0.0136 |
| 1.69 | 0.4545 | 0.0455 | 2.22 | 0.4868 | 0.0132 |
| 1.70 | 0.4554 | 0.0446 | 2.23 | 0.4871 | 0.0129 |
| 1.71 | 0.4564 | 0.0436 | 2.24 | 0.4875 | 0.0125 |
| 1.72 | 0.4573 | 0.0427 | 2.25 | 0.4878 | 0.0122 |
| 1.73 | 0.4582 | 0.0418 | 2.26 | 0.4881 | 0.0119 |
| 1.74 | 0.4591 | 0.0409 | 2.27 | 0.4884 | 0.0116 |
| 1.75 | 0.4599 | 0.0401 | 2.28 | 0.4887 | 0.0113 |
| 1.76 | 0.4608 | 0.0392 | 2.29 | 0.4890 | 0.0110 |
| 1.77 | 0.4616 | 0.0384 | 2.30 | 0.4893 | 0.0107 |
| 1.78 | 0.4625 | 0.0375 | 2.31 | 0.4896 | 0.0104 |
| 1.79 | 0.4633 | 0.0367 | 2.32 | 0.4898 | 0.0102 |
| 1.80 | 0.4641 | 0.0359 | 2.33 | 0.4901 | 0.0099 |
| 1.81 | 0.4649 | 0.0351 | 2.34 | 0.4904 | 0.0096 |
| 1.82 | 0.4656 | 0.0344 | 2.35 | 0.4906 | 0.0094 |
| 1.83 | 0.4664 | 0.0336 | 2.36 | 0.4909 | 0.0091 |
| 1.84 | 0.4671 | 0.0329 | 2.37 | 0.4911 | 0.0089 |
| 1.85 | 0.4678 | 0.0322 | 2.38 | 0.4913 | 0.0087 |
| 1.86 | 0.4686 | 0.0314 | 2.39 | 0.4916 | 0.0084 |
| 1.87 | 0.4693 | 0.0307 | 2.40 | 0.4918 | 0.0082 |
| 1.88 | 0.4699 | 0.0301 | 2.41 | 0.4920 | 0.0080 |
| 1.89 | 0.4706 | 0.0294 | 2.42 | 0.4922 | 0.0078 |
| 1.90 | 0.4713 | 0.0287 | 2.43 | 0.4925 | 0.0075 |
| 1.91 | 0.4719 | 0.0281 | 2.44 | 0.4927 | 0.0073 |
| 1.92 | 0.4726 | 0.0274 | 2.45 | 0.4929 | 0.0071 |
| 1.93 | 0.4732 | 0.0268 | 2.46 | 0.4931 | 0.0069 |
| 1.94 | 0.4738 | 0.0262 | 2.47 | 0.4932 | 0.0068 |
| 1.95 | 0.4744 | 0.0256 | 2.48 | 0.4934 | 0.0066 |
| 1.96 | 0.4750 | 0.0250 | 2.49 | 0.4936 | 0.0064 |
| 1.97 | 0.4756 | 0.0244 | 2.50 | 0.4938 | 0.0062 |
| 1.98 | 0.4761 | 0.0239 | 2.51 | 0.4940 | 0.0060 |
| 1.99 | 0.4767 | 0.0233 | 2.52 | 0.4941 | 0.0059 |
| 2.00 | 0.4772 | 0.0228 | 2.53 | 0.4943 | 0.0057 |
| 2.01 | 0.4778 | 0.0222 | 2.54 | 0.4945 | 0.0055 |
| 2.02 | 0.4783 | 0.0217 | 2.55 | 0.4946 | 0.0054 |
| 2.03 | 0.4788 | 0.0212 | 2.56 | 0.4948 | 0.0052 |
| 2.04 | 0.4793 | 0.0207 | 2.57 | 0.4949 | 0.0051 |
| 2.05 | 0.4798 | 0.0202 | 2.58 | 0.4951 | 0.0049 |
| 2.06 | 0.4803 | 0.0197 | 2.59 | 0.4952 | 0.0048 |
| 2.07 | 0.4808 | 0.0192 | 2.60 | 0.4953 | 0.0047 |

| (a) | (b) Area Between Mean and Z | (c) Area Beyond Z | (a) | (b) Area Between Mean and Z | (c) Area Beyond Z |
|---|---|---|---|---|---|
| Z | | | Z | | |
| 2.61 | 0.4955 | 0.0045 | 3.11 | 0.4991 | 0.0009 |
| 2.62 | 0.4956 | 0.0044 | 3.12 | 0.4991 | 0.0009 |
| 2.63 | 0.4957 | 0.0043 | 3.13 | 0.4991 | 0.0009 |
| 2.64 | 0.4959 | 0.0041 | 3.14 | 0.4992 | 0.0008 |
| 2.65 | 0.4960 | 0.0040 | 3.15 | 0.4992 | 0.0008 |
| 2.66 | 0.4961 | 0.0039 | 3.16 | 0.4992 | 0.0008 |
| 2.67 | 0.4962 | 0.0038 | 3.17 | 0.4992 | 0.0008 |
| 2.68 | 0.4963 | 0.0037 | 3.18 | 0.4993 | 0.0007 |
| 2.69 | 0.4964 | 0.0036 | 3.19 | 0.4993 | 0.0007 |
| 2.70 | 0.4965 | 0.0035 | 3.20 | 0.4993 | 0.0007 |
| 2.71 | 0.4966 | 0.0034 | 3.21 | 0.4993 | 0.0007 |
| 2.72 | 0.4967 | 0.0033 | 3.22 | 0.4994 | 0.0006 |
| 2.73 | 0.4968 | 0.0032 | 3.23 | 0.4994 | 0.0006 |
| 2.74 | 0.4969 | 0.0031 | 3.24 | 0.4994 | 0.0006 |
| 2.75 | 0.4970 | 0.0030 | 3.25 | 0.4994 | 0.0006 |
| 2.76 | 0.4971 | 0.0029 | 3.26 | 0.4994 | 0.0006 |
| 2.77 | 0.4972 | 0.0028 | 3.27 | 0.4995 | 0.0005 |
| 2.78 | 0.4973 | 0.0027 | 3.28 | 0.4995 | 0.0005 |
| 2.79 | 0.4974 | 0.0026 | 3.29 | 0.4995 | 0.0005 |
| 2.80 | 0.4974 | 0.0026 | 3.30 | 0.4995 | 0.0005 |
| 2.81 | 0.4975 | 0.0025 | 3.31 | 0.4995 | 0.0005 |
| 2.82 | 0.4976 | 0.0024 | 3.32 | 0.4995 | 0.0005 |
| 2.83 | 0.4977 | 0.0023 | 3.33 | 0.4996 | 0.0004 |
| 2.84 | 0.4977 | 0.0023 | 3.34 | 0.4996 | 0.0004 |
| 2.85 | 0.4978 | 0.0022 | 3.35 | 0.4996 | 0.0004 |
| 2.86 | 0.4979 | 0.0021 | 3.36 | 0.4996 | 0.0004 |
| 2.87 | 0.4979 | 0.0021 | 3.37 | 0.4996 | 0.0004 |
| 2.88 | 0.4980 | 0.0020 | 3.38 | 0.4996 | 0.0004 |
| 2.89 | 0.4981 | 0.0019 | 3.39 | 0.4997 | 0.0003 |
| 2.90 | 0.4981 | 0.0019 | 3.40 | 0.4997 | 0.0003 |
| 2.91 | 0.4982 | 0.0018 | 3.41 | 0.4997 | 0.0003 |
| 2.92 | 0.4982 | 0.0018 | 3.42 | 0.4997 | 0.0003 |
| 2.93 | 0.4983 | 0.0017 | 3.43 | 0.4997 | 0.0003 |
| 2.94 | 0.4984 | 0.0016 | 3.44 | 0.4997 | 0.0003 |
| 2.95 | 0.4984 | 0.0016 | 3.45 | 0.4997 | 0.0003 |
| 2.96 | 0.4985 | 0.0015 | 3.46 | 0.4997 | 0.0003 |
| 2.97 | 0.4985 | 0.0015 | 3.47 | 0.4997 | 0.0003 |
| 2.98 | 0.4986 | 0.0014 | 3.48 | 0.4997 | 0.0003 |
| 2.99 | 0.4986 | 0.0014 | 3.49 | 0.4998 | 0.0002 |
| 3.00 | 0.4987 | 0.0013 | 3.50 | 0.4998 | 0.0002 |
| 3.01 | 0.4987 | 0.0013 | 3.60 | 0.4998 | 0.0002 |
| 3.02 | 0.4987 | 0.0013 | 3.70 | 0.4999 | 0.0001 |
| 3.03 | 0.4988 | 0.0012 | | | |
| 3.04 | 0.4988 | 0.0012 | 3.80 | 0.4999 | 0.0001 |
| 3.05 | 0.4989 | 0.0011 | | | |
| 3.06 | 0.4989 | 0.0011 | 3.90 | 0.4999 | <0.0001 |
| 3.07 | 0.4989 | 0.0011 | 4.00 | 0.4999 | <0.0001 |
| 3.08 | 0.4990 | 0.0010 | | | |
| 3.09 | 0.4990 | 0.0010 | | | |
| 3.10 | 0.4990 | 0.0010 | | | |

# Appendix B

# Distribution of *t*

| Degrees of Freedom (*df*) | Level of Significance for One-Tailed Test | | | | | |
|---|---|---|---|---|---|---|
| | 0.10 | 0.05 | 0.025 | 0.01 | 0.005 | 0.0005 |
| | Level of Significance for Two-Tailed Test | | | | | |
| | 0.20 | 0.10 | 0.05 | 0.02 | 0.01 | 0.001 |
| 1 | 3.078 | 6.314 | 12.706 | 31.821 | 63.657 | 636.619 |
| 2 | 1.886 | 2.920 | 4.303 | 6.965 | 9.925 | 31.599 |
| 3 | 1.638 | 2.353 | 3.182 | 4.541 | 5.841 | 12.924 |
| 4 | 1.533 | 2.132 | 2.776 | 3.747 | 4.604 | 8.610 |
| 5 | 1.476 | 2.015 | 2.571 | 3.365 | 4.032 | 6.869 |
| 6 | 1.440 | 1.943 | 2.447 | 3.143 | 3.707 | 5.959 |
| 7 | 1.415 | 1.895 | 2.365 | 2.998 | 3.499 | 5.408 |
| 8 | 1.397 | 1.860 | 2.306 | 2.896 | 3.355 | 5.041 |
| 9 | 1.383 | 1.833 | 2.262 | 2.821 | 3.250 | 4.781 |
| 10 | 1.372 | 1.812 | 2.228 | 2.764 | 3.169 | 4.587 |
| 11 | 1.363 | 1.796 | 2.201 | 2.718 | 3.106 | 4.437 |
| 12 | 1.356 | 1.782 | 2.179 | 2.681 | 3.055 | 4.318 |
| 13 | 1.350 | 1.771 | 2.160 | 2.650 | 3.012 | 4.221 |
| 14 | 1.345 | 1.761 | 2.145 | 2.624 | 2.977 | 4.140 |
| 15 | 1.341 | 1.753 | 2.131 | 2.602 | 2.947 | 4.073 |
| 16 | 1.337 | 1.746 | 2.120 | 2.583 | 2.921 | 4.015 |
| 17 | 1.333 | 1.740 | 2.110 | 2.567 | 2.898 | 3.965 |
| 18 | 1.330 | 1.734 | 2.101 | 2.552 | 2.878 | 3.922 |
| 19 | 1.328 | 1.729 | 2.093 | 2.539 | 2.861 | 3.883 |
| 20 | 1.325 | 1.725 | 2.086 | 2.528 | 2.845 | 3.850 |
| 21 | 1.323 | 1.721 | 2.080 | 2.518 | 2.831 | 3.819 |
| 22 | 1.321 | 1.717 | 2.074 | 2.508 | 2.819 | 3.792 |
| 23 | 1.319 | 1.714 | 2.069 | 2.500 | 2.807 | 3.768 |
| 24 | 1.318 | 1.711 | 2.064 | 2.492 | 2.797 | 3.745 |
| 25 | 1.316 | 1.708 | 2.060 | 2.485 | 2.787 | 3.725 |
| 26 | 1.315 | 1.706 | 2.056 | 2.479 | 2.779 | 3.707 |
| 27 | 1.314 | 1.703 | 2.052 | 2.473 | 2.771 | 3.690 |
| 28 | 1.313 | 1.701 | 2.048 | 2.467 | 2.763 | 3.674 |
| 29 | 1.311 | 1.699 | 2.045 | 2.462 | 2.756 | 3.659 |
| 30 | 1.310 | 1.697 | 2.042 | 2.457 | 2.750 | 3.646 |
| 40 | 1.303 | 1.684 | 2.021 | 2.423 | 2.704 | 3.551 |
| 60 | 1.296 | 1.671 | 2.000 | 2.390 | 2.660 | 3.460 |
| 120 | 1.289 | 1.658 | 1.980 | 2.358 | 2.617 | 3.373 |
| ∞ | 1.282 | 1.645 | 1.960 | 2.326 | 2.576 | 3.291 |

Table III of Fisher & Yates: *Statistical Tables for Biological, Agricultural and Medical Research*, published by Longman Group Ltd., London (1974), 6th edition (previously published by Oliver & Boyd Ltd., Edinburgh). Reprinted by permission of Pearson Education Limited.

# Appendix C        Distribution of Chi Square

| df | 0.99 | 0.98 | 0.95 | 0.90 | 0.80 | 0.70 | 0.50 | 0.30 | 0.20 | 0.10 | 0.05 | 0.02 | 0.01 | 0.001 |
|---|---|---|---|---|---|---|---|---|---|---|---|---|---|---|
| 1 | 0.000 | 0.001 | 0.004 | 0.016 | 0.064 | 0.148 | 0.455 | 1.074 | 1.642 | 2.706 | 3.841 | 5.412 | 6.635 | 10.828 |
| 2 | 0.020 | 0.040 | 0.103 | 0.211 | 0.446 | 0.713 | 1.386 | 2.408 | 3.219 | 4.605 | 5.991 | 7.824 | 9.210 | 13.816 |
| 3 | 0.115 | 0.185 | 0.352 | 0.584 | 1.005 | 1.424 | 2.366 | 3.665 | 4.642 | 6.251 | 7.815 | 9.837 | 11.345 | 16.266 |
| 4 | 0.297 | 0.429 | 0.711 | 1.064 | 1.649 | 2.195 | 3.357 | 4.878 | 5.989 | 7.779 | 9.488 | 11.668 | 13.277 | 18.467 |
| 5 | 0.554 | 0.752 | 1.145 | 1.610 | 2.343 | 3.000 | 4.351 | 6.064 | 7.289 | 9.236 | 11.070 | 13.388 | 15.086 | 20.515 |
| 6 | 0.872 | 1.134 | 1.635 | 2.204 | 3.070 | 3.828 | 5.348 | 7.231 | 8.558 | 10.645 | 12.592 | 15.033 | 16.812 | 22.458 |
| 7 | 1.239 | 1.564 | 2.167 | 2.833 | 3.822 | 4.671 | 6.346 | 8.383 | 9.803 | 12.017 | 14.067 | 16.622 | 18.475 | 24.322 |
| 8 | 1.646 | 2.032 | 2.733 | 3.490 | 4.594 | 5.527 | 7.344 | 9.524 | 11.030 | 13.362 | 15.507 | 18.168 | 20.090 | 26.124 |
| 9 | 2.088 | 2.532 | 3.325 | 4.168 | 5.380 | 6.393 | 8.343 | 10.656 | 12.242 | 14.684 | 16.919 | 19.679 | 21.666 | 27.877 |
| 10 | 2.558 | 3.059 | 3.940 | 4.865 | 6.179 | 7.267 | 9.342 | 11.781 | 13.442 | 15.987 | 18.307 | 21.161 | 23.209 | 29.588 |
| 11 | 3.053 | 3.609 | 4.575 | 5.578 | 6.989 | 8.148 | 10.341 | 12.899 | 14.631 | 17.275 | 19.675 | 22.618 | 24.725 | 31.264 |
| 12 | 3.571 | 4.178 | 5.226 | 6.304 | 7.807 | 9.034 | 11.340 | 14.011 | 15.812 | 18.549 | 21.026 | 24.054 | 26.217 | 32.909 |
| 13 | 4.107 | 4.765 | 5.892 | 7.042 | 8.634 | 9.926 | 12.340 | 15.119 | 16.985 | 19.812 | 22.362 | 25.472 | 27.688 | 34.528 |
| 14 | 4.660 | 5.368 | 6.571 | 7.790 | 9.467 | 10.821 | 13.339 | 16.222 | 18.151 | 21.064 | 23.685 | 26.873 | 29.141 | 36.123 |
| 15 | 5.229 | 5.985 | 7.261 | 8.547 | 10.307 | 11.721 | 14.339 | 17.322 | 19.311 | 22.307 | 24.996 | 28.259 | 30.578 | 37.697 |
| 16 | 5.812 | 6.614 | 7.962 | 9.312 | 11.152 | 12.624 | 15.338 | 18.418 | 20.465 | 23.542 | 26.296 | 29.633 | 32.000 | 39.252 |
| 17 | 6.408 | 7.255 | 8.672 | 10.085 | 12.002 | 13.531 | 16.338 | 19.511 | 21.615 | 24.769 | 27.587 | 30.995 | 33.409 | 40.790 |
| 18 | 7.015 | 7.906 | 9.390 | 10.865 | 12.857 | 14.440 | 17.338 | 20.601 | 22.760 | 25.989 | 28.869 | 32.346 | 34.805 | 42.312 |
| 19 | 7.633 | 8.567 | 10.117 | 11.651 | 13.716 | 15.352 | 18.338 | 21.689 | 23.900 | 27.204 | 30.144 | 33.687 | 36.191 | 43.820 |
| 20 | 8.260 | 9.237 | 10.851 | 12.443 | 14.578 | 16.266 | 19.337 | 22.775 | 25.038 | 28.412 | 31.410 | 35.020 | 37.566 | 45.315 |
| 21 | 8.897 | 9.915 | 11.591 | 13.240 | 15.445 | 17.182 | 20.337 | 23.858 | 26.171 | 29.615 | 32.671 | 36.343 | 38.932 | 46.797 |
| 22 | 9.542 | 10.600 | 12.338 | 14.041 | 16.314 | 18.101 | 21.337 | 24.939 | 27.301 | 30.813 | 33.924 | 37.659 | 40.289 | 48.268 |
| 23 | 10.196 | 11.293 | 13.091 | 14.848 | 17.187 | 19.021 | 22.337 | 26.018 | 28.429 | 32.007 | 35.172 | 38.968 | 41.638 | 49.728 |
| 24 | 10.856 | 11.992 | 13.848 | 15.659 | 18.062 | 19.943 | 23.337 | 27.096 | 29.553 | 33.196 | 36.415 | 40.270 | 42.980 | 51.179 |
| 25 | 11.524 | 12.697 | 14.611 | 16.473 | 18.940 | 20.867 | 24.337 | 28.172 | 30.675 | 34.382 | 37.652 | 41.566 | 44.314 | 52.620 |
| 26 | 12.198 | 13.409 | 15.379 | 17.292 | 19.820 | 21.792 | 25.336 | 29.246 | 31.795 | 35.563 | 38.885 | 42.856 | 45.642 | 54.052 |
| 27 | 12.879 | 14.125 | 16.151 | 18.114 | 20.703 | 22.719 | 26.336 | 30.319 | 32.912 | 36.741 | 40.113 | 44.140 | 46.963 | 55.476 |
| 28 | 13.565 | 14.847 | 16.928 | 18.939 | 21.588 | 23.647 | 27.336 | 31.391 | 34.027 | 37.916 | 41.337 | 45.419 | 48.278 | 56.892 |
| 29 | 14.256 | 15.574 | 17.708 | 19.768 | 22.475 | 24.577 | 28.336 | 32.461 | 35.139 | 39.087 | 42.557 | 46.693 | 49.588 | 58.301 |
| 30 | 14.953 | 16.306 | 18.493 | 20.599 | 23.364 | 25.508 | 29.336 | 33.530 | 36.250 | 40.256 | 43.773 | 47.962 | 50.892 | 59.703 |

Table IV of Fisher & Yates: *Statistical Tables for Biological, Agricultural and Medical Research*, published by Longman Group Ltd., London (1974), 6th edition (previously published by Oliver & Boyd Ltd., Edinburgh). Reprinted by permission of Pearson Education Limited.

# Distribution of *F*

$\alpha = 0.05$

| dfb dfw | 1 | 2 | 3 | 4 | 5 | 6 | 8 | 12 | 24 | ∞ |
|---|---|---|---|---|---|---|---|---|---|---|
| 1 | 161.45 | 199.50 | 215.71 | 224.58 | 230.16 | 233.99 | 238.88 | 243.91 | 249.05 | 254.31 |
| 2 | 18.51 | 19.00 | 19.16 | 19.25 | 19.30 | 19.33 | 19.37 | 19.41 | 19.45 | 19.50 |
| 3 | 10.13 | 9.55 | 9.28 | 9.12 | 9.01 | 8.94 | 8.85 | 8.74 | 8.64 | 8.53 |
| 4 | 7.71 | 6.94 | 6.59 | 6.39 | 6.26 | 6.16 | 6.04 | 5.91 | 5.77 | 5.63 |
| 5 | 6.61 | 5.79 | 5.41 | 5.19 | 5.05 | 4.95 | 4.82 | 4.68 | 4.53 | 4.36 |
| 6 | 5.99 | 5.14 | 4.76 | 4.53 | 4.39 | 4.28 | 4.15 | 4.00 | 3.84 | 3.67 |
| 7 | 5.59 | 4.74 | 4.35 | 4.12 | 3.97 | 3.87 | 3.73 | 3.57 | 3.41 | 3.23 |
| 8 | 5.32 | 4.46 | 4.07 | 3.84 | 3.69 | 3.58 | 3.44 | 3.28 | 3.12 | 2.93 |
| 9 | 5.12 | 4.26 | 3.86 | 3.63 | 3.48 | 3.37 | 3.23 | 3.07 | 2.90 | 2.71 |
| 10 | 4.96 | 4.10 | 3.71 | 3.48 | 3.33 | 3.22 | 3.07 | 2.91 | 2.74 | 2.54 |
| 11 | 4.84 | 3.98 | 3.59 | 3.36 | 3.20 | 3.09 | 2.95 | 2.79 | 2.61 | 2.40 |
| 12 | 4.75 | 3.89 | 3.49 | 3.26 | 3.11 | 3.00 | 2.85 | 2.69 | 2.51 | 2.30 |
| 13 | 4.67 | 3.81 | 3.41 | 3.18 | 3.03 | 2.92 | 2.77 | 2.60 | 2.42 | 2.21 |
| 14 | 4.60 | 3.74 | 3.34 | 3.11 | 2.96 | 2.85 | 2.70 | 2.53 | 2.35 | 2.13 |
| 15 | 4.54 | 3.68 | 3.29 | 3.06 | 2.90 | 2.79 | 2.64 | 2.48 | 2.29 | 2.07 |
| 16 | 4.49 | 3.63 | 3.24 | 3.01 | 2.85 | 2.74 | 2.59 | 2.42 | 2.24 | 2.01 |
| 17 | 4.45 | 3.59 | 3.20 | 2.96 | 2.81 | 2.70 | 2.55 | 2.38 | 2.19 | 1.96 |
| 18 | 4.41 | 3.55 | 3.16 | 2.93 | 2.77 | 2.66 | 2.51 | 2.34 | 2.15 | 1.92 |
| 19 | 4.38 | 3.52 | 3.13 | 2.90 | 2.74 | 2.63 | 2.48 | 2.31 | 2.11 | 1.88 |
| 20 | 4.35 | 3.49 | 3.10 | 2.87 | 2.71 | 2.60 | 2.45 | 2.28 | 2.08 | 1.84 |
| 21 | 4.32 | 3.47 | 3.07 | 2.84 | 2.68 | 2.57 | 2.42 | 2.25 | 2.05 | 1.81 |
| 22 | 4.30 | 3.44 | 3.05 | 2.82 | 2.66 | 2.55 | 2.40 | 2.23 | 2.03 | 1.78 |
| 23 | 4.28 | 3.42 | 3.03 | 2.80 | 2.64 | 2.53 | 2.37 | 2.20 | 2.01 | 1.76 |
| 24 | 4.26 | 3.40 | 3.01 | 2.78 | 2.62 | 2.51 | 2.36 | 2.18 | 1.98 | 1.73 |
| 25 | 4.24 | 3.39 | 2.99 | 2.76 | 2.60 | 2.49 | 2.34 | 2.16 | 1.96 | 1.71 |
| 26 | 4.23 | 3.37 | 2.98 | 2.74 | 2.59 | 2.47 | 2.32 | 2.15 | 1.95 | 1.69 |
| 27 | 4.21 | 3.35 | 2.96 | 2.73 | 2.57 | 2.46 | 2.31 | 2.13 | 1.93 | 1.67 |
| 28 | 4.20 | 3.34 | 2.95 | 2.71 | 2.56 | 2.45 | 2.29 | 2.12 | 1.91 | 1.65 |
| 29 | 4.18 | 3.33 | 2.93 | 2.70 | 2.55 | 2.43 | 2.28 | 2.10 | 1.90 | 1.64 |
| 30 | 4.17 | 3.32 | 2.92 | 2.69 | 2.53 | 2.42 | 2.27 | 2.09 | 1.89 | 1.62 |
| 40 | 4.08 | 3.23 | 2.84 | 2.61 | 2.45 | 2.34 | 2.18 | 2.00 | 1.79 | 1.51 |
| 60 | 4.00 | 3.15 | 2.76 | 2.53 | 2.37 | 2.25 | 2.10 | 1.92 | 1.70 | 1.39 |
| 120 | 3.92 | 3.07 | 2.68 | 2.45 | 2.29 | 2.18 | 2.02 | 1.83 | 1.61 | 1.25 |
| ∞ | 3.84 | 2.99 | 2.60 | 2.37 | 2.21 | 2.10 | 1.94 | 1.75 | 1.52 | 1.00 |

Table V of Fisher & Yates: *Statistical Tables for Biological, Agricultural and Medical Research*, published by Longman Group Ltd., London (1974), 6th edition (previously published by Oliver & Boyd Ltd., Edinburgh). Reprinted by permission of Pearson Education Limited.

$\alpha = 0.01$

| dfb dfw | 1 | 2 | 3 | 4 | 5 | 6 | 8 | 12 | 24 | ∞ |
|---|---|---|---|---|---|---|---|---|---|---|
| 1 | 4052 | 4999 | 5403 | 5625 | 5764 | 5859 | 5981 | 6106 | 6234 | 6366 |
| 2 | 98.5 | 99.00 | 99.17 | 99.25 | 99.30 | 99.33 | 99.37 | 99.42 | 99.46 | 99.50 |
| 3 | 34.12 | 30.82 | 29.46 | 28.71 | 28.24 | 27.91 | 27.49 | 27.05 | 26.60 | 26.13 |
| 4 | 21.20 | 18.00 | 16.69 | 15.98 | 15.52 | 15.21 | 14.80 | 14.37 | 13.93 | 13.46 |
| 5 | 16.26 | 13.27 | 12.06 | 11.39 | 10.97 | 10.67 | 10.29 | 9.89 | 9.47 | 9.02 |
| 6 | 13.75 | 10.92 | 9.78 | 9.15 | 8.75 | 8.47 | 8.10 | 7.72 | 7.31 | 6.88 |
| 7 | 12.25 | 9.55 | 8.45 | 7.85 | 7.46 | 7.19 | 6.84 | 6.47 | 6.07 | 5.65 |
| 8 | 11.26 | 8.65 | 7.59 | 7.01 | 6.63 | 6.37 | 6.03 | 5.67 | 5.28 | 4.86 |
| 9 | 10.56 | 8.02 | 6.99 | 6.42 | 6.06 | 5.80 | 5.47 | 5.11 | 4.73 | 4.31 |
| 10 | 10.04 | 7.56 | 6.55 | 5.99 | 5.64 | 5.39 | 5.06 | 4.71 | 4.33 | 3.91 |
| 11 | 9.65 | 7.21 | 6.22 | 5.67 | 5.32 | 5.07 | 4.74 | 4.40 | 4.02 | 3.60 |
| 12 | 9.33 | 6.93 | 5.95 | 5.41 | 5.06 | 4.82 | 4.50 | 4.16 | 3.78 | 3.36 |
| 13 | 9.07 | 6.70 | 5.74 | 5.21 | 4.86 | 4.62 | 4.30 | 3.96 | 3.59 | 3.17 |
| 14 | 8.86 | 6.51 | 5.56 | 5.04 | 4.69 | 4.46 | 4.14 | 3.80 | 3.43 | 3.00 |
| 15 | 8.68 | 6.36 | 5.42 | 4.89 | 4.56 | 4.32 | 4.00 | 3.67 | 3.29 | 2.87 |
| 16 | 8.53 | 6.23 | 5.29 | 4.77 | 4.44 | 4.20 | 3.89 | 3.55 | 3.18 | 2.75 |
| 17 | 8.40 | 6.11 | 5.18 | 4.67 | 4.34 | 4.10 | 3.79 | 3.46 | 3.08 | 2.65 |
| 18 | 8.29 | 6.01 | 5.09 | 4.58 | 4.25 | 4.01 | 3.71 | 3.37 | 3.00 | 2.57 |
| 19 | 8.18 | 5.93 | 5.01 | 4.50 | 4.17 | 3.94 | 3.63 | 3.30 | 2.92 | 2.49 |
| 20 | 8.10 | 5.85 | 4.94 | 4.43 | 4.10 | 3.87 | 3.56 | 3.23 | 2.86 | 2.42 |
| 21 | 8.02 | 5.78 | 4.87 | 4.37 | 4.04 | 3.81 | 3.51 | 3.17 | 2.80 | 2.36 |
| 22 | 7.95 | 5.72 | 4.82 | 4.31 | 3.99 | 3.76 | 3.45 | 3.12 | 2.75 | 2.31 |
| 23 | 7.88 | 5.66 | 4.76 | 4.26 | 3.94 | 3.71 | 3.41 | 3.07 | 2.70 | 2.26 |
| 24 | 7.82 | 5.61 | 4.72 | 4.22 | 3.90 | 3.67 | 3.36 | 3.03 | 2.66 | 2.21 |
| 25 | 7.77 | 5.57 | 4.68 | 4.18 | 3.85 | 3.63 | 3.32 | 2.99 | 2.62 | 2.17 |
| 26 | 7.72 | 5.53 | 4.64 | 4.14 | 3.82 | 3.59 | 3.29 | 2.96 | 2.58 | 2.13 |
| 27 | 7.68 | 5.49 | 4.60 | 4.11 | 3.78 | 3.56 | 3.26 | 2.93 | 2.55 | 2.10 |
| 28 | 7.64 | 5.45 | 4.57 | 4.07 | 3.75 | 3.53 | 3.23 | 2.90 | 2.52 | 2.06 |
| 29 | 7.60 | 5.42 | 4.54 | 4.04 | 3.73 | 3.50 | 3.20 | 2.87 | 2.49 | 2.03 |
| 30 | 7.56 | 5.39 | 4.51 | 4.02 | 3.70 | 3.47 | 3.17 | 2.84 | 2.47 | 2.01 |
| 40 | 7.31 | 5.18 | 4.31 | 3.83 | 3.51 | 3.29 | 2.99 | 2.66 | 2.29 | 1.80 |
| 60 | 7.08 | 4.98 | 4.13 | 3.65 | 3.34 | 3.12 | 2.82 | 2.50 | 2.12 | 1.60 |
| 120 | 6.85 | 4.79 | 3.95 | 3.48 | 3.17 | 2.96 | 2.66 | 2.34 | 1.95 | 1.38 |
| ∞ | 6.63 | 4.61 | 3.78 | 3.32 | 3.02 | 2.80 | 2.51 | 2.18 | 1.79 | 1.00 |

# Using Statistics: Ideas for Research Projects

This appendix presents outlines for four research projects, each of which requires the use of SPSS to analyze the 2013 GSS or the 2012 CCHS data used throughout this textbook, although most of the projects can be done with other data sets that may be available to your instructor. The research projects should be completed at various intervals during the course, and each project permits a great deal of choice on the part of the student. The first project stresses description and should be done after completing Chapters 2 and 3. The second involves estimation and should be completed in conjunction with Chapter 6. The third and fourth projects use hypothesis testing and measures of association and should be done after Part 3 (or 4).

## PROJECT 1— DESCRIPTIVE STATISTICS

1. From either the 2013 GSS (short version: *2013_GSS_Shortened.sav*) or the 2012 CCHS (short version: *2012_CCHS_Shortened.sav*) data set, select five variables and use the **Frequencies** command to get frequency distributions and summary statistics. *(NOTE: Select at least one variable from each level of measurement.)* Click the **Statistics** button and request the mean, median, mode, standard deviation, and range. See Demonstration 3.1 for guidelines and examples. Make a note of all relevant information when it appears on screen or make a hardcopy. See Appendix G for a list of variables available in the GSS and CCHS.

2. For each variable, get a bar chart or histogram to summarize the overall shape of the distribution of the variable. See Demonstrations 2.2 and 4.1 for guidelines and examples.

3. Inspect the frequency distributions and graphs and choose appropriate measures of central tendency and, for ordinal level and interval-ratio-level variables, dispersion. Also, for interval-ratio variables check for skew both by using the histogram and by comparing the mean and median (see Section 3.5). Write a sentence or two of description for each variable, being careful to include a description of the overall shape of the distribution (see Chapter 2) and central tendency and dispersion (see Chapter 3).

4. Below are examples of *minimal* summary sentences, using fictitious data:

   *For a nominal-level variable* (e.g., marital status), report the mode and some detail about the overall distribution. For example:

   "Most respondents were married (57.5%), but divorced (17.4%) and single (21.3%) individuals were also common."

*For an ordinal-level variable* (e.g., occupational prestige), use the median (and, perhaps, the mode) and the range.

"The median prestige score was 44.3, and the range extended from 34 to 87. The most common score was 42."

*For an interval-ratio level variable* (e.g., population density for 124 nations), use the mean (and, perhaps, the median or mode) and the standard deviation (and, perhaps, the range).

"For these nations, population density (population per square kilometre) ranged from a low of 4.00 to a high of 12,000. The standard deviation was 1,000. The nations averaged 351 people per square kilometre, and the median density was 193. The distribution is positively skewed, and some nations have very high population density."

## PROJECT 2— ESTIMATION

In this exercise, you will use the 2012 CCHS (short version: *2012_CCHS_ Shortened.sav*) sample to estimate the characteristics of the Canadian population. You will use SPSS to generate the sample statistics to find the confidence interval and state each interval in words.

### A. Estimating Means

1. There are relatively few interval-ratio variables in the 2012 CCHS, and for this part of the project, you may use ordinal variables that have *at least* three categories or scores. Choose a total of three variables that fit this description *other than* the variables you used in Exercise 6.1. *(NOTE: Your instructor may specify a different number of variables.)*

2. Use the **Explore** command to get the 95% confidence interval for the first of your variables. Repeat this procedure for the remaining variables.

3. For each variable, write a summary sentence reporting the variable, the interval itself, the confidence level, and sample size. Write in plain English, as if you were reporting results in a newspaper. Most importantly, you should make it clear that you are estimating characteristics of the entire Canadian population. For example, a summary sentence might look like this:

"Based on a random sample of 1,500, it is estimated at the 95% level that Canadian drivers average between 98.46 and 102.22 kilometres per hour when driving on highways."

### B. Estimating Proportions

1. Choose three variables that are nominal or ordinal with *two or three* categories *other than* the variables you used in Exercise 6.3. *(NOTE: Your instructor may specify a different number of variables.)*

2. Use the **Frequencies** command to get the percentage of the sample in the various categories of each variable. Change the percentages (remember to use the "valid percents" column) to find proportions and construct confidence intervals for one category of each variable (e.g., the % female for *dhh_sex*) using Formula 6.3.

3. For each variable, write a summary sentence reporting the variable, the interval, the confidence level, and sample size. Write in plain English, as if you were reporting results in a newspaper. Remember to make it clear that you are estimating a characteristic of the Canadian population.

4. For any one of the intervals you constructed, identify each of the following concepts and terms and briefly explain their role in estimation: sample, population, statistic, parameter, EPSEM, representative, and confidence level.

## PROJECT 3— SIGNIFICANCE TESTING

Use the 2012 CCHS (short version: *2012_CCHS_Shortened.sav*) data set for this project.

### A. Chi Square (Chapter 7)

1. Choose two different dependent variables of any level of measurement that have five or fewer (preferably 2–3) scores. For each dependent variable, choose an independent variable that might logically be a cause. Independent variables can be any level of measurement as long as they have five or fewer (preferably 2–3) categories. Output will be easier to analyze if you use variables with few categories. You may use the same independent variable for both tests.

2. Click **Analyze**, **Descriptive Statistics**, and then **Crosstabs**. The **Crosstabs** dialog box will appear. Highlight your first dependent variable and move it into the **Rows** box. Next, highlight your independent variable and move it into the **Columns** box. Click the **Statistics** button at the bottom of the window and click the box next to **Chi square**. Click **Continue** and **OK**. Make a note of the results or keep a hardcopy. Repeat for your second dependent variable.

3. Write up the results of the test. At a minimum, your report should clearly identify the independent and dependent variables, the value of the test statistic (step 4), the results of the test (step 5), the degrees of freedom, and the alpha level you used. It is almost always desirable to also report the column percentages (see Section 7.9).

### B. Two-Sample *t* Test (Chapter 11)

1. Choose two different dependent variables that are measured at the interval-ratio level (since there are relatively few interval-ratio variables in the 2012 CCHS, you may instead use ordinal variables that have three

or more scores). Choose independent variables that might logically be a cause of your dependent variables. Remember that, for a *t* test, independent variables can have *only* two categories. Independent variables can be any level of measurement, and you may use the same independent variable for both tests.

2. Click **Analyze**, **Compare Means**, and then **Independent Samples T Test**. Put your dependent variable(s) in the **Test Variable(s)** box and your independent variable in the **Grouping Variable** box. You will also need to specify the scores used to define the groups on the independent variable. See SPSS Demonstration 11.1 for an example. Make a note of the test results (group means, obtained *t* score, significance, sample size) or keep a hardcopy. Repeat the procedure for the second dependent variable.

3. Write up the results of the test. At a minimum, your report should clearly identify the independent and dependent variables, the sample statistics, the value of the test statistic (step 4), the results of the test (step 5), and the alpha level you used.

### C. Analysis of Variance (Chapter 12)

1. Choose two different interval-ratio dependent variables (again, given the small number of interval-ratio variables in the 2012 CCHS, you may instead use ordinal variables that have three or more scores). Choose independent variables that might logically be a cause of your dependent variables and that have between three and five categories. You may use the same independent variables for both tests.

2. Click **Analyze**, **Compare Means**, and then **One-way ANOVA**. The **One-way ANOVA** window will appear. Find your dependent variable in the variable list on the left and click the arrow to move the variable name into the **Dependent List** box. Note that you can request more than one dependent variable at a time. Next, find the name of your independent variable and move it to the **Factor** box. Click **Options** and then click the box next to **Descriptive** in the **Statistics** box to request means and standard deviations. Click **Continue**. Then, click the **Post Hoc** button and check the box next to "**Tukey**" in the **Equal Variances Assumed** box. This will generate the Tukey HSD post hoc test for the one-way ANOVA. Click **Continue** and **OK**. Make a note of the test results or keep a hardcopy. Repeat, if necessary, for your second dependent variable.

3. Write up the results of the test. At a minimum, your report should clearly identify the independent and dependent variables, the sample statistics (category means), the value of the test statistic (step 4), the results of the test (step 5), the degrees of freedom, and the alpha level you used. If the null hypothesis is rejected as determined by the *F* ratio, use the post hoc test results to report which group means are significantly different from each other.

**PROJECT 4—
ANALYZING THE
STRENGTH AND
SIGNIFICANCE OF
RELATIONSHIPS**

**A. Using Bivariate Tables**

1. From the 2013 GSS data set (short version: *2013_GSS_Shortened.sav*), select either

   **a.** One dependent variable and three independent variables (possible causes) or

   **b.** One independent variable and three possible dependent variables (possible effects).

   Variables can be from any level of measurement but must have only a few (2–5) categories or "scores." Develop research questions or hypotheses about the relationships between variables. Make sure that the causal links you suggest are sensible and logical.

2. Use the **Crosstabs** procedure to generate bivariate tables. See any of the Demonstrations at the end of Chapters 8 or 9 for examples. Click **Analyze**, **Descriptive Statistics**, and **Crosstabs** and place your dependent variable(s) in the rows and independent variable(s) in the columns. On the **Crosstabs** dialog box, click the **Statistics** button and choose chi square, phi or V, and gamma for every table you request. On the **Crosstabs** dialog box, click the **Cells** button and get column percentages for every table you request. Make a note of results as they appear on the screen or get hardcopies.

3. Write a report that presents and analyzes these relationships. Be clear about which variables are dependent and which are independent. For each combination of variables, report the test of significance and measure of association. In addition, for each relationship, report and discuss column percentages, pattern or direction of the relationship, and strength of the relationship.

4. *OPTIONAL MULTIVARIATE ANALYSIS* (*NOTE: Multivariate analysis for variables organized in table format is covered on the website for this textbook*). Pick one of the bivariate relationships you produced in step 2 and find a logical control variable for this relationship. Run **Crosstabs** for the bivariate relationship again while controlling for the third variable. Compare the partial tables with each other and with the bivariate table. Is the original bivariate relationship direct? Is there evidence of a spurious or intervening relationship? Do the variables have an interactive relationship? Write up the results of this analysis and include them in your summary paper for this project.

**B. Using Interval-Ratio Variables**

1. From the 2012 CCHS (short version: *2012_CCHS_Shortened.sav*), select either

   **a.** One dependent variable and three independent variables (possible causes) or

      **b.** One independent variable and three possible dependent variables (possible effects).

      Variables should be interval-ratio in level of measurement, but you may use ordinal-level variables as long as they have three or more scores. Develop research questions or hypotheses about the relationships between variables. Make sure that the causal links you suggest are sensible and logical.

2. Use the **Regression** and **Scatterplot** (click **Graphs**, **Legacy Dialogs**, then **Scatter/Dot**) procedures to analyze the bivariate relationships. Make a note of results (including $r$, $r^2$, slope, beta-weights, and $a$) as they appear on the screen or print hardcopies.

3. Write a report that presents and analyzes these relationships. Be clear about which variables are dependent and which are independent. For each combination of variables, report the significance of the relationship (if relevant) and the strength and direction of the relationship. Include $r$, $r^2$, and the beta-weights in your report.

4. *OPTIONAL MULTIVARIATE ANALYSIS.* Pick one of the bivariate relationships you produced in step 2 and find another logical independent variable. Run **Regression** again with both independent variables and analyze the results. How much improvement is there in the explained variance after the second independent variable is included? Write up the results of this analysis and include them in your summary paper for this project.

# Appendix F

# An Introduction to IBM SPSS Statistics for Windows

Computers have affected virtually every aspect of human society, and, as you would expect, their impact on the conduct of social research has been profound. Researchers routinely use computers to organize data and compute statistics—activities that humans often find dull, tedious, and difficult but which computers accomplish with accuracy and ease. This division of labour allows social scientists to spend more time on analysis and interpretation—activities that humans typically enjoy but which are beyond the power of computers (so far, at least).

These days, the skills needed to use computers successfully are quite accessible, even for people with little or no experience. This appendix will prepare you to use a statistics program called IBM SPSS Statistics for Windows, often referred to as simply "SPSS." We use Version 24, though Versions 10 to 23 of SPSS are compatible with the information and instructions presented here and throughout the textbook. If you have used a mouse to "point and click" and run a computer program, you are ready to learn how to use this program. Even if you are completely unfamiliar with computers, you will find this program accessible. After you finish this appendix, you will be ready to do the exercises found at the end of most chapters of this textbook.

A word of caution before we begin: This appendix is intended only as an introduction to SPSS. It will give you an overview of the program and enough information so that you can complete the assignments in the textbook. It is unlikely, however, that this appendix will answer all your questions or provide solutions to all the problems you might encounter. So, this is a good place to tell you that SPSS has an extensive and easy-to-use "help" facility that will provide assistance as you request it. You should familiarize yourself with this feature and use it as needed. To get help, simply click on the **Help** command on the toolbar across the top of the screen.

SPSS is a **statistical package** (or **statpak**), a set of computer programs that work with data and compute statistics as requested by the user (you). Once you have entered the data for a particular group of observations, you can easily and quickly produce an abundance of statistical information without doing any computations yourself. Also, you can access the power of the computer without having to write computer programs yourself.

Why bother to learn this technology? The truth is that the labour-saving capacity of computers is sometimes exaggerated, and there are research situations in which they are unnecessary. If you are working with a small number of observations or need only a few, uncomplicated statistics, then statistical packages are probably not going to be helpful. However, as the number of cases increases and as your requirements for statistics become more sophisticated, computers and statpaks will become more and more useful.

An example should make this point clearer. Suppose you have gathered a sample of 150 respondents and the *only* thing you want to know about these people is their average age. To compute an average, as you know, you add the scores and divide by the total number of cases. How long do you think it would take you to add 150 two-digit numbers (ages) with a hand calculator? (Don't even think about doing it by hand.) If you entered the scores at the (pretty fast) rate of one per second, or sixty scores a minute, it would take about three or four minutes to enter the ages and get the average. Even if you worked slowly and carefully and did the addition a second and third time to check your math, you could probably complete all calculations in less than 20 minutes. If this were all the information you needed, computers and statpaks would not save you any time.

Such a simple research project is not very realistic, however. Typically, researchers deal with not one but scores or even hundreds of variables, and samples have hundreds or thousands of cases. While you could add 150 numbers in perhaps three or four minutes, how long would it take to add the scores for 1,500 cases? What are the chances of processing 1,500 numbers without making significant errors of arithmetic? The more complex the research situation, the more valuable and useful statpaks become. SPSS can produce statistical information in a few keystrokes or clicks of the mouse that might take you minutes, hours, or even days to produce with a hand calculator.

Clearly, this is technology worth mastering by any social researcher. With SPSS, you can avoid the drudgery of mere computation, spend more time on analysis and interpretation, and conduct research projects with very large data sets. Mastery of this technology might be very handy indeed in your upper-level courses, in a wide variety of jobs, or in graduate school.

## F.1 GETTING STARTED—DATABASES AND COMPUTER FILES

Before statistics can be calculated, SPSS must first have some data to process. A **database** is an organized collection of related information such as the responses to a survey. For purposes of computer analysis, a database is organized into a **file**, a collection of information that is stored under the same name on the hard drive of the computer or in some other medium. Words as well as numbers can be saved in files. If you've ever used a word processing program to type a letter or term paper, you probably saved your work in a file so that you could update or make corrections at a later time. Data can be stored in files indefinitely. Because it can take months to conduct a thorough data analysis, the ability to save a database is another advantage of using computers.

For the SPSS exercises in this textbook, we will use data from two well-established Canadian social surveys, the Canadian Community Health Survey (CCHS) and the General Social Survey (GSS). Both surveys contain questions on a large variety of issues from a sample of Canadians. The CCHS and GSS are conducted annually and have been the basis for hundreds of research projects by professional social researchers. The GSS is a rich source of information about public opinion in Canada and includes data on everything from attitudes about crime to social identity. The CCHS provides information on the health status, health care utilization, and health determinants of Canadians.

The CCHS and GSS are especially valuable because the respondents are chosen so that the samples as a whole are representative of the entire Canadian population. A representative sample reproduces, in miniature form, the characteristics of the population from which it was taken (see Chapter 5). So, when you analyze either the CCHS or GSS database, you are in effect analyzing Canadian society. The data are real, and the relationships you will analyze reflect some of the most important and sensitive issues in Canadian life.

The 2012 and 2013 versions of the CCHS and GSS, respectively, are provided with this textbook. The complete 2012 CCHS and 2013 GSS databases each contain hundreds of items of information for thousands of respondents. Some of you will be using a student version of SPSS, which is limited in the number of cases and variables it can process. To accommodate these limits, we have reduced the databases to about 50 items of information and 1,500 respondents.

The 2012 CCHS and 2013 GSS data files are summarized in Appendix G. Please turn to this appendix and familiarize yourself with it. Note that the variables are listed alphabetically by their variable names. In many cases, the variable names (e.g., *sex*) are easy to figure out. In other cases, variable names are not so obvious. Appendix G also shows the wording of the item that generated the variable. It is also a code book; it lists all the codes (or scores) for each survey item along with their meanings.

It's important that you understand the difference between a statpak (SPSS) and a database (like the CCHS or GSS) and what we are ultimately after here. A database consists of information. A statpak organizes the information in the database and produces statistics. Our goal is to apply the statpak to the database to produce output (e.g., statistics and graphs) that we can analyze and use to answer questions. The process might be diagrammed as in Figure F.1.

**FIGURE F.1    The Data Analysis Process**

| Database | → | Statpak | → | Output | → | Analysis |
|----------|---|---------|---|--------|---|----------|
| (raw information) | | (computer programs) | | (statistics and graphs) | | (interpretation) |

Statpaks like SPSS are general research tools that can be used to analyze databases of all sorts; they are not limited to the 2012 CCHS or 2013 GSS. In the same way, the 2012 CCHS or 2013 GSS could be analyzed with statpaks other than those used in this textbook. Other widely used statpaks include SAS and Stata—each of which may be available on your campus.

## F.2 STARTING SPSS AND LOADING THE 2013 GSS

If you are using the complete, professional version of SPSS, you will probably be working in a computer lab, and you can begin running the program immediately. If you are using the student version of the program on your personal computer, the first thing you need to do is install the software. Follow the instructions that came with the program and return to this appendix when installation is complete.

To start SPSS, find the icon (or picture) on the screen of your monitor that has an "IBM SPSS Statistics" label attached to it. Use the computer mouse to move the arrow on the monitor screen over this icon and then double-click the left button on the mouse. This will start up the SPSS program.

After a few seconds the SPSS screen will appear and ask, in the middle of the screen, what would you like to do. Of the choices listed, click the "Open another file…" option in the box labelled **Recent Files:**. Find the 2013 General Social Survey data set, labelled *2013_GSS_Shortened.sav*, which we will work with in the remainder of this appendix. Once you've located the data set, click on the name of the file with the left-hand button on the mouse, then click the **Open** button near the bottom of the window, and SPSS will load the data. The next screen you will see is the SPSS Data Editor screen.

Note that there is a list of commands across the very top of the screen. These commands begin with **File** at the far left and end with **Help** at the far right. This is the main menu bar for SPSS. When you click any of these words, a **menu** of commands and choices will drop down. Basically, you tell SPSS what to do by clicking on your desired choices from these menus. Sometimes, submenus will appear, and you will need to specify your choices further.

SPSS provides the user with a variety of options for displaying information about the data file and output on the screen. We highly recommend that you tell the program to display lists of variables by name (e.g., *actlimit*) rather than labels (e.g., Are you limited in the amount or kind of activity you can do). Lists displayed this way will be easier to read and compare to Appendix G. To do this, click **Edit** on the main menu bar and then click **Options** from the drop-down submenu. A dialog box labelled "Options" will appear with a series of "tabs" along the top. The "General" options should be displayed but, if not, click on this tab. On

**TABLE F.1   Summary of Commands**

| | |
|---|---|
| To start SPSS | Click the SPSS icon on the screen of the computer monitor |
| To open a data file | Double-click on the data file name |
| To set display options for lists of variables | Click **Edit** from the main menu bar, then click **Options**. On the "General" tab make sure that "Display names" and "Alphabetical" are selected and then click **OK**. |

the "General" screen, find the box labelled "Variable Lists" and, if they are not already selected, click "Display names" and "Alphabetical" and then click **OK**. If you make changes, a message may appear on the screen that tells you that changes will reset all dialog box settings and close all open dialog boxes. Click **OK**.

In this section, you learned how to start up SPSS, load a data file, and set some of the display options for this program. These procedures are summarized in Table F.1.

## F.3 WORKING WITH THE 2013 GSS DATABASE

Note that in the SPSS Data Editor window the data are organized into a two-dimensional grid with columns running up and down (vertically) and rows running across (horizontally). Each column is a variable or item of information from the survey. The names of the variables are listed at the tops of the columns. Remember that you can find the meaning of these variable names in the GSS 2013 code book in Appendix G.

Another way to decipher the meaning of variable names is to click **Utilities** on the menu bar and then click **Variables**. The Variables window opens. This window has two parts. On the left is a list of all variables in the database arranged in alphabetical order with the first variable highlighted. On the right is the Variable Information window with information about the highlighted variable. The Variable Information window displays a fragment of the question that was actually asked during the survey along with some other information.

The same information can be displayed for any variable in the data set. For example, find the variable *sex* in the list. You can do this by using the arrow keys on your keyboard or the slider bar on the right of the variable list window. You can also move through the list by typing the first letter of the variable name you are interested in. For example, type "s" and you will be moved to the first variable name in the list that begins with that letter. Now you can see that the variable measures sex and that a score of "1" indicates that the respondent is male and "2" is female. What do *brthcan* and *marstat* measure? Close this window by clicking the **Cancel** button at the bottom of the window.

**TABLE F.2  Summary of Commands**

| To move around in the Data window | 1. Click the cell you want to highlight or<br>2. Use the arrow keys on your keyboard or<br>3. Move the slider buttons or<br>4. Click the arrows on the right-hand and bottom margins |
|---|---|
| To get information about a variable | 1. From the menu bar, click **Utilities** and then click **Variables**. Scroll through the list of variable names until you highlight the name of the variable in which you are interested. Variable information will appear in the window on the right<br>2. See Appendix G |

Examine the window displaying the 2013 GSS a little more. Each row of the window (reading across or from left to right) contains the scores of a particular respondent on all the variables in the database. Note that the upper-left-hand cell is highlighted (shaded a darker colour than the other cells). This cell contains the score of respondent #1 on the first variable. The second row contains the scores of respondent #2, and so forth. You can move around in this window with the arrow keys on your keyboard. The highlight moves in the direction of the arrow, one cell at a time.

In this section, you learned to read information in the Data Editor window and to decipher the meaning of variable names and scores. These commands are summarized in Table F.2, and we are now prepared to actually perform some statistical operations with the 2013 GSS database.

## F.4 PUTTING SPSS TO WORK ON THE 2013 GSS DATABASE: PRODUCING STATISTICS

At this point, the database on the screen is just a mass of numbers with little meaning for you. That's okay because you will not have to actually read any information from this screen. Virtually all of the statistical operations you will conduct will begin by clicking the **Analyze** command from the menu bar, selecting a procedure and statistics, and then naming the variable or variables you would like to process.

To illustrate, let's have SPSS produce a frequency distribution for the variable *sex*. Frequency distributions are tables that display the number of times each score of a variable occurred in the sample (see Chapter 2). So, when we complete this procedure, we will know the number of males and females in the 2013 GSS sample.

With the 2013 GSS loaded, begin by clicking the **Analyze** command on the menu bar. From the menu that drops down, click **Descriptive Statistics** and then **Frequencies**. The Frequencies window appears with the variables listed in alphabetical order in the box on the left. The first variable (*agegr10*) will be highlighted. Use the slider button or the arrow keys on the right-hand margin of this box to scroll through the variable list until you highlight the variable *sex*, or type "s" to move to the approximate location.

Once the variable you want to process has been highlighted, click the arrow button in the middle of the screen to move the variable name to the box on the right-hand side of the screen. SPSS will produce frequency distributions for all variables listed in this box, but, for now, we will confine our attention to *sex*. Click the **OK** button in the upper-right-hand corner of the Frequencies window and, in seconds, a frequency distribution will be produced.

SPSS sends all tables and statistics to the Output window or SPSS viewer. This window is now "closest" to you, and the Data Editor window is "behind" the Output window. If you wanted to return to the Data Editor, click on any part of it if it is visible, and it will move to the "front" and the Output window will be "behind" it. To display the Data Editor window if it is not visible, minimize the Output window by clicking the "-" box in the upper-right-hand corner.

**Frequencies**  The output from SPSS, slightly modified, is reproduced as Table F.3. What can we tell from this table? The score labels (male and female) are printed at the left with the number of cases (frequency) in each category of the variable one column to the right. As you can see, there are 800 males and 791 females in the sample. The next two columns give information about percentages and the last column to the right displays cumulative percentages. We will defer a discussion of this last column until a later exercise.

One of the percentage columns is labelled Percent and the other is labelled Valid Percent. The difference between these two columns lies in the handling of missing values. The Percent column is based on all cases, including people who did not respond to the item and people who said they did not have the requested information. The Valid Percent column excludes all missing scores. Because we will almost always want to ignore missing scores, we will pay attention only to the Valid Percent column. Note that for sex, there are no missing scores (gender was determined by the interviewer), and the two columns are identical.

**TABLE F.3  An Example of SPSS Output (Respondents' Sex)**

|  |  | Frequency | Percent | Valid Percent | Cumulative Percent |
|---|---|---|---|---|---|
| Valid | Male | 800 | 50.3 | 50.3 | 50.3 |
|  | Female | 791 | 49.7 | 49.7 | 100.0 |
|  | Total | 1,592 | 100.0 | 100.0 |  |

## F.5 COMPUTING, RECODING, AND LABELLING VARIABLES

SPSS provides a variety of ways to transform and manipulate variables. This section demonstrates how to use SPSS to create and recode variables. We will use the SPSS compute command to create a *new* variable and the SPSS recode command to transform the values of an *existing* variable. We will also demonstrate how to add labels to make variables more meaningful.

**Creating a New Variable with the Compute Command**   In this demonstration, we will use the SPSS **Compute** command to create new variables and summary scales. Let's begin by considering two of the questions from the 2013 GSS that measure health in Canada: *srh_110* and *srh_115*. Each item examines a unique aspect of health. Specifically, the questions ask about a person's general health (*srh_110*) and mental health (*srh_115*). Because these two aspects of health are distinct, each item should be analyzed in its own right. Suppose, however, that you wanted to create a summary scale that indicated a person's *overall* health.

One way to do this would be to add the scores on the two variables together. This would create a new variable, which we will call *health*, with a maximum possible score of 10 since each of the two variables contains five scores (1, 2, 3, 4, and 5—meaning "excellent," "very good," "good," "fair," and "poor"). The minimum possible score will then be 2, since if a person selected "1" for both variables, the lowest possible sum is 2.

A respondent that consistently answered "excellent" (coded as "1") to both items would receive a score of 2 on the new summary variable. Thus, lower scores represent better health than higher scores. We might label this as "excellent" overall health. A score of 3 would occur when a respondent answered "excellent" to one item and "very good" (coded as "2") to the remaining item, and would indicate "very good" overall health. The other scores on this scale would be 4, 5, 6, 7, 8, 9, and 10, the highest possible score which is given to a respondent that answered "poor" (coded as "5") to both items. This would be consistent with "very poor" overall health. Once created, *health* could be analyzed, transformed, and manipulated exactly like a variable actually recorded in the data file.

To create this scale, use the **Compute** command. Click **Transform** and then **Compute Variable** from the main menu. The **Compute Variable** window will appear. Find the **Target Variable** box in the upper-left-hand corner of this window. The first thing we need to do is assign a name to the new variable we are about to compute (*health*) and type that name in this box.

Next, we need to tell SPSS how to compute the new variable. In this case, *health* will be computed by adding the scores of *srh_110* and *srh_115*. Find *srh_110* in the variable list on the left and click the arrow button in the middle of the screen to transfer the variable name to the **Numeric Expression** box. Next, click the plus sign (+) on the calculator pad under the **Numeric Expression** box, and the sign will appear next to *srh_110*. Then, highlight *srh_115* in the variable list and click the arrow button to transfer the variable name to the **Numeric Expression** box.

The expression in the **Numeric Expression** box should now read *health = srh_110 + srh_115*. Click **OK**, and *health* will be created and added to the data set. If you want to keep this new variable permanently, click **Save** from the **File** menu, and the updated data set with *health* added will be saved. However, if you are using the student version of SPSS, remember that your data set is limited to 50 variables.

We now have a new variable that measures overall health—a more general summary item that was created from two existing items related to specific aspects of a person's health. It is always a good idea to check the frequency distribution for computed and recoded variables to make sure that the computations were carried out correctly. Use the **Frequencies** procedure (click **Analyze**, **Descriptive Statistics**, and **Frequencies**) to get tables for *srh_110, srh_115,* and *health.* Your output will look like this:

### Self-rated General Health

| | | Frequency | Percent | Valid Percent | Cumulative Percent |
|---|---|---|---|---|---|
| Valid | Excellent | 387 | 24.3 | 24.7 | 24.7 |
| | Very good | 600 | 37.7 | 38.4 | 63.1 |
| | Good | 412 | 25.9 | 26.3 | 89.4 |
| | Fair | 123 | 7.7 | 7.9 | 97.3 |
| | Poor | 42 | 2.7 | 2.7 | 100.0 |
| | Total | 1565 | 98.3 | 100.0 | |
| Missing | Refusal | 0 | .0 | | |
| | Not stated | 27 | 1.7 | | |
| | Total | 27 | 1.7 | | |
| Total | | 1592 | 100.0 | | |

### Self-rated Mental Health

| | | Frequency | Percent | Valid Percent | Cumulative Percent |
|---|---|---|---|---|---|
| Valid | Excellent | 590 | 37.0 | 37.7 | 37.7 |
| | Very good | 588 | 37.0 | 37.6 | 75.4 |
| | Good | 297 | 18.6 | 19.0 | 94.4 |
| | Fair | 67 | 4.2 | 4.3 | 98.7 |
| | Poor | 21 | 1.3 | 1.3 | 100.0 |
| | Total | 1563 | 98.2 | 100.0 | |
| Missing | Don't know | 1 | .1 | | |
| | Refusal | 1 | .1 | | |
| | Not stated | 27 | 1.7 | | |
| | Total | 29 | 1.8 | | |
| Total | | 1592 | 100.0 | | |

**Overall Health**

|  |  | Frequency | Percent | Valid Percent | Cumulative Percent |
|---|---|---|---|---|---|
| Valid | 2.00 (excellent) | 305 | 19.1 | 19.5 | 19.5 |
|  | 3.00 | 242 | 15.2 | 15.5 | 35.0 |
|  | 4.00 | 443 | 27.9 | 28.4 | 63.4 |
|  | 5.00 | 220 | 13.8 | 14.1 | 77.5 |
|  | 6.00 | 222 | 13.9 | 14.2 | 91.7 |
|  | 7.00 | 68 | 4.2 | 4.3 | 96.0 |
|  | 8.00 | 34 | 2.1 | 2.2 | 98.2 |
|  | 9.00 | 20 | 1.2 | 1.3 | 99.5 |
|  | 10.00 (very poor) | 9 | .5 | .5 | 100.0 |
|  | Total | 1562 | 98.2 | 100.0 |  |
| Missing | System | 29 | 1.8 |  |  |
| Total |  | 1592 | 100.0 |  |  |

Looking at the first two tables we see that physical and mental health both vary by item. For example, about 25% of respondents feel that their general health is excellent, while more than a third (37%) feel that their mental health is excellent.

The new variable, *health* shown in the final table above, summarizes each respondent's overall health. (Note, as a convenience we added labels to the first and last values to improve the readability of this table. We will demonstrate how to add labels at the end of this section.)

We see that about 20% of the sample feel their overall health is excellent (scored 2), while 0.5% feel their health is very poor (scored 10). Thus, there are many more Canadians who feel they have "excellent" overall health than there are those who feel their overall health is "very poor." Most Canadians, however, fall somewhere in between these two extremes. In fact, about 28% of the sample scored a 4, meaning that their health is at least "good" in one aspect, but not necessarily in the other aspect.

Notice that the total number of valid (non-missing) respondents is not equal for the three variables. In most practical settings, such as in our current example, researchers encounter missing values in some or all of their questions. If these cases were included in the computation of the new variable, the validity of the scale would be diminished, and a variety of errors and miscalculations could result. Fortunately, when SPSS executes a **Compute** statement, it automatically eliminates any cases that are missing scores on any of the constituent items.

**Collapsing Categories with the Recode Command** We often need to make a variable more compact by collapsing its scores into fewer categories.

SPSS provides a number of ways to change the scores of a variable, and one of the most useful of these is the **Recode** command.

As an example of using this command, we will create a new version of the variable *incm* (respondent's annual personal income) that has fewer categories and is more suitable for display in a frequency distribution. When we are finished, we will have two different versions of the same variable in the data set: the original version and a new version with collapsed categories. We recommend that the new version be added to the permanent data file because it will be used in future demonstrations.

We have decided to collapse the values of *incm* into four categories. We begin by collapsing all respondents with values 1 (no income) through 6 ($20,000–$29,999) on *incm* into a value of 1. This collapsed category includes all respondents with total annual incomes of $29,999 or less. The next recodes involve collapsing values 7 ($30,000–$39,999) through 8 ($40,000–$49,999) on *incm* into a value of 2, values 9 ($50,000–$59,999) through 10 ($60,000–$79,999) on *incm* into a value of 3, and finally values 11 ($80,000–$99,999) through 12 ($100,000 or more) on *incm* into a value of 4. As you will see, recoding requires many small steps, so please be patient and execute the commands as they are discussed.

1. In the **SPSS Data Editor** window, click **Transform** from the menu bar where you can find two types of recode commands: **Recode into Same Variables** and **Recode into Different Variables**. If we choose the former (**Recode into Same Variables**), the new version of the variable will replace the old version—the original version of *incm* (total household income) would disappear. We definitely do not want this to happen, so we will choose (click on) **Recode into Different Variables**. This option will allow us to keep both the old and new versions of the variable.

2. The **Recode into Different Variables** dialog box will open. A list box containing an alphabetical list of variables is on the left. Use your mouse to highlight *incm* and then click on the arrow button to move the variable to the **Input Variable → Output Variable** box. The input variable is the old version of *incm,* and the output variable is the new, recoded version we will soon create.

3. In the **Output Variable** box on the right, click in the **Name** text box and type a name for the new (output) variable. We suggest *income4* (total household income grouped into four categories) for the new variable, but you can assign any name as long as it does not duplicate the name of some other variable in the data set. Next, click on the **Label** text box, in order to provide a short descriptive label for your new variable. We suggest *recode version of total annual income*. Click the **Change** button and the expression *incm → income4* will appear in the **Input Variable → Output Variable** box.

4. Click on the **Old and New Values** button in the middle of the screen, and a new dialog box will open.

5. Read down the left-hand column in the **Old Value** box until you find the **Range** button. Click on the button, and the cursor will move to the small text box immediately below. Type 1 into the first **Range** text box and then click on the second text box and type 6. In the **New Value** box in the upper-right-hand corner of the screen, click the **Value** button. Type 1 in the **Value** text box and then click the **Add** button directly below. The expression "1 thru 6 → 1" will appear in the **Old** → **New** dialog box. This completes the first recode instruction to SPSS.

    Note, alternatively, for the first category, you can choose the **Range, LOWEST through value** button. The cursor will move to the small box immediately below. Then type 6 in the text box. Do not forget to type 1 in the **New Value** box and click the **Add** button. The expression "Lowest thru 6 → 1" appears in the **Old** → **New** box.

6. Continue recoding by returning to the **Range** text boxes on the left. Type 7 in the first box under the **Range** option and 8 in the second box, and then click the **Value** button in the **New Value** box. Type 2 in the **Value** text box and then click the **Add** button. The expression "7 thru 8 → 2" appears in the **Old** → **New** box.

7. Return again to the **Range** text boxes, and specify the low and high points of next interval. Type 9 in the first box under the **Range** option and 10 in the second box and then click the **Value** button in the **New Values** box. Type 3 in the **Value** text box and then click the **Add** button. The expression "9 thru 10 → 3" appears in the **Old** → **New** box.

8. For the last recode, return to the **Range** text boxes. Type 11 in the first box under the **Range** option and 12 in the second box and then click the **Value** button in the **New Value** box. Type 4 in the **Value** text box and then click the **Add** button. The expression "11 thru 12 → 4" appears in the **Old** → **New** box.

    Note, the values 98 and 99 are defined as missing in the original variable *incm*, and are automatically redefined during the recode procedure as missing and relabelled as "." [period] in the new variable *income4*. Because this is done automatically by SPSS, these cases are referred to as "system" missing values.

9. Now click the **Continue** button at the bottom of the screen, and you will return to the **Recode into Different Variable** dialog box. Click **OK**, and SPSS will execute the transformation.

You now have a data set with one more variable named *income4* (or whatever name you gave the recoded variable). SPSS adds the new variable to the data set, and you can find it in the last column to the right in the data window (or in the bottom row if you are using the Variable View display instead of the Data View display). You can make the new variable a permanent part of the data set by saving the data file at the end of the session. If you do not wish to save the new, expanded data file, click **No** when you are asked if you want to save the data file. Remember that if you are using the student version of SPSS you are limited to a maximum of 50 variables, and you will not be able to save more than two new variables (unless you delete other variables to make space) because there are already 48 variables in the 2013 GSS data set.

Finally, to make sure that no mistakes were made in the recoding process, produce a cross-tabulation between the original variable (*incm*) and the new variable (*income4*), using the **Crosstabs** command, to ensure that cases from the original response categories have been grouped as expected into the new response categories. (Since *incm* and *income4* are not independent or dependent variables, it does not matter which variable you put in the columns and which you put in the rows.) In addition, produce a frequency distribution for *income4* using the **Frequencies** command, to ensure that the missing cases have, indeed, again been categorized as "missing" (the earlier cross-tabulation does not include information about the missing cases). The cross-tabulation and frequency table should look like this:

### *incm* * *income4* Cross-tabulation

Count

| | | income4 | | | | Total |
|---|---|---|---|---|---|---|
| | | 1.00 | 2.00 | 3.00 | 4.00 | |
| incm | 1 | 107 | 0 | 0 | 0 | 107 |
| | 2 | 46 | 0 | 0 | 0 | 46 |
| | 3 | 42 | 0 | 0 | 0 | 42 |
| | 4 | 74 | 0 | 0 | 0 | 74 |
| | 5 | 64 | 0 | 0 | 0 | 64 |
| | 6 | 138 | 0 | 0 | 0 | 138 |
| | 7 | 0 | 153 | 0 | 0 | 153 |
| | 8 | 0 | 137 | 0 | 0 | 137 |
| | 9 | 0 | 0 | 93 | 0 | 93 |
| | 10 | 0 | 0 | 123 | 0 | 123 |
| | 11 | 0 | 0 | 0 | 81 | 81 |
| | 12 | 0 | 0 | 0 | 122 | 122 |
| Total | | 471 | 290 | 216 | 203 | 1180 |

This cross-tabulation shows us that the categories of *incm* have been correctly collapsed in *income4*. The first six categories of *incm* have been collapsed into the first category of *income4*, with all the cases from *incm*'s first six categories now showing up together in the "1" column of *income4*. Check the other categories of *income4*, too, to ensure that all categories of *incm* have been correctly collapsed.

The frequency table of *income4* also confirms that *incm* has been correctly recoded, with the cases that were originally missing for *incm*, now also missing for *income4*.

### income4

|  |  | Frequency | Percent | Valid Percent | Cumulative Percent |
|---|---|---|---|---|---|
| Valid | 1.00 | 471 | 29.6 | 39.9 | 39.9 |
|  | 2.00 | 290 | 18.2 | 24.5 | 64.4 |
|  | 3.00 | 217 | 13.6 | 18.4 | 82.8 |
|  | 4.00 | 203 | 12.8 | 17.2 | 100.0 |
|  | Total | 1180 | 74.1 | 100.0 |  |
| Missing | System | 412 | 25.9 |  |  |
| Total |  | 1592 | 100.0 |  |  |

The sample is particularly clustered around categories 1 and 2, or between < $30,000 and $30,000 to $49,999—over 60% of the sample is in these two lowest categories. Fewer respondents are in the highest income groups.

**Adding Labels**   This table can be made easier to read and more meaningful by attaching variable value labels. To do this, click the **Variable View** tab located at the bottom of the SPSS Data Editor screen. The first column, **Name**, in the variable view window contains the names of the variables in the data file. Scroll up or down this window until you locate the variable name *income4*, which will be in the last row. Next, click on the cell in the **Values** column, which initially indicates "**None**" of the values has been labelled, then click on the button with the three dots in it. The **Value Labels** dialog box will open. Type the first value (1) into the **Value** text box and its label into the **Value Label** text box (< $30,000, or any other label that you want to use for the value). Then click **Add**. Next, enter the second value (2) into the **Value** text box and its label into the **Value Label** text box ($30,000–$49,999). Repeat this exercise for each value, making sure to click **Add** after each entry. (You can fix or delete any entry by highlighting it in the large display box and clicking **Change** or **Remove**.) Click **OK** after all values labels have been added.

SPSS output will now display all labels. For example, the **Frequencies** command will produce a frequency distribution for *income4* as follows:

### *Income4*

| | | Frequency | Percent | Valid Percent | Cumulative Percent |
|---|---|---|---|---|---|
| Valid | <$30,000 | 471 | 29.6 | 39.9 | 39.9 |
| | $30,000–$49,999 | 290 | 18.2 | 24.5 | 64.4 |
| | $50,000–$79,999 | 217 | 13.6 | 18.4 | 82.8 |
| | $80,000+ | 203 | 12.8 | 17.2 | 100.0 |
| | Total | 1180 | 74.1 | 100.0 | |
| Missing | System | 412 | 25.9 | | |
| Total | | 1592 | 100.0 | | |

## F.6 EDITING OUTPUT

SPSS output can be edited directly in the **Output** window. To edit a table, double-click on any part of the table. Next, double-click the exact area of the table to be edited, and make the appropriate revision. To edit a graph, double-click on any part of the graph in the **Output** window and the SPSS **Chart Editor** window will appear. This window gives you a wide array of options for the final appearance of the chart.

For example, if you want to change the colour of some elements (e.g., bars or background) in the chart, first you need to click on the elements to be highlighted, then click on the **Edit** menu and choose **Properties**. (Alternatively, you can directly open the **Properties** dialog box by right-clicking anywhere on the highlighted elements then choosing **Properties Window**.) The **Properties** dialog box will appear where you can find different options under each tab. For example, the options for changing the colour of the elements is the **Fill & Border** tab. Explore these options at your leisure using the **Help** button at the bottom of the window as necessary. You need to close the **SPSS Chart Editor** window and return to the **Output** window to see the changes you have made.

## F.7 PRINTING, SAVING, PASTING, AND EXPORTING OUTPUT

Once you've gone to the trouble of producing statistics, a table, or a graph, you will probably want to keep a permanent record. There are three ways to do this. First, you can print a copy of the contents of the SPSS Viewer to take with you. To do this, click on **File** and then click **Print** from the **File** menu. Alternatively, find the icon of a printer (third from the left) in the row of icons just below the menu bar and click on it.

The second way to create a permanent record of SPSS output is to save the window to the computer's hard drive or other medium. To do this, click **Save** from the **File** menu. The Save dialog box opens. Give the output a name (some abbreviation such as "freqsex" might do) and, if necessary, specify the location of your storage device. Click **OK**, and the table will be permanently saved.

Third, tables and charts in the Output window can be used in many applications, including word processors. Specifically, SPSS output tables and charts can be pasted into a word-processing document. Formats are retained and can be edited in the word processor. (Note that charts are pasted in graph format and tables in table format.)

To paste, click on any part of the table or chart in the SPSS Output window, then click **Copy** from the **Edit** menu. Next, open your word processor, and click **Paste** from the **Edit** menu. Repeat this process separately for each table or chart that you want to paste into the word-processor document.

Alternatively, SPSS output tables and charts can be exported to a document. From the SPSS Output window, click **Export** from the **File** menu. Next, select **Word/RTF file (*.docx)** from the **File Type** drop-down list, and click **OK**. Then, open your word processor, click **Open** from the **Edit** menu, and double-click the file name to open it. You may have to change the folder specification to locate the file. By default, SPSS names the file OUTPUT and saves it in the SPSS program folder.

**F.8 ENDING YOUR SPSS SESSION**

Once you have saved or printed your work, you may end your SPSS session. Click on **File** from the menu bar and then click **Exit**. If you haven't already done so, you will be asked if you want to save the contents of the Output window. You may save the frequency distribution at this point if you wish. Otherwise, click **NO**. The program will close, and you will be returned to the screen from which you began.

# Information and Code Books for the 2012 Canadian Community Health Survey and 2013 General Social Survey

## G.1 INTRODUCTION TO CCHS AND GSS

Four data sets from two social surveys, the 2012 Canadian Community Health Survey (CCHS) and the 2013 Canadian General Social Survey (GSS), are provided on the website for this textbook. The data sets are named *CCHS_2012_Full.sav*, *CCHS_2012_Shortened.sav*, *GSS_2013_Full.sav*, and *GSS_2013_Shortened.sav*. SPSS uses the file extension ".sav" as a saved data format. These files will load easily into most versions of SPSS.

The CCHS and GSS are conducted by Statistics Canada. The GSS is a public opinion poll that has been conducted annually since 1985 on representative samples of Canadians aged 15 years and older living in private households in the 10 provinces. The content and focus of the survey change each year. The 2013 GSS contained items on social networks and patterns of civic participation in Canada, as well as demographic and background characteristics of the respondents.

The CCHS is also administered annually to a representative sample. It collects information on health-related topics, including health status, health care use, and determinants of health, from persons 12 years of age or older residing in private households in all provinces and territories. Because many variables in the CCHS are not applicable to younger Canadians, we have restricted the sample to adults (i.e., persons 18 and over).

## G.2 CCHS AND GSS DATA SETS

The original CCHS and GSS data sets each contain dozens of variables on a sample of thousands of cases. We have shortened the CCHS (*CCHS_2012_Shortened.sav*) and GSS (*GSS_2013_Shortened.sav*) data sets to about 50 variables and 1,500 randomly selected cases to be compatible with the student version of SPSS. (SPSS Student Version, created for classroom instruction, is in essence the full version of the SPSS base software but limited to a maximum of 50 variables and 1,500 cases.) These shortened data sets are used for all of the end-of-chapter exercises.

For those using the full, professional version of SPSS for Windows, we additionally provide the complete CCHS and GSS data sets (*CCHS_2012_Full.sav* and *GSS_2013_Full.sav*). They include the original random samples for the variables in the shortened CCHS and GSS data sets.

Variables in the CCHS and GSS data sets were selected to best meet the objectives of this textbook, and to provide students with the ability to examine issues of current and emerging interest. The code book for the CCHS and GSS data sets are provided below. The variable names, shown in the left margin, are those used in the data file to identify the variables. A description or the exact question as it was asked on the CCHS and GSS questionnaires for each variable is provided. The numbers beside each response are the scores recorded in each data set.

The website for this textbook provides further information on the CCHS and GSS. Detailed descriptions and frequency distributions for all variables in the full sample, as well as information on other issues such as sampling design and data collection, are contained in the files named *CCHS_2012_Guide.pdf* and *2013_GSS_Guide.pdf* on the website.

In sum, the four data sets provided with, and used throughout, this textbook are the following:

1. *CCHS_2012_Full.sav.* The full (complete sample) version of the 2012 Canadian Community Health Survey.
2. *CCHS_2012_Shortened.sav.* The short (1,500 randomly selected cases) version of the 2012 Canadian Community Health Survey.
3. *GSS_2013_Full.sav.* The full (complete sample) version of the 2013 General Social Survey (GSS).
4. *GSS_2013_Shortened.sav.* The short (1,500 randomly selected cases) version of the 2013 General Social Survey (GSS).

## G.3 SPSS STUDENT VERSION

The SPSS Student Version is available at many campus bookstores.

## G.4 MISSING DATA AND SAMPLE DESIGN IN THE CCHS AND GSS

It is important to comment on two features of the data sets. First, social survey data like the CCHS and GSS typically contain "missing data." Missing data occur when a respondent did not (e.g., refused to) or could not (e.g., lacked the information to) answer a specific question. Most variables in the original CCHS and GSS data sets had relatively few missing cases. Thus, with the CCHS, the missing cases for these variables were simply excluded from the data files supplied with this textbook. On the other hand, a few other variables contained significantly more missing cases. Deleting these cases may produce biased data and results, so for these variables, missing data were retained but defined as missing in data sets. These missing data will be automatically eliminated from all statistical analysis, unless SPSS is commanded to do otherwise. Conversely, the data sets for the GSS retained the missing cases in order to provide a concrete sense of some of the practical challenges that can arise when dealing with missing data. Missing data are a common problem in survey research; if significant in number, they may jeopardize the integrity of the inquiry.

Second, the CCHS and GSS, like the vast majority of Statistics Canada surveys, use a "complex" sampling design that is ultimately based on the principle of EPSEM (see Chapter 5). It is said to be "complex" as opposed to "simple" (as in "simple" random sampling) because of the types and combinations of sampling methods used—the CCHS and GSS use a stratified, multi-stage cluster design with probability sampling at all stages to select a representative sample of Canadians.

However, the CCHS and GSS both use an *unequal* probability of selection method. That is, they under- and over-sample various groups of individuals to ensure that subpopulations of interest to each survey, such as persons 65 and older, are represented in the sample. Because individuals do not have an equal probability of selection, it is necessary to "weight" (correct) the sample to approximate an EPSEM sample. A weight variable was calculated by Statistics Canada for each survey, called *wts_m* and *wght_per* in the CCHS and GSS data files respectively. The weight variable is included in each data file. Once you open the file in SPSS, the weight variable is automatically "turned on" to correct for this bias. In the *GSS_2013_Shortened.sav* data file, for example, with the weight turned on, the sample of 1,500 cases actually converts to a size of 1,592.

## G.5 GSS CODE BOOK

**agegr10**

Age group of respondent (groups of 10).
1. 15 to 24 years
2. 25 to 34 years
3. 35 to 44 years
4. 45 to 54 years
5. 55 to 64 years
6. 65 to 74 years
7. 75 years and over

**amb_01**

Are you an Aboriginal person, that is, First Nations, Métis or Inuk (Inuit)? First Nations includes Status and Non-Status Indians. (Asked of respondents who were born in Canada, the United States, Germany, or Greenland.)
1. Yes
2. No
6. Valid skip
7. Don't know
8. Refusal
9. Not stated

**brthcan**

Place of birth of respondent—Canada.
1. Born in Canada
2. Born outside Canada
7. Don't know
8. Refusal
9. Not stated

**brthmacr**

Place of birth of respondent—Geographical macro-region. (Asked of respondents who were not born in Canada.)
1. Americas
2. Europe

3. Africa
4. Asia
5. Oceania
96. Valid skip
97. Don't know
98. Refusal
99. Not stated

**cerd230c**   Number of types of groups, organizations, and associations the respondent participated in the last 12 months.
0. None
5. 5 or more

**discrim**   Respondent has been a victim of discrimination in the past five years.
1. Yes
2. No
7. Don't know
8. Refusal
9. Not stated

**ehg_all**   What is the highest certificate, diploma, or degree that you completed?
1. Less than high school diploma or its equivalent
2. High school diploma or a high school equivalency certificate
3. Trade certificate or diploma
4. College/CEGEP/other non-university certificate or diploma
5. University certificate or diploma below the bachelor's level
6. Bachelor's degree (e.g. B.A., B.Sc., LL.B.)
7. University certificate, diploma, degree above the B.A. level
97. Don't know
98. Refusal
99. Not stated

**ethnic7**   Ethnic or cultural origins of respondent (7 categories).
1. Canadian only
2. British Isles origins only
3. French only
4. Other European only
5. Canadian and other
6. British Isles & other/French & other/British & French & other
7. Other
97. Don't know
98. Refusal
99. Not stated

**grp_10c**   Number of groups—12 months. (Asked if the respondent participated in at least 1 group, organization, or association in the past 12 months.)

9. 9 groups or more
96. Valid skip
97. Don't know
98. Refusal
99. Not stated

**grp_40**    [Including participation both on and off the Internet, how/How] often did you participate in group activities and meetings?
1. At least once a week
2. A few times a month
3. Once a month
4. Once or twice a year
5. Not in the past year
6. Valid skip
7. Don't know
8. Refusal

**hsdsizec**    Household size of respondent.
6. 6 or more

**icr_10**    In the 12 months, have you used the Internet to access a social-networking website (such as Facebook or Twitter)? (Asked if the respondent used the Internet anytime in the past 12 months.)
1. Yes
2. No
6. Valid skip
7. Don't know
8. Refusal

**icr_30**    How often do you access your social networking site(s)? (For respondents with a social-networking site.)
1. Several times a day
2. About once a day
3. 3–5 times a week
4. 1–2 times a week
5. A few times per month
6. Less than once a month
7. Never
96. Valid skip
97. Don't know
98. Refusal

**incm**    Annual personal income of the respondent—2012.
1. No income
2. Less than $5,000

3. $5,000 to $9,999
4. $10,000 to $14,999
5. $15,000 to $19,999
6. $20,000 to $29,999
7. $30,000 to $39,999
8. $40,000 to $49,999
9. $50,000 to $59,999
10. $60,000 to $79,999
11. $80,000 to $99,999
12. $100,000 or more
97. Don't know
98. Refusal
99. Not stated

**incmhsd**    Total household income—2012.
1. No income or loss
2. Less than $5,000
3. $5,000 to $9,999
4. $10,000 to $14,999
5. $15,000 to $19,999
6. $20,000 to $29,999
7. $30,000 to $39,999
8. $40,000 to $49,999
9. $50,000 to $59,999
10. $60,000 to $79,999
11. $80,000 to $99,999
12. $100,000 to $149,999
13. $150,000 or more
97. Don't know
98. Refusal
99. Not stated

**ium_10**    In the past month, did you use the Internet?
1. Yes
2. No
7. Don't know
8. Refusal

**iuy_01**    In the past 12 months, did you use the Internet? (Asked if the respondent did not use the Internet in the past month.)
1. Yes
2. No
6. Valid skip
7. Don't know
8. Refusal

**lanhsdc**     What language do you speak most often at home?
1. English only
2. French only
3. Other languages
4. Multiple languages
7. Don't know
8. Refusal
9. Not stated

**livarr06**     Living arrangement of respondent's household (6 categories).
1. Alone
2. Spouse only
3. Spouse and single/non-single child(ren)
4. Single/non-single child(ren) only
5. Living with one or two parents
6. Other living arrangement

**luc_rst**     Population centres indicator.
1. Larger urban population centres (CMA/CA)
2. Rural areas/small population centres (non-CMA/CA)
3. Prince Edward Island

**mar_110**     During the past 12 months, was your main activity working at a paid job or business, looking for paid work, going to school, caring for children, household work, retired or something else?
1. Working at a paid job or business
2. Looking for paid work
3. Going to school
5. Household work
6. Retired
7. Maternity/paternity or parental leave
8. Long-term illness
9. Volunteering/care-giving other than for children
10. Other—Specify
97. Don't know
98. Refusal

**marstat**     Marital status of respondent.
1. Married
2. Living common-law
3. Widowed
4. Separated
5. Divorced
6. Single, never married
97. Don't know
98. Refusal

**mcr_300c**    How many hours do you spend watching television during a typical week?
　　50. 50 hours or more
　　97. Don't know
　　98. Refusal

**neighbourhood**    How long have you lived in this neighbourhood? (This is a recoded version of one of the survey variables.)
　　1. Less than 6 months
　　2. 6 months to less than 1 year
　　3. 1 year to less than 3 years
　　4. 3 years to less than 5 years
　　5. 5 years to less than 10 years
　　6. 10 years and over
　　97. Don't know
　　98. Refusal
　　99. Not stated

**pct_10**    Generally speaking, would you say that most people can be trusted or that you cannot be too careful in dealing with people?
　　1. Most people can be trusted
　　2. You cannot be too careful in dealing with people
　　7. Don't know
　　8. Refusal
　　9. Not stated

**prcode**    Province of residence of the respondent.
　　10. Newfoundland and Labrador
　　11. Prince Edward Island
　　12. Nova Scotia
　　13. New Brunswick
　　24. Quebec
　　35. Ontario
　　46. Manitoba
　　47. Saskatchewan
　　48. Alberta
　　59. British Columbia

**qin_50**    About how many people in your neighbourhood do you know well enough to ask for a favour?
　　0. None
　　1. 1 to 5
　　2. 6 to 10
　　3. Over 10
　　7. Don't know
　　8. Refusal
　　9. Not stated

**ree_02**    Not counting events such as weddings or funerals, during the past 12 months, how often did you participate in religious activities or attend religious services or meetings?
>    1. At least once a week
>    2. At least once a month
>    3. At least 3 times a year
>    4. Once or twice a year
>    5. Not at all
>    7. Don't know
>    8. Refusal
>    9. Not stated

**relig7**    Religion of respondent—7 categories.
>    1. Buddhist
>    2. Christian
>    3. Hindu
>    4. Jewish
>    5. Islam (Muslim)
>    6. Other
>    7. No religion
>    97. Don't know
>    98. Refusal
>    99. Not stated

**rfe_10c**    How many relatives do you have who you feel close to, (that is, who you feel at ease with, can talk to about what is on your mind, or call on for help)? (Asked only to respondents with living relatives.)
>    200. 200 or more
>    996. Valid skip
>    997. Don't know
>    998. Refusal

**scf_100c**    How many close friends do you have (that is, people who are not your relatives, but who you feel at ease with, can talk to about what is on your mind, or call on for help)?
>    200. 200 or more
>    997. Don't know
>    998. Refusal

**scf_110c**    Not counting your close friends or relatives, how many other friends do you have?
>    200. 200 or more
>    997. Don't know
>    998. Refusal

**scp_110**     In the past month, outside of work or school, how many new people did you meet either face-to-face or online? Include people you had not met before and whom you intend to stay in contact with.
97. Don't know
98. Refusal

**scp_115**     Did you meet this person on the Internet? (Asked if the respondent used the internet in the past month, and the number of new people reported in scp_110 = 1.)
1. Yes
2. No
6. Valid skip
7. Don't know
8. Refusal

**scp_120c**     Of these scp_110 people, how many did you meet on the Internet? (Asked if the respondent used the Internet in the past month, and the number of new people reported in scp_110 > 1.)
5. 5 or more
6. Valid skip
7. Don't know
8. Refusal

**sex**     Sex of respondent.
1. Male
2. Female

**slm_01**     Using a scale of 0 to 10 where 0 means "Very dissatisfied" and 10 means "Very satisfied," how do you feel about your life as a whole right now?
0. Very dissatisfied
1. 1
2. 2
3. 3
4. 4
5. 5
6. 6
7. 7
8. 8
9. 9
10. Very satisfied
97. Don't know
98. Refusal
99. Not stated

**socnet**

Respondent has a social networking account. (Asked if the respondent used the internet to access a social-networking site in the past 12 months.)
1. Yes
2. No
6. Valid skip
7. Don't know
8. Refusal
9. Not stated

**srh_110**

In general, would you say your health is ...?
1. Excellent
2. Very good
3. Good
4. Fair
5. Poor
7. Don't know
8. Refusal
9. Not stated

**srh_115**

In general, would you say your mental health is ...?
1. Excellent
2. Very good
3. Good
4. Fair
5. Poor
7. Don't know
8. Refusal
9. Not stated

**vcg_300**

In the past 12 months, did you do unpaid volunteer work for any organization?
1. Yes
2. No
7. Don't know
8. Refusal

**vcg_310**

On average, about how many hours per month did you volunteer? (Asked if the respondent volunteered in the past 12 months.)
1. 15 hours or more per month
2. Between 5 and less than 15 hours per month
3. Between 1 and less than 5 hours per month
4. Less than 1 hour per month
6. Valid skip
7. Don't know
8. Refusal

**vcg_320**   Have you met new people through volunteering in the past 12 months? (Asked if the respondent volunteered in the past 12 months.)
  1. Yes
  2. No
  6. Valid skip
  7. Don't know
  8. Refusal

**vismin**   Visible minority status of the respondent.
  1. Visible minority
  2. Not a visible minority
  7. Don't know
  8. Refusal
  9. Not stated

**wet_110**   For how many weeks during the past 12 months were you employed? (Asked of respondents who were employed or self-employed anytime in the past 12 months.)
  96. Valid skip
  97. Don't know
  98. Refusal
  99. Not stated

**wght_per**   Person weight.
  99999.9996. Valid skip
  99999.9997. Don't know
  99999.9998. Refusal
  99999.9999. Not stated

**wkwehrc**   Number of paid hours usually worked in a week (all jobs). (Asked of respondents who spent time working at any job.)
  75.0  75 hours or more
  99.6. Valid skip
  99.7. Don't know
  99.8. Refusal
  99.9. Not stated

## G.6 CCHS CODE BOOK

**alc_2**   During the past 12 months, how often did you drink alcoholic beverages?
  1. No drinks in last 12 months
  2. < Once a month
  3. Once a month
  4. 2 to 3 times a month

     5. Once a week
     6. 2 to 3 times a week
     7. 4 to 6 times a week
     8. Every day

**alwddly**    Average number of drinks consumed per day in the past week.
     996. Did not drink in last 12 months (***defined as missing in the data set***)

**alwdwky**    Total number of drinks consumed in the past week.
     996. Did not drink in last 12 months (***defined as missing in the data set***)

**ccc_280**    Do you have a mood disorder such as depression, bipolar disorder, or mania?
     1. Yes
     2. No

**ccc_290**    Do you have an anxiety disorder such as a phobia, obsessive-compulsive disorder, or panic disorder?
     1. Yes
     2. No

**dhh_own**    Dwelling owned by a member of the household?
     1. Owned
     2. Rented

**dhh_sex**    Sex.
     1. Male
     2. Female

**dhhgage**    Age.
     3. 18 to 19 years
     4. 20 to 24 years
     5. 25 to 29 years
     6. 30 to 34 years
     7. 35 to 39 years
     8. 40 to 44 years
     9. 45 to 49 years
     10. 50 to 54 years
     11. 55 to 59 years
     12. 60 to 64 years
     13. 65 to 69 years
     14. 70 to 74 years
     15. 75 to 79 years
     16. 80 years or more

**dhhghsz**          Household size.
                                1.  1 person
                                2.  2 persons
                                3.  3 persons
                                4.  4 persons
                                5.  5 or + persons

**dhhglvg**          Living arrangement.
1. Unattached alone
2. Unattached other
3. Spouse/partner
4. Parent, spouse, child
5. Parent, child
6. Child, parent, sibling
7. Child, 2 parent, sibling
8. Other

**dhhgms**          Marital status.
1. Married
2. Common law
3. Widow/sep/divorced
4. Single/never married

**edudr04**          Highest level of education.
1. < Sec. school gr.
2. Sec. school gr.
3. Some post-sec. ed.
4. Post-sec. cert.

**flu_162**          When did you have your last seasonal flu shot?
1. <1 year
2. 1 to <2 years
3. 2 years or more
6. Never had a flu shot

**fscdhfs2**          Food security situation of the household in the previous 12 months.
0. Food secure
1. Moderate food insecurity
2. Severe food insecurity

**fvcdfru**          Total number of times per day eats fruit.

**fvcdjui**          Total number of times per day drinks fruit juice.

**fvcdtot**          Total number of times per day eats fruits *and* vegetables.

**fvcdvegtot**          Total number of times per day eats vegetables.

**fvcgtot**    Total number of times per day eats fruits *and* vegetables—grouped.
   1. Less than 5 per day
   2. 5–10 times per day
   3. >10 times per day

**gen_02**    Compared to one year ago, how would you say your health is now?
   1. Much better
   2. Somewhat better
   3. About the same
   4. Somewhat worse
   5. Much worse

**gen_07**    Thinking about the amount of stress in your life, would you say that most days are stressful?
   1. Not at all
   2. Not very
   3. A bit
   4. Quite a bit
   5. Extremely

**gen_09**    Would you say that most days at work are stressful?
   0. Not in labour force (***defined as missing in the data set***)
   1. Not at all
   2. Not very
   3. A bit
   4. Quite a bit
   5. Extremely

**gendhdi**    Perceived health status.
   0. Poor
   1. Fair
   2. Good
   3. Very good
   4. Excellent

**gendmhi**    Perceived mental health status.
   0. Poor
   1. Fair
   2. Good
   3. Very good
   4. Excellent

**gengswl**    Satisfaction with life in general.
   1. Very satisfied
   2. Satisfied
   3. Neither

4. Dissatisfied
5. Very dissatisfied

**geogprv**        Province of residence.
10. Nfld. & Labrador
11. Prince Edward Island
12. Nova Scotia
13. New Brunswick
24. Quebec
35. Ontario
46. Manitoba
47. Saskatchewan
48. Alberta
59. British Columbia
60. Yukon/NWT/Nunavut

**hcu_1aa**        Do you have a regular medical doctor?
1. Yes
2. No

**hwtgbmi**        Body mass index (BMI) score.

**hwtghtm**        Height (in metres).

**hwtgisw**        Body mass index (BMI)—grouped.
1. Underweight
2. Normal weight
3. Overweight
4. Obese

**hwtgwtk**        Weight (in kilograms).

**incdrca**        Distribution of household income. (This variable is a distribution of respondents in *approximate* deciles—ten categories of approximately, but not exactly, ten percentage each.)
1. Decile 1
2. Decile 2
3. Decile 3
4. Decile 4
5. Decile 5
6. Decile 6
7. Decile 7
8. Decile 8
9. Decile 9
10. Decile 10

**incghh**  Household income.
1. No or <$20,000
2. $20,000−$39,999
3. $40,000−$59,999
4. $60,000−$79,999
5. $80,000 or more

**lbsghpw**  Total usual hours worked per week in current job(s).
996. Not in labour force (***defined as missing in the data set***)

**pacdee**  Average daily energy expenditure doing leisure-time physical activities (expressed in kilocalories expended per kilogram of body weight during physical activities).

**pacdfm**  Average number of times per month respondents took part in leisure time physical activity(ies) lasting more than 15 minutes.

**pacdlti**  Transportation- *and* leisure-time physical activity index—grouped.
1. Active
2. Moderate active
3. Inactive

**pacdpai**  Leisure-time physical activity index—grouped.
1. Active
2. Moderate active
3. Inactive

**pacdtle**  Average daily energy expenditure doing transportation- *and* leisure-time physical activities (expressed in kilocalories expended per kilogram of body weight during physical activities).

**pmhdcla**  Positive mental health classification.
1. Flourishing
2. Languishing
3. Moderate mental health

**pmhdscr**  Positive mental health continuous score (higher scores indicate higher level of positive mental health).
99. Not stated (***defined as missing in the data set***)

**sacdtot**  Total number of hours spent in a typical week in sedentary activities.
1. Less 5 hours
2. 5 to 9 hours
3. 10 to 14 hours
4. 15 to 19 hours
5. 20 to 24 hours

6. 25 to 29 hours
7. 30 to 34 hours
8. 35 to 39 hours
9. 40 to 44 hours
10. 45 or more hours

**sdcdfols**  First official language spoken.
    1. English
    2. French
    3. English & French
    4. Neither

**sdcgcgt**  Cultural or racial origin.
    1. White
    2. Visible minority

**sdcgres**  Length/time in Canada since immigration.
    1. 0 to 9 years
    2. 10 or more years
    3. Canadian-born

**smk_204**  Number of cigarettes smoked daily (current daily smokers only).
    996. Not applicable (***defined as missing in the data set***)

**smk_05b**  Number of cigarettes smoked daily (current occasional smokers only).
    996. Not applicable (***defined as missing in the data set***)

**smkdsty**  Type of smoker.
    1. Daily
    2. Occasional
    3. Always occasionally
    4. Former daily
    5. Former occasional
    6. Never smoked

**smkdycs**  Number of years smoked daily (current daily smokers only).
    996. Not applicable (***defined as missing in the data set***)

# Answers to Odd-Numbered Computational Problems

In addition to answers, this section suggests some problem-solving strategies and provides examples of how to interpret the numerical answers. You should try to solve and interpret the problems on your own before consulting this section.

In solving these problems, we let our calculators or computers do most of the work. We worked with whatever level of precision these devices permitted and, generally, didn't round off until the end or until we had to record an intermediate sum. We always rounded off to two places of accuracy (or, two places beyond the decimal point, or to 100ths). If you follow these same conventions, your answers will almost always match our answers. However, there is no guarantee that our answers will always be exact matches, and you should be aware that small discrepancies might occur and that they are almost always trivial. If the difference between your answer and our answer doesn't seem trivial, you should double-check to make sure you haven't made an error or solve the problem again using a greater degree of precision.

Finally, please allow us a brief disclaimer about mathematical errors in this section. Let us assure you, first of all, that we know how important this section is for most students and that we worked hard to be certain that these answers are correct. Human fallibility being what it is, however, we know that we cannot make absolute guarantees. Should you find any errors, please let us know so that we can make corrections in the future.

## CHAPTER 2

**2.1 a.** Complex A: $(5/20) \times 100 = 25.00\%$
Complex B: $(10/20) \times 100 = 50.00\%$
**b.** Complex A: $4{:}5 = 0.80$
Complex B: $6{:}10 = 0.60$
**c.** Complex A: $(0/20) = 0.00$
Complex B: $(1/20) = 0.05$
**d.** $(6/(4 + 6)) = (6/10) = 60.00\%$
**e.** Complex A: $8{:}5 = 1.60$
Complex B: $2{:}10 = 0.20$

**2.3** Bank robbery rate =
$(47/211{,}732) \times 100{,}000 = 22.20$
Murder rate $= (13/211{,}732) \times 100{,}000 = 6.14$
Auto theft rate $= (23/211{,}732) \times 100{,}000 = 10.86$

**2.5** For sex:

| Sex | Frequency |
|---|---|
| Male | 9 |
| Female | 6 |
| Total | 15 |

For age, set $k = 10$. $R = 77 - 23$, or 54, so we can round off interval size to 5 ($i = 5$). The first interval will be $20-24$, to include the low score of 23, and the highest interval will be $75-79$.

| Age | Frequency |
|---|---|
| $20-24$ | 1 |
| $25-29$ | 2 |

| Age | Frequency |
|-----|-----------|
| 30–34 | 3 |
| 35–39 | 2 |
| 40–44 | 1 |
| 45–49 | 3 |
| 50–54 | 1 |
| 55–59 | 1 |
| 60–64 | 0 |
| 65–69 | 0 |
| 70–74 | 0 |
| 75–79 | 1 |
| | 15 |

**2.9** Set $k = 10$. $R = 92 - 5$, or 87, so set $i$ at 10.

| Score | Frequency |
|-------|-----------|
| 0–9 | 3 |
| 10–19 | 7 |
| 20–29 | 6 |
| 30–39 | 0 |
| 40–49 | 2 |
| 50–59 | 2 |
| 60–69 | 3 |
| 70–79 | 0 |
| 80–89 | 0 |
| 90–99 | 2 |
| | 25 |

# CHAPTER 3

**3.1** "Region of birth" is a nominal-level variable, "support for legalization" and "opinion of food" are ordinal, and "expenses" and "number of movies" are interval-ratio. The mode, the most common score, is the only measure of central tendency available for nominal-level variables. For the ordinal-level variables, *don't forget to array the scores from high to low* before locating the median. There are ten lower-year students ($n$ is even), so the median will be the score halfway between the scores of the two middle cases. There are 11 upper-year students ($n$ is odd), so the median will be the score of the middle case. To find the mean for the interval-ratio variables, add the scores and divide by the number of cases.

| Variable | Lower Year | Upper Year |
|----------|-----------|-----------|
| Region of birth: | Mode = Atlantic | Mode = Atlantic |
| Legalization: | Median = 3 | Median = 5 |
| Expenses: | Mean = 48.50 | Mean = 63.00 |
| Movies: | Mean = 5.80 | Mean = 5.18 |
| Food: | Median = 6 | Median = 4 |

**3.3**

| Variable | Level of Measurement | Measure of Central Tendency |
|----------|---------------------|----------------------------|
| Sex | Nominal | Mode = male |
| Social class | Ordinal | Median = "medium" (the middle case is in this category) |
| Number of years in the party | I-R | Mean = 26.15 |
| Education | Ordinal | Median = high school |
| Marital status | Nominal | Mode = married |
| Number of children | I-R | Mean = 2.39 |

**3.5**

| Variable | Level of Measurement | Measure of Central Tendency |
|----------|---------------------|----------------------------|
| Marital status | Nominal | Mode = married |
| Sex | Nominal | Mode = female |
| Age | I-R | Mean = 27.53 |
| Attitude on legalization of marijuana | Ordinal | Median = 7 |

**3.7** The median is 27.50 and the mean 26.90. Since $Q_1$ is 15 (the median of the lower half of the data) and $Q_3$ is 35 (the median of the upper half of the data), the interquartile range is $35 - 15$, or 20. The standard deviation is 12.28.

**3.9**

| Statistic | 2000 | 2005 |
|-----------|------|------|
| Standard deviation | 40.86 | 29.46 |

The standard deviation became smaller over the time period. This indicates that the dispersion in the group (the differences in income from province to province) decreased.

**3.11** Mean = 40.25, Median = 44.50. The lower value for the mean indicates a negative skew or a few very *low* scores. For this small group of nations, the skew is caused by the score of Mexico (10), which is much lower than the scores of the other seven nations (which are grouped between 37 and 51).

**3.13** To find the median, the scores for both groups first must be ranked from high to low. Both groups have 25 cases ($n$ = odd), so the median is the score of the 13th case. For first-year students, the median is 35 and, for final-year students, the median is 30. The mean score for first-year students is 31.72. For final-year students, the mean is 28.60.

# CHAPTER 4

## 4.1

| $X_i$ | Z Score | % Area Above | % Area Below |
|---|---|---|---|
| 5 | −1.67 | 95.25 | 4.75 |
| 6 | −1.33 | 90.82 | 9.18 |
| 7 | −1.00 | 84.13 | 15.87 |
| 8 | −0.67 | 74.86 | 25.14 |
| 9 | −0.33 | 62.93 | 37.07 |
| 11 | 0.33 | 37.07 | 62.93 |
| 12 | 0.67 | 25.14 | 74.86 |
| 14 | 1.33 | 9.18 | 90.82 |
| 15 | 1.67 | 4.75 | 95.25 |
| 16 | 2.00 | 2.28 | 97.72 |
| 18 | 2.67 | 0.38 | 99.62 |

## 4.3

| | Z Scores | Area |
|---|---|---|
| **a.** | 0.10 & 1.10 | 32.45% |
| **b.** | 0.60 & 1.10 | 13.86% |
| **c.** | 0.60 | 27.43% |
| **d.** | 0.90 | 18.41% |
| **e.** | 0.60 & −0.40 | 38.11% |
| **f.** | 0.10 & −0.40 | 19.52% |
| **g.** | 0.10 | 53.98% |
| **h.** | 0.30 | 61.79% |
| **i.** | 0.60 | 72.57% |
| **j.** | 1.10 | 86.43% |

## 4.5

| $X_i$ | Z Score | Number of Students Above | Number of Students Below |
|---|---|---|---|
| 60 | −2.00 | 195 | 5 |
| 57 | −2.50 | 199 | 1 |
| 55 | −2.83 | 199 | 1 |
| 67 | −0.83 | 159 | 41 |
| 70 | −0.33 | 126 | 74 |
| 72 | 0.00 | 100 | 100 |
| 78 | 1.00 | 32 | 168 |
| 82 | 1.67 | 10 | 190 |
| 90 | 3.00 | 1 | 199 |
| 95 | 3.83 | 1 | 199 |

Note: Number of students (a discrete variable) has been rounded off to the nearest whole number.

## 4.7

| | Z Score | Area |
|---|---|---|
| **a.** | −2.20 | 1.39% |
| **b.** | 1.80 | 96.41% |
| **c.** | −0.20 & 1.80 | 54.34% |
| **d.** | 0.80 & 2.80 | 20.93% |
| **e.** | −1.20 | 88.49% |
| **f.** | 0.80 | 21.19% |

**4.9** With a Z score of 2.33 (corresponding as closely as possible to an area between the mean and Z of 0.4900)
   **a.** $X_i$ = 1116.50
   **b.** $X_i$ = 123.30

**4.11** With a Z score of 0.00 (corresponding to an area between the mean and Z of 0.0000)
   **a.** $X_i$ = 1000.00
   **b.** $X_i$ = 100.00

## 4.13

| | Z Score | Area |
|---|---|---|
| **a.** | −1.00 & 1.50 | 0.7745 |
| **b.** | 0.25 & 1.50 | 0.3345 |
| **c.** | 1.50 | 0.0668 |
| **d.** | 0.25 & −2.25 | 0.5865 |
| **e.** | −1.00 & −2.25 | 0.1465 |
| **f.** | −1.00 | 0.1587 |

**4.15** Yes. The raw score of 110 translates into a $Z$ score of $+2.88$. 99.80% of the area lies below this score, so this individual was in the top 1% on this test.

**4.17** For the first event, the probability is 0.0919 and, for the second, the probability is 0.0655. The first event is more likely.

# CHAPTER 6

**6.1 a.** $5.2 \pm 0.11$
   **b.** $100 \pm 0.71$
   **c.** $20 \pm 0.40$
   **d.** $1,020 \pm 5.41$
   **e.** $7.3 \pm 0.23$
   **f.** $33 \pm 0.79$

**6.3**

| Confidence Level | Alpha | Area Beyond $Z$ | $Z$ Score |
|---|---|---|---|
| 95% | 0.05 | 0.0250 | $\pm1.96$ |
| 94% | 0.06 | 0.0300 | $\pm1.88$ or $\pm1.89$ |
| 92% | 0.08 | 0.0400 | $\pm1.75$ or $\pm1.76$ |
| 97% | 0.03 | 0.0150 | $\pm2.17$ |
| 98% | 0.02 | 0.0100 | $\pm2.33$ |
| 99.9% | 0.001 | 0.0005 | $\pm3.27$ |

**6.5 a.** $2.30 \pm 0.04$
   **b.** $2.10 \pm 0.01$, $0.78 \pm 0.07$
   **c.** $6.00 \pm 0.37$

**6.7 a.** $178.23 \pm 1.97$. The estimate is that students spent between \$176.26 and \$180.20 on books.
   **b.** $1.5 \pm 0.04$ The estimate is that students visited the clinic between 1.46 and 1.54 times on the average.
   **c.** $2.8 \pm 0.12$    **d.** $3.5 \pm 0.19$

**6.9** $0.14 \pm 0.07$ The estimate is that between 0.07 and 0.21 of the population consists of unmarried couples living together.

**6.11 a.** $P_s = (823/1{,}496) = 0.55$
      Confidence interval: $0.55 \pm 0.03$
      Between 0.52 and 0.58 of the population agrees with the statement.

**b.** $P_s = (650/1{,}496) = 0.43$
   Confidence interval: $0.43 \pm 0.03$
**c.** $P_s = (375/1{,}496) = 0.25$
   Confidence interval: $0.25 \pm 0.03$
**d.** $P_s = (1{,}023/1{,}496) = 0.68$
   Confidence interval: $0.68 \pm 0.03$
**e.** $P_s = (800/1{,}496) = 0.53$
   Confidence interval: $0.53 \pm 0.03$

**6.13**

| Alpha ($\alpha$) | Confidence Level | Confidence Interval |
|---|---|---|
| 0.10 | 90% | $100 \pm 0.73$ |
| 0.05 | 95% | $100 \pm 0.88$ |
| 0.01 | 99% | $100 \pm 1.15$ |
| 0.001 | 99.9% | $100 \pm 1.47$ |

**6.15** The confidence interval is $0.51 \pm 0.05$. The estimate would be that between 46% and 56% of the population prefer candidate A. The population parameter ($P_u$) is equally likely to be anywhere in the interval (i.e., it's just as likely to be 46% as it is to be 56%), so a winner cannot be predicted.

**6.17** The confidence interval is $0.23 \pm 0.08$. At the 95% confidence level, the estimate would be that between 240 (15%) and 496 (31%) of the 1,600 incoming students would be extremely interested. The estimated numbers are found by multiplying $n$ (1,600) by the upper (0.31) and lower (0.15) limits of the interval.

**6.19 a.** $43.87 \pm 0.48$
   **b.** $2.86 \pm 0.08$
   **c.** $1.81 \pm 0.06$
   **d.** $0.29 \pm 0.02$
   **e.** $0.18 \pm 0.02$
   **f.** $0.36 \pm 0.02$
   **g.** $0.81 \pm 0.02$

# CHAPTER 7

**7.1 a.** $1.11$
   **b.** $0.00$
   **c.** $1.52$
   **d.** $1.46$

**7.3** A computing table is highly recommended as a way of organizing the computations for chi square:

Computational Table for Problem 7.3

| (1) | (2) | (3) | (4) | (5) |
|---|---|---|---|---|
| $f_o$ | $f_e$ | $f_o - f_e$ | $(f_o - f_e)^2$ | $(f_o - f_e)^2/ f_e$ |
| 6 | 5 | 1 | 1 | 0.20 |
| 7 | 8 | −1 | 1 | 0.13 |
| 4 | 5 | −1 | 1 | 0.20 |
| 9 | 8 | 1 | 1 | 0.13 |
| $n = 26$ | $n = 26$ | 0 | | $\chi^2$ (obtained) = 0.65 |

**a.** There is 1 degree of freedom in a 2 × 2 table. With alpha set at 0.05, the critical value for the chi square would be 3.841. The obtained chi square is 0.65, so we fail to reject the null hypothesis of independence between the variables. There is no statistically significant relationship between sex and services received.

**7.5**

Computational Table for Problem 7.5

| (1) | (2) | (3) | (4) | (5) |
|---|---|---|---|---|
| $f_o$ | $f_e$ | $f_o - f_e$ | $(f_o - f_e)^2$ | $f_o - f_e)^2/f_e$ |
| 21 | 17.50 | 3.50 | 12.25 | 0.70 |
| 29 | 32.50 | −3.50 | 12.25 | 0.38 |
| 14 | 17.50 | −3.50 | 12.25 | 0.70 |
| 36 | 32.50 | 3.50 | 12.25 | 0.38 |
| $n = 100$ | $n = 100.0$ | 0 | | $\chi^2$ (obtained) = 2.16 |

**a.** With 1 degree of freedom and alpha set at 0.05, the critical region will begin at 3.841. The obtained chi square of 2.16 does not fall within this area, so the null hypothesis cannot be rejected. There is no statistically significant relationship between unionization and salary.

**7.7 a.** The obtained chi square is 5.12. There is a statistically significant relationship ($df = 1$, alpha = 0.05).

**7.9** The obtained chi square is 6.68.

**7.11** The obtained chi square is 12.58.

**7.13** The obtained chi square is 19.34.

**7.15**

| Problem | Chi Square | Significant at $\alpha = 0.05$? |
|---|---|---|
| a. | 25.19 | Yes |
| b. | 1.80 | No |
| c. | 5.23 | No |
| d. | 28.43 | Yes |
| e. | 14.17 | Yes |

# CHAPTER 8

Tables display conditional distributions (or column percentages).

**8.1**

| Efficiency | Authoritarianism | |
|---|---|---|
| | Low | High |
| Low | 37.04 | 70.59 |
| High | 62.96 | 29.41 |
| Totals | 100.00 | 100.00 |

The conditional distributions change, so there is a relationship between the variables. The change from column to column is quite large and the maximum difference is $(70.59 - 37.04) = 33.55$. Using Table 8.5 as a guideline, we can say that this relationship is strong. From inspection of the percentages, we can see that efficiency decreases as authoritarianism increases—workers with dictatorial bosses are less productive (or, maybe, bosses become more dictatorial when workers are inefficient), so this relationship is negative in direction.

**8.3**

| ˄015 Election | 2011 Election | |
|---|---|---|
| | Voted | Didn't Vote |
| Voted | 87.31 | 11.44 |
| Didn't Vote | 12.69 | 88.56 |
| Totals | 100.00 | 100.00 |

The maximum difference for this table is $(87.31 - 11.44)$ or 75.87. This is a very strong relationship. People are very consistent in their voting habits.

**8.5**

| Problem | $\phi$ | $\lambda$ |
|---|---|---|
| 8.1 | 0.33 | 0.32 |
| 8.2 a. | 0.04 | 0.00 |
| b. | 0.18 | 0.00 |
| c. | 0.16 | 0.00 |
| 8.3 | 0.75 | 0.71 |
| 8.4 | 0.02 | 0.00 |

**8.7 a.**

| Supports Same-sex Marriage | Political Ideology | | |
|---|---|---|---|
| | Liberal | Moderate | Conservative |
| Favour | 59.42 | 39.39 | 26.88 |
| Oppose | 40.58 | 60.61 | 73.12 |
| Totals | 100.00 | 100.00 | 100.00 |

The maximum difference of 32.55 indicates a strong relationship. Liberals support same-sex marriage, conservatives are opposed, and moderates are intermediate.

**b.**

| Supports Capital Punishment? | Political Ideology | | |
|---|---|---|---|
| | Liberal | Moderate | Conservative |
| Favour | 62.41 | 76.41 | 78.84 |
| Oppose | 37.59 | 23.59 | 21.16 |
| Totals | 100.00 | 100.00 | 100.00 |

The maximum difference of 16.43 reveals a moderate relationship, with conservatives and moderates most likely to support capital punishment and liberals least likely to support it.

**c.**

| Supports the Right to Suicide? | Political Ideology | | |
|---|---|---|---|
| | Liberal | Moderate | Conservative |
| Favour | 76.05 | 63.24 | 55.00 |
| Oppose | 23.95 | 36.76 | 45.00 |
| Totals | 100.00 | 100.00 | 100.00 |

The maximum difference of 21.05 indicates a moderate relationship. Liberals are most likely to support the right to suicide and conservatives are least likely to support it.

**d.**

| Supports Traditional Gender Roles? | Political Ideology | | |
|---|---|---|---|
| | Liberal | Moderate | Conservative |
| Favour | 11.50 | 14.11 | 18.24 |
| Oppose | 88.50 | 85.89 | 81.76 |
| Totals | 100.00 | 100.00 | 100.00 |

A maximum difference of 6.74 indicates a very weak relationship between political ideology and support for traditional gender roles.

**e.**

| Supports Marijuana Be Legalized? | Political Ideology | | |
|---|---|---|---|
| | Liberal | Moderate | Conservative |
| Favour | 56.65 | 47.27 | 32.30 |
| Oppose | 43.35 | 52.73 | 67.70 |
| Totals | 100.00 | 100.00 | 100.00 |

The maximum difference of 24.35 indicates a strong moderate relationship. Liberals support legalization, conservatives are opposed, and moderates are intermediate.

# CHAPTER 9

**9.1 a.** $G = 0.71$ **b.** $G = 0.69$ **c.** $G = -0.88$ These relationships are strong. Facility in English/French and income increase with length of residence. Use the percentages to help interpret the direction of a relationship. In the first table, 80% of recent immigrants were "Low" in English/French facility while 60% of long-term immigrants were "High." In this relationship, low scores on one variable are associated with low scores on the other, and scores increase together (as one increases, the other increases), so this is a positive relationship. In contrast, contact with country of origin decreases with length of residence ($-0.88$). Most recent immigrants have higher levels of contact, and most long-term immigrants have lower levels.

**9.3** $G = -0.61$ This is a strong negative relationship. As authoritarianism increases, efficiency decreases.

**9.5** $G = 0.27$ Be careful interpreting the direction of this relationship. The positive sign of gamma means that cases tend to fall along the diagonal from upper left to lower right. In this case, white-collar families are more associated with organized sports and blue-collar families with sandlot sports. Computing percentages will help you identify the direction of the relationship.

**9.7 a.** $G = 0.22$, $Z$ (obtained) = 0.92

**9.9** $G = -0.15$

**9.11** $r_s = -0.46$, $t$ (obtained) = $-1.55$

**9.13** $r_s = 0.33$

For these nations, there is a moderate positive relationship between diversity and inequality. The greater the diversity, the greater the inequality.

**9.15 a.** $G = -0.14$
**b.** $G = -0.17$
**c.** $G = -0.14$
**d.** $G = 0.39$
**e.** $G = -0.13$

Income has moderate negative relationships with the first three and the last dependent variables. Be careful in interpreting direction for these tables and remember that a negative gamma means that cases tend to be clustered along the diagonal from lower left to upper right. Computing percentages will clarify direction. For example, for the first table, low income is associated with opposition to same-sex marriage (62% of the people in this column said "Oppose") and high income is associated with support (47% of the people in this column said "Favour" and this is the highest percentage of support across the three income groups).

Income has a strong positive relationship with support for traditional gender roles. Note the way in which the dependent variable is coded: "Favour" means support for traditional gender roles. A positive relationship means that cases tend to fall along the diagonal from upper

left to lower right. In this case, favouring is greater for low income and declines as income increases. Is this truly a "positive" relationship? As always, percentages will help clarify the direction of the relationship.

# CHAPTER 10

**10.1 a.**

| Alpha | Form | Z (Critical) |
|---|---|---|
| 0.05 | One-tailed | ±1.65 |
| 0.10 | Two-tailed | ±1.65 |
| 0.06 | Two-tailed | ±1.88 |
| 0.01 | One-tailed | ±2.33 |
| 0.02 | Two-tailed | ±2.33 |

**b.**

| Alpha | Form | n | t (Critical) |
|---|---|---|---|
| 0.10 | Two-tailed | 31 | ±1.697 |
| 0.02 | Two-tailed | 24 | ±2.500 |
| 0.01 | Two-tailed | 121 | ±2.617 |
| 0.01 | One-tailed | 31 | ±2.457 |
| 0.05 | One-tailed | 61 | ±1.671 |

**c. 1.** $Z$ (obtained) = $-3.77$
**2.** $t$ (obtained) = $+2.24$
**3.** $t$ (obtained) = $+5.76$
**4.** $Z$ (obtained) = $+0.07$
**5.** $Z$ (obtained) = $-0.77$

**10.3 a.** $t$ (obtained) = $-40.54$
**b.** $t$ (obtained) = $+29.09$

**10.5** $t$ (obtained) = $+6.04$

**10.7 a.** $t$ (obtained) = $-13.66$
**b.** $t$ (obtained) = $+25.50$

**10.9** $t$ (obtained) = $+4.50$

**10.11** $Z$ (obtained) = $+3.06$

**10.13** $Z$ (obtained) = $-1.48$

**10.15 a.** $Z$ (obtained) = $-0.74$
**b.** $Z$ (obtained) = $+2.19$
**c.** $Z$ (obtained) = $-8.55$
**d.** $Z$ (obtained) = $-18.07$

**e.** $Z$ (obtained) = $+2.09$
**f.** $Z$ (obtained) = $-53.33$

**10.17** $t$ (obtained) = $-1.14$

# CHAPTER 11

**11.1 a.** $\sigma = 1.38$, $Z$ (obtained) = $-2.53$
**b.** $\sigma = 1.60$, $Z$ (obtained) = $2.50$

**11.3 a.** $Z$ (obtained) = $1.71$
**b.** $Z$ (obtained) = $-2.50$

**11.5 a.** $\sigma = 0.08$ $Z$ (obtained) = $-12.07$
**b.** Phone calls: $\sigma = 0.12$ $Z$ (obtained) = $-3.33$
E-mail messages: $\sigma = 0.15$ $Z$ (obtained) = $19.78$

**11.7 a.** $\sigma = 0.13$, $Z$ (obtained) = $-1.24$
**b.** $\sigma = 0.12$, $Z$ (obtained) = $15.88$

**11.9** (Canada) $\sigma = 0.0095$, $t$ (obtained) = $-31.54$
(Nigeria) $\sigma = 0.0075$, $t$ (obtained) = $-146.80$
(China) $\sigma = 0.0064$, $t$ (obtained) = $77.54$
(Mexico) $\sigma = 0.0107$, $t$ (obtained) = $-74.94$
(Japan) $\sigma = 0.0115$, $t$ (obtained) = $-43.49$

The large values for the $t$ scores indicate that the differences are significant at very low alpha levels (i.e., they are extremely unlikely to have been caused by random chance alone). Note that women are significantly happier than men in every nation except China, where men are significantly happier.

**11.11** $P_u = 0.45$, $\sigma_p = 0.06$, $Z$ (obtained) = $0.67$

**11.13 a.** $P_u = 0.46$, $\sigma_p = 0.06$, $Z$ (obtained) = $2.17$
**b.** $P_u = 0.80$, $\sigma_p = 0.07$, $Z$ (obtained) = $-1.43$
**c.** $P_u = 0.72$, $\sigma_p = 0.08$, $Z$ (obtained) = $0.75$

**11.15 a.** $Z$ (obtained) = $1.50$
**b.** $Z$ (obtained) = $-2.75$
**c.** $Z$ (obtained) = $4.00$
**d.** $t$ (obtained) = $1.85$
**e.** $t$ (obtained) = $-5.70$
**f.** $t$ (obtained) = $-5.52$

# CHAPTER 12

**12.1**

| Problem | Grand Mean | SST | SSB | SSW | $F$ Ratio | $\eta^2$ |
|---|---|---|---|---|---|---|
| **a.** | 12.17 | 231.67 | 173.17 | 58.50 | 13.32 | 0.7475 |
| **b.** | 6.87 | 455.73 | 78.53 | 377.20 | 1.25 | N/A |
| **c.** | 31.65 | 8,362.55 | 5,053.35 | 3,309.20 | 8.14 | 0.6043 |

**12.3**

| Problem | Grand Mean | SST | SSB | SSW | $F$ Ratio | $\eta^2$ |
|---|---|---|---|---|---|---|
| **a.** | 4.39 | 86.28 | 45.78 | 40.50 | 8.48 | 0.5306 |
| **b.** | 16.44 | 332.44 | 65.44 | 267.00 | 1.84 | N/A |

For problem 12.3a, with alpha = 0.05 and $df = 2, 15$, the critical $F$ ratio would be 3.68. We would reject the null hypothesis and conclude that decision making *does* vary significantly by type of relationship. By inspection of the group means, it seems that the "cohabitational" category accounts for most of the differences. Moreover, eta-squared indicates that we can improve our prediction of the dependent variable (power and decision making) by 74.75% by taking the independent variable (relationship type) into account.

**12.5** SST = 213.61, SSB = 2.11, SSW = 211.50 $F$ (obtained) = 0.07, $\eta^2$ is not appropriate since $F$ (obtained) $<$ $F$ (critical).

**12.7** SST = 429.48, SSB = 124.06, SSW = 305.42 $F$ (obtained) = 5.96, $\eta^2 = 0.2889$

**12.9**

| Nation | Grand Mean | SST | SSB | SSW | $F$ Ratio | $\eta^2$ |
|---|---|---|---|---|---|---|
| Mexico | 3.78 | 300.98 | 154.08 | 146.90 | 12.59 | 0.5119 |
| Canada | 6.88 | 156.38 | 20.08 | 136.30 | 1.77 | N/A |
| United States | 5.13 | 286.38 | 135.28 | 151.10 | 10.74 | 0.4724 |

At alpha = 0.05 and $df = 3, 36$, the critical $F$ ratio is 2.92. There is a significant difference in support for doctor-assisted suicide by class in Mexico and the United States but not in Canada.

The category means for Mexico suggest that the upper class accounts for most of the differences. For the United States, there is more variation across the category means and the working class seems to account for most of the differences. Going beyond the ANOVA test and comparing the grand means, support is highest in Canada and lowest in Mexico.

Overall, eta-squared indicates that we can improve our prediction of the dependent variable (support for doctor-assisted suicide) in Mexico by 51.19%, and in the United States by 47.24%, when we take the independent variable (social class) into account. (We do not calculate eta-squared for Canada because $F$ (obtained) $< F$ (critical).)

## CHAPTER 13

**13.1** *(HINT: When finding the slope, remember that "Turnout" is the dependent or Y variable.)*

| | For Turnout ($Y$) and | | |
| | Unemployment | Education | Neg. Campaigning |
|---|---|---|---|
| Slope ($b$) | 3.00 | 12.67 | −0.90 |
| $Y$ intercept ($a$) | 39.00 | −94.73 | 114.01 |
| Reg. Eq. | $Y = (39) + (3)X$ | $Y = (-94.73) + (12.67)X$ | $Y = (114.01) + (-0.90)X$ |
| $r$ | 0.94 | 0.98 | −0.87 |
| $r^2$ | 0.89 | 0.97 | 0.76 |
| $t$ (obtained) | 4.70 | 9.80 | −3.08 |

**13.3** *(HINT: When finding the slope, remember that "Number of visitors" is the dependent or Y variable.)*

| | |
|---|---|
| Slope ($b$) | −0.37 |
| $Y$ intercept ($a$) | 13.42 |
| $r$ | −0.31 |
| $r^2$ | 0.09 |

**13.5**

| Dependent Variables | | Independent Variables | | |
|---|---|---|---|---|
| | | Density | Growth | Urbanization |
| Auto theft | $a$ | 417.08 | 135.47 | −215.46 |
| | $b$ | −0.23 | 17.50 | 7.96 |
| | $r$ | −0.13 | 0.89 | 0.67 |
| | $r^2$ | 0.02 | 0.79 | 0.45 |
| Robbery | $a$ | 59.97 | 94.37 | −96.70 |
| | $b$ | 0.37 | 1.44 | 2.81 |
| | $r$ | 0.71 | 0.27 | 0.87 |
| | $r^2$ | 0.51 | 0.07 | 0.76 |
| Homicide | $a$ | 3.87 | 3.01 | −0.58 |
| | $b$ | 0.00 | 0.11 | 0.07 |
| | $r$ | 0.26 | 0.61 | 0.65 |
| | $r^2$ | 0.07 | 0.38 | 0.43 |

**c.** For a growth rate of −1, the predicted homicide rate would be 2.90. For a population density of 250, the predicted robbery rate would be 152.47. For a city with 50% urbanization, the predicted rate of auto theft would be 182.54.

**13.7** $b = 0.05$, $a = 53.18$, $r = 0.39$, $r^2 = 0.16$

**13.9**

| Relationship | $r$ | $r^2$ | $t$ (Obtained) |
|---|---|---|---|
| Prestige and age | −0.30 | 0.09 | −1.14 |
| Attendance and number of children | −0.39 | 0.15 | −1.52 |
| Number of children and hours of TV | 0.18 | 0.03 | 0.66 |
| Age and hours of TV | 0.16 | 0.03 | 0.57 |
| Age and number of children | 0.67 | 0.45 | 3.24 |
| Hours of TV and prestige | −0.19 | 0.04 | −0.69 |

## CHAPTER 14

**14.1 a.** For turnout ($Y$) and unemployment ($X$) while controlling for negative advertising ($Z$), $r_{yx.z} = 0.97$. The relationship between $X$ and $Y$ is not affected by the control variable $Z$.

**b.** For turnout ($Y$) and negative advertising ($X$) while controlling for unemployment ($Z$), $r_{yx.z} = -0.92$. The bivariate relationship is not affected by the control variable.

**c.** Turnout ($Y$) = 70.25 + (2.09) unemployment ($X_1$) + (−0.43) negative advertising ($X_2$). For unemployment ($X_1$) = 10 and negative advertising ($X_2$) = 75, turnout ($Y$) = 58.90.

**d.** For unemployment ($X_1$): $b_1^* = 0.66$. For negative advertising ($X_2$): $b_2^* = -0.41$. Unemployment has a stronger effect on turnout than negative advertising. Note that the independent variables' effect on turnout is in opposite directions.

**e.** $R^2 = 0.98$

**14.3 a.** For strife ($Y$) and unemployment ($X$), controlling for urbanization ($Z$), $r_{yx.z} = 0.79$.

**b.** For strife ($Y$) and urbanization ($X$), controlling for unemployment ($Z$), $r_{yx.z} = 0.20$.

**c.** Strife ($Y$) = $(-14.61) + (4.94)$ unemployment ($X_1$) + (0.16) urbanization ($X_2$). With unemployment = 10 and urbanization = 90, strife ($Y'$) would be 49.19.

**d.** For unemployment ($X_1$): $b_1^* = 0.78$. For urbanization ($X_2$): $b_2^* = 0.12$.

**e.** $R^2 = 0.65$

**14.5 a.** Turnout ($Y$) = 83.80 + $(-1.16)$ working-class ($X_1$) + (2.88) unemployment ($X_2$).

**b.** For $X_1 = 0$ and $X_2 = 5$, $Y' = 98.20$

**c.** $Z_y = (-1.27)Z_1 + (0.84)Z_2$

**d.** $R^2 = 0.51$

**14.7 a.** $Z_y = (-0.001)$ HS grads ($Z_1$) + $(-0.74)$ Rank ($Z_2$)

**b.** $R^2 = 0.54$

# Glossary

Each entry includes a brief definition and refers to the page number where the term was introduced.

**Alpha ($\alpha$).** The probability of error or the probability that a confidence interval does not contain the population value. Alpha levels are usually set at 0.10, 0.05, 0.01, or 0.001. (p. 173)

**Alpha error.** See *Type I error.* (p. 210)

**Alpha level.** The proportion of the area under the sampling distribution that contains unlikely sample outcomes if the null is true. Also, the probability of Type I error. Alpha is associated with the critical statistic score. (p. 209)

**Analysis of variance (ANOVA).** A test of significance appropriate for situations in which we are concerned with the differences among more than two sample means. (p. 384)

**ANOVA.** See *Analysis of variance.* (p. 384)

**Association.** The relationship between two (or more) variables. Two variables are said to be associated if the distribution of one variable changes for the various categories or scores of the other variable. (p. 244)

**Bar chart.** A graphic display device for discrete variables. Response categories are represented by bars of equal width, the height of each corresponding to the number (or percentage) of cases in the response category. (p. 61)

**Beta error.** See *Type II error.* (p. 233)

**Beta-weights ($b^*$).** Standardized partial slopes. (p. 465)

**Bias.** A criterion used to select sample statistics as estimators. A statistic is unbiased if the mean of its sampling distribution is equal to the population value of interest. (p. 169)

**Bivariate normal distributions.** The model assumption in the test of significance for Pearson's $r$ that both variables are normally distributed. (p. 435)

**Bivariate table.** A table that displays the joint frequency distribution of two variables. (p. 213)

**Boxplot.** A graphic device based on the median, interquartile range, and range. It is used to display the centre, dispersion, and overall range of scores in a distribution of ordinal-level or interval-ratio-level variable scores. (p. 88)

**Cells.** The cross-classification categories of the variables in a bivariate table. (p. 213)

**Central Limit Theorem.** A theorem that specifies the mean, standard deviation, and shape of the sampling distribution, given that the sample is large. (p. 157)

**Chi square test.** A non-parametric test of hypothesis for variables that have been organized into a bivariate table. (p. 212)

**$\chi^2$ (critical).** The score on the sampling distribution of all possible sample chi squares that marks the beginning of the critical region. (p. 215)

**$\chi^2$ (obtained).** The test statistic as computed from sample results. (p. 215)

**Clustered bar chart.** A bivariate (or multivariate) bar chart that displays the conditional distributions of $Y$ of a contingency table. (p. 248)

**Coefficient of determination ($r^2$).** The proportion of all variation in $Y$ that is explained by $X$. Found by squaring the value of Pearson's $r$. (p. 430)

**Coefficient of multiple determination ($R^2$).** A statistic that equals the total variation explained in the dependent variable by all independent variables combined. (p. 467)

**Column.** The vertical dimension of a bivariate table. By convention, each column represents a score on the independent variable. (p. 213)

**Column percentages.** Percentages computed within each column of a bivariate table. (p. 220)

**Conditional distribution of $Y$.** The distribution of scores on the dependent variable for a specific score or category of the independent variable when the variables have been organized into table format. (p. 245)

**Conditional mean of $Y$.** The mean of all scores on $Y$ for each value of $X$. (p. 422)

**Confidence interval.** An estimate of a population value in which a range of values is specified. (p. 169)

**Confidence level.** A frequently used alternative way of expressing alpha, the probability that a confidence interval will not contain the population value. Confidence levels of 90%, 95%, 99%, and 99.9% correspond to alphas of 0.10, 0.05, 0.01, and 0.001, respectively. (p. 173)

**Continuous variable.** A variable with a unit of measurement that can be subdivided infinitely. (p. 20)

**Control variable.** A "third variable" ($Z$) that might affect a bivariate relationship. (p. 453)

**Cramer's V (V).** A chi square–based measure of association. Appropriate for nominally measured variables that have been organized into a bivariate table of any number of rows and columns. (p. 257)

**Critical region (region of rejection).** The area under the sampling distribution that, in advance of the test itself, is defined as including unlikely sample outcomes, given that the null hypothesis is true. (p. 209)

**Cumulative frequency.** An optional column in a frequency distribution that displays the number of cases in an interval and all preceding intervals. (p. 54)

**Cumulative percentage.** An optional column in a frequency distribution that displays the percentage of cases in an interval and all preceding intervals. (p. 54)

**Data.** Any information collected as part of a research project and expressed as numbers. (p. 10)

**Database.** An organized collection of related information. (p. 501)

**Data reduction.** Summarizing many scores with a few statistics. A major goal of descriptive statistics. (p. 17)

**Dependent variable.** A variable that is identified as an effect, result, or outcome variable. The dependent variable is thought to be caused by the independent variable. In a bivariate relationship, the variable that is taken as the effect. (p. 12)

**Descriptive statistics.** The branch of statistics concerned with (1) summarizing the distribution of a single variable or (2) measuring the relationship between two or more variables. (p. 16)

**Deviations.** The distances between the scores and the mean. (p. 96)

**Direct relationship.** A multivariate relationship in which a control variable has no effect on the bivariate relationship. (p. 454)

**Discrete variable.** A variable with a basic unit of measurement that cannot be subdivided. (p. 19)

**Dispersion.** The amount of variety or heterogeneity in a distribution of scores. (p. 78)

**Efficiency.** The extent to which sample outcomes are clustered around the mean of the sampling distribution. (p. 169)

**EPSEM.** The Equal Probability of SElection Method for selecting samples. Every element or case in the population must have an equal probability of selection for the sample. (p. 151)

**Error bar.** A graphic display device used to illustrate the confidence interval of a sample statistic. (p. 181)

**Eta-squared ($\eta^2$).** The PRE measure of association used with one-way ANOVA. (p. 400)

**Expected frequency ($f_e$).** The cell frequencies that would be expected in a bivariate table if the variables were independent. (p. 215)

**Explained variation.** The proportion of all variation in $Y$ that is attributed to the effect of $X$. (p. 431)

**F ratio.** The test statistic computed in step 4 of the ANOVA test. (p. 389)

**File.** A database (or any other information) that is stored under the same name in the memory of the computer or other storage media. (p. 71)

**Five-numbered summary.** A group of statistics consisting of the lowest score $L$, first quartile $Q_1$, median, third quartile $Q_3$, and highest score $H$ of a distribution of scores, and the basis for the boxplot. (p. 88)

**Five-step model.** A step-by-step guideline for conducting tests of hypotheses. A framework that organizes decisions and computations for all tests of significance. (p. 208)

**Frequency distribution.** A table that displays the number of cases in each response category of a variable. (p. 46)

**Frequency polygon.** A graphic display device for interval-ratio variables. Intervals are represented by dots placed over the midpoints, the height of each corresponding to the number (or percentage) of cases in the interval. All dots are connected by a straight line, and the line is dropped to the horizontal axis at the midpoint of the adjacent interval at the ends. (p. 63)

**Gamma (*G*).** A measure of association appropriate for any two variables measured with "collapsed" ordinal scales. (p. 279)

**Histogram.** A graphic display device for interval-ratio variables. Intervals are represented by contiguous bars of equal width (equal to the real limits), the height of each corresponding to the number (or percentage) of cases in the interval. (p. 62)

**Homoscedasticity.** The model assumption in the test of significance for Pearson's $r$ that the variance of the $Y$ scores is uniform across all values of $X$. (p. 435)

**Hypothesis.** A statement about the relationship between variables that is derived from a theory. Hypotheses are more specific than theories, and all terms and concepts are fully defined. (p. 13)

**Hypothesis testing (significance testing).** Statistical tests that estimate the probability of sample outcomes if assumptions about the population (the null hypothesis) are true. (p. 207)

**Independence.** The null hypothesis in the chi square test. Two variables are independent if, for all cases, the classification of a case on one variable has no effect on the probability that the case will be classified in any particular category of the second variable. (p. 214)

**Independent random samples.** Random samples gathered so that the selection of a case for one sample has no effect on the probability that any particular case will be selected for the other samples. (p. 356)

**Independent variable.** A variable that is identified as a causal variable. The independent variable is thought to cause the dependent variable. In a bivariate relationship, the variable that is taken as the cause. (p 12)

**Inferential statistics.** The branch of statistics concerned with making generalizations from samples to populations. (p. 18)

**Interquartile range (*Q*).** The distance from the third quartile to the first. (p. 86)

**Interval-ratio variable.** A variable whose response categories can be classified, ordered, and have equal distance between them. (p. 25)

**Intervals.** The response categories created to produce the frequency distributions for interval-ratio variables. (p. 50)

**Intervening relationship.** A multivariate relationship in which the independent and dependent variables are linked primarily through the control variable. (p. 455)

**Kendall's tau-b ($\tau_b$).** A measure of association appropriate for two variables measured with "collapsed" ordinal scales with an equal number of categories. (p. 279)

**Kendall's tau-c ($\tau_c$).** A measure of association appropriate for two variables measured with "collapsed" ordinal scales with an unequal number of categories. (p. 279)

**Lambda ($\lambda$).** A measure of association appropriate for nominal-level variables that have been organized into a bivariate table. Lambda is based on the logic of PRE. (p. 261)

**Level of measurement.** The mathematical characteristics of a variable and a major criterion for selecting statistical techniques. It is determined from an examination of the variable's response categories. Variables can be measured at any of three levels, each permitting certain mathematical operations and statistical techniques. (p. 21)

**Linear relationship.** A relationship between two variables in which the observation points (dots) in the scatterplot can be approximated with a straight line. (p. 420)

**Marginals.** The row and column subtotals of a bivariate table. (p. 213)

**Margin of error.** The radius (half the size) of a confidence interval for a sample mean or sample proportion. It is also called the margin of sampling error, or just sampling error. (p. 169)

**Maximum difference.** A way to assess the strength of an association between variables that have been organized into a bivariate table. The maximum difference is the largest difference between column percentages for any row of the table. (p. 251)

**Mean ($\overline{X}$ or $\mu$).** The arithmetic average of the scores; $\overline{X}$ represents the mean of a sample, and $\mu$, the mean of a population. (p. 91).

**Mean deviation.** The average of the absolute deviations of the scores around the mean. (p. 96)

**Mean square between (MSB).** An estimate of the population variance calculated by dividing the sum of squares between (SSB) by the degrees of freedom between (*dfb*). (p. 389)

**Mean square within (MSW).** An estimate of the population variance calculated by dividing the sum of squares within (SSW) by the degrees of freedom within (*dfw*). (p. 389)

**Measures of association.** Statistics that summarize the strength and direction of the relationship between variables. For ordinal-level and interval-ratio-level variables, this statistic also indicates the direction of the relationship. (p 17)

**Measures of central tendency.** Statistics that summarize a distribution of scores by reporting the most typical, average, or central value of the distribution. (p. 78)

**Measures of dispersion.** Statistics that indicate the amount of variety or heterogeneity in a distribution of scores. (p. 78)

**Median (Md).** The point in a distribution of scores above and below which half of the cases fall. (p. 84)

**Menu.** A list of options in a statistical package. (p. 503)

**Midpoint.** The point halfway between the upper and lower limits of a class interval. (p. 52)

**Mode.** The most common value in a distribution, or the largest category of a variable. (p. 80)

**Multiple correlation.** A multivariate technique for examining the combined effects of more than one independent variable on a dependent variable. (p. 467)

**Multiple correlation coefficient (R).** A statistic that indicates the strength of the correlation between a dependent variable and two or more independent variables. (p. 467)

**Multiple regression.** A multivariate technique that breaks down the separate effects of the independent variables on the dependent variable. (p. 460)

**Negative association.** A bivariate relationship in which the variables vary in opposite directions. As one variable increases, the other decreases, and high scores on one variable are associated with low scores on the other. (p. 252)

**Nominal variable.** A variable whose response categories can be classified but not ordered. (p. 22)

**Non-parametric.** A "distribution-free" test. These tests do not assume a normal sampling distribution. (p. 212)

**Normal curve.** A bell-shaped theoretical distribution of scores that is unimodal and symmetrical. The standard normal curve always has a mean of 0 and a standard deviation of 1. (p. 123)

**Null hypothesis ($H_0$).** A statement of "no difference" or "no relationship." In the context of the chi square test of independence, the variables are assumed to be independent in the population. (p. 208)

**Observed frequency ($f_o$).** The cell frequencies actually observed and recorded in a bivariate table. (p. 215)

**One-tailed test.** A type of hypothesis test that can be used when (1) the direction of the difference can be predicted or (2) concern focuses on outcomes in only one tail of the sampling distribution. (p. 331)

**One-way analysis of variance.** An application of ANOVA in which the effect of a single independent variable on a dependent is observed. (p. 385)

**Ordinal variable.** A variable whose response categories can be classified and ordered. (p. 23)

**Outliers.** Extreme high or low scores in a distribution. (p. 86)

**$p$.** The area under the sampling distribution that indicates the exact likelihood of rejecting the null hypothesis when it is true (i.e., the exact risk of a Type I error). $p$ is associated with the test (obtained) statistic. (p. 209)

**Panelled pie chart.** A bivariate (or multivariate) pie chart that displays the conditional distributions of *Y* of a contingency table. (p. 248)

**Parameter.** A characteristic of a population. (p. 150)

**Partial correlation.** A multivariate technique for examining a bivariate relationship while controlling for other variables. (p. 453)

**Partial correlation coefficient.** A statistic that shows the relationship between two variables while controlling for other variables; $r_{yx.z}$ is the symbol for the partial correlation coefficient when controlling for one variable. (p. 455)

**Partial slopes.** In a multiple regression equation, the slope of the relationship between a particular independent variable and the dependent variable while controlling for all other independents in the equation. (p. 460)

**Pearson's *r* (*r*).** A measure of association for variables that have been measured at the interval-ratio level. $\rho$ is the symbol for the population value of Pearson's *r*. (p. 427)

**Percentage (%).** The number of cases in a response category of a variable divided by the number of cases in all response categories, with the entire quantity then multiplied by 100. (p. 39)

**Phi ($\phi$).** A chi square–based measure of association. Appropriate for nominal-level variables that have been organized into a $2 \times 2$ bivariate table. (p. 256)

**Pie chart.** A graphic display device especially for discrete variables with only a few response categories. A circle (the pie) is divided into segments proportional in size to the percentage of cases in each response category of the variable. (p. 60)

**Point estimate.** An estimate of a population value in which a single value is specified. (p. 169)

**Pooled estimate.** An estimate of the standard deviation of the sampling distribution of the difference in sample means based on the standard deviations of both samples. (p. 362)

**Pooled estimate of the population proportion.** An estimate of the population proportion based on the proportions of both samples. (p. 365)

**Population.** The total collection of all cases in which the researcher is interested. (p. 18)

**Positive association.** A bivariate relationship in which the variables vary in the same direction. As one variable increases, the other also increases, and high scores on one variable are associated with high scores on the other. (p. 252)

**Post hoc test.** A technique for determining which pair(s) of means is significantly different. (p. 400)

**Probability.** A ratio of the number of successes to the number of possible events. (p. 138)

**Proportion (*p*).** The number of cases in a response category divided by the number of cases in all response categories. (p. 39)

**Proportional reduction in error (PRE).** The logic that underlies the definition and computation of statistics such as lambda. All PRE statistics compare the number of errors made when predicting the dependent variable while ignoring the independent variable ($E_1$) with the number of errors made while taking the independent variable into account ($E_2$). (p. 260)

**Range (*R*).** The highest score minus the lowest score. (p. 85)

**Rate.** The number of actual occurrences of some phenomenon or trait divided by the number of possible occurrences per some unit of time. (p. 45)

**Ratio.** The number of cases in one response category divided by the number of cases in another response category. (p. 43)

**Real limits.** The intervals of a frequency distribution when stated as continuous response categories. (p. 53)

**Region of rejection.** See *Critical region.* (p. 209)

**Regression line.** The single best-fitting straight line that summarizes the relationship between two variables. The regression line is fitted to the data points by the least-squares criterion, whereby the line touches all conditional means of *Y* or comes as close to doing so as possible. (p. 418)

**Representative.** The quality a sample is said to have if it reproduces the major characteristics of the population from which it was drawn. (p. 151)

**Research.** Any process of gathering information systematically and carefully to answer questions or test theories. Statistics are useful for research projects in which the information is represented in numerical form or as data. (p. 10)

**Research hypothesis ($H_1$).** A statement that contradicts the null hypothesis. In the context of the chi square test of independence, the research hypothesis says that the variables are dependent in the population. (p. 208)

**Response category.** A variable's possible attributes, qualities, or characteristics. (p. 21)

**Row.** The horizontal dimension of a table, conventionally representing a score on the dependent variable. (p. 213)

**Sample.** A carefully chosen subset of a population. In inferential statistics, information is gathered from a sample and then generalized to a population. (p. 18)

**Sampling distribution.** The distribution of a statistic for all possible sample outcomes of a certain size. Under conditions specified in two theorems, the sampling distribution will be normal in shape with a mean equal to the population value and a standard deviation equal to the population standard deviation divided by the square root of *n*. (p. 153)

**Scatterplot.** A graphic display device that depicts the relationship between two variables. (p. 417)

**Significance testing.** See *Hypothesis testing.* (p. 207)

**Simple random sample.** A method for choosing cases from a population by which every case has an equal chance of being included. (p. 152)

**Skew.** The extent to which a distribution of scores has a few cases that are extremely high (positive skew) or extremely low (negative skew). It is an important characteristic of distribution shape. (p. 94)

**Slope (*b*).** The amount of change in a variable per unit change in the other variable. *b* is the symbol for the slope of a regression line. (p. 423)

**Somers' *d* ($d_{yx}$).** A measure of association appropriate for two variables measured with "collapsed" ordinal scales where one variable is identified as the dependent. (p. 279)

**Spearman's rho ($r_s$).** A measure of association for ordinal variables that are "continuous" in form. (p. 279)

**Spurious relationship.** A multivariate relationship in which the bivariate relationship becomes substantially weaker after controlling for a third variable. The independent ($X$) and dependent ($Y$) variables are not causally linked. Rather, both are caused by the control variable ($Z$). (p. 454)

**Standard deviation (*s* or *σ*).** The square root of the sum of the squared deviations of the scores around the mean, divided by the number of cases. The most important and useful descriptive measure of dispersion; *s* represents the standard deviation of a sample; *σ*, the standard deviation of a population. (p. 97)

**Standard error.** The standard deviation of a sampling distribution. (p. 156)

**Standardized partial slopes (beta-weights).** The slope of the relationship between a particular independent variable and the dependent when all scores are expressed as $Z$ scores. (p. 465)

**Standard normal curve table.** See Appendix A; a detailed description of the area between a $Z$ score and the mean of a standardized normal distribution. (p. 128)

**Stated limits.** The intervals of a frequency distribution when stated as discrete response categories. (p. 53)

**Statistical package (statpak).** A set of computer programs designed to manipulate and statistically analyze data. (p. 500)

**Statistics.** A set of mathematical techniques for organizing and analyzing data. Sometimes the term refers to the numbers obtained with statistical techniques. (p. 10)

**Student's *t* distribution.** A distribution used in the construction of confidence intervals and hypothesis tests when the population standard deviation is unknown. (p. 177)

**Sum of squares between (SSB).** The sum of the squared deviations of the sample means from the overall mean, weighted by sample size. (p. 387)

**Sum of squares within (SSW).** The sum of the squared deviations from the category means. (p. 387)

***t* (critical).** The *t* score that marks the beginning of the critical region of a *t* distribution. (p. 338)

***t* (obtained).** The test statistic computed in step 4 of the five-step model for tests. The sample outcome is expressed as a *t* score. (p. 388)

**Test statistic.** The obtained statistic. The value computed in step 4 of the five-step model that converts the sample outcome into a chi square score. (p. 209)

**Theory.** A generalized explanation of the relationship between two or more variables. (p. 11)

**Total sum of squares (SST).** The sum of the squared deviations of the scores from the overall mean. (p. 387)

**Total variation.** The spread of the $Y$ scores around the mean of $Y$. (p. 430)

**Two-tailed test.** A type of hypothesis test used when (1) the direction of the difference cannot be predicted or (2) concern focuses on outcomes in both tails of the sampling distribution. (p. 331)

**Type I error (alpha error).** The probability of rejecting a null hypothesis that is true. (p. 210)

**Type II error (beta error).** The probability of failing to reject a null hypothesis that is false. (p. 211)

**Unexplained variation.** The proportion of the total variation in $Y$ that is not accounted for by $X$. (p. 432)

**Variable.** Any trait that can change values from case to case. (p. 12)

**Variance ($s^2$ or $\sigma^2$).** The sum of the squared deviations of the scores around the mean, divided by the number of cases. A measure of dispersion used primarily in inferential statistics and also in correlation and regression techniques; $s^2$ represents the variance of a sample; $\sigma^2$, the variance of a population. (p. 97)

**X.** Symbol used for any independent variable. (p. 244)

**Y.** Symbol used for any dependent variable. (p. 244)

**Y'.** Symbol for predicted score on $Y$. (p. 421)

**Y intercept (*a*).** The point where the regression line crosses the $Y$ axis. (p. 423)

**Z (critical).** The $Z$ score that marks the beginning of the critical region of a $Z$ distribution. (p. 328)

**Z (obtained).** The test statistic computed in step 4 of the five-step model. The sample outcomes is expressed as a $Z$ score. (p. 329)

**Z scores.** Standard scores; the way scores are expressed after they have been standardized to the theoretical normal curve. (p. 126)

**Zero-order correlations.** Correlation coefficients for bivariate relationships. (p. 455)

# Index

# Glossary of Symbols

The number in parentheses indicates the chapter in which the symbol is introduced.

| | |
|---|---|
| $a$ | Point at which the regression line crosses the $Y$ axis (13) |
| ANOVA | The analysis of variance (12) |
| $b$ | Slope of the regression line (13) |
| $b_i$ | Partial slope of the linear relationship between the $i$th independent variable and the dependent variable (14) |
| $b_i^*$ | Standardized partial slope of the linear relationship between the $i$th independent variable and the dependent variable (14) |
| $df$ | Degrees of freedom (7) |
| $d_{yx}$ | Somers' $d$ (9) |
| $\eta^2$ | Eta-squared (12) |
| $f$ | Frequency (2) |
| $F$ | $F$ ratio (9) |
| $f_e$ | Expected frequency (7) |
| $f_o$ | Observed frequency (7) |
| $G$ | Gamma for a sample (9) |
| $H_0$ | Null hypothesis (7) |
| $H_1$ | Research hypothesis (7) |
| $IQV$ | Index of qualitative variation (3) |
| $\lambda$ | Lambda (8) |
| $\mu$ | Mean of a population |
| Md | Median (3) |
| Mo | Mode (3) |
| $N$ | Number of cases in the population (3) |
| $n$ | Number of cases in the sample (2) |
| $n_d$ | Number of pairs of cases ranked in different order on two variables (9) |

| | |
|---|---|
| $n_s$ | Number of pairs of cases ranked in the same order on two variables (9) |
| % | Percentage (2) |
| $p$ | Proportion (2) |
| $\phi$ | Phi (8) |
| $P_s$ | A sample proportion (6) |
| $P_u$ | A population proportion (6) |
| PRE | Proportional reduction in error (8) |
| $Q$ | Interquartile range (3) |
| $r$ | Pearson's correlation coefficient for a sample (13) |
| $r^2$ | Coefficient of determination (13) |
| $R$ | Range (3) |
| $r_s$ | Spearman's rho for a sample (9) |
| $r_{yx.z}$ | Partial correlation coefficient (14) |
| $R^2$ | Multiple correlation coefficient (14) |
| $s$ | Sample standard deviation (3) |
| $\sigma$ | Population standard deviation (3) |
| SSB | The sum of squares between (12) |
| SST | The total sum of squares (12) |
| SSW | The sum of squares within (12) |
| $s^2$ | Sample variance (3) |
| $t$ | Student's $t$ score (10) |
| $V$ | Cramer's $V$ (8) |
| $X$ | Any independent variable (8) |
| $\overline{X}$ | Mean of a sample (3) |
| $X_i$ | Any score in a distribution (3) |
| $Y$ | Any dependent variable (8) |
| $Y'$ | A predicted score on $Y$ (13) |
| $Z$ | Standard scores (4) |